ADVANCED MATHEMATICS
for Engineers

ADVANCED

MATHEMATICS

———————————— for Engineers —

By H. W. REDDICK
and F. H. MILLER

Third Edition prepared by

F. H. MILLER

PROFESSOR AND HEAD OF THE
DEPARTMENT OF MATHEMATICS
THE COOPER UNION SCHOOL
OF ENGINEERING

JOHN WILEY & SONS, INC., NEW YORK
CHAPMAN & HALL, LIMITED, LONDON

Library of Congress Catalog Card Number: 55–6102

PRINTED IN THE UNITED STATES OF AMERICA

Preface to the Third Edition

In this revision, extensive changes have been made in the problem lists. Previous problems involving general relationships and results have been retained, but formal ones of the drill variety and those entailing numerical computations have, for the most part, been replaced by fresh ones. Problems have also been added to many of the lists, and new sets likewise accompany topics appearing in this edition for the first time; as a result, the number of problems in this book is more than twenty per cent greater than in the second edition.

Among the changes made in the text, the following may be noted. A theorem on reversion of power series has been included in Art. 38. An introductory account of Legendre's equation has been added to Chapter VI, and physical applications of Legendre polynomials appear there and in Chapter VII, where Laplace's equation in spherical coordinates is considered. Chapter IX has been recast: the previous discussion of permutations, combinations, and elementary probability theory has been shortened, and two articles on the important topic of numerical methods for solving ordinary and partial differential equations have been inserted. A third section, on Laplace transforms and their applications, has been added to Chapter XI.

Answers to all problems are again given in the back of the book.

FREDERIC H. MILLER

NEW YORK, N. Y
January, 1955

v

Preface to the Second Edition

In this new edition, the plan and features of the original book have, for the most part, been retained. Notable changes are principally of four kinds, which may be described briefly as follows:

1. An appendix, concerned with a short discussion of dimensional analysis and systems of physical units, has been added. It is believed that the basic concepts and methods of dimensional analysis are of considerable value to the engineer, and that the engineering student should therefore be acquainted with the rudiments of the subject. Moreover, since various systems of units are employed in this book and elsewhere, an indication of the bases of these systems and of their relationships should also be a part of the student's training.

2. The problem lists have been completely revised. All the original problems have been kept, with only occasional changes of wording for the sake of clarity, and numerous additional problems have been inserted. Some of the new problems will serve as further drill problems to illustrate the principles established in the text; others exemplify new kinds of physical problems. In all, the number of problems has been increased by more than fifty per cent.

3. Discussions of a few new topics have been added. In particular, a mechanical-brake problem involving elliptic integrals has been inserted in Chapter III, the treatment of Fourier series in Chapter V has been somewhat extended, and the vibrating membrane is considered in Chapter VII as a typical problem dealing with a partial differential equation containing three independent variables.

4. A number of derivations and illustrative examples have been replaced or revised in order to clarify the concepts and theory and to aid the student further in his work with the problems.

One minor change should also be mentioned. The natural logarithm of x is now denoted by $\ln x$, and the symbol $\log x$ is used only for the common logarithm. This notation has been adopted to conform with the present trend in scientific writing.

As in the first edition, answers to all the problems are given in the back of the book.

H. W. R.
F. H. M.

New York, N. Y.
September, 1946

Preface to the First Edition

The present book has evolved from courses given by the authors to juniors and seniors in civil, electrical, mechanical, and chemical engineering at The Cooper Union Institute of Technology. These courses were designed to show some of the various roles played by advanced mathematics in engineering technology.

In constructing such courses, the problem of what to include and what to omit is particularly difficult. Here, as opposed to the mathematics courses previously encountered by the engineering student, there is no well-defined, unifying thread; rather, the whole must be made up of a number of more or less distinct topics. It is hoped that the selection of material included in this book will afford each teacher a sufficiently broad range of topics from which to make his individual choice.

Anyone about to take up the study of advanced mathematics should have had as background a thorough training in engineering mathematics through the calculus, and would normally continue with the elementary theory of ordinary differential equations. For a number of years it has been recognized that some knowledge of methods of solving differential equations is a valuable tool for the engineer, inasmuch as so many physical problems arising in all fields of engineering are naturally formulated in the guise of differential relations. Accordingly, Chapter I is devoted to the standard methods of manipulating the common types of ordinary differential equations. In addition, differential equations arise again and again in the later chapters so that, upon completion of his course, the student should have acquired not only as full a knowledge of the theory of differential equations as is usually obtained in a separate course, but also more practice in their applications to his special field. However, it may be considered desirable in some schools to offer a separate course in differential equations and to follow it by a course beginning with the second chapter of this book. It is, of course, entirely feasible to follow this procedure and to consult the first chapter whenever necessary or as indicated in the text.

The authors believe that it is becoming more and more important in engineering training to include courses wherein the student will meet many of the topics, pertinent to his field, which are discussed in this volume. As the Table of Contents shows, topics of value to all branches of engineering have been included. Throughout, emphasis has been placed on physical applications by presenting, with each principal topic, problems relating to the four main fields of engineering. The order of arrangement minimizes the number of references forward in the text; at the same time, one chapter leads naturally into the next so as to yield as much continuity of treatment as possible. The assignment of the more difficult material to the later chapters takes advantage of the growing mathematical maturity of the student as he proceeds in the text.

With the interests and needs of engineering students constantly in mind, the authors have not attempted overmuch rigor. The engineer rightly wants to know how each piece of mathematical theory can be utilized in his work, and questions of rigor are of secondary importance to him. Nevertheless, comprehension of the underlying theory and of some of the subtler points is necessary if the ideas are to be correctly applied to a new problem. This viewpoint has not been overlooked. Critical discussions are introduced whenever they are deemed necessary. References are given when lack of space, or insufficient background on the part of the student, prevents the insertion of the entire argument; on the other hand, the details of each demonstration are set forth wherever possible.

The authors make no claim to originality of content or of treatment, but they have taken particular care to present definitions, statements of physical laws, theorems, problems, and the physical units employed, in a thorough and clearcut manner. They have endeavored to produce, also, a textbook sufficiently flexible that material may be chosen for courses of various lengths suitable for students of civil, electrical, mechanical, or chemical engineering. For example, Part II of Chapter X may be omitted without disturbing the continuity. In fact, any combination of topics from Chapters VIII to XI may be chosen, except that the material in Part III of Chapter X is essential to the proper understanding of Part II of Chapter XI. Thus, while a minimum course may properly contain most of the fundamental material of Chapters I–VII, with selected applications and problems, a longer course will naturally include also various of the more specialized subjects treated in the later chapters.

H. W. REDDICK
F. H. MILLER

New York, N. Y.
July, 1938

Contents

Chapter III· ELLIPTIC INTEGRALS

Chapter IV· INFINITE SERIES

Chapter V· FOURIER SERIES

Chapter VI· GAMMA, BESSEL, AND LEGENDRE FUNCTIONS

Chapter VII· PARTIAL DERIVATIVES AND PARTIAL
DIFFERENTIAL EQUATIONS

Chapter VIII· VECTOR ANALYSIS

Chapter IX· PROBABILITY AND NUMERICAL METHODS

Chapter X· FUNCTIONS OF A COMPLEX VARIABLE

Part I. Elementary Theory of Analytic Functions

Part II. The Schwarz-Christoffel Transformation and Its Applications

CHAPTER I

Ordinary Differential Equations

1. Introduction. A vast number of the problems the engineer encounters in advanced work have to do with differential equations. The mathematical treatment of such problems consists, in general, of three phases or processes. In the first place, the physical principles forming the background of the problem are expressed mathematically by the formulation of one or more differential equations; these relations, involving rates of change of one variable with respect to another, are thus symbolic statements of certain physical laws. Secondly, the differential equations must be manipulated mathematically so as to obtain other relations among the variables of the problem. Finally, we interpret these new relations, which are the logical consequences of the original ones, so as to get additional information concerning the manner in which the physical quantities involved depend upon one another.

We shall see in our subsequent work numerous examples of this mode of reasoning. The first and third steps of the process will depend upon the particular problem under discussion, and it will appear in this and later chapters how they are carried out. The second step, the manipulation of differential equations, is of a more formal and general nature, and is the principal concern of the present chapter. Our purpose, then, will be to classify and examine a number of types of differential equations with which the engineer has to deal.

We shall call an equation containing one or more derivatives a *differential equation*. The differential equation may sometimes, as a matter of analytical convenience, be written in a form in which differentials rather than derivatives appear, but such an equation will always be equivalent to one involving derivatives.

By the *order* of a differential equation is meant the order of the highest-ordered derivative contained in the equation.

Differential equations may be divided into two main classes, *ordinary* and *partial* differential equations. If all derivatives appearing in the differential equation are ordinary derivatives, the equation is said to be an ordinary differential equation. If, on the other hand, the derivatives present in the equation are partial derivatives, the equation is called a partial differential equation.

1

In this chapter, only ordinary equations will be considered. In Chapter VII we shall discuss some problems leading to partial differential equations, and shall apply special devices to the manipulation of such equations.

If there is only one dependent variable whose relation to the independent variable is desired, we shall have in general a single differential equation; if there are two or more dependent variables to be considered we shall be led to a system of *simultaneous differential equations*, and the number of equations in the system will usually be equal to the number of dependent variables.

By a *solution* of a differential equation we mean any functional relation among the variables, free of derivatives and reducing the given equation to an identity. For example, the relation

$$y = e^{2x} \tag{1}$$

is a solution of the differential equation of second order,

$$\frac{d^2y}{dx^2} - 5\frac{dy}{dx} + 6y = 0, \tag{2}$$

since substitution in (2) of y and its derivatives as given by (1) yields the identity

$$4e^{2x} - 10e^{2x} + 6e^{2x} \equiv 0. \tag{3}$$

A more general solution of (2) is $y = c_1 e^{2x}$, where c_1 is an arbitrary constant, and a still more general solution is $y = c_1 e^{2x} + c_2 e^{3x}$, where c_1 and c_2 are both arbitrary constants. Now it is shown * in the theory of differential equations that an equation of order n possesses a solution containing n essential arbitrary constants, and that no solution of such an equation can contain more than n. A solution containing the maximum number of constants is called *the general solution;* thus $y = c_1 e^{2x} + c_2 e^{3x}$ is the general solution of (2). Any solution obtainable from the general solution by giving specific values to one or more of the arbitrary constants is called *a particular solution;* for instance, $y = e^{2x}$ and $y = c_1 e^{2x}$ are particular solutions of (2).

In a physical problem, the differential equation involved is usually accompanied by certain auxiliary conditions on the variables. For some, notably the linear differential equations discussed in Part II, it is easiest first to find the general solution of the equation and then obtain a particular solution satisfying the imposed auxiliary conditions, as well as the differential equation, by determining the specific values of the arbitrary constants in the general solution. For others, the

---

* See, for example, E. L. Ince, "Ordinary Differential Equations."

constants may be evaluated as they appear in the process of solving the differential equation. Examples of both methods of attack will arise in the problems treated in this and subsequent chapters. A fully determinate physical problem should provide a sufficient number of initial or boundary conditions for the evaluation of all constants that may appear.

We proceed now to classify some types of ordinary differential equations, and to discuss the standard methods of solving them.

PART I. EQUATIONS OF THE FIRST ORDER AND MISCELLANEOUS EQUATIONS OF HIGHER ORDER

2. Variables separable. The type form of the differential equation of first order is

$$\frac{dy}{dx} = f(x, y). \tag{1}$$

It may happen that the function $f(x, y)$ is such that the variables may be separated, so that the equation may be written in the form

$$F(x)\, dx + G(y)\, dy = 0. \tag{2}$$

The general solution of the equation may then be obtained at once by integrating; we get

$$\int F(x)\, dx + \int G(y)\, dy = c, \tag{3}$$

where c is an arbitrary constant. That (3) satisfies equation (2) is immediately apparent, for differentiation of (3) leads to the relation (2).

As a simple example, let there be given the equation

$$\frac{dy}{dx} = e^{x-2y}. \tag{4}$$

Since $e^{x-2y} = e^x \cdot e^{-2y}$, we may write

$$e^x\, dx - e^{2y}\, dy = 0, \tag{5}$$

whence

$$e^x - \tfrac{1}{2}e^{2y} = c. \tag{6}$$

If the function $f(x, y)$ contains no constants whose values are unspecified, a single corresponding pair of values of x and y suffices to determine c, and hence a particular solution of equation (2) subject to the given value-pair is obtainable. If, however, the differential equation involves additional constants of unknown value, further conditions on x and y

must be given in order that the functional relation (3) be of use for computation.

To illustrate the latter situation, consider two liquids A and B boiling together in a vessel. Suppose that it is found experimentally that the ratio of the rates at which A and B are evaporating at any instant is proportional to the ratio of the respective amounts of A and B still in the liquid state. Letting y and x denote the respective amounts of A and B present in liquid form at time t, the physical law stated yields the differential equation

$$\frac{\dfrac{dy}{dt}}{\dfrac{dx}{dt}} = k\frac{y}{x}, \tag{7}$$

where k is an unknown constant of proportionality. In this form, the differential equation involves one independent variable t and the two dependent variables x and y, but if we desire merely the functional relation between x and y we may eliminate t and write

$$\frac{dy}{dx} = k\frac{y}{x}. \tag{8}$$

Here $f(x, y) = ky/x$, and consequently the variables may be separated. We have

$$\frac{dy}{y} = k\frac{dx}{x}, \tag{9}$$

whence, by integrating, we get

$$\ln y = k \ln x + \ln c. \tag{10}$$

Since only logarithmic functions of x and of y appear here, it is convenient to write the arbitrary constant of integration in the form $\ln c$ instead of merely c. Taking antilogarithms, we then obtain

$$y = cx^k. \tag{11}$$

Evidently we should need two sets of values of x and y to determine the particular solution from which further corresponding values of x and y could be obtained.

3. Integrable combinations. If it appears that we cannot separate the variables in the equation

$$\frac{dy}{dx} = f(x, y), \tag{1}$$

it may still be possible to put it in a form which allows us to integrate by combinations.

For example, consider the equation

$$\frac{dy}{dx} = \frac{2x + y}{3 - x}, \tag{2}$$

or

$$(2x + y)\, dx + (x - 3)\, dy = 0. \tag{3}$$

Here the coefficient of dx contains y and that of dy contains x, and no manipulation in the equation will separate the variables. Now the terms $2x\, dx$ and $-3\, dy$ are capable of integration individually, and thus need give no concern. The remainder of the left-hand member of (3), $y\, dx + x\, dy$, consists of the sum of two terms neither of which can be integrated by itself. But as a combination, this sum may be integrated; we recognize it as the differential of the product xy. Consequently, if we write (3) as

$$2x\, dx - 3\, dy + (x\, dy + y\, dx) = 0,$$

we get, upon integration,

$$x^2 - 3y + xy = c. \tag{4}$$

Evidently (4) is the general solution of (2), for

$$d(x^2 - 3y + xy) \equiv 2x\, dx - 3\, dy + x\, dy + y\, dx = 0,$$

whence (2) results.

When equation (1), written in differential form,

$$M(x, y)\, dx + N(x, y)\, dy = 0, \tag{5}$$

is such that $M\, dx + N\, dy$ is the exact differential of some function $u(x, y)$,

$$M\, dx + N\, dy \equiv du,$$

we say that (5) is an *exact differential equation*, and its solution is

$$u(x, y) = c. \tag{6}$$

Thus (3) is an exact equation. Note also that any equation with variables separable may be written as an exact equation.

Exact differential equations for which the variables are not separable are comparatively rare in applied work, and when they do occur an examination of them usually brings into evidence the integrable combinations without much difficulty, so that they are readily solved. Sometimes an equation may easily be made exact by multiplying it, when written in the form $M\,dx + N\,dy = 0$, by a suitable function of x and y. To illustrate, consider the equation

$$(2xy^2 + y)\,dx - x\,dy = 0. \tag{7}$$

No term of this equation is individually integrable, nor is it exact as it stands. But the combination $y\,dx - x\,dy$ occurs in the differential

$$d\left(\frac{x}{y}\right) = \frac{y\,dx - x\,dy}{y^2},$$

which suggests that we divide (7) by y^2, or, in other words, multiply it by $1/y^2$. Doing this, we get

$$2x\,dx + \frac{y\,dx - x\,dy}{y^2} = 0. \tag{8}$$

This is now exact, and integration yields immediately

$$x^2 + \frac{x}{y} = c, \qquad x^2 y + x = cy. \tag{9}$$

The factor $1/y^2$ by which (7) was multiplied so as to get the exact equation (8) is called an *integrating factor*. The process of solving a

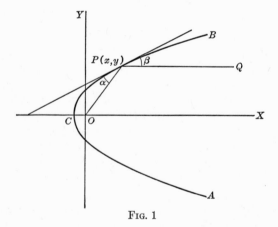

Fig. 1

first-order differential equation can often be made short and simple by noting that some combinations of terms may be made integrable by the use of an integrating factor, whereas the standard methods for solving the equation may be long or complicated. Practice and the experience gained thereby will do much to aid the student in finding such short cuts. We give here a few of the frequently occurring integrable combinations and the functions of which these combinations are the exact differentials.

$$\text{(I)} \qquad x\,dy + y\,dx = d(xy),$$

$$\text{(II)} \qquad \frac{x\,dy - y\,dx}{x^2} = d\left(\frac{y}{x}\right),$$

$$\text{(III)} \qquad \frac{x\,dy - y\,dx}{y^2} = d\left(-\frac{x}{y}\right),$$

$$\text{(IV)} \qquad \frac{x\,dy - y\,dx}{x^2 + y^2} = \frac{\dfrac{x\,dy - y\,dx}{x^2}}{1 + \left(\dfrac{y}{x}\right)^2} = d\left(\tan^{-1}\frac{y}{x}\right),$$

$$\text{(V)} \qquad \frac{x\,dy - y\,dx}{x^2 - y^2} = \frac{\dfrac{x\,dy - y\,dx}{x^2}}{1 - \left(\dfrac{y}{x}\right)^2} = d\left(\frac{1}{2}\ln\frac{x+y}{x-y}\right),$$

$$\text{(VI)} \qquad \frac{2xy\,dy - y^2\,dx}{x^2} = d\left(\frac{y^2}{x}\right),$$

$$\text{(VII)} \qquad \frac{2xy\,dx - x^2\,dy}{y^2} = d\left(\frac{x^2}{y}\right).$$

$$(10)$$

An interesting illustration of the usefulness of the above method arises in connection with the following physical problem. It is required to find the shape of a reflector such that light emanating from a point source is reflected parallel to a fixed line, so that the beam of light consists of parallel rays. Take the origin O as the point source and the x-axis parallel to the fixed line. The reflector will then have the shape of a surface of revolution generated by rotating a certain curve ACB about the x-axis (Fig. 1). If the tangent be drawn to any point $P(x, y)$ on the required curve, the angle α between it and the incident ray OP must, by the physical law of reflection, be equal to the angle β between the tangent line and the horizontal reflected ray PQ. Now $\tan\beta = dy/dx$, and $\tan \angle XOP = y/x$. Hence, since $\angle XOP = \alpha + \beta = 2\beta$, we have

$$\frac{y}{x} = \frac{2\dfrac{dy}{dx}}{1 - \left(\dfrac{dy}{dx}\right)^2}. \qquad (11)$$

Solving for dy/dx, we get

$$y\left(\frac{dy}{dx}\right)^2 + 2x\frac{dy}{dx} - y = 0,$$

or

$$\frac{dy}{dx} = \frac{-x \pm \sqrt{x^2 + y^2}}{y}, \tag{12}$$

a pair of differential equations. When the curve opens to the right, as in the figure, y and dy/dx have the same sign on either the upper or lower half of the curve, so that $y\,dy/dx > 0$ and the positive sign in (12) applies; when the reflected rays proceed to the left, $y\,dy/dx < 0$, and the negative sign in (12) is proper. If desired, therefore, we may fix our attention on either equation obtainable from (12); however, it is just as easy here to consider both possibilities simultaneously. We have

$$x\,dx + y\,dy = \pm\sqrt{x^2 + y^2}\,dx,$$

and thus see that the combination $x\,dx + y\,dy = \frac{1}{2}d(x^2 + y^2)$ appears. Moreover, the function $\sqrt{x^2 + y^2}$ of the combination $(x^2 + y^2)$ is also present, and we therefore form the integrable combination

$$\pm\frac{x\,dx + y\,dy}{\sqrt{x^2 + y^2}} = dx.$$

Integrating, we get

$$\pm\sqrt{x^2 + y^2} = x + c,$$

$$x^2 + y^2 = x^2 + 2cx + c^2,$$

and

$$y^2 = 2c\left(x + \frac{c}{2}\right). \tag{13}$$

These are our generating curves, a family of parabolas with foci at the origin, the point source of light. When c is positive, the parabolas open to the right; and when c is negative, they open to the left. The student will remember that paraboloids of revolution do have the property of reflecting a beam of parallel rays when a point source of light is placed at the focus; this is the well-known "focal property" of a parabola. We have here shown that, conversely, only parabolas possess this characteristic.

PROBLEMS

Find the general solution of each of the following differential equations.

1. $\dfrac{dy}{dx} = x^3 y^5.$

2. $\dfrac{dy}{dx} = x^2 e^{-3y}.$

3. $\dfrac{dy}{dx} = \dfrac{\sin 2x}{y}.$

4. $\dfrac{dy}{dx} = \cot x \tan y.$

5. $\dfrac{dy}{dx} = \dfrac{(2-y)^2}{2\sqrt{1+x}}.$

6. $\dfrac{dy}{dx} = \dfrac{y \ln x}{x}.$

7. $\dfrac{dy}{dx} = \dfrac{1+y^2}{\sec x}.$

8. $\dfrac{dy}{dx} = \dfrac{4x + xy^2}{y - x^2 y}.$

9. $\dfrac{dy}{dx} = \dfrac{2x - y}{x}.$

10. $\dfrac{dy}{dx} = \dfrac{x - 2y}{2x - y}.$

11. $\dfrac{dy}{dx} = \dfrac{2xy^2}{1 - 2x^2 y}.$

12. $\dfrac{dy}{dx} = \dfrac{y}{x + 4y^3}.$

13. $\dfrac{dy}{dx} = \dfrac{x + 2y}{2x}.$

14. $\dfrac{dy}{dx} = \dfrac{x^3 - xy^2 - 1}{x^2 y - y^3}.$

15. $\dfrac{dy}{dx} = \dfrac{y}{x - 2x^2 y}.$

16. $\dfrac{dy}{dx} = \dfrac{y - x^2 - y^2}{x}.$

17. $\dfrac{dy}{dx} = \dfrac{3x^3 - 3xy^2 + y}{x}.$

18. $\dfrac{dy}{dx} = \dfrac{2y\sqrt{y}}{2x\sqrt{y} - x^2}.$

19. $\dfrac{dy}{dx} = \dfrac{\sin y}{1 - x \cos y}.$

20. $\dfrac{dy}{dx} = \dfrac{x^3 + y}{x - x^2 y}.$

21. $\dfrac{dy}{dx} = \dfrac{2y^3 + y}{x - 2xy^2}.$

22. $\dfrac{dy}{dx} = \dfrac{2xy}{3y^2 - x^2}.$

23. $\dfrac{dy}{dx} = \dfrac{e^{-y}}{2y + xe^{-y}}.$

24. $\dfrac{dy}{dx} = \dfrac{2x + y \sin x}{\cos x}.$

25. Using each of the relations (10-II)–(10-V) of Art. 3, obtain the solution of the equation $x\,dy - y\,dx = 0$ in the form $y = cx$.

4. Homogeneous equations. A function $g(x, y)$ is said to be *homogeneous of degree m* if, for any quantity r, we have identically

$$g(rx, ry) = r^m g(x, y),$$

that is, if the replacement of x and y by rx and ry, respectively, yields the original function multiplied by r^m. If, in particular, such replacement leaves the function unaltered, so that it is homogeneous of degree zero, then with $r = 1/x$ we have $g(x, y) = g(1, y/x)$, and g may be expressed as a function of the single argument or combination y/x.

For example, consider the function

$$g(x, y) = \frac{x^2 - 2xy + 3y^2}{2x^2 + y^2} + \sin\frac{y}{x} + \ln\frac{\sqrt{x^2 + y^2}}{x}.$$

Then we have

$$g(rx, ry) = \frac{r^2x^2 - 2r^2xy + 3r^2y^2}{2r^2x^2 + r^2y^2} + \sin\frac{ry}{rx} + \ln\frac{\sqrt{r^2x^2 + r^2y^2}}{rx}$$

$$= g(x, y),$$

so that this function is homogeneous of degree zero. We may therefore write it as a function of the single argument y/x:

$$g\left(1, \frac{y}{x}\right) = \frac{1 - 2\frac{y}{x} + 3\left(\frac{y}{x}\right)^2}{2 + \left(\frac{y}{x}\right)^2} + \sin\left(\frac{y}{x}\right) + \ln\sqrt{1 + \left(\frac{y}{x}\right)^2}.$$

Likewise, if $g(rx, ry) = g(x, y)$, we get by choosing $r = 1/y$, $g(x, y) = g(x/y, 1)$, a function of the single argument x/y.

If the right-hand member $f(x, y)$ of the differential equation

$$\frac{dy}{dx} = f(x, y) \tag{1}$$

is homogeneous of degree zero, we may put it in the form

$$\frac{dy}{dx} = F\left(\frac{y}{x}\right); \tag{2}$$

in this event, equation (1) is said to be a *homogeneous differential equation*. Either of the substitutions

$$y = vx \tag{3_1}$$

or

$$x = vy \tag{3_2}$$

will then reduce (2) to an equation in which the variables x and v, or y and v, are separable. We shall show this to be true for the substitution (3_1); an entirely analogous argument holds when the relation (3_2) is employed. Using (3_1), equation (2) becomes

$$\frac{dy}{dx} = v + x\frac{dv}{dx} = F(v). \tag{4}$$

Now when $F(v) = v$, equation (4) reduces to $x\,dv/dx = 0$, whence $v = c$, and $y = cx$ is the complete solution. This is, of course, a trivial problem, for when $F(v) = v$, equation (2), which takes the form $dy/dx = y/x$, is immediately solvable by separating the variables. Supposing, therefore, that $F(v) \neq v$, (4) gives us

$$x\frac{dv}{dx} = F(v) - v,$$

and

$$\frac{dv}{F(v) - v} = \frac{dx}{x}. \tag{5}$$

Since the variables x and v have been separated, integration of (5) yields a relation between x and v (and an arbitrary constant). Replacing v by its value y/x, we then get the desired functional relation between x and y.

As an example, consider the equation *

$$\frac{dy}{dx} = \frac{x - 2y}{2x - y}, \tag{6}$$

which is readily seen to be homogeneous. Letting $y = vx$, we get

$$v + x\frac{dv}{dx} = \frac{1 - 2v}{2 - v},$$

$$x\frac{dv}{dx} = \frac{1 - 2v}{2 - v} - v = \frac{1 - 4v + v^2}{2 - v},$$

$$\frac{2 - v}{1 - 4v + v^2}\,dv = \frac{dx}{x},$$

$$\frac{-4 + 2v}{1 - 4v + v^2}\,dv + 2\frac{dx}{x} = 0,$$

$$\ln(1 - 4v + v^2) + 2\ln x = \ln c,$$

$$\ln x^2(1 - 4v + v^2) = \ln c,$$

$$x^2\left(1 - \frac{4y}{x} + \frac{y^2}{x^2}\right) = c,$$

$$x^2 - 4xy + y^2 = c. \tag{7}$$

Equation (6) might equally well have been solved by means of the substitution (3_2). Sometimes it may happen that the solution of a

* See Problem 10, Art. 3.

homogeneous equation is more quickly or easily obtained by one of the substitutions (3) than by the other, but this is usually difficult to predict beforehand. Generally speaking, the only guide in making a choice between the two possible substitutions is the following. Write the given homogeneous equation in the form $M\,dx + N\,dy = 0$; if the coefficient M of dx contains fewer or simpler terms than N, set $x = vy$, $dx = v\,dy + y\,dv$; and if N is simpler than M, set $y = vx$, $dy = v\,dx + x\,dv$. This procedure will simplify somewhat the multiplication of one of the coefficients by the new differential expression.

5. Linear equations. A differential equation of the first order is said to be *linear* when it is of the first degree in the dependent variable and its derivative. Thus the equation

$$\frac{dy}{dx} = f(x, y) \tag{1}$$

is linear if $f(x, y)$ is of the first degree in y; it may then be written in the form

$$\frac{dy}{dx} + Py = Q, \tag{2}$$

where P and Q are functions of x only. Since the left-hand member of (2) consists of the sum of two terms, one containing y and the other its derivative, the possibility is suggested of multiplying (2) throughout by some function of x so as to have on the left the exact derivative of a product, i.e., it may be possible to render the equation exact by the use of an integrating factor that involves x only. Hence we seek tentatively a function $R(x)$ such that

$$R\frac{dy}{dx} + RPy \tag{3}$$

shall be the derivative of some combination. Now the first term in the expression (3) will arise if we differentiate the product Ry, and we therefore try to find R such that

$$R\frac{dy}{dx} + RPy = \frac{d}{dx}(Ry) = R\frac{dy}{dx} + y\frac{dR}{dx}.$$

This relation will evidently hold if

$$\frac{dR}{dx} = RP. \tag{4}$$

But, since P is a function of x only, (4) is a separable differential equation for the determination of the integrating factor R. We thus have

$$\frac{dR}{R} = P\,dx,$$

$$\ln R = \int P\,dx,$$

$$R = e^{\int P\,dx}. \tag{5}$$

We have omitted the introduction of a constant of integration since we seek merely one integrating factor, and as simple a one as possible. The function R given by (5) thus serves to solve the linear equation (2); we have, in fact,

$$e^{\int P\,dx}\frac{dy}{dx} + e^{\int P\,dx}\,Py = Qe^{\int P\,dx},$$

$$e^{\int P\,dx}\,y = \int Qe^{\int P\,dx}\,dx + c,$$

$$y = e^{-\int P\,dx}\int Qe^{\int P\,dx}\,dx + ce^{-\int P\,dx}. \tag{6}$$

Equation (6) is in effect a formula for the solution of (2). The function y as given by (6) thus will be completely determined provided merely that the two indicated integrations are performed.

Linear differential equations (including those of order higher than the first, which are considered in Part II of this chapter) are of considerable importance in engineering applications because of their frequent occurrence. Some of the physical problems leading to linear equations of first order will be discussed in Art. 7 and in later chapters; we now examine a formal problem in order to illustrate the manner in which a linear equation is solved. Consider the equation

$$\frac{dy}{dx} = \frac{e^x - 3xy}{x^2}. \tag{7}$$

This may be written in the form (2),

$$\frac{dy}{dx} + \frac{3}{x}y = \frac{e^x}{x^2}, \tag{8}$$

so that it is linear with $P = 3/x$, $Q = e^x/x^2$. We have here

$$R = e^{\int P\,dx} = e^{\int 3\frac{dx}{x}}$$

$$= e^{3\ln x} = x^3. \tag{9}$$

In the last step we have made use of the identity $e^{\ln A} = A$, which is of frequent utility in our work. Multiplying (8) by x^3, we then get

$$x^3 \frac{dy}{dx} + 3x^2 y = xe^x,$$

which is evidently exact, as it should be. Consequently

$$x^3 y = \int xe^x \, dx = (x - 1)e^x + c,$$

and

$$y = \frac{(x - 1)e^x}{x^3} + \frac{c}{x^3}. \tag{10}$$

In all the foregoing, Arts. 2–5, we have arbitrarily assigned to x and y the roles of independent and dependent variables, respectively. Evidently this is a matter of nomenclature only, and similar discussions may be applied to the equation

$$\frac{dx}{dy} = \phi(x, y). \tag{11}$$

If a given differential equation is homogeneous when written in the form $dy/dx = f(x, y)$, it is apparent that the equation $dx/dy = 1/f(x, y) = \phi(x, y)$ will likewise be homogeneous. If the equation is one in which the variables are separable or one for which an integrating factor may be found by inspection, it is again immaterial whether we consider the form $dy/dx = f(x, y)$ or the form $dx/dy = \phi(x, y)$. But it may happen that a given differential equation, when written in the form (1), is not linear in y and dy/dx, whereas it will be linear in x and dx/dy when written in the form (11). For example, the equation

$$\frac{dy}{dx} = \frac{y^2}{e^y - 3xy}$$

is obviously not linear in y and dy/dx, but if we write it

$$\frac{dx}{dy} = \frac{e^y - 3xy}{y^2} = \frac{e^y}{y^2} - \frac{3}{y} x,$$

we see that it is linear in x and dx/dy—it is, in fact, identical in form with (7), only x and y having been interchanged. If, therefore, a specific equation does not appear to be susceptible to the methods of Arts. 2–4 and is not linear in y and dy/dx when written in the form (1), it is well to put the equation in the form (11) to see whether it may be linear in x and dx/dy.

PROBLEMS

Solve each of the differential equations in Problems 1–20.

1. $\dfrac{dy}{dx} = \dfrac{3y^3 - x^3}{3xy^2}.$

2. $\dfrac{dy}{dx} = 4e^{2x} + 2y.$

3. $\dfrac{dy}{dx} = \dfrac{y}{x} - \cot \dfrac{y}{x}.$

4. $\dfrac{dy}{dx} = \dfrac{3 - xy}{2x^2}.$

5. $\dfrac{dy}{dx} = (1 + y)\csc x - \cot x.$

6. $\dfrac{dy}{dx} = \dfrac{4x^2 + 3y^2}{2xy}.$

7. $\dfrac{dy}{dx} = \dfrac{x^2 + 2y}{x}.$

8. $\dfrac{dy}{dx} = \dfrac{4x^2 - 2y}{x}.$

9. $\dfrac{dy}{dx} = \dfrac{y - x \sin x - \cos x}{x}.$

10. $\dfrac{dy}{dx} = \dfrac{xe^{-y/x} + y}{x}.$

11. $\dfrac{dy}{dx} = \dfrac{y}{x + \sqrt{xy}}.$

12. $\dfrac{dy}{dx} = \dfrac{4 \ln x - 2x^2 y}{x^3}.$

13. $\dfrac{dy}{dx} = \dfrac{y - \sqrt{x^2 - y^2}}{x}.$

14. $\dfrac{dy}{dx} = \dfrac{\sin x - (x - y)\cos x}{\sin x}.$

15. $\dfrac{dy}{dx} = \dfrac{1}{x - y}.$

16. $\dfrac{dy}{dx} = \dfrac{y - 1}{ye^y - x}.$

17. $\dfrac{dy}{dx} = 1 + \dfrac{y}{x} - \cos^2 \dfrac{y}{x}$

18. $\dfrac{dy}{dx} = \dfrac{y}{x} + \dfrac{y}{x \ln (y/x)}.$

19. $\dfrac{dy}{dx} = \dfrac{\sqrt{x^2 + y^2} + y}{x}.$

20. $\dfrac{dy}{dx} = \dfrac{2x + 2y}{3x + y}.$

21. Solve Problem 22 of the list following Art. 3 by considering the equation as homogeneous.

22. Solve Problem 24 of the list following Art. 3 by considering the equation as linear.

23. Solve the equation $dy/dx = y/(x + y)$ by three methods.

24. (a) By making the substitutions $x = x_1 + h$, $y = y_1 + k$, and then determining proper values of the constants h and k, show that the equation

$$\frac{dy}{dx} = \frac{a_1 x + b_1 y + c_1}{a_2 x + b_2 y + c_2},$$

where $a_1/b_1 \neq a_2/b_2$, may be transformed into the homogeneous equation

$$\frac{dy_1}{dx_1} = \frac{a_1 x_1 + b_1 y_1}{a_2 x_1 + b_2 y_1}.$$

Hence solve the equation

$$\frac{dy}{dx} = \frac{2x + 2y - 6}{3x + y - 7}.$$

(b) If, in the equation of part (a), $a_1/b_1 = a_2/b_2$, show that the substitution $z = a_1 x + b_1 y$ will transform this equation into one in which the variables are separable. Hence solve the equation

$$\frac{dy}{dx} = \frac{x + 2y - 3}{2x + 4y - 1}.$$

25. Show that *Bernoulli's equation*,

$$\frac{dy}{dx} + Py = Qy^n,$$

where P and Q are functions of x only and n is a constant other than zero or unity, may be transformed into a linear equation by the substitution $z = y^{1-n}$. Hence solve the equation

$$\frac{dy}{dx} = \frac{xy^2 + 2y}{x}.$$

If n is zero or unity, how may the equation be solved?

6. Equations of order higher than the first. The simplest type of differential equation of order n is

$$\frac{d^n y}{dx^n} = F(x), \tag{1}$$

for we get by immediate integration,

$$\frac{d^{n-1}y}{dx^{n-1}} = \int F(x)\,dx + c_1,$$

$$\frac{d^{n-2}y}{dx^{n-2}} = \iint F(x)\,dx^2 + c_1 x + c_2,$$

$$\cdot\ \cdot\ \cdot\ \cdot\ \cdot\ \cdot\ \cdot\ \cdot\ \cdot\ \cdot\ \cdot\ \cdot\ \cdot\ \cdot,$$

so that n integrations yield y as the sum of an n-fold integral of $F(x)$ and a polynomial of degree $n-1$ with n arbitrary constants as its coefficients.

Consider next an equation from which the dependent variable y is lacking. We make the substitution *

$$p = \frac{dy}{dx}, \tag{2}$$

together with the resulting substitutions,

$$\frac{dp}{dx} = \frac{d^2 y}{dx^2}, \qquad \frac{d^2 p}{dx^2} = \frac{d^3 y}{dx^3}, \qquad \cdots, \qquad \frac{d^{n-1}p}{dx^{n-1}} = \frac{d^n y}{dx^n}, \tag{3}$$

and consequently the original equation of order n with y as dependent variable is replaced by an equation of order $n-1$ with p as dependent variable. If, in particular, the given equation is of second order, this substitution gives us an equation of the first order to which one of the

---

* If dy/dx is also lacking, but two or more higher derivatives appear, we set p equal to the derivative of lowest order present and make corresponding substitutions for the higher derivatives.

methods already discussed may apply. When p may be found in terms of x and $n - 1$ arbitrary constants, an integration will then give us the general solution of the original equation.

As an example, consider the equation

$$\frac{d^2y}{dx^2} + 2\frac{dy}{dx} - 6x - 3 = 0. \tag{4}$$

The dependent variable y does not appear in this equation, so that we may substitute $p = dy/dx$, $dp/dx = d^2y/dx^2$. Then equation (4), of the second order in x and y, becomes

$$\frac{dp}{dx} + 2p - 6x - 3 = 0, \tag{5}$$

which is linear of the first order in p and dp/dx. We solve this by the method of Art. 5, getting, since e^{2x} is an integrating factor,

$$e^{2x}p = \int (6x + 3)e^{2x}\, dx = 3xe^{2x} + c_1,$$

$$p = \frac{dy}{dx} = 3x + c_1 e^{-2x},$$

and

$$y = \frac{3x^2}{2} + c_1' e^{-2x} + c_2, \tag{6}$$

where $c_1' = -c_1/2$ and c_2 are arbitrary constants.

An equation from which the independent variable x is lacking may likewise be transformed into an equation of lower order by means of the substitution (2).* Here, however, it is necessary to get an equation in y and p, so that instead of the relations (3) we require expressions for $d^k y/dx^k$ $(k = 2, 3, \cdots, n)$ in terms of p and its derivatives with respect to y. We have

$$\frac{d^2y}{dx^2} = \frac{dp}{dx} = \frac{dp}{dy}\frac{dy}{dx} = p\frac{dp}{dy},$$

$$\frac{d^3y}{dx^3} = \frac{d}{dx}\left(p\frac{dp}{dy}\right) = \frac{d}{dy}\left(p\frac{dp}{dy}\right) \cdot \frac{dy}{dx} = p^2\frac{d^2p}{dy^2} + p\left(\frac{dp}{dy}\right)^2, \tag{7}$$

and so on. If the equation of order $n - 1$, obtained by substituting the values of $dy/dx, \cdots, d^n y/dx^n$ as given by (2) and (7), can be solved for p in terms of y, we can find x as a function of y by integration.

* See footnote, p. 16.

To illustrate the procedure, let us solve the equation

$$y\frac{d^2y}{dx^2} + \left(\frac{dy}{dx}\right)^2 + 4 = 0. \tag{8}$$

Since x is absent, we set $dy/dx = p$, $d^2y/dx^2 = p\, dp/dy$, getting

$$yp\frac{dp}{dy} + p^2 + 4 = 0,$$

$$\frac{p\, dp}{p^2 + 4} + \frac{dy}{y} = 0,$$

$$\tfrac{1}{2}\ln(p^2 + 4) + \ln y = \ln c_1,$$

$$(p^2 + 4)y^2 = c_1^2,$$

$$p^2 = \frac{c_1^2}{y^2} - 4 = \frac{c_1^2 - 4y^2}{y^2},$$

$$p = \frac{dy}{dx} = \frac{\pm\sqrt{c_1^2 - 4y^2}}{y},$$

$$\frac{y\, dy}{\sqrt{c_1^2 - 4y^2}} = \pm\, dx,$$

$$-\sqrt{c_1^2 - 4y^2} = \pm 4(x + c_2),$$

$$16(x + c_2)^2 + 4y^2 = c_1^2.^* \tag{9}$$

There are other types of equations that may be solved by special methods, but we shall consider in this book only one other class of equations of order higher than the first. These, designated as linear differential equations, are of such great importance in engineering that we shall devote all of Part II of this chapter to their study.

PROBLEMS

Solve the following differential equations; y', y'', and y''', respectively, denote dy/dx, d^2y/dx^2, and d^3y/dx^3.

1. $y'' = x\cos x - 24x^2$.   **2.** $yy'' = y'^2$.
3. $x^2y'' + 2xy' = 1$.   **4.** $y'' + y'^2 + 1 = 0$.
5. $(1 + y'^2)^3 = 4y''^2$.   **6.** $x^3y''' + x^2y'' = 2x - 3$.

* It may be observed that this particular example can be solved more easily if we notice that the first two terms of equation (8) represent the exact derivative of $y\, dy/dx$; hence one integration yields $y\, dy/dx + 4x = C_1/2$. A second integration then gives us the solution $y^2 + 4x^2 = C_1x + C_2$, which is equivalent to (9).

7. $xy'' - 2xy'^2 - y' = 0.$ 8. $yy'' + y'^2 = 2y'.$
9. $yy'' + 2y'^2 = 0.$ 10. $2yy'' + y^2 = y'^2.$
11. $y'' + k^2 y^2 = 0.$ 12. $yy'' - y'^2 + y' = 0.$
13. $y^2 y'' = y'.$ 14. $x^2 y'' + y'^2 + xy' = 3x^2.$
15. $yy'' = 2y'^2 + 4y^2.$ 16. $xy'' + y'^2 = 1.$
17. $xy'' - 2xy'^2 = y'.$ 18. $2x^2 y'' + y'^2 = 4xy'.$
19. $yy'' + y'^2 + 1 = 0.$ 20. $y'y''' + y'^2 = 2y''^2.$

7. Applications. We shall treat in this article a few geometric and physical problems leading to differential equations. Further problems into which first and higher order differential equations enter are considered in connection with other topics in later sections of this book.

(*a*) *Orthogonal trajectories.* By an orthogonal trajectory of a family of curves is meant a curve that cuts *each* member of the given family at right angles. Thus, if the given family consists of the straight lines $y = c$ parallel to the x-axis, the straight line $x = $ const. will be an orthogonal trajectory, and the aggregate of lines $x = c'$ will constitute a family of orthogonal trajectories to the family $y = c$.

In the preceding simple example, it was easy to obtain the orthogonal trajectories by geometric intuition. To illustrate the general procedure, let us find the orthogonal trajectories of the family of circles

$$x^2 + y^2 = cx, \tag{1}$$

all of which pass through the origin and have their centers on the x-axis. In order that two curves shall intersect at right angles, it is evidently necessary that the slope of one curve at the point of intersection be equal to the negative reciprocal of the slope of the other curve at that point. Hence we first find the expression for the slope of the circles at the point (x, y) and then take the negative reciprocal of this expression as the value of dy/dx for the orthogonal trajectories. Differentiating, with respect to x, the equation of our family of circles, we get

$$2x + 2y \frac{dy}{dx} = c. \tag{2}$$

Eliminating the arbitrary constant c between the given equation (1) and the derived equation (2), we have

$$x^2 + y^2 = 2x^2 + 2xy \frac{dy}{dx},$$

and the slope of the circles is given by

$$\frac{dy}{dx} = \frac{y^2 - x^2}{2xy}. \tag{3}$$

Consequently the differential equation of the required trajectories will be

$$\frac{dy}{dx} = \frac{2xy}{x^2 - y^2}. \tag{4}$$

This is a homogeneous differential equation which may be solved by the method of Art. 4. However, if we write it in the form

$$2xy\,dx - x^2\,dy + y^2\,dy = 0, \tag{5}$$

the combination $2xy\,dx - x^2\,dy$ suggests the differential of x^2/y: $d(x^2/y) = (2xy\,dx - x^2\,dy)/y^2$. Hence $1/y^2$ is an integrating factor for (5), and we have

$$\frac{2xy\,dx - x^2\,dy}{y^2} + dy = 0,$$

$$\frac{x^2}{y} + y = c',$$

$$x^2 + y^2 = c'y. \tag{6}$$

The orthogonal trajectories (6) of the circles (1) are therefore also circles passing through the origin but with their centers on the y-axis.

In our definition of orthogonal trajectories we have emphasized the fact that each member of the given family is to be cut at right angles. It is therefore important that we eliminate the arbitrary constant between the given equation of the family and the derived equation in order to obtain an expression for the slope of any one of the given family. Thus (3) represents the slope of the circle through the point (x, y), and since this may be any point we have an expression for the slope of each circle. If we had taken the value of dy/dx as given by (2),

$$\frac{dy}{dx} = \frac{c - 2x}{2y},$$

and had taken instead of (4) the relation

$$\frac{dy}{dx} = \frac{2y}{2x - c},$$

we should have obtained

$$\frac{dy}{y} = \frac{2\,dx}{2x - c},$$

$$\ln y = \ln (2x - c) + \ln c'',$$

$$y = c''(2x - c), \tag{7}$$

a doubly infinite family of straight lines. Now, for any particular value
of c, equation (1) gives us a particular circle with center at $(c/2, 0)$,
and then (7) represents the family of straight lines cutting that circle
at right angles. For a given value of c', equation (6) gives us a curve
cutting all the curves (1) orthogonally, whereas (7) yields merely a
system of straight lines no one of which cuts all the circles (1) at right
angles. Hence equation (6) represents the true orthogonal trajectories
of our circles (1).

The concept of orthogonal trajectories has been presented here as a
purely geometric application. It is, however, also of considerable
importance physically in connection with field problems, as we shall
see in Chapter X.

(b) *Dynamics.* Of fundamental importance in mechanics are
Newton's three laws of motion, which we state here for ready reference.

I. A particle persists in its state of rest, or of motion in a straight
line with constant velocity, unless some force acts to change that state.

II. The rate of change of momentum of a particle is proportional to
the force acting on it and is in the same direction as the force.

III. Action and reaction are equal in magnitude and opposite in
direction.

The second law, which includes the first as a special case, states that
the force F acting on a particle of constant mass m moving with varying velocity v is proportional to the time rate of change of the momentum mv, or

$$F = k \frac{d}{dt}(mv) = km \frac{dv}{dt} = kma,$$

where $a = dv/dt$ is the acceleration of the particle and k is a constant
of proportionality depending upon the system of units employed.*
When c.g.s. (centimeter-gram-second) units are used, so that mass is
measured in grams and acceleration in centimeters per second per
second, we may take F in dynes, so that $k = 1$, or we may take F in
grams, so that $k = 1/g$, where g is the gravitational constant, approximately equal to 980.5 cm./sec.^{2} When f.p.s. (foot-pound-second)
units are used, so that mass is measured in pounds and acceleration
in feet per second per second, F may be measured in poundals, making
$k = 1$, or in pounds, making $k = 1/g$, where now $g = 32.17$ ft./sec.^{2}
approximately.

Consider now a mass of 100 lb. being drawn along a rough surface.
Let the force in the direction of motion be 30 lb., let the force of friction
be 20 lb., and let there be an air resistance whose magnitude in pounds

* See Appendix.

is equal to twice the speed in feet per second at any instant. If the body starts from rest at time $t = 0$, what will be the velocity and the displacement from the initial position at time t?

Let x (ft.) be the displacement from the initial position ($x = 0$), and let v (ft./sec.) be the velocity at time t (sec.). Here the force acting in the direction of motion will be positive, and the forces opposing the motion will be negative. Consequently the resultant force F (lb.) will be $30 - 20 - 2v = 10 - 2v$, and we have as the equation of motion

$$10 - 2v = \frac{100}{g}\frac{dv}{dt}, \tag{8}$$

where $g = 32.17$ ft./sec.^{2} This is a differential equation of the first order in which the variables are separable, so that we write

$$\frac{dv}{5 - v} = \frac{g}{50}\,dt. \tag{9}$$

Instead of finding the general solution of (9) and then determining the arbitrary constant, it is more convenient to integrate (9) between limits. Since the body starts from rest at time $t = 0$, we have $v = 0$ when $t = 0$. This corresponding pair of values will serve as lower limits in our integration, the upper limits being $v = v$ and $t = t$. Hence we have

$$\int_0^v \frac{dv}{5 - v} = \int_0^t \frac{g}{50}\,dt, \tag{10}$$

$$\left[\ln(5 - v)\right]_0^v = \left[-\frac{gt}{50}\right]_0^t,$$

$$\ln\frac{5 - v}{5} = -\frac{gt}{50},$$

$$\frac{5 - v}{5} = e^{-gt/50},$$

and

$$v = \frac{dx}{dt} = 5(1 - e^{-gt/50}) \text{ ft./sec.} \tag{11}$$

Likewise, since $x = 0$ when $t = 0$, we get

$$\int_0^x dx = \int_0^t 5(1 - e^{-gt/50})\,dt,$$

$$x = 5\left(t + \frac{50}{g}e^{-gt/50} - \frac{50}{g}\right) \text{ ft.} \tag{12}$$

Equations (11) and (12) give us the velocity and displacement as functions of t.

We see that both v and x are zero for $t = 0$, as they should be. Moreover, both v and x increase with increased t, but x increases without limit while v tends to a limiting value:

$$\lim_{t \to \infty} v = 5 \text{ ft./sec.} \tag{13}$$

This agrees with the value of v found by setting $dv/dt = 0$ in equation (8). The values of v and of x at a particular time t are readily found by using a table such as Peirce's.* Thus, when $t = 1$ sec., we get

$$v\Big]_{t=1} = 5(1 - e^{-32.17/50}) = 5(1 - e^{-0.6434})$$

$$= 5(1 - 0.5255) = 2.37 \text{ ft./sec.,}$$

$$x\Big]_{t=1} = 5\left[1 + \frac{50(0.5255 - 1)}{32.17}\right] = 1.31 \text{ ft.}$$

(c) *Chemical solutions.* Consider a tank initially holding 100 gal. of a salt solution in which 50 lb. of salt are dissolved. Suppose that 3 gal. of brine, each containing 2 lb. of dissolved salt, run into the tank per minute, and that the mixture, kept uniform by stirring, runs out of the tank at the rate of 2 gal./min. Find the amount of salt in the tank at any time t.

Let Q be the number of pounds of salt present at the end of t minutes. Then dQ/dt will be the rate at which the salt content is changing. This in turn will be the number of pounds gained per minute owing to the inflow of brine, minus the number of pounds lost per minute owing to the outflow of the mixture. The rate of gain will evidently be 3 (gal./min.) $\times$ 2 (lb./gal.) = 6 (lb./min.). Let C (lb./gal.) denote the concentration; then the rate of loss will be 2 (gal./min.) $\times C$ (lb./gal.) = $2C$ (lb./min.). Now the number of gallons of brine present after t minutes will be $100 + t$, since the original number, 100, is increased by 1 gal. each minute. Hence $C = Q/(100 + t)$, and we get the relation

$$\frac{dQ}{dt} = 6 - \frac{2Q}{100 + t}. \tag{14}$$

This is a linear differential equation of the first order (Art. 5), the integrating factor for which is readily found to be $(100 + t)^2$. Thus we find, upon integration, the general solution

$$(100 + t)^2 Q = 2(100 + t)^3 + k,$$

* B. O. Peirce, "A Short Table of Integrals." We shall make frequent reference to this book.

where k is a constant. Using the initial conditions, $Q = 50$ when $t = 0$, we obtain $k = -1,500,000$, and therefore

$$Q = 2(100 + t) - \frac{1,500,000}{(100 + t)^2} \text{ lb.} \tag{15}$$

It is seen that Q is an increasing function of t. At the end of 30 min., for example, we have

$$Q\Big]_{t=30} = 260 - \frac{1,500,000}{16,900} = 171 \text{ lb.}$$

(d) *Heat flow*. Experimental studies of the flow of heat in a body lead to the following laws:

I. The quantity of heat in a body is proportional to its mass and to its temperature.

II. Heat flows from a higher to a lower temperature.

III. The rate of flow across an area is proportional to the area and to the temperature gradient, i.e., the rate of change of temperature with respect to distance, normal to the area.

Let us apply laws II and III to a problem in steady-state heat flow, that is, flow, the rate of which is independent of the time.* We shall use c.g.s. units. Let q (cal./sec.) be the constant quantity of heat flowing through an area A (cm.^{2}), perpendicular to the direction of flow, in each second, let u (°C.) be the temperature at a point P of the body, and let x (cm.) be the distance, taken as positive in the direction of flow, from some point chosen as origin to the point P. Then by law III, the magnitude of q will be $KA\,du/dx$, where the constant K is a property of the material of the body and is called the thermal conductivity (cal./cm. deg. sec.). But, by law II, the temperature decreases in the direction of flow, and consequently du/dx will be negative. Hence we have the relation

$$q = -KA \frac{du}{dx}. \tag{16}$$

Now consider a cylindrical pipe containing steam and covered with an insulating material of thermal conductivity K. Let the inner and outer radii of the insulating cylindrical shell be x_1 and x_2, respectively, and let the corresponding temperatures be u_1 and u_2, respectively. Under steady-state conditions, heat will flow radially, and the area A perpendicular to the direction of flow will be the lateral surface of a cylinder of radius x, where $x_1 \leqq x \leqq x_2$. For a length L

* The more general problem of heat flow at a rate varying with the time leads to a partial differential equation; see Chapter VII, Art. 71.

(cm.) of pipe, we therefore have $A = 2\pi x L$, and consequently our differential equation (16) here takes the form

$$q = -2\pi K L x \frac{du}{dx}. \tag{17}$$

Separating the variables and integrating between limits, we get

$$q \int_{x_1}^{x_2} \frac{dx}{x} = -2\pi K L \int_{u_1}^{u_2} du$$

$$q \ln \frac{x_2}{x_1} = -2\pi K L (u_2 - u_1),$$

and

$$q = \frac{2\pi K L (u_1 - u_2)}{\ln (x_2/x_1)}. \tag{18}$$

Hence the rate of flow of heat through a cylindrical shell is directly proportional to the difference of inner and outer temperatures and inversely proportional to the logarithm of the ratio of outer to inner radius.

(e) *Electric circuits.* We shall consider here merely a simple circuit containing a resistance and an inductance in series with a source of electromotive force (e.m.f.).* Resistance is that circuit parameter which opposes the current, and which causes the dissipation of energy in the form of heat. If a potential drop E_R (volts) across a coil is proportional to the current I (amperes) flowing through the coil, we have Ohm's law,

$$E_R = RI, \tag{19}$$

where R (ohms) is the resistance. Inductance is that circuit parameter which opposes a change in current, and is analogous to inertia in mechanics. If a change in the magnetic flux linking with a circuit, due to a variation of current flowing in the circuit, gives rise to a counter e.m.f., there will be a corresponding drop in potential E_L proportional to the time rate of change of current,

$$E_L = L \frac{dI}{dt}, \tag{20}$$

where L is the inductance and t the time; when E_L is given in volts, I in amperes, and t in seconds, L will be measured in henries.

* Series circuits containing resistance, inductance, and capacitance are considered in Art. 14 (d). More complicated network problems are discussed in Chapter XI.

The fundamental laws for electric circuits and networks are known as Kirchhoff's laws:

I. The algebraic sum of all the potential drops around a closed circuit is zero.

II. The algebraic sum of all the currents flowing into a junction is zero.

In dealing with a single closed circuit, only law I is needed. For our case, it leads immediately to the relation

$$E - RI - L\frac{dI}{dt} = 0,$$

or

$$L\frac{dI}{dt} + RI = E, \tag{21}$$

where E is the impressed e.m.f. and I is the instantaneous current at time t. Let us solve the differential equation (21) under the assumption that a constant e.m.f. E is impressed at time $t = 0$, no current having flowed previously. Since the variables are then separable, we have

$$\int_0^I \frac{dI}{E - RI} = \int_0^t \frac{dt}{L},$$

$$\left[\ln (E - RI)\right]_0^I = -\left[\frac{Rt}{L}\right]_0^t,$$

$$\ln\frac{E - RI}{E} = -\frac{Rt}{L},$$

$$I = \frac{E}{R}(1 - e^{-Rt/L}). \tag{22}$$

Inspection of equation (22) shows us that the current increases with increase of t, and approaches as a limit the Ohm's law value E/R. Usually the ratio R/L is numerically large, so that after only a short time the current value I differs from E/R by a negligible amount.

(f) *Deflection of beams.* Consider first a rod under tension (Fig. 2), and assume that Hooke's law is obeyed, so that the force F is proportional to the elongation e produced. The work done by the force $F = ke$ will then be

$$W = \int_0^e F\, de = k\int_0^e e\, de = \tfrac{1}{2}ke^2 = \tfrac{1}{2}Fe.$$

Fig. 2

Thus the work done is equal to the product of the average force, $\frac{1}{2}(0 + F)$, and the distance through which the varying force acts.

We now think of the rod as being a fiber of a small piece of a bent beam (Fig. 3). Let ΔA (ft.^{2}) be the cross-section area of the fiber and

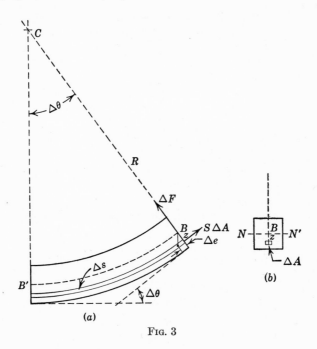

Fig. 3

let S (lb./ft.^{2}) be the stress per unit cross-section area, so that the force $S \, \Delta A$ now corresponds to an elongation Δe (ft.). If Δs (ft.) is the natural unstretched length of the fiber, $\Delta e/\Delta s$ is the stretch per unit length. Consequently we have, by Hooke's law,

$$S = E \frac{\Delta e}{\Delta s}, \qquad (23)$$

where the constant of proportionality, E (lb./ft.^{2}), is Young's modulus, or the modulus of elasticity.

The surface containing those fibers whose lengths are unaltered when the beam is bent is called the *neutral surface*. The curve of one of these fibers, BB', is called the *elastic curve* of the beam. The line NN', lying in the neutral surface and shown in the cross-section view of Fig. 3(b), is called the neutral axis for that section. Let R (ft.) be the length of BC, the radius of curvature of the fiber BB', and let z

(ft.) be the distance of ΔA from NN'. Then we have the proportion

$$\frac{\Delta e}{\Delta s} = \frac{z}{R}. \tag{24}$$

The moment of the force $S \, \Delta A$ about NN' is $zS \, \Delta A$. Summing all such moments over the cross-section of the beam, we get the bending moment M producing the deflection of the beam:

$$M = \int zS \, dA = \int zE \frac{\Delta e}{\Delta s} \, dA = \int zE \frac{z}{R} \, dA = \frac{E}{R} \int z^2 \, dA$$

by (23) and (24). But the last integral represents the moment of inertia I (ft.[4]) of the cross-sectional area of the beam with respect to the neutral axis NN'. Hence

$$M = \frac{EI}{R}. \tag{25}$$

Since the force $S \Delta A$ acting on the fiber of length Δs corresponds to the elongation Δe, the work done in deforming this fiber, and hence the potential energy stored in the fiber, is $\Delta W = \frac{1}{2} S \, \Delta A \, \Delta e$. Making use of relations (23) and (24), we then get

$$\Delta W = \frac{1}{2} E \frac{\Delta e}{\Delta s} \Delta A \, \Delta e = \frac{1}{2} E z^2 \, \Delta A \, \frac{\Delta s}{R^2}.$$

Integrating first over the area A, we find that the potential energy stored in the portion of the beam of length Δs and radius of curvature R is $\frac{1}{2} EI \, \Delta s / R^2$; integrating again along the entire length L (ft.) of the beam, we get

$$W = \frac{EI}{2} \int_0^L \frac{ds}{R^2} \tag{26}$$

as the total potential energy stored in the beam.

Now we have, from differential calculus,

$$R = \frac{(1 + y'^2)^{3/2}}{y''}, \qquad ds = (1 + y'^2)^{1/2} \, dx, \qquad \frac{ds}{R^2} = \frac{y''^2 \, dx}{(1 + y'^2)^{5/2}}.$$

When the bending is small, y' is small, and we may neglect y'^2 in comparison with unity, obtaining the close approximations

$$R = \frac{1}{y''}, \qquad \frac{ds}{R^2} = y''^2 \, dx.$$

Using these approximations, equations (25) and (26) become

$$M = EIy'', \tag{27}$$

$$W = \frac{EI}{2} \int_0^L y''^2 \, dx. \tag{28}$$

Formula (27) is applied in several problems in this chapter; formula (28) will be used in connection with the beam problem of Art. 52, Chapter V.

Suppose that the beam rests on supports at the ends and is slightly bent under the action of a number of concentrated loads (Fig. 4).

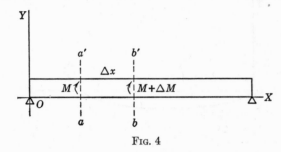

FIG. 4

Take two sections, aa' at x and bb' at $x + \Delta x$, with no forces between them acting on the beam, and let M and $M + \Delta M$ be the bending moments at the two sections. We now define the *vertical shear* Q at the section aa' as the algebraic sum of all the vertical forces acting on the beam to the left of aa', including the reaction at the end. Choosing the upward direction as positive, Q will be positive or negative according as the resultant force to the left of aa' is upward or downward. For the difference between the bending moments at the two sections, we have approximately

$$\Delta M = Q \, \Delta x,$$

whence, in the limit,

$$\frac{dM}{dx} = Q. \tag{29}$$

Using the approximation (27) for M, (29) becomes

$$EIy''' = Q. \tag{30}$$

Suppose now that the beam carries a load q per unit length. Then ΔQ, the (negative) increment in Q in going from section aa' to section bb', is approximately

$$\Delta Q = -q \, \Delta x,$$

which gives, from (30), in the limit,

$$EIy^{\text{iv}} = -q. \tag{31}$$

When this equation is used with the y-axis positive toward the convex side of the curve, as in the application of Art. 25, Chapter II, it becomes

$$EIy^{iv} = q. \tag{31'}$$

As an example let us find the equation of the elastic curve of a beam L ft. long resting on supports at the ends and slightly bent under a uniform load of q lb./ft. We take the origin at the left support and the y-axis positive upwards, then consider the bending moment at a section through P at a distance x from the origin (Fig. 5). We set the

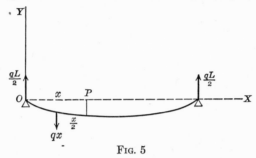

Fig. 5

expression for bending moment at P, EIy'' (equation (27)), equal to the sum of the moments of all the forces acting on the beam on one side of P, say to the left. Since y'' is positive on a curve when it is concave toward the positive direction of the y-axis, we write a moment as positive when it tends to produce concavity in the direction of the positive y-axis. Since y'' is negative on a curve when it is concave toward the negative y-axis, we write a moment as negative when it tends to produce concavity in the direction of the negative y-axis. The load qL is equally distributed on the supports causing an upward force $qL/2$ at the left support, and the load on OP, acting downward at the middle point of OP, is qx. The differential equation of the elastic curve of the beam is therefore

$$EIy'' = \frac{qL}{2} x - qx \cdot \frac{x}{2}. \tag{32}$$

Here x and y are in feet, E in pounds per square foot, and I in feet to the fourth power. Integrating,

$$EIy' = \frac{qLx^2}{4} - \frac{qx^3}{6} + C_1.$$

Since $y' = 0$ when $x = L/2$, $C_1 = -qL^3/24$. Integrating again,

$$EIy = \frac{qLx^3}{12} - \frac{qx^4}{24} - \frac{qL^3 x}{24} + C_2.$$

Since $x = 0$ when $y = 0$, $C_2 = 0$, and the elastic curve of the beam is

$$y = \frac{-q}{24EI}(x^4 - 2Lx^3 + L^3x).$$

The maximum deflection is the value of $-y$ when $x = L/2$, that is

$$\text{Max. defl.} = \frac{q}{24EI}\left(\frac{L^4}{16} - \frac{2L^4}{8} + \frac{L^4}{2}\right) = \frac{5qL^4}{384EI}.$$

We could have obtained the differential equation (32) by starting with equation (31), $EIy^{\text{iv}} = -q.$

Integrating,

$$EIy''' = -qx + C.$$

Since the shear $Q = EIy''' = 0$ when $x = L/2$, $C = qL/2$. Integrating again,

$$EIy'' = -\frac{qx^2}{2} + \frac{qL}{2}x + C'.$$

Since the bending moment $M = EIy'' = 0$ when $x = 0$, $C' = 0$. Hence

$$EIy'' = -\frac{qx^2}{2} + \frac{qLx}{2}.$$

It is clear that this differential equation (32) holds for any position of the point P, that is, for all values of x in the range $0 \leqq x \leqq L$. Accordingly, we are justified in using deflection values y and slope values y', wherever they are known in that range, for the evaluation of the constants of integration C_1 and C_2, and the resulting elastic curve equation is valid throughout that range.

Suppose now that our beam, of length L ft. and simply supported at its ends as before, carries a concentrated load of W lb. at its center instead of a uniform load of q lb./ft. Then for any point P in the left half of the beam we have

$$EIy_1'' = \frac{W}{2}x, \qquad 0 \leqq x \leqq \frac{L}{2}, \tag{33}$$

and for a section in the right half,

$$EIy_2'' = \frac{W}{2}x - W\left(x - \frac{L}{2}\right) = \frac{W}{2}(L - x), \qquad \frac{L}{2} \leqq x \leqq L. \tag{34}$$

Using the conditions $y_1 = 0$ for $x = 0$, $y_1' = 0$ for $x = L/2$, (33) yields, as the equation of the left half of the elastic curve,

$$EIy_1 = \tfrac{1}{48}Wx(4x^2 - 3L^2), \qquad 0 \leqq x \leqq L/2; \tag{35}$$

similarly, with $y_2 = 0$ for $x = L$ and $y_2' = 0$ for $x = L/2$, we get

$$EIy_2 = \tfrac{1}{48}W(L - x)(L^2 - 8Lx + 4x^2), \qquad L/2 \leqq x \leqq L, \quad (36)$$

for the right half of the elastic curve. Because of symmetry, only (33) and its solution (35) are needed in this particular problem; (34) and (36) are obtainable, if desired, by replacing x by $L - x$ in (33) and (35), respectively.

PROBLEMS

1. Find the orthogonal trajectories of the family of hyperbolas $x^2 - y^2 = cy$.

2. Find the orthogonal trajectory, through the point $(0, 1)$, of the system of curves $y = 2x + ce^x$.

3. Find the orthogonal trajectories of the ellipses $4x^2 + y^2 = cx$.

4. Find the curves that cut the circles $x^2 + y^2 = c$ at an angle of $45°$.

5. If a cylindrical can with vertical axis contains a liquid and is rotated about its axis with constant angular velocity ω, show that the surface of the liquid forms a paraboloid of revolution.

6. A 20-lb. weight moves in a horizontal straight line under the joint action of a constant force of 12 lb., in the direction of motion, and a resisting force whose magnitude in pounds is equal to four times the instantaneous velocity in feet per second. If the body starts from rest, find its velocity and the distance traveled after $\tfrac{1}{2}$ sec.

7. A weight of 100 lb. falls from rest. If the resistance of the air is proportional to the speed, and if the limiting speed is 173 ft./sec., find the speed at the end of 5 sec.

8. A body falls in a medium offering resistance proportional to the speed at any instant. If the limiting speed is 50 ft./sec., and if the body attains half that speed in 1 sec., what was the initial speed?

9. A 10-lb. weight is projected downward with an initial velocity of 15 ft./sec. If the air resistance is proportional to the speed, and if the limiting speed is 30 ft./sec., how far has the body traveled when it has reached a speed of 20 ft./sec.?

10. A 100-lb. weight falls from rest against resistance proportional to the speed at any instant. If the body attains speeds of v_1 and v_2 ft./sec. after 1 and 2 sec. in motion, respectively, find an expression for the limiting velocity.

11. A 10-lb. weight falls from rest against a resistance proportional to the speed at any time t (sec.). (a) Letting L (ft./sec.) denote the limiting speed, find an expression for the velocity v (ft./sec.). (b) Find the ratio of the times required to reach $\tfrac{1}{2}$ and $\tfrac{9}{10}$ of the limiting speed.

12. A body falls from rest against resistance proportional to the square root of the speed at any instant. If the limiting speed is 36 ft./sec., find the time required to attain a speed of 25 ft./sec.

13. A 10-lb. weight falls from rest against a resistance proportional to e^v, where v (ft./sec.) is the speed. If the limiting speed is 3 ft./sec., how long will it take the body to attain a speed of 2 ft./sec.?

14. A body falls from rest against a resistance proportional to the cube of the speed at any instant. If the limiting speed is 10 ft./sec., find the time required to attain a speed of 8 ft./sec.

15. A body falls into a liquid of the same density as the body. The entering velocity is 16 ft./sec., and the velocity 1 sec. later is 9 ft./sec. Assuming resistance proportional to $v^{3/2}$, where v (ft./sec.) is velocity, find the time required for the speed to be reduced to 10% of its initial value.

16. A body falls into a liquid of the same density as the body, the entering velocity being 1 ft./sec. at time $t = 0$. When $t = t_1$ and $t = t_2$ sec., the velocity has the respective values v_1 and v_2 ft./sec. Assuming that the resistance is proportional to v^n ($n \neq 1$), show that the constant n satisfies the relation $t_2(v_1^{1-n} - 1) = t_1(v_2^{1-n} - 1)$, and hence may be determined.

17. A rope is wound on a rough circular cylinder of radius a (ft.) and with horizontal axis (Fig. 6). Let the coefficient of friction be μ, let T (lb.) be the tension in the rope at any point P, and let θ be the angle AOP. Neglecting the weight of the rope, show that, when the rope is on the point of slipping in the counterclockwise direction,

$$\frac{dT}{d\theta} = \mu T,$$

whence

$$T = T_0 e^{\mu\theta},$$

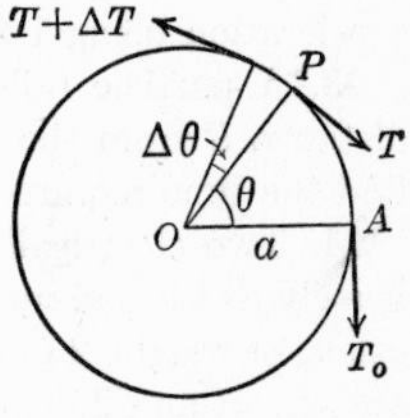

FIG. 6

where T_0 is the tension at A.

18. If the rope of Problem 17 is of linear density ρ (lb./ft.), show that when friction is neglected the tension T is given by

$$\frac{dT}{d\theta} = \rho a \cos \theta,$$

whence, assuming $T = 0$ for $\theta = 0$,

$$T = \rho a \sin \theta.$$

19. (a) Taking into account both the weight of the rope of Problems 17 and 18, and the friction, show that

$$\frac{dT}{d\theta} = \mu T + \rho a(\cos \theta + \mu \sin \theta).$$

(b) If one end of the rope is at the level of the axis of the cylinder and the other hangs down to a distance L (ft.) below the axis, show that

$$L = \frac{2\mu a}{1 + \mu^2}(1 + e^{\pi\mu}).$$

(c) If one end of the rope is at the top of the cylinder and the other is at the level of the axis, show that

$$\tan 2\alpha = e^{(\pi/2)\tan \alpha},$$

where $\mu = \tan \alpha$.

20. A particle moves in a horizontal line acted upon only by an attractive force which varies inversely as the cube of the distance x from a fixed point O. If the particle starts from rest when $x = 20$ ft., and if $x = 10$ ft. when $t = 1$ sec., find the time it takes to travel three-fourths the total distance to O.

21. A particle of weight w (lb.) is constrained to move in a horizontal circular path of radius a (ft.). (a) If the particle is subjected only to a resistance proportional to the square of the speed at any instant, show that the differential equation of motion may be written as

$$w \frac{d^2\theta}{dt^2} + kga \left(\frac{d\theta}{dt}\right)^2 = 0,$$

where θ (rad.) is the angular displacement and t (sec.) is time. (b) If the particle starts with an initial speed v_0 (ft./sec.), show that

$$\theta = \frac{w}{kga} \ln \left(1 + \frac{kgv_0t}{w} \right).$$

22. A particle moves from rest at a distance of 16 ft. from a center of attraction, the force varying inversely as the three-halves power of the distance, and the initial acceleration being 1 ft./sec.^{2} Find the time required to reach the center.

23. A particle falls from rest toward the earth (radius $R = 3960$ miles) at a distance R from the earth's surface. Using the inverse square law of attraction, find the time required to reach the earth.

24. Two electrically charged particles repel each other with a force varying inversely as the square of the distance between them. One particle is fixed, and the other, of weight 2 grams, is free to move without friction. Initially both particles are at rest and 20 cm. apart. (a) Find the initial force of repulsion if the velocity is 100 cm./sec. when the particles are 40 cm. apart. (b) Determine the time required for the particles to be 80 cm. apart.

25. A tank initially contains 50 gal. of fresh water. Brine, containing 2 lb./gal. of salt, flows into the tank at the rate of 2 gal./min., and the mixture, kept uniform by stirring, runs out at the same rate. How long will it take for the quantity of salt in the tank to increase from 40 to 80 lb.?

26. A tank contains 50 gal. of fresh water. Brine containing 2 lb./gal. of salt runs into the tank at the rate of 2 gal./min., and the mixture, kept uniform by stirring, runs out at the rate of 1 gal./min. Find (a) the amount of salt present when the tank contains 60 gal. of brine; (b) the concentration of salt in the tank at the end of 20 min.

27. A tank originally contains 100 gal. of brine holding 100 lb. of salt in solution. Two gallons of brine, each containing 3 lb. of dissolved salt, enter the tank per minute, and the mixture, assumed uniform, leaves at the rate of 3 gal./min. (a) Find the time for the concentration to reach 90% of its maximum value. (b) Find the maximum amount of salt in the tank, and sketch a graph showing the variation of salt content with time.

28. A tank contains 100 gal. of brine. Three gallons of brine, each containing 2 lb. of dissolved salt, enter the tank per minute, and the mixture, assumed uniform, leaves at the rate of 2 gal./min. If the concentration is to be 1.8 lb./gal. at the end of 1 hour, how many pounds of salt should there be present in the tank originally?

29. A tank contains 100 gal. of water. Brine containing A lb./gal. of salt enters the tank at the rate of 3 gal./min. The mixture, thoroughly stirred, leaves the tank at the rate of 2 gal./min. If the concentration is to be 2 lb./gal. at the end of 20 min., find the value of A.

30. A tank contains fresh water. Brine holding 2 lb./gal. of salt runs into the tank at the rate of 4 gal./min., and the mixture, assumed uniform, runs out at the rate of 3 gal./min. If the concentration is to reach 90% of its maximum value in 30 min., how many gallons of water should there be in the tank originally?

31. A tank holds 100 gal. of brine. Brine containing 4 lb./gal. of salt flows into the tank at the rate of 1 gal./min., and the mixture, kept uniform, flows out at the rate of 2 gal./min. If the maximum amount of salt in the tank occurs at the end of 20 min., what was the initial salt content of the tank?

32. Tank A initially contains 50 gal. of brine in which 50 lb. of salt are dissolved. Two gallons of fresh water enter A per minute, and the mixture, assumed uniform, passes from A into a second tank B, initially containing 50 gal. of fresh water, at the same rate. The resulting mixture, also kept uniform, leaves B at the rate of 2 gal./min. Find the amount of salt in tank B at the end of 1 hour.

33. Tank A contains 100 gal. of brine holding 50 lb. of salt in solution, and tank B contains 100 gal. of water. If the brine runs out of A into B at the rate of 3 gal./min. while the mixture, kept thoroughly stirred, is pumped back from B to A at the same rate, when will A contain twice as much salt as B?

34. A pipe 20 meters long and 30 cm. in diameter contains steam at $100°$ C. The pipe is covered by a layer of insulation 10 cm. thick and having a thermal conductivity $K = 0.00225$ cal./cm. deg. sec. If the temperature of the outer surface of the insulation is kept at $35°$ C., find (a) the heat loss in calories per hour; (b) the temperature halfway through the insulation.

35. A pipe 20 cm. in diameter contains steam at $100°$ C. and is covered with a certain insulation 5 cm. thick. The outside temperature is kept at $40°$ C. By how much should the thickness of insulation be increased in order that the rate of heat loss shall be decreased 20%?

36. A steam pipe of radius 3 cm. and at $100°$ C. is wrapped with a 1-cm. layer of insulation of thermal conductivity 0.0003 cal./cm. deg. sec. and then that layer is wrapped with a 2-cm. layer of insulation of conductivity 0.0002 cal./cm. deg. sec. At what temperature must the outside surface be maintained in order that 0.008 cal. will flow from each square centimeter of pipe surface each second?

37. A pipe, 10 cm. in diameter, contains steam at $100°$ C. It is to be covered with two coats of insulating material, each 2.5 cm. thick, one of asbestos ($K = 0.00060$ cal./cm. deg. sec.) and the other of magnesia ($K = 0.00017$ cal./cm. deg. sec.). If the outside surface temperature is $30°$ C., find the heat loss per hour from a meter length of pipe when the asbestos is inside and the magnesia outside, and vice versa. Compare the two results for efficiency of insulation.

38. Generalize Problem 37 as follows. Let r be the radius of the pipe, let K_1 and K_2 be the thermal conductivities of inner and outer coats, respectively, let t be the common thickness of the two coats, and suppose the pipe and outside temperatures to be fixed. Show that less heat loss is obtained when $K_1 < K_2$.

39. According to Newton's law, the rate at which heat is lost by a heated body is proportional to the difference in temperature between the body and the surrounding medium when that temperature difference is small. If a thermometer is taken outdoors, where the temperature is $5°$ C., from a room in which the temperature is $20°$, and the reading drops $10°$ in 1 min., how long after its removal will the reading be $6°$?

40. An inductance of 2 henries and a resistance of 20 ohms are connected in series with an e.m.f. of E volts. If the current is zero when time $t = 0$, find the current at the end of 0.01 sec. if (a) $E = 100$ volts; (b) $E = 100 \sin 150t$ volts.

41. A constant inductance of 1 henry and a variable resistance R are connected in series with a constant e.m.f. E (volts). If $R = 1/(5 + t)$ (ohms) at time t (sec.), and if the current $I = 0$ at $t = 0$, what is E to be in order that the current be 30 amp. when $t = 5$ sec.?

42. A coil of inductance 1 henry and resistance 10 ohms is connected in series with an e.m.f. of $E_0 \sin 10t$ volts, where t (sec.) is time. When $t = 0$, the current I (amp.) is zero. If $I = 5$ amp. when $t = 0.1$ sec., what must be the value of E_0?

43. An inductance of 1 henry and a resistance of 2 ohms are connected in series with an e.m.f. of Ee^{-t} volts. No current is flowing initially. (*a*) If the current $I = 10$ amp. when $t = 1$ sec., how much must E be? (*b*) If $E = 50$ volts, when will the current be 5 amp.?

44. An inductance L (henries) and a resistance R (ohms) are connected in series with an e.m.f. of Ee^{-at} volts, where E and a are positive constants and t is time (sec.). Initially the current I (amp.) is zero. Find an expression for I as a function of t, and determine at what time the current reaches its maximum value.

45. When a resistance R (ohms) and a capacitance C (farads) are connected in series with an e.m.f. E (volts), the charge Q (coulombs) on the condenser and the current I (amp.) are given by

$$R\frac{dQ}{dt} + \frac{Q}{C} = E, \qquad I = \frac{dQ}{dt}, \qquad R\frac{dI}{dt} + \frac{I}{C} = \frac{dE}{dt}.$$

If $R = 2000$ ohms, $C = 5 \times 10^{-6}$ farad, and $I = 10$ amp. for $t = 0$, find the current when $t = 0.01$ sec. if (*a*) $E = 100$ volts; (*b*) $E = 100 \sin 120\pi t$ volts.

46. An e.m.f. of 100 volts is applied to a circuit containing a resistance of 1000 ohms and a capacitance of 5×10^{-6} farad in series. When the condenser is fully charged and current no longer flows through the resistance, the e.m.f. is removed and the circuit closed. Using the relations of Problem 45, find the current and the charge on the condenser 0.01 sec. after the removal of the e.m.f.

47. Radium decomposes at a rate proportional to the amount present. If the half-period is 1600 years, i.e., if half of any given amount is decomposed in 1600 years, find the percentage remaining at the end of 100 years.

48. In a certain chemical reaction, a molecule of one substance A combines with one of a second substance B to form one molecule of C. If a and b are the amounts of A and B, respectively, at time $t = 0$, the amount of C at time t is given by

$$\frac{dx}{dt} = k(a - x)(b - x),$$

where k is a constant and $x = 0$ when $t = 0$. If $x = 1$ when $t = 10$ min., find x at the end of 20 min. (*a*) when $a = 4$, $b = 3$; (*b*) when $a = b = 4$.

49. A tank of cross-sectional area A (ft.^{2}) at water level has an orifice of area B (ft.^{2}) at the bottom. If h (ft.) is the depth of water in the tank at any time t (sec.), the rate of flow from the tank is given by

$$A\frac{dh}{dt} = -0.6B\sqrt{2gh},$$

where $g = 32.17$ ft./sec.^{2} Find the time required to empty a cylindrical tank 4 ft. in diameter and 8 ft. long through a hole 2 in. in diameter if the tank is initially full and its axis is (*a*) vertical; (*b*) horizontal.

50. Two tanks, one in the form of a right circular cylinder with vertical axis and the other a right circular cone with vertex down, have equal base radii and identical orifices. If the time required to empty completely is the same for both tanks, find the ratio of their altitudes.

51. A tank in the form of a right circular cone, with vertex down, has an orifice at the bottom whose area, controlled by a float valve, is proportional to the depth of water in the tank at each instant. Of the time to empty completely, what percentage is required for half the volume of water to escape?

52. (*a*) If p (lb./in.^{2}) is the atmospheric pressure and ρ (lb./in.^{3}) is the density of air at a height of h (in.) above the surface of the earth, show that

$$\frac{dp}{dh} + \rho = 0.$$

(b) Assuming that p is proportional to ρ, and taking $p = 14.7$ and 12.0 lb./in.^{2} at the surface of the earth and at a height of 1 mile, respectively, find the pressure at a height of 3 miles.

53. Using the same data as in Problem 52, but assuming that p is proportional to $\rho^{1.4}$, find the theoretical height of the atmosphere.

54. If sea water under a pressure of P lb./ft.^{2} weighs $64(1 + 2 \times 10^{-8}P)$ lb./ft.^{3}, find the weight of a cubic foot of water at a depth of 2 miles below sea level.

55. A beam L ft. long is held horizontal at its ends by having its ends embedded in masonry. Find the equation of the elastic curve and the maximum deflection of the beam if it carries a uniform load of q lb./ft. *Note:* This problem differs from the example of the text in that there is, in addition, an unknown moment exerted by the masonry which keeps the beam horizontal at the end; but we also have the additional condition that $dy/dx = 0$ at the end.

56. Work Problem 55 if, in addition, there is a concentrated load of P lb. at the middle point of the beam.

57. A cantilever beam (one end free and the other fixed horizontally) of length L ft. weighs q lb./ft. and carries a load of P lb. at its free end. Taking the origin at the free end, find the equation of the elastic curve. Show that the same effect at the free end can be produced by distributing a load of W lb. uniformly along the beam as by applying a load of 37.5% of W lb. at the free end.

58. A beam L ft. long, weighing q lb./ft., is simply supported at one end and is fixed horizontally at the other. Find the distance from the simply supported end to the point of maximum deflection.

59. A beam 12 ft. long and weighing 2 lb./in. is simply supported at two points 35 in. from each end. Determine whether the middle point of the elastic curve is above or below the level of the points corresponding to the supports, and draw the elastic curve.

60. A 12-ft. beam, weighing 20 lb./ft., is simply supported at its left end and at a point 4 ft. from its right end. Taking the origin at the left end, find the equation of the portion of the elastic curve between supports and the distance from the left end to the point of maximum deflection within that span.

61. Making use of the result of Problem 60, find the equation of the portion of the elastic curve for $8 \leqq x \leqq 12$.

62. A beam 6 ft. long and of negligible weight is simply supported at its ends. Two concentrated loads, each equal to 100 lb., are supported at the points of trisection of the beam. Find the distance from an end to the nearer point where the deflection has half its maximum value.

63. A beam 8 ft. long is simply supported at its ends. Three concentrated loads, each equal to P lb., are supported at distances 2, 4, and 6 ft., respectively, from one end. Neglecting the weight of the beam, find the maximum deflection.

64. One end of a 2-ft. beam is fixed horizontally in masonry, its midpoint is simply supported, and a concentrated load of 20 lb. is applied to its other end. Neglecting the weight of the beam, find the reaction at the simple support.

65. A beam 4 ft. long and of negligible weight is simply supported at its ends and carries a load of 100 lb./ft. uniformly distributed over the central 2 ft. of its length. Find the ratio of the maximum deflection of this beam to that of a simply supported 4-ft. beam having the load of 200 lb. uniformly distributed over its entire length.

66. A 6-ft. beam, simply supported at its points of trisection, carries a load of 9 lb. at each end. Neglecting the weight of the beam, find the ratio of the deflection at the center to that at an end of the beam.

67. A cantilever beam is L ft. long and has a rectangular cross-section of breadth b ft. and depth h ft. It carries a load whose density is w lb./ft.^{3} and whose depth is proportional to the distance from the free end. Neglecting the weight of the beam, find the maximum deflection.

68. A beam of length $2L$ ft., carrying a uniform load of q lb./ft., is supported at its ends and at its middle point. Taking the origin at the middle point, find the equation of the elastic curve of the right half of the beam. Show that the maximum deflection is $(39 + 55\sqrt{33})qL^4/2^{16}EI$, and that this is 42% of the value it would have if the beam were cut in two at its middle point.

69. A simply supported beam L ft. long carries a concentrated load of P lb. at a distance of c ft. from the left end. (a) Taking the origin at the left end, find the equation of the elastic curve of the portion of the beam to the left of P and of that to the right of P. (b) If $c < L/2$, show that the distance from the left end to the point of maximum deflection is greater than c and less than $L/2$, and find the maximum deflection.

PART II.   LINEAR EQUATIONS OF HIGHER ORDER

8. Definitions and properties. In engineering applications, the most important and most frequently occurring differential equations of order higher than the first are those called linear equations. A *linear differential equation of order n* is one of the form

$$a_0(x)\frac{d^n y}{dx^n} + a_1(x)\frac{d^{n-1}y}{dx^{n-1}} + \cdots + a_{n-1}(x)\frac{dy}{dx} + a_n(x)y = f(x), \quad (1)$$

where $a_0, a_1, \cdots, a_n, f$ are functions of the independent variable x only, $a_0 \neq 0$. It derives its name from the fact that it is linear, i.e., of the first degree, in the dependent variable y and its derivatives.

We have already considered, in Art. 5, the linear equation of first order, and we found a formula in terms of the coefficients P and Q for the general solution of this particular linear equation. Unfortunately, it is impossible to find a similar formula for the general solution of (1) when n is greater than unity. It is possible, however, to find the general solutions of certain linear equations of special types, as we shall see.

Before discussing methods of solving an equation of the form (1), let us investigate the properties of such an equation. We can deduce one of its properties from our knowledge about the first-order linear equation,

$$\frac{dy}{dx} + Py = Q. \quad (2)$$

It was found in Art. 5 that the general solution of (2) is of the form

$$y = u + cv, \tag{3}$$

where u and v are functions of x determined from P and Q, and c is an arbitrary constant. Now if we set $c = 0$ in (3), we get a particular solution $y = u$; that is,

$$\left(\frac{d}{dx} + P\right)u = Q$$

identically. Moreover, since $v = e^{-\int P\,dx}$ by equation (6), Art. 5, we have

$$\left(\frac{d}{dx} + P\right)cv = -cPe^{-\int P\,dx} + cPe^{-\int P\,dx} = 0$$

identically. Thus the right member of the general solution (3) of equation (2) consists of the sum of two parts; one of these parts, u, when substituted for y in the left-hand side of (2) yields the function Q, while the other, cv, yields zero. In other words, $y = u$ is a particular solution of (2), free of any arbitrary element, and $y = cv$ is the general solution of the equation obtained from (2) by replacing the right member by zero.

This property of the first-order equation is possessed by the linear equation (1) of any order n. For, if $y = Y_P$ is any particular solution of (1), and if $y = Y_c$, involving n arbitrary constants, is the general solution of the equation

$$a_0 \frac{d^n y}{dx^n} + a_1 \frac{d^{n-1}y}{dx^{n-1}} + \cdots + a_{n-1}\frac{dy}{dx} + a_n y = 0, \tag{4}$$

obtained from (1) by replacing $f(x)$ by zero, then

$$a_0 \frac{d^n(Y_P + Y_c)}{dx^n} + a_1 \frac{d^{n-1}(Y_P + Y_c)}{dx^{n-1}} + \cdots + a_n(Y_P + Y_c)$$

$$= \left(a_0 \frac{d^n Y_P}{dx^n} + \cdots + a_n Y_P\right) + \left(a_0 \frac{d^n Y_c}{dx^n} + \cdots + a_n Y_c\right)$$

$$= f + 0. \tag{5}$$

Since $y = Y_P + Y_c$ is, by (5), a solution of equation (1), and, moreover, is one containing n arbitrary constants, it is the general solution of (1).

Any function Y_P, satisfying (1), is called a *particular integral* of (1), and the expression Y_c, satisfying (4), is called the *complementary function* of (1). An equation of the form (4) is said to be a *homogeneous*

linear equation; an equation of type (1), with $f(x) \neq 0$, is called
non-homogeneous. The result found may then be stated as follows.
The general solution of a non-homogeneous linear equation is made up
of the sum of a particular integral of the given equation and the
general solution of the corresponding homogeneous equation.

Now suppose that $y = y_1$ is any solution of the homogeneous equation (4), so that

$$a_0 \frac{d^n y_1}{dx^n} + a_1 \frac{d^{n-1} y_1}{dx^{n-1}} + \cdots + a_n y_1 = 0 \qquad (6)$$

identically. Then $y = c_1 y_1$, where c_1 is an arbitrary constant, will also
satisfy (4). For we have

$$a_0 \frac{d^n (c_1 y_1)}{dx^n} + a_1 \frac{d^{n-1} (c_1 y_1)}{dx^{n-1}} + \cdots + a_n (c_1 y_1)$$

$$= c_1 \left(a_0 \frac{d^n y_1}{dx^n} + a_1 \frac{d^{n-1} y_1}{dx^{n-1}} + \cdots + a_n y_1 \right) = 0,$$

by (6). If $y = y_1$ and $y = y_2$ are any two solutions of (4), we can
show also that $y = y_1 + y_2$ will be a solution. For by hypothesis we
have

$$a_0 \frac{d^n y_1}{dx^n} + a_1 \frac{d^{n-1} y_1}{dx^{n-1}} + \cdots + a_n y_1 = 0,$$

$$a_0 \frac{d^n y_2}{dx^n} + a_1 \frac{d^{n-1} y_2}{dx^{n-1}} + \cdots + a_n y_2 = 0,$$

whence

$$a_0 \frac{d^n (y_1 + y_2)}{dx^n} + a_1 \frac{d^{n-1} (y_1 + y_2)}{dx^{n-1}} + \cdots + a_n (y_1 + y_2)$$

$$= a_0 \frac{d^n y_1}{dx^n} + a_1 \frac{d^{n-1} y_1}{dx^{n-1}} + \cdots + a_n y_1$$

$$+ a_0 \frac{d^n y_2}{dx^n} + a_1 \frac{d^{n-1} y_2}{dx^{n-1}} + \cdots + a_n y_2$$

$$= 0.$$

From these two facts it further follows that, if $y = y_1$, $y = y_2$, $\cdots$,
$y = y_n$ are n solutions of the homogeneous equation (4), the linear
combination

$$c_1 y_1 + c_2 y_2 + \cdots + c_n y_n, \qquad (7)$$

where the c's are arbitrary constants, will likewise satisfy (4). Now it may happen that there exists among the functions $y_1, y_2, \cdots, y_n$ a linear relation

$$b_1 y_1 + b_2 y_2 + \cdots + b_n y_n = 0, \tag{8}$$

where the b's are definite constants not all zero, satisfied identically in x. For example, suppose that $y_1 = \sin x$, $y_2 = \cos x$, $y_3 = \cos (x + \pi/3)$. Then since

$$y_3 = \cos \left(x + \frac{\pi}{3} \right) = \cos x \cos \frac{\pi}{3} - \sin x \sin \frac{\pi}{3}$$

$$= \frac{1}{2} \cos x - \frac{\sqrt{3}}{2} \sin x,$$

there exists the identical linear relation

$$\frac{\sqrt{3}}{2} y_1 - \frac{1}{2} y_2 + y_3 = 0,$$

of the form (8) with $b_1 = \sqrt{3}/2$, $b_2 = -\frac{1}{2}$, $b_3 = 1$. When a relation (8) does exist among $y_1, y_2, \cdots, y_n$, these n functions are said to be *linearly dependent;* and when no such relation exists, the functions are *linearly independent.** If $y_1, y_2, \cdots, y_n$ are linearly dependent, the linear combination (7) may be expressed in a form involving less than n arbitrary constants. Thus, for $y_1 = \sin x$, $y_2 = \cos x$, $y_3 = \cos (x + \pi/3)$, we have

$$c_1 y_1 + c_2 y_2 + c_3 y_3 = c_1 \sin x + c_2 \cos x + \frac{c_3}{2} \cos x - \frac{c_3 \sqrt{3}}{2} \sin x$$

$$= c_1' \sin x + c_2' \cos x,$$

where $c_1' = c_1 - c_3 \sqrt{3}/2$, $c_2' = c_2 + c_3/2$. If, however, $y_1, y_2, \cdots, y_n$ are linearly independent, the constants $c_1, c_2, \cdots, c_n$ in (7) are all essential, and hence the linear combination (7) will be the complementary function of equation (1):

$$Y_c = c_1 y_1 + c_2 y_2 + \cdots + c_n y_n, \tag{9}$$

and $y = Y_c$ will be the general solution of (4).

---

* There are several ways of testing a set of functions for linear dependence, the most common of which depends upon the vanishing or non-vanishing of a functional determinant called the Wronskian. It is beyond the scope of this book to consider the theory involved; the interested student is referred to E. L. Ince, "Ordinary Differential Equations."

In order to solve a linear equation (1), we therefore proceed as follows. We first find n linearly independent solutions $y = y_1$, $y = y_2$, $\cdots$, $y = y_n$ of the corresponding homogeneous equation (4) and form the complementary function (9); if $f(x) = 0$, $y = Y_c$ gives us the general solution of the equation. If $f(x) \neq 0$, we next find a particular integral Y_P; then $y = Y_P + Y_c$ will be the general solution sought.

When the coefficients a_0, a_1, $\cdots$, a_n of equation (1) involve x, the process of finding the general solution usually requires special methods. When, however, the a's are all constants, or when the given equation may be transformed into a linear equation with constant coefficients, the methods for finding the general solution are of an elementary nature. We devote the remainder of Part II of this chapter to a discussion of these methods.

9. Operators. In order to solve a linear equation with constant coefficients,

$$a_0 \frac{d^n y}{dx^n} + a_1 \frac{d^{n-1} y}{dx^{n-1}} + \cdots + a_{n-1} \frac{dy}{dx} + a_n y = f(x), \tag{1}$$

we introduce the concept of a differential operator. Let D be a symbol denoting the operation of differentiation with respect to the independent variable,

$$\mathrm{D} \equiv \frac{d}{dx}. \tag{2}$$

D is not a quantity, but an *operator;* when placed to the left of any function of x, it indicates that the function is to be differentiated, and the result of operating on the function with D is the derivative of that function. Thus,

$$\mathrm{D}(3x^2) = 6x, \qquad \mathrm{D}(\sin 2x) = 2 \cos 2x, \qquad \mathrm{D}(xe^x) = (x+1)e^x.$$

We may generalize the definition (2) by writing D^r to indicate the operation of finding the rth derivative,

$$\mathrm{D}^r \equiv \frac{d^r}{dx^r} \qquad (r = 0, 1, 2, \cdots); \tag{2'}$$

thus,

$$\mathrm{D}^2(3x^2) = 6, \qquad \mathrm{D}^3(\sin 2x) = -8 \cos 2x, \qquad \mathrm{D}^r(xe^x) = (x+r)e^x.$$

Although these operators are not algebraic quantities, they have many of the properties of such quantities, for they obey the following fundamental laws of algebra:

$$\text{Addition} \begin{cases} \text{(I)} & \text{The commutative law, } a + b = b + a. \\ \text{(II)} & \text{The associative law, } a + (b + c) = (a + b) + c. \end{cases}$$

$$\text{Multiplication} \begin{cases} \text{(III) The commutative law, } ab = ba. \\ \text{(IV) The associative law, } a(bc) = (ab)c. \\ \text{(V) \ The distributive law, } a(b + c) = ab + ac. \\ \text{(VI) The index law, } a^r a^s = a^{r+s}, \ r \text{ and } s \text{ positive} \\ \qquad \text{integers.} \end{cases}$$

By the formulas of the calculus, for u a function of x, we have analogously,

$$\text{(I)} \qquad (D^r + D^s)u = (D^s + D^r)u.$$

$$\text{(II)} \qquad [D^r + (D^s + D^t)]u = [(D^r + D^s) + D^t]u.$$

$$\text{(III)} \qquad (D^r \cdot D^s)u = (D^s \cdot D^r)u.$$

$$\text{(IV)} \qquad D^r(D^s \cdot D^t)u = (D^r \cdot D^s)D^t u.$$

$$\text{(V)} \qquad D^r(D^s + D^t)u = (D^r \cdot D^s + D^r \cdot D^t)u.$$

$$\text{(VI)} \qquad (D^r \cdot D^s)u = D^{r+s}u.$$

Moreover,

$$D^r(cu) = cD^r u,$$

when c is any constant. Hence we may say that these operators, and sums of such operators *with constant coefficients*, behave *as if* they were algebraic quantities, and may be manipulated algebraically subject to the above laws.

Using operator notation, equation (1) may be written as

$$(a_0 D^n + a_1 D^{n-1} + \cdots + a_{n-1}D + a_n)y = f(x),$$

or, briefly, as

$$\phi(D)y = f(x), \tag{3}$$

where

$$\phi(D) \equiv a_0 D^n + a_1 D^{n-1} + \cdots + a_{n-1}D + a_n. \tag{4}$$

We employ the functional notation $\phi(D)$ to indicate that the operator (4) is a polynomial function of D with constant coefficients, and as such may be treated in accordance with the above laws in the same manner as any other polynomial in a single letter or argument. In particular, $\phi(D)$ may be expressed in factored form as the product of n linear expressions in D. If $r_1, r_2, \cdots, r_n$ are the n roots of the equation

$$\phi(m) \equiv a_0 m^n + a_1 m^{n-1} + \cdots + a_{n-1}m + a_n = 0, \tag{5}$$

we have

$$\phi(m) \equiv a_0(m - r_1)(m - r_2)\cdots(m - r_n),$$

and consequently

$$\phi(D) \equiv a_0(D - r_1)(D - r_2)\cdots(D - r_n). \tag{6}$$

It should be noted that the roots r_1, r_2, $\cdots$, r_n of the auxiliary equation (5) may be arranged in any order, so that the order of the factors in (6) is immaterial.

Let us illustrate what we are doing by means of a concrete example. Consider the operator

$$\phi(D) \equiv D^2 - 3D + 2,$$

and let $\phi(D)$ operate on the function $u = x^2 - 3 \sin x$. Then we have

$$\phi(D)u = (D^2 - 3D + 2)(x^2 - 3 \sin x)$$

$$= D^2(x^2 - 3 \sin x) - 3D(x^2 - 3 \sin x) + 2(x^2 - 3 \sin x)$$

$$= 2 + 3 \sin x - 6x + 9 \cos x + 2x^2 - 6 \sin x$$

$$= 2 - 6x + 2x^2 - 3 \sin x + 9 \cos x.$$

Now the roots of the auxiliary equation,

$$\phi(m) \equiv m^2 - 3m + 2 = 0,$$

are 1 and 2. Hence

$$\phi(D) \equiv (D - 1)(D - 2),$$

or, alternatively,

$$\phi(D) \equiv (D - 2)(D - 1).$$

Then

$$\phi(D)u = (D - 1)[(D - 2)(x^2 - 3 \sin x)]$$

$$= (D - 1)(2x - 3 \cos x - 2x^2 + 6 \sin x)$$

$$= 2 + 3 \sin x - 4x + 6 \cos x - 2x + 3 \cos x + 2x^2 - 6 \sin x$$

$$= 2 - 6x + 2x^2 - 3 \sin x + 9 \cos x,$$

or

$$\phi(D)u = (D - 2)[(D - 1)(x^2 - 3 \sin x)]$$

$$= (D - 2)(2x - 3 \cos x - x^2 + 3 \sin x)$$

$$= 2 + 3 \sin x - 2x + 3 \cos x - 4x + 6 \cos x + 2x^2 - 6 \sin x$$

$$= 2 - 6x + 2x^2 - 3 \sin x + 9 \cos x.$$

We thus get the same result when operating upon $u = x^2 - 3 \sin x$ with all three forms of $\phi(D)$.

The factored form (6) of the operator (4), obtained by the algebraic process of determining the roots of the auxiliary equation (5), will be of considerable utility in our later work.

We proceed now to the consideration of a few formulas involving operators. To begin with, we have

$$De^{mx} = me^{mx}, \qquad D^2e^{mx} = m^2e^{mx}, \qquad \cdots, \qquad D^ne^{mx} = m^ne^{mx},$$

where m is any constant, whence

$$\begin{aligned}
\phi(D)e^{mx} &= (a_0D^n + a_1D^{n-1} + \cdots + a_{n-1}D + a_n)e^{mx} \\
&= (a_0m^n + a_1m^{n-1} + \cdots + a_{n-1}m + a_n)e^{mx} \\
&= \phi(m)e^{mx}. \qquad (7)
\end{aligned}$$

Now if u is a function of x,

$$D(e^{mx}u) = e^{mx}Du + me^{mx}u = e^{mx}(D + m)u,$$

$$\begin{aligned}
D^2(e^{mx}u) &= D[e^{mx}(D + m)u] = e^{mx}(D^2 + mD)u + me^{mx}(D + m)u \\
&= e^{mx}(D^2 + 2mD + m^2)u \\
&= e^{mx}(D + m)^2u.
\end{aligned}$$

These two relations suggest that

$$D^r(e^{mx}u) = e^{mx}(D + m)^ru \qquad (8)$$

for any positive integer r. Let us prove the truth of equation (8) by mathematical induction. If we operate on both members of (8) with D, we get

$$\begin{aligned}
D^{r+1}(e^{mx}u) &= D[e^{mx}(D + m)^ru] \\
&= e^{mx}D(D + m)^ru + me^{mx}(D + m)^ru \\
&= e^{mx}(D + m)^{r+1}u. \qquad (9)
\end{aligned}$$

Therefore, if (8) is true for any particular value of r, it is true for the next higher value of the exponent, since (9) is the same relation as (8) except that $r + 1$ replaces r. But we have found that (8) holds for $r = 1$ and for $r = 2$. Consequently, it holds for $r = 2 + 1 = 3$, and therefore for $r = 3 + 1 = 4$, and so on, so that it is true for any positive integer r. It follows that

$$\begin{aligned}
\phi(D)(e^{mx}u) &= (a_0D^n + a_1D^{n-1} + \cdots + a_{n-1}D + a_n)(e^{mx}u) \\
&= e^{mx}[a_0(D + m)^n + a_1(D + m)^{n-1} + \cdots \\
&\qquad + a_{n-1}(D + m) + a_n]u \\
&= e^{mx}\phi(D + m)u. \qquad (10)
\end{aligned}$$

Formula (10) tells us that, when operating with $\phi(D)$ on the product of e^{mx} and any other function u, we may shift e^{mx} from the right-hand side of the operator to the left if we change D in the operator into $D + m$ and act with the resulting operator on u alone.

As an example, let $\phi(D) = D^2 - D + 4$, and let $m = 3$. Then, by (10),

$$(D^2 - D + 4)(e^{3x}u) = e^{3x}[(D + 3)^2 - (D + 3) + 4]u$$

$$= e^{3x}(D^2 + 5D + 10)u.$$

To verify this relation in a particular case, suppose that $u = x^2$. Then we have, on the one hand,

$$(D^2 - D + 4)(e^{3x}x^2) = D^2(e^{3x}x^2) - D(e^{3x}x^2) + 4e^{3x}x^2$$

$$= 2e^{3x} + 12xe^{3x} + 9x^2e^{3x} - 2xe^{3x}$$

$$- 3x^2e^{3x} + 4x^2e^{3x}$$

$$= e^{3x}(2 + 10x + 10x^2),$$

and, on the other,

$$e^{3x}(D^2 + 5D + 10)x^2 = e^{3x}(2 + 10x + 10x^2).$$

Thus the two methods yield the same result.

The theorem expressed by the relation (10) has the following corollary. If, in particular, $\phi(D) = (D - m)^r$, then

$$(D - m)^r(e^{mx}u) = e^{mx}D^ru. \qquad (11)$$

For example, if $m = 3$, $r = 2$, and $u = x^2$,

$$(D - 3)^2(e^{3x}x^2) = e^{3x}D^2x^2 = 2e^{3x},$$

as may be readily verified by operating upon $e^{3x}x^2$ with $(D - 3)^2$ directly.

PROBLEMS

Perform the indicated operations in Problems 1–5.

1. $(2D^2 - 3D + 5)(x \cos x - 3)$.
2. $(D^2 + 2D - 3)(\tan x - 2/x)$.
3. $(3D^2 + D + 2)(\ln 2x - 1/x^2)$.
4. $(D^3 + 2D - 4)(e^{-x} \sin x + e^{2x})$.
5. $(2D^3 - D^2 + 1)(\ln \cos x - 2 \tan x)$.

In Problems 6–10, resolve the given operator $\phi(D)$ into linear factors, and arrange these factors in all possible orders. Operate upon the given function u with $\phi(D)$ written in each form, and verify the fact that the results obtained are the same.

6. $\phi(D) = D^2 - 1$; $u = e^x + 2e^{-x}$.
7. $\phi(D) = D^2 + 3D + 2$; $u = e^{-2x} + 3x^2$.

8. $\phi(D) = 2D^2 + 3D - 5$; $u = \cos x - 2e^x$.

9. $\phi(D) = D^2 + 2D + 2$; $u = e^{-x} \sin x + 2x^3$.

10. $\phi(D) = D^3 - 2D^2 + D - 2$; $u = \sin x - 2 \cos x + e^{2x}$.

Using formula (10), or its special form (11), carry out the indicated operations in Problems 11–19.

11. $(D^2 + 2D - 1)(e^x \cos x)$.

12. $(D^2 - 2D + 5)(e^x \sin 2x)$.

13. $(D^2 + 4D - 6)(xe^{-2x})$.

14. $(D^3 - 6D^2 + 12D - 8)(x^2 e^{2x})$.

15. $(D^3 - 2D^2 + D)(xe^x)$.

16. $(D^2 - 6D + 9)(e^{3x} \cos^2 x)$.

17. $(D - m)^r [e^{mx}(c_1 + c_2 x + \cdots + c_r x^{r-1})]$.

18. $(D - \ln 2)^3 (2^x x^2)$.

19. $(D + a)^r a^x$.

20. Using Leibnitz's formula for the rth derivative of a product,

$$D^r(uv) = vD^r u + r(D^{r-1}u)(Dv) + \frac{r(r-1)}{2!}(D^{r-2}u)(D^2 v) + \cdots$$
$$+ r(Du)(D^{r-1}v) + uD^r v,$$

where the coefficients are the binomial coefficients, derive formula (10).

10. The complementary function.

We are now in a position to solve completely the homogeneous linear equation with constant coefficients,

$$\phi(D)y \equiv (a_0 D^n + a_1 D^{n-1} + \cdots + a_{n-1}D + a_n)y = 0. \qquad (1)$$

Let $r_1, r_2, \cdots, r_n$ be the roots of the auxiliary equation

$$\phi(m) \equiv a_0 m^n + a_1 m^{n-1} + \cdots + a_{n-1}m + a_n = 0, \qquad (2)$$

and write the operator $\phi(D)$ in factored form,

$$\phi(D) \equiv a_0(D - r_1)(D - r_2) \cdots (D - r_{n-1})(D - r_n).$$

Then equation (1) may be written

$$a_0(D - r_1)(D - r_2) \cdots (D - r_{n-1})(D - r_n)y = 0. \qquad (3)$$

It is easy to see that any solution of the equation

$$(D - r_n)y = 0 \qquad (4)$$

will likewise be a solution of equation (3). For, if y_n is a function satisfying (4), so that $(D - r_n)y_n = 0$ identically, we get

$$\phi(D)y_n \equiv a_0(D - r_1)(D - r_2) \cdots (D - r_{n-1})[(D - r_n)y_n]$$
$$= a_0(D - r_1)(D - r_2) \cdots (D - r_{n-1})(0)$$
$$= 0.$$

Now the solution of equation (4) is readily found. We have

$$\frac{dy}{dx} - r_n y = 0,$$

$$\frac{dy}{y} = r_n \, dx,$$

$$\ln y = r_n x + \ln c_n,$$

$$y = c_n e^{r_n x},$$

where c_n is an arbitrary constant. Consequently $y_n = c_n e^{r_n x}$ is a solution of equation (1). But r_n is any one of the roots of the auxiliary equation (2), and therefore

$$y_1 = c_1 e^{r_1 x}, \qquad y_2 = c_2 e^{r_2 x}, \qquad \cdots, \qquad y_n = c_n e^{r_n x},$$

where the c's are arbitrary, are all solutions of (1). Since, as shown in Art. 8, the sum of two or more solutions of a linear homogeneous equation is also a solution, the linear combination

$$c_1 e^{r_1 x} + c_2 e^{r_2 x} + \cdots + c_n e^{r_n x} \tag{5}$$

will satisfy (1).

If the roots r_1, r_2, $\cdots$, r_n of (2) are all different, the functions $e^{r_1 x}$, $e^{r_2 x}$, $\cdots$, $e^{r_n x}$, will be linearly independent, so that the n c's are all essential. Consequently (5) will be the complementary function sought, and

$$y = c_1 e^{r_1 x} + c_2 e^{r_2 x} + \cdots + c_n e^{r_n x} \tag{6}$$

will be the general solution of the linear homogeneous equation (1) when r_1, r_2, $\cdots$, r_n are distinct numbers.

As an example, consider the equation

$$(2D^2 + 5D - 3)y = 0.$$

The auxiliary equation is here

$$2m^2 + 5m - 3 = 0,$$

and, since $2m^2 + 5m - 3 = (2m - 1)(m + 3)$, the roots are $\frac{1}{2}$ and -3. Hence we have as the general solution of the given equation

$$y = c_1 e^{x/2} + c_2 e^{-3x}.$$

Consider now the case in which the auxiliary equation possesses repeated roots. To illustrate this situation, let there be given the equation

$$(D^2 - 4D + 4)y = 0.$$

Here the auxiliary equation,

$$m^2 - 4m + 4 = 0, \qquad \text{or} \qquad (m - 2)^2 = 0,$$

has the double root 2. Evidently the relation

$$y = c_1 e^{2x} + c_2 e^{2x} = (c_1 + c_2) e^{2x}$$

cannot be the general solution, for the sum of two arbitrary constants may be replaced by a single arbitrary element, $c = c_1 + c_2$, whence the relation $y = ce^{2x}$ is seen to be merely a particular solution. To overcome this difficulty we proceed tentatively as follows. Since $y = ce^{2x}$ is a solution, we try the effect of substituting $y = ue^{2x}$, where u is a function to be determined if possible; that is, we wish to find out whether e^{2x} multiplied by something more general than a constant will likewise satisfy the equation. In this process, we may advantageously apply formula (11) of Art. 9; we have

$$(D^2 - 4D + 4)(e^{2x}u) = (D - 2)^2(e^{2x}u)$$
$$= e^{2x}D^2u.$$

It appears, therefore, that if u is such that $D^2u = 0$, $e^{2x}u$ will satisfy the given equation. Solving the simple differential equation $D^2u = 0$, we get by repeated integration, $Du = c_1$, $u = c_1 x + c_2$. Hence

$$y = (c_1 x + c_2)e^{2x}$$

will satisfy the equation $(D^2 - 4D + 4)y = 0$, and since we now have two essential arbitrary constants, we have succeeded in finding the general solution.

The above process is easily generalized. Let the given equation,

$$\phi(D)y = 0, \tag{7}$$

be such that the auxiliary equation $\phi(m) = 0$ possesses a p-fold root r_1. Then the polynomial $\phi(m)$ contains the factor $(m - r_1)^p$, or $\phi(m) = \phi_1(m)(m - r_1)^p$, where $\phi_1(m)$ is a polynomial of degree $n - p$, with $\phi_1(r_1) \neq 0$. Hence the differential equation may be written

$$\phi_1(D)(D - r_1)^p y = 0. \tag{8}$$

Since $y = e^{r_1 x}$ is a solution of (8), let $y = e^{r_1 x}u$. We get by use of formula (11), Art. 9,

$$\phi_1(D)(D - r_1)^p(e^{r_1 x}u) = \phi_1(D)e^{r_1 x}D^pu = 0,$$

whence integration of $D^pu = 0$, p times, gives us

$$u = c_1 + c_2 x + \cdots + c_p x^{p-1},$$

and

$$y = (c_1 + c_2 x + \cdots + c_p x^{p-1})e^{r_1 x} \tag{9}$$

is a solution of (7). If $\phi_1(m) = 0$ has a repeated root r_2 ($r_2 \neq r_1$), a solution of (7) corresponding to this root may be found similarly. Continuing this process as often as may be necessary, we arrive at the general solution.

As another example of this type of problem, consider the equation

$$(D^5 - 2D^3 + D)y = 0.$$

We find as roots of the auxiliary equation $m^5 - 2m^3 + m = 0$, the numbers 1, 1, -1, -1, 0. Corresponding to the double root 1, we have the solution $y = (c_1 + c_2 x)e^x$; corresponding to -1, we get $(c_3 + c_4 x)e^{-x}$; and corresponding to the single root 0, we have $c_5 e^{0x} = c_5$. Hence the general solution is

$$y = (c_1 + c_2 x)e^x + (c_3 + c_4 x)e^{-x} + c_5.$$

The result (9) may be easily remembered by noting that the portion of the general solution arising from a p-fold root r_1 is given by $e^{r_1 x}$ multiplied by a polynomial in x of degree one less than the number of times the root r_1 occurs. It is good practice also to check the final result by making sure that the general solution contains as many arbitrary constants as the order of the given equation indicates.

We have now formally completed our discussion of the complementary function, and may obtain by purely algebraic means the general solution of any linear homogeneous equation with constant coefficients. However, the case in which the auxiliary equation possesses complex roots requires special investigation in order that the corresponding portion of the solution be properly interpreted and written in a form useful for further manipulation. This is particularly important in engineering work, for, as we shall see in Art. 14 and from time to time in later chapters, the linear differential equations arising in physical problems very often have as their most useful solutions those corresponding to complex roots of the auxiliary equation.

Consider, for example, the equation

$$(D^2 + k^2)y = 0,$$

which appears in connection with a large variety of vibration problems. Here we have $m^2 + k^2 = 0$, so that $m = \pm ik$, where $i = \sqrt{-1}$, and therefore the general solution of the above equation takes the form

$$y = c_1 e^{ikx} + c_2 e^{-ikx}.$$

Now e^x, with x real, may be expanded in a Maclaurin's series,

$$e^x = 1 + x + \frac{x^2}{2!} + \frac{x^3}{3!} + \cdots.$$

If we mechanically replace x by ikx in this series, and make use of the relations $i^2 = -1, i^3 = -i, i^4 = 1, \cdots$, we get

$$e^{ikx} = 1 + ikx - \frac{k^2 x^2}{2!} - i\frac{k^3 x^3}{3!} + \frac{k^4 x^4}{4!} + i\frac{k^5 x^5}{5!} - \cdots$$

$$= \left(1 - \frac{k^2 x^2}{2!} + \frac{k^4 x^4}{4!} - \cdots\right) + i\left(kx - \frac{k^3 x^3}{3!} + \frac{k^5 x^5}{5!} - \cdots\right).$$

But the first of the series in parentheses is the familiar expansion of $\cos kx$, and the second series represents $\sin kx$. Formally, therefore, it appears that

$$e^{ikx} = \cos kx + i \sin kx. \tag{10_1}$$

In a like manner, or by changing x into $-x$ in (10_1), we find

$$e^{-ikx} = \cos kx - i \sin kx. \tag{10_2}$$

The relation (10_1), which really includes (10_2), is known as *Euler's relation*. It should be noted that we have not proved Euler's relation, since we have used a series originally derived under the assumption that the variable is real, to obtain a result involving complex quantities. Let us nevertheless make use of (10_1) and (10_2) in the general solution above, and examine what we get. We find

$$y = c_1(\cos kx + i \sin kx) + c_2(\cos kx - i \sin kx)$$

$$= (c_1 + c_2) \cos kx + i(c_1 - c_2) \sin kx.$$

Since c_1 and c_2 are arbitrary, $(c_1 + c_2)$ and $i(c_1 - c_2)$ are also arbitrary. Denote the latter expressions by A and B, respectively, so that we have

$$y = A \cos kx + B \sin kx.$$

Is this the general solution of the equation $(D^2 + k^2)y = 0$? A sure answer to this question is obtained by substituting for y the above expression. We then get

$$(D^2 + k^2)(A \cos kx + B \sin kx)$$

$$= (-k^2 A \cos kx - k^2 B \sin kx + k^2 A \cos kx + k^2 B \sin kx) \equiv 0;$$

thus we do have the general solution.

Let us now consider the matter of complex roots of the auxiliary equation in the general case. We shall suppose that the coefficients $a_0, a_1, \cdots, a_n$ of equation (1) are all real constants; this assumption is nearly always fulfilled in the equations arising in practice. Then the algebraic theory of equations tells us that any complex roots of the equation $\phi(m) = 0$ will occur in conjugate pairs. Let $\alpha \pm i\beta$ be such a pair, so that the corresponding part of the solution of the differential equation is

$$y = c_1 e^{(\alpha+i\beta)x} + c_2 e^{(\alpha-i\beta)x}. \tag{11}$$

If we take for granted that

$$e^{a+ib} = e^a e^{ib} = e^a(\cos b + i \sin b), \tag{12}$$

equation (11) becomes

$$y = e^{\alpha x}[(c_1 + c_2) \cos \beta x + i(c_1 - c_2) \sin \beta x]$$
$$= e^{\alpha x}(A \cos \beta x + B \sin \beta x), \tag{13}$$

where A and B are arbitrary. We may show that (13) satisfies the equation $\phi(D)y = 0$ when $\phi(\alpha \pm i\beta) = 0$, as follows. Corresponding to the root pair $\alpha \pm i\beta$, we must evidently have $(m - \alpha)^2 + \beta^2$ as a factor of $\phi(m)$. Hence $\phi(D) = \phi_1(D)[(D - \alpha)^2 + \beta^2]$, and

$$\phi(D)[e^{\alpha x}(A \cos \beta x + B \sin \beta x)]$$
$$= \phi_1(D)[(D - \alpha)^2 + \beta^2]e^{\alpha x}(A \cos \beta x + B \sin \beta x)$$
$$= \phi_1(D)e^{\alpha x}(D^2 + \beta^2)(A \cos \beta x + B \sin \beta x)$$

by formula (10) of Art. 9. But

$$(D^2 + \beta^2)(A \cos \beta x + B \sin \beta x) = 0,$$

and consequently (13) is a solution.

Since the relation (12) is formally obtained from the series for e^x by setting $x = a + ib$, and since the form (13), into which (11) transforms by use of (12), satisfies the differential equation, it is manifestly desirable that the exponential function with complex exponent be defined so as to make (12) true. It is shown in Chapter X that such a definition is consistent and desirable on other grounds as well; we shall in all our subsequent work consider (12) as a known and valid relation, and shall make free use of it.

The expression $e^{\alpha x}(A \cos \beta x + B \sin \beta x)$, with A and B arbitrary, can be written in two other useful forms. These arise from the trigonometric identities

$$A \cos \theta + B \sin \theta = \sqrt{A^2 + B^2} \sin \left(\theta + \tan^{-1} \frac{A}{B}\right)$$
$$= \sqrt{A^2 + B^2} \cos \left(\theta - \tan^{-1} \frac{B}{A}\right),$$

which are easily verified by expanding the right-hand members. We then have

$$e^{\alpha x}(A \cos \beta x + B \sin \beta x) = Ce^{\alpha x} \sin (\beta x + C'),$$

$$= Ce^{\alpha x} \cos (\beta x + C''), \qquad (14)$$

where C, C', C'' are new arbitrary constants,

$$C = \sqrt{A^2 + B^2}, \qquad C' = \tan^{-1} \frac{A}{B}, \qquad C'' = -\tan^{-1} \frac{B}{A}.$$

As another example, consider

$$(D^3 - 2D^2 + 10D)y = 0.$$

We find

$$m^3 - 2m^2 + 10m = 0,$$

$$m = 0, \qquad 1 \pm 3i,$$

and therefore the general solution may be written in any of the forms

$$y = c_1 + e^x(c_2 \sin 3x + c_3 \cos 3x),$$

$$y = c_1 + c_2'e^x \sin (3x + c_3'),$$

$$y = c_1 + c_2'e^x \cos (3x + c_3'').$$

When repeated complex roots appear, the procedure is similar to that given above; it is necessary merely to interpret the exponential factor with complex exponent. Thus, if the complex root pair $\alpha \pm i\beta$ occurs p times, the corresponding part of the general solution is

$$\left. \begin{array}{l} e^{\alpha x}[(A_1 + A_2x + \cdots + A_px^{p-1}) \cos \beta x \\ \qquad\qquad + (B_1 + B_2x + \cdots + B_px^{p-1}) \sin \beta x], \\ \text{or} \\ e^{\alpha x}[C_1 \sin (\beta x + C_1') + C_2x \sin (\beta x + C_2') + \cdots \\ \qquad\qquad + C_px^{p-1} \sin (\beta x + C_p')], \\ \text{or} \\ e^{\alpha x}[C_1 \cos (\beta x + C_1'') + C_2x \cos (\beta x + C_2'') + \cdots \\ \qquad\qquad + C_px^{p-1} \cos (\beta x + C_p'')]. \end{array} \right\} \qquad (15)$$

PROBLEMS

Find the general solution of each of the following differential equations.

1. $(D^2 + 5D + 6)y = 0.$ 2. $(2D^2 - 5D - 3)y = 0.$
3. $(D^3 - 4D^2 + 3D)y = 0.$ 4. $(D^3 - 3D^2 - D + 3)y = 0.$

5. $(9D^2 - 6D + 1)y = 0.$

6. $(4D^3 - 4D^2 + D)y = 0.$

7. $(D^3 - 6D^2 + 12D - 8)y = 0.$

8. $(D^4 - 2D^3 + D^2)y = 0.$

9. $(D^3 + 9D)y = 0.$

10. $(D^2 - 4D + 5)y = 0.$

11. $(D^3 + 3D^2 + 9D - 13)y = 0.$

12. $(D^5 + 8D^3 + 16D)y = 0.$

13. $(D^4 - 2D^2)y = 0.$

14. $(D^3 + 8)y = 0.$

15. $(D^4 - 2D^3)y = 0.$

16. $(D^4 + 4D^2)y = 0.$

17. $(D^4 - 81)y = 0.$

18. $(D^5 + 9D^3)y = 0.$

19. $(D^6 - 4D^4 + 4D^2)y = 0.$

20. $(D^4 + 4)y = 0.$

11. Particular integrals. Having discussed ways of obtaining the complementary function Y_c of a linear differential equation with constant coefficients,

$$\phi(D)y \equiv (a_0D^n + a_1D^{n-1} + \cdots + a_{n-1}D + a_n)y = f(x), \quad (1)$$

we turn now to a consideration of methods for finding a particular integral Y_P. For brevity, we shall say that Y_P *corresponds* to the right-hand member $f(x)$.

In the first place, we note that, if the right-hand member $f(x)$ of equation (1) consists of the sum of two or more terms, then the process of finding Y_P may be broken up into parts, where in each part we find the portion of Y_P corresponding to one term of $f(x)$. For suppose that $f(x) = f_1(x) + f_2(x)$, and consider the equations

$$\phi(D)y = f_1(x), \qquad \phi(D)y = f_2(x).$$

If $y = Y_{P1}$ satisfies the first of these equations and $y = Y_{P2}$ satisfies the second, so that

$$\phi(D)Y_{P1} = f_1(x), \qquad \phi(D)Y_{P2} = f_2(x),$$

identically, then

$$\phi(D)(Y_{P1} + Y_{P2}) = \phi(D)Y_{P1} + \phi(D)Y_{P2} = f_1(x) + f_2(x),$$

so that $y = Y_{P1} + Y_{P2}$ will be a particular integral of (1). Thus, if we find Y_{P1} corresponding to $f_1(x)$ and also Y_{P2} corresponding to $f_2(x)$, the sum $Y_{P1} + Y_{P2}$ will correspond to $f_1(x) + f_2(x)$.

Since there are, as we shall see, several methods of determining a particular integral, it follows from what has been said that we may, if we find it convenient, apply one method to find the part of Y_P corresponding to one term of $f(x)$ and use a different method to find the portion of Y_P corresponding to another term of $f(x)$.

We shall confine our attention in the following discussion of methods of attack to the problem of finding a particular integral $y = Y_P$ corresponding to a right-hand member $f(x)$ consisting of a single term.

(a) *Reduction of order.* One method of getting a particular integral is suggested by writing the operator $\phi(D)$ in factored form,

$$\phi(D)y \equiv a_0(D - r_1)(D - r_2)\cdots(D - r_{n-1})(D - r_n)y = f(x). \quad (2)$$

If we let $u = a_0(D - r_2)(D - r_3)\cdots(D - r_n)y$, equation (2) is replaced by the first-order equation

$$(D - r_1)u = f(x).$$

We may solve this equation for u by the method of Art. 5. Supposing this done, and the expression so found (omitting the constant of integration since we are seeking the simplest particular integral) substituted in the expression defining u, we get

$$a_0(D - r_2)(D - r_3)\cdots(D - r_n)y = u.$$

This is another linear equation for y similar to the original equation (2), with the known function u as right-hand member instead of $f(x)$, and of order $n - 1$ instead of n. We may treat this in the same way as before; letting $v = a_0(D - r_3)\cdots(D - r_n)y$, solving the new first-order equation

$$(D - r_2)v = u,$$

and substituting back, we have

$$a_0(D - r_3)\cdots(D - r_n)y = v,$$

an equation of order $n - 2$. Evidently we may continue this process, solving a first-order equation at each stage and reducing the order of the equation by unity each time, until we ultimately obtain y.

As an example, consider the equation

$$(D^3 - 2D^2 + D)y = x.$$

Factoring the operator, we get

$$(D - 1)(D - 1)Dy = x.$$

Then the complementary function is $Y_c = c_1 + (c_2 + c_3x)e^x$. Letting $u = (D - 1)Dy$, we have $(D - 1)u = x$, whence

$$ue^{-x} = -e^{-x}(x + 1), \qquad u = -x - 1.$$

Consequently

$$(D - 1)Dy = -x - 1.$$

Letting $v = Dy$, we find

$$(D - 1)v = -x - 1,$$

$$ve^{-x} = e^{-x}(x + 1) + e^{-x},$$

$$v = x + 2.$$

Hence
$$Dy = x + 2,$$
and
$$Y_P = \frac{x^2}{2} + 2x.$$
Thus
$$y = \frac{x^2}{2} + 2x + c_1 + (c_2 + c_3x)e^x.$$

Although this method will always work in theory, it may sometimes lead to laborious and difficult integration problems. Thus, if the right-hand member in our example had been x^4 instead of x, the three integrations involved would have been much longer and more tedious. It should be remarked also that the order in which the factors of $\phi(D)$ are written may often affect the amount of work necessary to complete the solution; the student should solve the preceding equation for each of the other two orders of factors and compare his solutions with the one given.

(b) *Undetermined coefficients.* The next method we shall describe has the decided advantage that it requires no integration but only differentiation. On the other hand, it does not apply to every form of right-hand member $f(x)$. We shall show that it does apply to any function $f(x)$ such that $f(x)$ and a finite number of its successive derivatives form a set of linearly dependent functions,

$$b_0f^{(S)}(x) + b_1f^{(S-1)}(x) + \cdots + b_{S-1}f'(x) + b_Sf(x) = 0. \tag{3}$$

For example, $f(x) = x^2e^{3x}$ is of the stated form, since we have

$$f'(x) = (3x^2 + 2x)e^{3x}, \qquad f''(x) = (9x^2 + 12x + 2)e^{3x},$$
$$f'''(x) = (27x^2 + 54x + 18)e^{3x},$$

and consequently

$$f'''(x) - 9f''(x) + 27f'(x) - 27f(x)$$
$$= e^{3x}(27x^2 + 54x + 18 - 81x^2 - 108x - 18 + 81x^2 + 54x - 27x^2)$$
$$= 0$$

identically; here $S = 3$, $b_0 = 1$, $b_1 = -9$, $b_2 = 27$, $b_3 = -27$.

It is easy to find the form that $f(x)$ must have in order that a relation of the type (3) shall hold. For (3) is evidently a linear homogeneous differential equation with constant coefficients,

$$(b_0D^S + b_1D^{S-1} + \cdots + b_{S-1}D + b_S)f = 0.$$

Hence, by the theory of Art. 10, $f(x)$ must be expressible as a sum of terms of the form

$$Cx^p e^{qx}, \qquad Cx^p e^{\alpha x} \cos \beta x, \qquad Cx^p e^{\alpha x} \sin \beta x, \qquad (4)$$

where p is a positive integer or zero; q, α, and β are any real constants (including zero); and C is any constant.

Suppose, therefore, that we have the equation

$$\phi(D)y \equiv (a_0 D^n + a_1 D^{n-1} + \cdots + a_{n-1}D + a_n)y = Cx^p e^{qx}. \qquad (5)$$

Consider first the simpler case in which $q = 0$, so that the given equation is of the form

$$\phi(D)y \equiv (a_0 D^n + a_1 D^{n-1} + \cdots + a_{n-1}D + a_n)y = Cx^p, \qquad (6)$$

with p a positive integer or zero. Since the required particular integral Y_P is to be such that $\phi(D)$ operating upon Y_P produces Cx^p, it is reasonable to assume that Y_P will be a polynomial in x, for a positive integral power of x will be obtained as the derivative of only another such power function. Now if the constant term a_n in $\phi(D)$ is not zero, the degree of the assumed polynomial Y_P need not exceed p. To illustrate, suppose the given equation to be

$$(D^2 - 1)y = x^2.$$

If we were to take as Y_P a polynomial of degree three, say

$$Y_P = Ax^3 + Bx^2 + Cx + E,$$

we should get

$$(D^2 - 1)(Ax^3 + Bx^2 + Cx + E)$$
$$= 6Ax + 2B - Ax^3 - Bx^2 - Cx - E,$$

which could not reduce to x^2 unless A were zero. Consequently, when $a_n \neq 0$, we assume as a particular integral of equation (6) the polynomial

$$Y_P = Ax^p + Bx^{p-1} + \cdots + Kx + L, \qquad (7)$$

with (at present) undetermined coefficients A, B, $\cdots$, L. We then substitute (7) in (6) and find values of A, B, $\cdots$, L that reduce the resulting equation to an identity.

As an example, consider the above equation,

$$(D^2 - 1)y = x^2.$$

We take

$$Y_P = Ax^2 + Bx + C,$$

whence

$$(D^2 - 1)(Ax^2 + Bx + C) = 2A - Ax^2 - Bx - C = x^2.$$

This will become an identity if the total coefficients of each power of x, in the two members, are equated. We then have

$$-A = 1, \qquad -B = 0, \qquad 2A - C = 0,$$

whence $A = -1$, $B = 0$, $C = -2$, and

$$Y_P = -x^2 - 2.$$

If, on the other hand, $a_n = 0$ in $\phi(D)$, the auxiliary equation $\phi(m) = 0$ will have the root $m = 0$. Suppose that $m = 0$ is an r-fold root, so that $\phi(D)Y_P = \phi_1(D) \cdot D^r Y_P = Cx^p$, where $\phi_1(0) \neq 0$. Since the constant term in $\phi_1(D)$ is not zero, the degree of $D^r Y_P$ need not exceed p, and hence the degree of Y_P need not exceed $p + r$. Moreover, since the complementary function of the equation

$$\phi_1(D)D^r y = Cx^p$$

will contain, by virtue of the r-fold root $m = 0$, the sum

$$c_1 + c_2 x + \cdots + c_r x^{r-1},$$

those terms of degree $r - 1$ or less in the assumed Y_P need not be included, since such terms can be absorbed by the complementary function. Hence we now set

$$Y_P = Ax^{p+r} + Bx^{p+r-1} + \cdots + Kx^{r+1} + Lx^r. \qquad (8)$$

It should be noted that Y_P as given by (8) is then equal to the expression (7), taken in the case where $a_n \neq 0$, multiplied by x^r. Thus (7) is merely a special case of (8), with $r = 0$.

To illustrate, consider the equation

$$(D^4 + D^2)y = 2x.$$

Here the auxiliary equation $m^4 + m^2 = 0$ has zero as a double root, and consequently we take

$$Y_P = x^2(Ax + B) = Ax^3 + Bx^2.$$

That is, if the operator in our equation had contained a constant term, we should have taken $Y_P = Ax + B$ in accordance with the right-hand member $2x$, but since $\phi(D)$ contains the factor $D^r = D^2$, we take $Ax + B$ multiplied by $x^r = x^2$. We now get

$$(D^4 + D^2)(Ax^3 + Bx^2) = 6Ax + 2B = 2x,$$

whence $A = \frac{1}{3}$, $B = 0$, and

$$Y_P = \frac{x^3}{3}.$$

We may now readily reduce the more general case of equation (5), with $q \neq 0$, to that already discussed. The exponential function e^{qx} reproduces itself, with mere change of coefficient, upon successive differentiation, and hence it is apparent that Y_P should contain the factor e^{qx} in order that $\phi(D)$ operating upon Y_P shall yield $x^p e^{qx}$. We therefore set $Y_P = ue^{qx}$, where u is a function to be determined, and apply formula (10) of Art. 9,

$$\phi(D)(ue^{qx}) = e^{qx}\phi(D + q)u.$$

Since we are to have $\phi(D)Y_P = Cx^p e^{qx}$, it follows that u should be such that

$$\phi(D + q)u \equiv F(D)u = Cx^p. \tag{9}$$

But this equation is of the form (6), and consequently the methods explained above may be applied to find the function u.

If $f(x) = Cx^p e^{qx}$, with $q \neq 0$, we may then either set

$$Y_P = (Ax^{p+r} + Bx^{p+r-1} + \cdots + Kx^{r+1} + Lx^r)e^{qx} \tag{10}$$

in the equation

$$\phi(D)y = Cx^p e^{qx} \tag{5}$$

directly, or we may set

$$u = Ax^{p+r} + Bx^{p+r-1} + \cdots + Kx^{r+1} + Lx^r$$

in equation (9), obtained from (5) by dropping the factor e^{qx} on the right and changing D into $D + q$. Here r is the number of times zero appears as a root of $F(m) = 0$, or, since $F(0) = \phi(q)$, the number of times q appears as a root of $\phi(m) = 0$.

To illustrate the procedure, consider the equation

$$\phi(D)y \equiv (D^2 - 3D + 2)y = (D - 1)(D - 2)y = xe^{2x}.$$

For the first method, since $p = 1$, $q = 2$, $r = 1$, we take

$$Y_P = Ax^2 e^{2x} + Bxe^{2x},$$

so that

$$DY_P = 2Ax^2 e^{2x} + 2Axe^{2x} + 2Bxe^{2x} + Be^{2x},$$

$$D^2 Y_P = 4Ax^2 e^{2x} + 8Axe^{2x} + 2Ae^{2x} + 4Bxe^{2x} + 4Be^{2x}.$$

Substituting in the given equation and dropping the common factor e^{2x}, we obtain

$$4Ax^2 + 8Ax + 2A + 4Bx + 4B - 6Ax^2 - 6Ax - 6Bx - 3B$$
$$+ 2Ax^2 + 2Bx = x,$$

$$A = \tfrac{1}{2}, \qquad B = -1,$$

and

$$Y_P = \left(\frac{x^2}{2} - x\right)e^{2x}.$$

By the second method, we get

$$\phi(D + 2)u = (D^2 + D)u = x,$$

$$u = Ax^2 + Bx, \qquad Du = 2Ax + B, \qquad D^2u = 2A,$$

$$2A + 2Ax + B = x,$$

$$A = \tfrac{1}{2}, \qquad B = -1,$$

$$Y_P = ue^{2x} = \left(\frac{x^2}{2} - x\right)e^{2x}.$$

We now have to consider equations of the forms

$$\phi(D)y = C_1 x^p e^{\alpha x} \cos \beta x, \tag{11_1}$$

$$\phi(D)y = C_2 x^p e^{\alpha x} \sin \beta x. \tag{11_2}$$

For definiteness, we fix our attention on the first of these equations; our discussion will apply equally well to the other equation. From the Euler relations,

$$e^{i\beta x} = \cos \beta x + i \sin \beta x,$$

$$e^{-i\beta x} = \cos \beta x - i \sin \beta x,$$

we get by addition

$$\cos \beta x = \tfrac{1}{2}(e^{i\beta x} + e^{-i\beta x}),$$

whence (11_1) becomes

$$\phi(D)y = \frac{C_1}{2} x^p [e^{(\alpha + i\beta)x} + e^{(\alpha - i\beta)x}].$$

Evidently the preceding theory may be applied to each of the two terms on the right; then we have from (10),

$$Y_P = Y_{P1} + Y_{P2}$$

$$= (Ax^{p+r} + \cdots + Lx^r)e^{(\alpha + i\beta)x} + (A'x^{p+r} + \cdots + L'x^r)e^{(\alpha - i\beta)x}$$

$$= e^{\alpha x}[(Ax^{p+r} + \cdots + Lx^r)(\cos \beta x + i \sin \beta x)$$

$$\qquad + (A'x^{p+r} + \cdots + L'x^r)(\cos \beta x - i \sin \beta x)]$$

$$= e^{\alpha x}[A_1 x^{p+r} + \cdots + L_1 x^r) \cos \beta x$$

$$\qquad + (A_2 x^{p+r} + \cdots + L_2 x^r) \sin \beta x], \tag{12}$$

where $A_1 = A + A'$, $A_2 = i(A - A')$, etc. Equation (12) is then the assumed form of Y_P for equation (11_1) and, as may be similarly shown, for equation (11_2) also. As before, r is the number of times $q = \alpha + i\beta$ appears as a root of $\phi(m) = 0$.

As an example, let there be given the equation

$$(D^2 + 1)y = (D + i)(D - i)y = x \sin x.$$

Here $p = 1$, $q = 0 + 1 \cdot i = i$, $r = 1$, and consequently we take

$$Y_P = A_1 x^2 \cos x + B_1 x \cos x + A_2 x^2 \sin x + B_2 x \sin x.$$

Then

$$DY_P = -A_1 x^2 \sin x + 2A_1 x \cos x - B_1 x \sin x + B_1 \cos x$$
$$+ A_2 x^2 \cos x + 2A_2 x \sin x + B_2 x \cos x + B_2 \sin x,$$

$$D^2 Y_P = -A_1 x^2 \cos x - 4A_1 x \sin x$$
$$+ 2A_1 \cos x - B_1 x \cos x - 2B_1 \sin x - A_2 x^2 \sin x$$
$$+ 4A_2 x \cos x + 2A_2 \sin x - B_2 x \sin x + 2B_2 \cos x,$$

$$(D^2 + 1)Y_P = (-4A_1 x - 2B_1 + 2A_2) \sin x$$
$$+ (2A_1 + 4A_2 x + 2B_2) \cos x$$
$$= x \sin x,$$

$$A_1 = -\tfrac{1}{4}, \qquad A_2 = 0, \qquad B_1 = 0 \qquad B_2 = \tfrac{1}{4},$$

and

$$Y_P = -\frac{x^2}{4} \cos x + \frac{x}{4} \sin x.$$

We may summarize all of the foregoing results as follows·
Given either of the equations

$$\phi(D)y = Cx^p e^{\alpha x} \cos \beta x, \qquad \phi(D)y = Cx^p e^{\alpha x} \sin \beta x, \qquad (13)$$

where p is any positive integer or zero, α and β are any real numbers (including zero), and C is any constant different from zero. Let r be the number of times $\alpha + i\beta$ appears as a root of $\phi(m) = 0$. Let

$$Y_P = (A_1 x^p + B_1 x^{p-1} + \cdots + L_1) x^r e^{\alpha x} \cos \beta x$$
$$+ (A_2 x^p + B_2 x^{p-1} + \cdots + L_2) x^r e^{\alpha x} \sin \beta x, \quad (14)$$

substitute in the given equation, and determine the constants A_1, A_2, $\cdots$, L_1, L_2 so as to reduce the resulting relation to an identity. The function Y_P thus obtained will be a particular integral of the given equation.

The student should convince himself that each of the special cases considered above properly falls under the above statement by particularizing the constants p, α, β.

In our work we have not shown that the linear algebraic equations of condition on the constants A_1, A_2, $\cdots$, L_1, L_2, obtained when (14) is substituted in either of equations (13) and the coefficients of like terms are equated, are necessarily consistent and suffice to determine these constants. This may be proved,* however, and the procedure outlined is always applicable.

When the right-hand member $f(x)$ consists of two or more terms of the forms given in (13), we may at once set up a single expression for Y_P corresponding to the entire right member. It may happen also that the parts of the complete Y_P corresponding to the sum of terms comprising $f(x)$ contain expressions of the same form. In this case, only one such expression with a single undetermined coefficient will evidently suffice in the assumed Y_P. To illustrate, consider the equation

$$(D^2 - 1)y = 3x^2 - 4x + 2e^x.$$

Corresponding to the terms $3x^2$, $-4x$, $2e^x$, we have, respectively,

$$Y_{P1} = A_1 x^2 + B_1 x + C_1, \quad Y_{P2} = A_2 x + B_2, \quad \text{and} \quad Y_{P3} = Exe^x.$$

Since the expressions $B_1 x$ and $A_2 x$ are of the same form, only one term in x need be taken in Y_P; likewise, since C_1 and B_2 are of the same form (which may be considered as either kx^0 or ke^{0x}), only one constant term need appear in Y_P. Consequently we set

$$Y_P = Ax^2 + Bx + C + Exe^x,$$

whence we get

$$2A + Exe^x + 2Ee^x - Ax^2 - Bx - C - Exe^x = 3x^2 - 4x + 2e^x,$$

$$A = -3, \quad B = 4, \quad C = -6, \quad E = 1,$$

and

$$Y_P = -3x^2 + 4x - 6 + xe^x.$$

The expression (14) may be applied to any of the cases considered, but it is somewhat difficult to remember, and, moreover, does not bring into evidence possible simplifications such as appeared in the above problem. In practice, it will be found more convenient to apply the following equivalent rule for the formation of Y_P when the right-hand

* See A. B. Coble, *American Math. Monthly*, Vol. 26, p. 12, 1919.

member of the differential equation consists of a sum of terms of the forms given in (13):

*Write the variable parts of the terms in the right-hand member $f(x)$ and the variable parts of any other terms obtainable by differentiating $f(x)$.** *Arrange the terms so found in groups such that all terms obtainable from a single term of $f(x)$ appear in only one group. Any group consisting of terms none of which appears as a term of the complementary function Y_c is left intact, but if, in some group, any term is a term of Y_c, all terms of this group are multiplied by the lowest positive integral power of x that will make them all different from any term of Y_c. We then multiply each term in all the groups by a general constant and take the sum of the expressions so obtained as Y_P.*

Thus, in the preceding example, we have as the variable parts of $f(x)$ and of the terms obtained by differentiation,

$$x^2, x, 1, e^x.$$

We then get two groups, the first,

(I) $$x^2, x, 1,$$

consisting of all terms obtainable from x^2, and the second,

(II) $$e^x,$$

containing the only term obtainable from e^x. Since, in this case, $Y_c = c_1 e^x + c_2 e^{-x}$, no terms in group (I) appear in Y_c, but e^x does. Hence e^x must be multiplied by x, which makes it distinct from anything in Y_c, and we get

$$Y_P = Ax^2 + Bx + C + Exe^x.$$

(*c*) *Variation of parameters.* The method of undetermined coefficients applies, as has been stated, only to a right-hand member $f(x)$ of a certain form. Although nearly all the linear differential equations arising in practice have a right-hand member of the form considered in (*b*), we occasionally encounter an equation to which undetermined coefficients do not apply. The method (*a*), in which the order of the equation is reduced step by step, may of course be used whenever method (*b*) breaks down; we give now, as an alternative method, and because of its elegance, complete generality, and importance in the theory of linear differential equations, another method, due to the French mathematician Lagrange, and called the method of variation of parameters.†

---

* When a term is a constant, we write 1.
† Sometimes called the method of variation of constants.

Lagrange's method applies to a linear equation of any order and with constant or variable coefficients. It assumes knowledge of the complementary function (which can certainly be obtained when the coefficients are constants by the method of Art. 10), and enables us then to find the general solution. We shall give the theory of the method for the linear equation of second order, and merely indicate the manner in which the method is applied to equations of order higher than the second.

Consider the equation

$$(a_0 D^2 + a_1 D + a_2)y = f(x), \tag{15}$$

where the a s are constants or depend upon x. Let the complementary function for (15) be known, and denote it by

$$Y_c = c_1 u + c_2 v, \tag{16}$$

where u and v are specific functions of x. We employ a device similar to that used in Art. 10 for finding the complete complementary function in the case where the auxiliary equation has equal roots; that is, we replace the constants in (16) by unknown functions or parameters P and Q and assume the general solution of (15) in the form

$$y = Pu + Qv. \tag{17}$$

The problem then is to find P and Q as functions of x such that (17) is the desired general solution. Using primes to denote differentiation with respect to x, we have

$$y' = Pu' + Qv' + P'u + Q'v.$$

Now in order to determine the two quantities P and Q, we need two relations involving them. If (17) is to be a solution, substitution in (15) will give us one such relation; we choose as the second relation

$$P'u + Q'v = 0. \tag{18}$$

There are two reasons for making this particular choice. In the first place, if we remove terms containing the derivatives of P and of Q from y', the resulting expression for y'' will contain no second derivatives of the parameters; this situation may be brought about by setting $P'u + Q'v$ equal to any function of x. Secondly, we choose zero as being the simplest function of x. Then y' becomes

$$y' = Pu' + Qv',$$

and a second differentiation gives us

$$y'' = Pu'' + Qv'' + P'u' + Q'v'.$$

Substituting for y, y', y'' their expressions as now given, (15) leads to the relation

$$a_0(Pu'' + Qv'' + P'u' + Q'v') + a_1(Pu' + Qv') + a_2(Pu + Qv) = f(x).$$

But since u and v are particular solutions of (15) when $f(x) = 0$,

$$a_0u'' + a_1u' + a_2u = 0 \quad \text{and} \quad a_0v'' + a_1v' + a_2v = 0.$$

Making use of these relations, the preceding equation reduces to

$$a_0P'u' + a_0Q'v' = f(x). \tag{19}$$

Since a_0, u, v, u', v', and f are known, equations (18) and (19) together constitute a pair of linear algebraic equations in the unknowns P' and Q'. We therefore solve * (18) and (19) simultaneously for P' and Q' and integrate the resulting expressions to get

$$P = F_1(x) + c_1, \qquad Q = F_2(x) + c_2,$$

where c_1 and c_2 are constants of integration. Substituting these in (17) then gives us

$$y = F_1(x)u + F_2(x)v + c_1u + c_2v. \tag{20}$$

This is the required general solution, with $Y_P = F_1u + F_2v$ and $Y_c = c_1u + c_2v$.

As an example, consider the equation †

$$(D^2 + 4)y = \tan 2x.$$

Here

$$Y_c = c_1 \cos 2x + c_2 \sin 2x,$$

and we therefore put

$$y = P \cos 2x + Q \sin 2x.$$

Then

$$y' = -2P \sin 2x + 2Q \cos 2x$$

if we set

$$P' \cos 2x + Q' \sin 2x = 0,$$

and

$$y'' = -4P \cos 2x - 4Q \sin 2x - 2P' \sin 2x + 2Q' \cos 2x.$$

---

* It may be shown that the determinant of the system, $a_0(uv' - u'v)$, cannot vanish if u and v are linearly independent; see Ince, *op. cit.* Hence it is always possible to find P' and Q'.

† The student should try to solve this equation by method (*a*) of this article.

Consequently

$$-4P \cos 2x - 4Q \sin 2x - 2P' \sin 2x + 2Q' \cos 2x$$
$$+ 4P \cos 2x + 4Q \sin 2x = \tan 2x$$

or

$$-2P' \sin 2x + 2Q' \cos 2x = \tan 2x.$$

Coupling this equation with the equation $P' \cos 2x + Q' \sin 2x = 0$, we get

$$P' = \frac{\begin{vmatrix} 0 & \sin 2x \\ \tan 2x & 2 \cos 2x \end{vmatrix}}{\begin{vmatrix} \cos 2x & \sin 2x \\ -2 \sin 2x & 2 \cos 2x \end{vmatrix}} = -\frac{\sin^2 2x}{2 \cos 2x},$$

$$Q' = \frac{\begin{vmatrix} \cos 2x & 0 \\ -2 \sin 2x & \tan 2x \end{vmatrix}}{2} = \frac{\sin 2x}{2},$$

whence

$$P = -\frac{1}{2} \int \frac{\sin^2 2x}{\cos 2x} \, dx = \frac{\sin 2x}{4} - \frac{1}{4} \ln (\sec 2x + \tan 2x) + c_1,$$

$$Q = -\frac{\cos 2x}{4} + c_2,$$

and

$$y = \frac{\sin 2x \cos 2x}{4} - \frac{1}{4} \cos 2x \ln (\sec 2x + \tan 2x) + c_1 \cos 2x$$
$$- \frac{\cos 2x \sin 2x}{4} + c_2 \sin 2x$$
$$= -\tfrac{1}{4} \cos 2x \ln (\sec 2x + \tan 2x) + c_1 \cos 2x + c_2 \sin 2x.$$

In the case of an equation of order n, we take as the expression for the general solution that obtained from the complementary function by replacing the constants by variable parameters,

$$y = Pu + Qv + Rw + \cdots.$$

For this to be a solution imposes one condition on P, Q, R, $\cdots$. Differentiating this expression, we get

$$y' = Pu' + Qv' + Rw' + \cdots + P'u + Q'v + R'w + \cdots.$$

Take as a second condition the equation

$$P'u + Q'v + R'w + \cdots = 0,$$

so that

$$y' = Pu' + Qv' + Rw' + \cdots.$$

Then

$$y'' = Pu'' + Qv'' + Rw'' + \cdots + P'u' + Q'v' + R'w' + \cdots,$$

and we take as the next condition

$$P'u' + Q'v' + R'w' + \cdots = 0,$$

whence

$$y'' = Pu'' + Qv'' + Rw'' + \cdots.$$

We treat similarly $y''', \cdots, y^{(n-1)}$, setting the portion containing the derivatives of the parameters equal to zero at each stage:

$$P'u'' + Q'v'' + R'w'' + \cdots = 0,$$

$$P'u''' + Q'v''' + R'w''' + \cdots = 0,$$

$$\cdots \cdots \cdots \cdots \cdots \cdots$$

Then compute $y^{(n)}$ and substitute $y, y', \cdots, y^{(n)}$ in the given equation. Solve the n linear algebraic equations in $P', Q', R', \cdots$ obtained by this process, integrate to get $P, Q, R, \cdots$, and substitute in the expression $y = Pu + Qv + Rw + \cdots$.

As may be supposed, the labor involved in applying this method increases rapidly as the order n increases, so that, from the practical standpoint, the usefulness of the method for large values of n is limited.

There are other methods of finding a particular integral, including symbolic methods into which inverse operators and resolution into partial fractions enter. We shall not discuss these methods here, however, as we have, in the foregoing, ample means of solving completely most of the linear equations arising in practice. Symbolic methods are considered in Chapter XI as a topic in operational calculus.

PROBLEMS

Find the general solution of each of the following equations.

1. $(D^2 - 4)y = 4x - 3e^x$.
2. $(D^2 - 5D + 6)y = 12x^2 - 20x + 4 + e^{2x}$.
3. $(D^3 + D^2)y = 6x + 6 - 2e^{-x}$.
4. $(D^2 + 1)y = 2 \cos x - 3 \cos 2x$.
5. $(D^2 + 2D + 5)y = 3e^{-x} \sin x - 10$.
6. $(D^4 - 3D^2 - 4)y = 24 \sin 2x - 40e^{-2x}$.
7. $(D^4 - 2D^3 + D^2)y = 6e^x - 2$.
8. $(D^3 + 4D)y = 24x^2 + 12 + 8 \sin 2x$.
9. $(2D^2 - 3D - 2)y = (15x^2 + 12x - 5)e^{2x} - 18e^x$.
10. $(D^2 + 4D + 3)y = 2x(\sin x + 2 \cos x) + 4 \sin x + 2 \cos x - 2e^{-x}$.
11. $(D^4 + D^2)y = 18x - 4 \sin x$.
12. $(D^2 - 4D + 5)y = 2e^{2x} \cos x - 5$.

13. $(D^2 - 8D + 16)y = 12e^{4x}/x^4.$

14. $(D^2 - 4D + 4)y = e^{2x} \sec^2 x.$

15. $(D^2 + 9)y = 18 - 9 \sec 3x.$

16. $(D^2 + 1)y = 3x - 8 \cot x.$

17. $(D^2 + 2D + 5)y = 4e^{-x} \tan 2x + 5e^x.$

18. $(D^3 + D)y = 2 - \sec x.$

19. $(D^3 - D)y = \dfrac{4}{e^x + 1}.$

20. $(D^3 - 3D^2 + 4D - 2)y = e^x \csc x.$

12. Euler's equation.* One of the most important of the linear equations with variable coefficients is Euler's equation,

$$(b_0 x^n D^n + b_1 x^{n-1} D^{n-1} + \cdots + b_{n-1} x D + b_n)y = f(x), \qquad (1)$$

where the b's are constants, $b_0 \neq 0$, and $D \equiv d/dx$. It is readily recognized from the fact that the powers of x and of D in any term of the operator are the same.

Euler's equation may always be transformed into a linear equation with constant coefficients by changing the independent variable from x to z by the substitution

$$x = e^z, \qquad \text{or} \qquad z = \ln x. \qquad (2)$$

Using D_z to denote d/dz, we have, since $dz/dx = 1/x$,

$$Dy = \frac{dy}{dx} = \frac{dy}{dz}\frac{dz}{dx} = \frac{1}{x} D_z y,$$

$$D^2 y = \frac{d}{dx}(Dy) = \frac{d}{dx}\left(\frac{1}{x} D_z y\right) = \frac{1}{x}\frac{d}{dx}(D_z y) - \frac{1}{x^2} D_z y$$

$$= \frac{1}{x}\frac{d}{dz}(D_z y)\frac{dz}{dx} - \frac{1}{x^2} D_z y = \frac{1}{x^2} D_z^2 y - \frac{1}{x^2} D_z y,$$

$$D^3 y = \frac{d}{dx}\left(\frac{1}{x^2} D_z^2 y - \frac{1}{x^2} D_z y\right)$$

$$= \frac{1}{x^2}\frac{d}{dz}(D_z^2 y)\frac{dz}{dx} - \frac{2}{x^3} D_z^2 y - \frac{1}{x^2}\frac{d}{dz}(D_z y)\frac{dz}{dx} + \frac{2}{x^3} D_z y$$

$$= \frac{1}{x^3} D_z^3 y - \frac{3}{x^3} D_z^2 y + \frac{2}{x^3} D_z y,$$

whence

$$xDy = D_z y,$$

$$x^2 D^2 y = D_z^2 y - D_z y = D_z(D_z - 1)y,$$

$$x^3 D^3 y = D_z^3 y - 3D_z^2 y + 2D_z y = D_z(D_z - 1)(D_z - 2)y.$$

* Also referred to as Cauchy's equation or as the homogeneous linear equation.

These results suggest the formula

$$x^r D^r y = D_z(D_z - 1)(D_z - 2)\cdots(D_z - r + 1)y. \qquad (3)$$

That the formula holds in general is readily proved by induction. For, if

$$D^r y = \frac{1}{x^r} D_z(D_z - 1)\cdots(D_z - r + 1)y$$

for any positive integer r, then

$$D^{r+1}y = D\left[\frac{1}{x^r} D_z(D_z - 1)\cdots(D_z - r + 1)y\right]$$

$$= \frac{1}{x^r} D_z[D_z(D_z - 1)\cdots(D_z - r + 1)y]\frac{dz}{dx}$$

$$- \frac{r}{x^{r+1}}[D_z(D_z - 1)\cdots(D_z - r + 1)y]$$

$$= \frac{1}{x^{r+1}} D_z(D_z - 1)\cdots(D_z - r + 1)(D_z - r)y,$$

or

$$x^{r+1}D^{r+1}y = D_z(D_z - 1)\cdots(D_z - r)y.$$

Since this is of the same form as (3) with r replaced by $r + 1$, it follows from the usual argument that (3) is true when r is any positive integer.

Substituting in (1) the values of $x^r D^r y$ ($r = 1, 2, \cdots, n$), as given by (3), and at the same time replacing x by e^z on the right, evidently yields a linear equation with constant coefficients,

$$(a_0 D_z^n + a_1 D_z^{n-1} + \cdots + a_{n-1}D_z + a_n)y = F(z), \qquad (4)$$

in the variables z and y, where the a's are constants and $F(z) = f(e^z)$. Equation (4) may then be solved by the methods previously given to obtain y as a function of z, whence replacement of z by $\ln x$ leads to the general solution of (1).

As an example, consider the equation

$$(x^3 D^3 + x^2 D^2 - 4xD)y = 3x^2.$$

This becomes

$$[D_z(D_z - 1)(D_z - 2) + D_z(D_z - 1) - 4D_z]y = 3e^{2z},$$

or

$$(D_z^3 - 2D_z^2 - 3D_z)y = 3e^{2z}.$$

Since the roots of $m^3 - 2m^2 - 3m = 0$ are $m = 0, -1, 3$, the complementary function of the new equation is

$$Y_c = c_1 + c_2 e^{-z} + c_3 e^{3z}.$$

Also, setting

$$Y_P = A e^{2z},$$

we get

$$8A - 8A - 6A = 3, \qquad A = -\tfrac{1}{2},$$

and

$$Y_P = -\tfrac{1}{2} e^{2z}.$$

Therefore

$$y = Y_P + Y_c = -\tfrac{1}{2} e^{2z} + c_1 + c_2 e^{-z} + c_3 e^{3z}$$

$$= -\frac{x^2}{2} + c_1 + \frac{c_2}{x} + c_3 x^3.$$

13. Simultaneous equations. We consider next a system of n linear equations involving one independent and n dependent variables. The orders of the derivatives in these equations may be any positive integers; also we suppose that the coefficients of the dependent variables and their derivatives are constants. Just as in the case of simultaneous linear algebraic equations, the first step is to combine the equations of the system so as to get a single equation containing only one of the dependent variables and its derivatives. In this elimination process, the algebraic properties of operators enable us to treat simultaneous linear differential equations in much the same way as a set of linear algebraic equations.

We shall illustrate the general process for a system of two equations,

$$\phi_1(D)y + \phi_2(D)z = f_1(x), \tag{1_1}$$

$$\phi_3(D)y + \phi_4(D)z = f_2(x), \tag{1_2}$$

where the ϕ's are operators with constant coefficients, $D \equiv d/dx$, and y and z are the dependent variables. Operate on the first equation with $\phi_4(D)$ and on the second with $\phi_2(D)$, obtaining

$$\phi_4(D)\phi_1(D)y + \phi_4(D)\phi_2(D)z = \phi_4(D)f_1,$$

$$\phi_2(D)\phi_3(D)y + \phi_2(D)\phi_4(D)z = \phi_2(D)f_2.$$

Since the operators $\phi_2(D)$ and $\phi_4(D)$ are commutative, subtraction eliminates z, giving us

$$[\phi_4(D)\phi_1(D) - \phi_2(D)\phi_3(D)]y = \phi_4(D)f_1 - \phi_2(D)f_2. \tag{2}$$

This equation, containing only x, y, and the derivatives of y, may be solved by the methods of Arts. 10–11.

We might also have eliminated y between (1_1) and (1_2), getting instead of (2),

$$[\phi_4(D)\phi_1(D) - \phi_2(D)\phi_3(D)]z = \phi_1(D)f_2 - \phi_3(D)f_1. \tag{3}$$

Since the left-hand operators in (2) and (3) are the same, the work of finding the complementary function will be the same for both cases.

Having found the general solution y from (2), or the general solution z from (3), we may proceed in either of two ways. On the one hand, we may substitute the expression found in (1_1), (1_2), or any relation obtained by combining these equations—whatever allows for the determination of the remaining dependent variable most easily. Alternatively, we may use both equations (2) and (3), obtaining expressions for y and for z. It must be remembered, however, that our problem is to find values of y and z satisfying equations (1_1) and (1_2). Consequently, if the first alternative is employed, say by using (1_1), then, whenever constants of integration are introduced, possible relations among the constants of integration must be determined by making sure that (1_2) is identically satisfied. If the second procedure is followed, an identity must likewise be obtained by substituting the expressions for y and for z in either (1_1) or (1_2); this will determine possible relations among the arbitrary constants.

Let us examine the various possibilities in solving the simultaneous equations

$$(D - 1)y - (2D + 1)z = 1 - x,$$
$$Dy + (D + 4)z = 1 + 4x. \tag{4}$$

Operating on the first equation with D, and on the second with $(D - 1)$, we get

$$D(D - 1)y - (2D^2 + D)z = -1,$$
$$(D - 1)Dy + (D^2 + 3D - 4)z = 4 - 1 - 4x = 3 - 4x.$$

Subtracting the first equation from the second gives us

$$(3D^2 + 4D - 4)z = 4 - 4x. \tag{5}$$

Since $3m^2 + 4m - 4 = (3m - 2)(m + 2)$, the complementary function for z is

$$Z_c = c_1 e^{2x/3} + c_2 e^{-2x}.$$

Also, taking for the particular integral

$$Z_P = Ax + B,$$

we get

$$4A - 4Ax - 4B = 4 - 4x,$$
$$A = 1, \qquad B = 0,$$
$$Z_P = x.$$

Hence
$$z = x + c_1 e^{2x/3} + c_2 e^{-2x}. \tag{6}$$

In this instance the best way to continue is as follows. Subtracting the first of equations (4) from the second, member for member, we get a relation free of derivatives of y:

$$y + (3D + 5)z = 5x.$$

We then get directly, without the need of further integration,

$$y = 5x - (3D + 5)z$$
$$= 5x - 3 - 2c_1 e^{2x/3} + 6c_2 e^{-2x} - 5x - 5c_1 e^{2x/3} - 5c_2 e^{-2x},$$

$$y = -3 - 7c_1 e^{2x/3} + c_2 e^{-2x}. \tag{7}$$

Equations (6) and (7) together constitute the general solution of the system (4).

For purposes of comparison with the above method, and to illustrate the second alternative method, let us find y directly from (4). Operating on the first equation with $(D + 4)$ and on the second with $(2D + 1)$, we get

$$(D^2 + 3D - 4)y - (D + 4)(2D + 1)z = -1 + 4 - 4x = 3 - 4x,$$

$$(2D^2 + D)y + (2D + 1)(D + 4)z = 8 + 1 + 4x = 9 + 4x.$$

Adding, we have
$$(3D^2 + 4D - 4)y = 12. \tag{8}$$

The complementary function is found as before,

$$Y_c = c_3 e^{2x/3} + c_4 e^{-2x}.$$

Also, we see by inspection that $Y_P = -3$. Hence

$$y = c_3 e^{2x/3} + c_4 e^{-2x} - 3. \tag{9}$$

Substituting from (6) and (9) into the first of equations (4) gives us

$$\tfrac{2}{3} c_3 e^{2x/3} - 2c_4 e^{-2x} - c_3 e^{2x/3} - c_4 e^{-2x} + 3$$
$$-2 - \tfrac{4}{3} c_1 e^{2x/3} + 4c_2 e^{-2x} - x - c_1 e^{2x/3} - c_2 e^{-2x} = 1 - x,$$

which will be an identical relation only if

$$-\tfrac{1}{3} c_3 - \tfrac{7}{3} c_1 = 0, \qquad -3c_4 + 3c_2 = 0.$$

Hence
$$c_3 = -7c_1, \qquad c_4 = c_2, \qquad \text{and} \qquad y = -7c_1 e^{2x/3} + c_2 e^{-2x} - 3,$$

as before. Substitution of the expressions (6) and (9) into the second of equations (4) would similarly have yielded $c_3 = -7c_1$, $c_4 = c_2$.

As indicated in the above example, the total number of arbitrary constants in the general solution of a system of simultaneous equations of form (1) will be equal to the degree in D of the determinant

$$\begin{vmatrix} \phi_1(D) & \phi_2(D) \\ \phi_3(D) & \phi_4(D) \end{vmatrix}.$$

Thus, since

$$\begin{vmatrix} D-1 & -(2D+1) \\ D & D+4 \end{vmatrix} = 3D^2 + 4D - 4$$

is of the second degree in D, two arbitrary constants appear in (6) and (7).

PROBLEMS

Find the general solution of each of the equations in Problems 1–8.

1. $(x^2D^2 + 2xD - 2)y = 4 + x^2$.
2. $(2x^2D^2 - xD - 2)y = 3x - 5x^2$.
3. $(x^2D^2 - xD + 1)y = 6x + 2x^2$.
4. $(x^2D^2 + 3xD + 5)y = 10 - 4/x$.
5. $(x^3D^3 + 3x^2D^2 + xD - 8)y = 7x - 4$.
6. $(x^3D^3 + 2x^2D^2 - xD + 1)y = 3x^2 \ln x - 8x$.
7. $(x^3D^3 - 3x^2D^2 + 7xD - 8)y = 12x^2(\ln x)^2$.
8. $[(2x-1)^2D^2 - 4(2x-1)D + 8]y = 8x$. *Hint:* Let $2x - 1 = e^z$.

In Problems 9–20, solve each system of equations.

9. $2y + Dz = e^{2x}$, $(2D - 3)y + D^2z = 2e^{2x} - 6$.
10. $Dy + 3z = 4x$, $D^2y + (2D + 1)z = 3$.
11. $(D + 1)y + Dz = e^x \sin x$, $(D + 3)y + (D + 2)z = e^x \cos x$.
12. $(D^2 - 3)y - z = e^x$, $Dz - 2y = 0$.
13. $(D^2 - D)y + z = 1$, $(D - 1)y + Dz = 4e^{-x}$.
14. $3Dy + 2z = 0$, $(D + 1)z + 3w = 15 - 3x$, $D^2y - 2w = -10$.
15. $Dy = z$, $Dz = w$, $Dw = y$.
16. $(3xD - 1)y + (xD + 4)z = 21$, $(2xD + 11)y + xDz = -11$.
17. $(xD - 1)y + 5z = 20x - 7$, $x^2D^2y + (6xD + 2)z = 32x - 2$.
18. $(xD + 2)y - 2z = 0$, $3y - (xD + 1)z = -x$.
19. $(x^2D^2 + 2)y + xDz = 4x$, $2xDy + z = 5$.
20. $(x^2D^2 + 2)y - 2xDz = 4 \sin \ln x$, $(xD - 5)y + 3z = 7 \sin \ln x$.

14. Applications.

It has been stated that linear differential equations are of marked importance in engineering because of their frequent occurrence. We shall at this point discuss only a few types of motion, electric circuits, and a chemical reaction; further applications will appear in connection with other topics later in this book.

(a) *Rectilinear motion with acceleration proportional to displacement.* Consider a particle moving in a straight line, which we take as the x-axis, under the action of a central force located at the origin O, the magnitude of the force being proportional to the displacement x of the particle at any time t. By Newton's second law of motion, the force is proportional to the acceleration; hence the given motion is such that the acceleration d^2x/dt^2 is proportional to the displacement x, or

$$\frac{d^2x}{dt^2} = Cx, \tag{1}$$

where C is a constant.

Equation (1) is a linear differential equation, and its solution is easily obtained by the methods of Art. 10. However, the form of the solution will depend upon whether the constant C is positive or negative. This indeterminacy is not surprising, for we have not as yet specified whether the force is one of attraction or of repulsion. Suppose first that we are dealing with an attractive force, which therefore acts always toward the origin O. Then if x is positive, the acceleration and the force will be negative, and if x is negative, d^2x/dt^2 will be positive. Hence, for any position of the particle, the acceleration and displacement will be oppositely signed, so that C in equation (1) must be negative. To emphasize this, write $C = -k^2$, whence our differential equation takes the form

$$\frac{d^2x}{dt^2} = -k^2x. \tag{1_1}$$

Letting D denote d/dt, (1_1) may be written as

$$(\mathrm{D}^2 + k^2)x = 0,$$

the general solution of which is

$$x = A \cos kt + B \sin kt, \tag{2_1}$$

where A and B are arbitrary constants. The displacement x from the center of attraction at time t is thus given by (2_1), and the velocity at this instant will be

$$\frac{dx}{dt} = -kA \sin kt + kB \cos kt. \tag{3_1}$$

If x_0 and v_0 are, respectively, the displacement and velocity when $t = 0$, we have the conditions

$$x = x_0, \qquad \frac{dx}{dt} = v_0 \qquad \text{for} \qquad t = 0$$

which suffice to determine A and B. From the first condition we get, by (2_1), $x_0 = A$; from the second, by (3_1), $v_0 = kB$. Hence

$$x = x_0 \cos kt + \frac{v_0}{k} \sin kt. \qquad (4_1)$$

Motion defined by a relation of the form (4_1) is called *simple harmonic motion*, and (1_1) accordingly is the differential equation of simple harmonic motion. If we write (4_1) in the alternative form

$$x = \sqrt{x_0^2 + \frac{v_0^2}{k^2}} \sin \left(kt + \tan^{-1} \frac{kx_0}{v_0} \right),$$

or, for brevity

$$x = a \sin (kt + \alpha), \qquad (5_1)$$

where $a = \sqrt{x_0^2 + v_0^2/k^2}$, $\alpha = \tan^{-1} (kx_0/v_0)$, we see that the particle oscillates between the extreme positions $x = \pm a$. The distance a from the center O to either extreme position is called the *amplitude* of the motion; it evidently depends upon the initial conditions.

Now let x_1 and $(dx/dt)_1$ denote the displacement and velocity at any time t_1,

$$x_1 = a \sin (kt_1 + \alpha),$$

$$\left(\frac{dx}{dt} \right)_1 = ka \cos (kt_1 + \alpha).$$

The smallest time interval T that must elapse before x and dx/dt again take on the values x_1 and $(dx/dt)_1$, respectively, will be such that $\sin [k(t_1 + T) + \alpha] = \sin (kt_1 + \alpha)$, $\cos [k(t_1 + T) + \alpha] = \cos (kt_1 + \alpha)$. But these relations will be true if $k(t_1 + T) + \alpha = kt_1 + \alpha + 2\pi$, or

$$T = \frac{2\pi}{k}, \qquad (6_1)$$

and for no smaller value of T. The time interval T, called the *period* of the motion, represents the time required for the particle to complete one oscillation, say from one extreme position to the other and back again. By the *frequency f* is meant the number of complete oscillations occurring in unit time, so that $fT = 1$, or

$$f = \frac{1}{T} = \frac{k}{2\pi}. \qquad (7_1)$$

The period and frequency are seen to depend only upon the constant k, and not upon the initial conditions.

If, now, the force is one of repulsion, it will be directed always *away from* the center. Consequently its algebraic sign, which is that of the acceleration, will be the same as that of the displacement, so that the constant C in equation (1) is here positive, $C = k^2$. Then we have

$$\frac{d^2x}{dt^2} = k^2x, \tag{1_2}$$

or

$$(\mathbf{D}^2 - k^2)x = 0,$$

whence

$$x = c_1 e^{kt} + c_2 e^{-kt}, \tag{2_2}$$

$$\frac{dx}{dt} = kc_1 e^{kt} - kc_2 e^{-kt}, \tag{3_2}$$

where c_1 and c_2 are arbitrary. Using the same initial conditions as in simple harmonic motion, we get $x_0 = c_1 + c_2$, $v_0 = kc_1 - kc_2$, and consequently

$$x = \frac{kx_0 + v_0}{2k} e^{kt} + \frac{kx_0 - v_0}{2k} e^{-kt}. \tag{4_2}$$

This type of motion is not oscillatory and does not occur in practice nearly so often as does the more important simple harmonic motion. We shall, however, meet these two kinds of motion again in Chapter II, where the close analytic analogy between them is exhibited by means of hyperbolic functions.

(b) *Damped vibrations.* Because of the occurrence of friction or other resisting forces, vibratory motion may often not be considered as simple harmonic. If the resisting forces are large, the motion may not even be oscillatory, i.e., the particle may simply move toward the equilibrium position. For small resisting forces, the vibrations will decrease in size as time goes on; we say then that the particle executes damped vibrations.

Suppose that a particle of weight m (lb.) is attracted toward the origin O by a force proportional to the displacement x (ft.), and that the motion takes place in a medium in which the resisting force is proportional to the velocity dx/dt (ft./sec.). By Newton's second law of motion, one expression for the resultant force acting on the mass is $\frac{m}{g} \frac{d^2x}{dt^2}$, where $g = 32.17$ ft./sec.^{2}, and this force will also be given by the algebraic sum of the attractive and resisting forces. As in simple harmonic motion, the attractive force will be represented by $-k^2x$, for its sign must be opposite that of x. The magnitude of the resisting force will be $K\,dx/dt$, where K is a positive constant of proportionality; it remains to determine the proper algebraic sign of this force. Now if the mass, at some time t, is moving in the direction of increasing x, so that dx/dt is positive, the resisting force will be negatively directed and consequently will be given algebraically by $-K\,dx/dt$; if, on the other hand, the motion is in the direction of x decreasing, so that $dx/dt < 0$, the resisting force will act in the positive direction and is therefore again equal to $-K\,dx/dt$. Hence for any position and for motion in either direction we have the relation

$$\frac{m}{g}\frac{d^2x}{dt^2} = -k^2x - K\frac{dx}{dt}. \tag{8}$$

Relation (8) is evidently a linear differential equation with constant coefficients. For simplicity, we write it in the form

$$(\mathrm{D}^2 + 2a\mathrm{D} + b^2)x = 0, \tag{9}$$

where $\mathrm{D} = d/dt$, and a and b are positive constants given by

$$2a = \frac{Kg}{m}, \qquad b^2 = \frac{k^2g}{m}.$$

The roots of the equation auxiliary to (9) are $-a \pm \sqrt{a^2 - b^2}$, and it is seen that the nature of the general solution will depend upon the relative values of a and b. If the motion takes place in a viscous medium, K will be large, and it may be so large that $a > b$; then we shall get

$$x = c_1 e^{(-a+\sqrt{a^2-b^2})t} + c_2 e^{(-a-\sqrt{a^2-b^2})t}, \tag{10_1}$$

where c_1 and c_2 are arbitrary constants. Since $\sqrt{a^2 - b^2} < a$, the coefficients $-a \pm \sqrt{a^2 - b^2}$ of t will both be negative, and therefore x will approach zero as t becomes infinite whatever the initial conditions may be. As a concrete example, suppose that $a = 5$, $b = 4$, and let the mass start from rest at $x = x_0$ when $t = 0$. Then we have from (10_1),

$$x = c_1 e^{-2t} + c_2 e^{-8t},$$

$$\frac{dx}{dt} = -2c_1 e^{-2t} - 8c_2 e^{-8t};$$

and from the initial conditions,

$$x_0 = c_1 + c_2, \qquad 0 = -2c_1 - 8c_2,$$

whence

$$c_1 = \frac{4x_0}{3}, \qquad c_2 = -\frac{x_0}{3}, \qquad \text{and} \qquad x = \frac{4x_0}{3}e^{-2t} - \frac{x_0}{3}e^{-8t}.$$

The nature of the resulting motion is indicated by the graph (Fig. 7). It is seen that no oscillation takes place, x being positive for all $t > 0$, and that the damping is rapid; when $t = 1$, $x = 0.180x_0$.

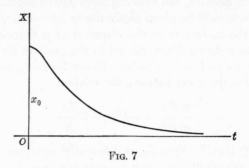

FIG. 7

If the medium is such that $a = b$, the general solution of (9) becomes

$$x = (c_1 + c_2 t)e^{-at}. \tag{10_2}$$

With the same initial conditions as before, namely $x = x_0$, $dx/dt = 0$ for $t = 0$, and taking $a = 4$, we get

$$x = x_0(1 + 4t)e^{-4t}.$$

This motion is non-oscillatory as in the preceding case.

Finally, if $a < b$, the roots of the auxiliary equation may be written $-a \pm \sqrt{b^2 - a^2}\, i$, and the general solution of (9) takes the form

$$x = e^{-at}(c_1 \cos \sqrt{b^2 - a^2}\, t + c_2 \sin \sqrt{b^2 - a^2}\, t). \tag{10_3}$$

If at time $t = t_1$ the body is passing through the origin in a given direction, then at time $t = t_1 + 2\pi/\sqrt{b^2 - a^2}$ it will again be passing O in the same direction; we call the interval $2\pi/\sqrt{b^2 - a^2}$ the *period* of the motion. The factor e^{-at} is called the *damping factor*. Taking $a = 1$, $b = 4$, and applying the conditions $x = x_0$, $dx/dt = 0$ for $t = 0$, it is found that

$$x = x_0 e^{-t}\left(\cos \sqrt{15}\, t + \frac{1}{\sqrt{15}} \sin \sqrt{15}\, t\right).$$

Hence we now have damped oscillatory motion, as indicated in Fig. 8, with period $T = 2\pi/\sqrt{15} = 1.62$ sec.

As a physical example of damped motion, consider a spring fixed at its upper end and supporting a weight of 10 lb. at its lower end. Assume that Hooke's law holds, so that any force producing an elongation of the spring is proportional to the elongation produced, the constant of proportionality being called the spring constant. Suppose that the 10-lb. weight stretches the spring 6 in. and that the resistance in pounds is numerically equal to $\frac{1}{10}$ the speed in feet per second. We wish to

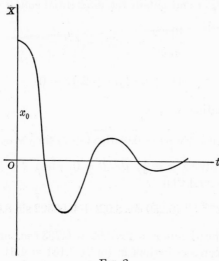

FIG. 8

find the equation of motion of the weight if it is drawn down 3 in. below its equilibrium position and released.

We first determine the spring constant. Since a force of 10 lb. stretches the spring 6 in. or $\frac{1}{2}$ ft., we have $10 = c(\frac{1}{2})$, and the spring constant is $c = 20$ lb./ft. In solving a problem of this type, it is important that we specify and keep clearly in mind the direction chosen as positive and the origin from which the displacement is measured. We shall take the downward direction as positive and our reference point O at the equilibrium position of the weight, that is, the position of the weight when it is hanging at rest (Fig. 9). Let x (ft.) be the displacement of the weight from its equilibrium position at any time t (sec.); then the elastic force tending to restore the

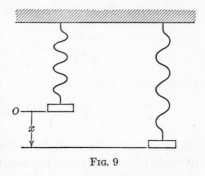

FIG. 9

weight to its equilibrium position is $-cx = -20x$, the minus sign denoting that this force and the displacement are opposite in sign. We also have a resisting force whose sign is opposite that of the velocity dx/dt, namely $-0.1\,dx/dt$, so that the resultant force tending to restore the weight to its equilibrium position is $-20x - 0.1\,dx/dt$. We equate this resultant force to the product of the moving mass and its acceleration and obtain the differential equation of motion:

$$\frac{10}{g}\frac{d^2x}{dt^2} = -20x - 0.1\frac{dx}{dt},$$

or

$$(D^2 + 0.01gD + 2g)x = 0.$$

Solving this equation, we get

$$x = e^{-0.005gt}(c_1 \cos \tfrac{1}{2}\sqrt{8g - 0.0001g^2}\,t + c_2 \sin \tfrac{1}{2}\sqrt{8g - 0.0001g^2}\,t).$$

Using the conditions $x = \frac{1}{4}$, $dx/dt = 0$ when $t = 0$, and setting $g = 32.17$, it is found that

$$x = e^{-0.161t}(0.250 \cos 8.02t + 0.00502 \sin 8.02t).$$

The period of vibration is $T = 2\pi/8.02 = 0.783$ sec., and the damping factor $e^{-0.161t}$ decreases by half in $(\ln 2)/0.161 = 4.31$ sec.

(c) *Forced vibrations.* The motion of the weight considered above was due to the inherent elastic forces of the spring-weight system and to the resistance; the vibrations are accordingly called free or natural vibrations. If, however, the system is subjected to an external periodic force, we say that the body executes forced vibrations.

Suppose that the particle of mass m is acted upon by the forces $-k^2x$ and $-K\,dx/dt$, as in the analysis leading to equation (8), and in addition is subjected to an external force $C \sin \omega t$ of amplitude C and period $2\pi/\omega$. Then (8) is replaced by

$$\frac{m}{g}\frac{d^2x}{dt^2} = -k^2x - K\frac{dx}{dt} + C \sin \omega t, \tag{11}$$

which may be written as

$$(D^2 + 2aD + b^2)x = \frac{gC}{m} \sin \omega t, \tag{12}$$

where, as before, $2a = Kg/m$ and $b^2 = k^2g/m$. Since the operators in (9) and (12) are the same, the complementary function for (12) will be given by (10_1), (10_2), or (10_3), according as $a > b$, $a = b$, $a < b$. Consequently the general solution of (12) is obtained by adding to the complementary function x_c, previously determined, a particular integral x_P of (12), and x_P will give us the effect of the external force.

We shall consider only the most important case, in which the resisting force is small, so that $a < b$ and

$$x_c = e^{-at}(c_1 \cos \sqrt{b^2 - a^2}\, t + c_2 \sin \sqrt{b^2 - a^2}\, t).$$

Let us suppose first that K is so small that we may take $a = 0$ without much error being introduced, i.e., we take the ideal situation,

$$(D^2 + b^2)x = \frac{gC}{m} \sin \omega t, \qquad (12_1)$$

for which

$$x_c = c_1 \cos bt + c_2 \sin bt.$$

It is evident that the form of a particular integral of (12_1) will depend upon whether $\omega \neq b$ or $\omega = b$. If $\omega \neq b$, we may set

$$x_P = A \sin \omega t + B \cos \omega t,$$

where A and B are undetermined coefficients; we then get

$$-\omega^2 A \sin \omega t - \omega^2 B \cos \omega t + b^2 A \sin \omega t + b^2 B \cos \omega t = \frac{gC}{m} \sin \omega t,$$

whence

$$A = gC/m(b^2 - \omega^2), \qquad B = 0,$$

and

$$x_P = \frac{gC}{m(b^2 - \omega^2)} \sin \omega t. \qquad (13_1)$$

Consequently the general solution of (12_1) is, for $\omega \neq b$,

$$x = \frac{gC}{m(b^2 - \omega^2)} \sin \omega t + c_1 \cos bt + c_2 \sin bt. \qquad (14_1)$$

Hence the effect of the sinusoidal force $C \sin \omega t$ is to superimpose a simple harmonic motion as given by (13_1); the period of this added motion is the same as that of the impressed force, and the amplitude is constant for a fixed value of ω but becomes larger as ω approaches b.

Now if the period of the external force is equal to the natural period $2\pi/b$ of the vibrating system, the differential equation of motion, when a is still negligible, is

$$(D^2 + b^2)x = \frac{gC}{m} \sin bt. \qquad (12_2)$$

Here we set

$$x_P = At \sin bt + Bt \cos bt,$$

and we then find

$$Dx_P = bAt \cos bt + A \sin bt - bBt \sin bt + B \cos bt,$$

$$D^2 x_P = -b^2 At \sin bt + 2bA \cos bt - b^2 Bt \cos bt - 2bB \sin bt,$$

whence

$$2bA \cos bt - 2bB \sin bt = \frac{gC}{m} \sin bt,$$

$$A = 0, \qquad B = -\frac{gC}{2bm},$$

$$x_P = -\frac{gC}{2bm} t \cos bt, \tag{13_2}$$

$$x = -\frac{gC}{2bm} t \cos bt + c_1 \cos bt + c_2 \sin bt. \tag{14_2}$$

From (13_2) we see that, since the coefficient of $\cos bt$ increases indefinitely with t, the vibrations get larger and larger. Of course this situation cannot occur in practice, since some resistance to the motion is always present, but it is evident that the displacement may become seriously large. If, for example, a weight is suspended by a spring and the upper end of the spring is made to move with simple harmonic motion of a period equal to the natural period of vibration, the displacement x may become so large that the elastic limit of the spring is exceeded, and a permanent set or distortion occurs.

Consider next the general equation (12), with $0 < a < b$. We put

$$x_P = A \sin \omega t + B \cos \omega t,$$

and substitution in (12) gives us

$$-\omega^2 A \sin \omega t - \omega^2 B \cos \omega t + 2a\omega A \cos \omega t - 2a\omega B \sin \omega t$$
$$+ b^2 A \sin \omega t + b^2 B \cos \omega t = \frac{gC}{m} \sin \omega t,$$

from which we find

$$A = \frac{gC(b^2 - \omega^2)}{m[(b^2 - \omega^2)^2 + 4a^2\omega^2]}, \qquad B = -\frac{2gCa\omega}{m[(b^2 - \omega^2)^2 + 4a^2\omega^2]},$$

$$x_P = \frac{gC}{m[(b^2 - \omega^2)^2 + 4a^2\omega^2]} [(b^2 - \omega^2) \sin \omega t - 2a\omega \cos \omega t]$$

$$= \frac{gC}{m\sqrt{(b^2 - \omega^2)^2 + 4a^2\omega^2}} \sin \left(\omega t - \tan^{-1} \frac{2a\omega}{b^2 - \omega^2} \right). \tag{13_3}$$

If, in particular, $\omega = b$, this reduces to

$$x_P = -\frac{gC}{2mab} \cos bt. \tag{14_3}$$

The period of x_P as given by (13_3) is $2\pi/\omega$, the same as that of the impressed force, and since the complementary function x_c approaches zero as t increases, the forced motion x_P ultimately predominates and the vibration becomes more and more nearly in tune with the external force. When $\omega = b$, we see from (14_3) that the amplitude of x_P may be dangerously large if a is small, i.e., if the resistance is small; this agrees with what has already been said. For fixed values of a and b, the amplitude in (13_3) will be a maximum when ω is such that $(b^2 - \omega^2)^2 + 4a^2\omega^2$ has its least value; if we set the derivative of this expression with respect to ω equal to zero, we find that the critical value of ω is

$$\omega_c = \sqrt{b^2 - 2a^2}. \tag{15_3}$$

When a is small compared to b, ω_c is nearly equal to b. If the period of the impressed force is $2\pi/\omega_c$, we say the force is in *resonance* with the vibrating mass. The phenomenon of resonance is of great importance in engineering. It is sometimes necessary, as in our spring problem, to avoid a resonant condition so that no undue stresses occur; on the other hand, resonance is desirable in many acoustical and radio-circuit problems.

(*d*) *Electric circuits.* In Art. 7(*e*) we considered a simple circuit containing an inductance L (henries) and a resistance R (ohms) in series with an e.m.f. E (volts), and were led to a linear differential equation of the first order. We shall discuss now a series circuit containing in addition to the parameters L and R a capacitance C.

The charge on a condenser varies directly as the potential difference across it, so that

$$Q = CE_C; \tag{16}$$

if the charge Q is given in coulombs and the potential E_C in volts, the capacitance C is measured in farads. Since current I (amp.) is the rate of flow of electric charge, we have also

$$I = \frac{dQ}{dt}, \qquad Q = \int I \, dt, \tag{17}$$

where time t is measured in seconds. Hence

$$I = C\frac{dE_C}{dt}, \qquad E_C = \frac{1}{C}\int I \, dt, \tag{18}$$

so that, just as inductance opposes a change in current, capacitance opposes a change in voltage.

Applying Kirchhoff's first law to the circuit shown in Fig. 10, in which an inductance L (henries), a resistance R (ohms), and a capacitance C (farads) are connected in series with an e.m.f. E (volts), we get

$$E - L\frac{dI}{dt} - RI - \frac{1}{C}\int I\,dt = 0. \tag{19}$$

Using relations (17), this may be written

$$\left(L\mathrm{D}^2 + R\mathrm{D} + \frac{1}{C}\right)Q = E, \tag{20}$$

where $\mathrm{D} = d/dt$. When $L \neq 0$, this second-order linear equation with constant coefficients may be solved for Q, I obtained from (17), and the

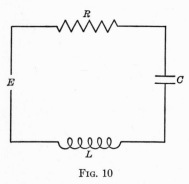

FIG. 10

two constants of integration determined when the values of Q and I for $t = 0$, say, are known. If $L = 0$, (20) reduces to an equation of first order, so that Q and I are completely determined when only one initial condition is given.

As an example, let $L = 1$ henry, $R = 100$ ohms, $C = 10^{-4}$ farad, and $E = 100$ volts. Suppose that no charges are present and no current is flowing at time $t = 0$, when the e.m.f. is applied, so that $Q = I = 0$ for $t = 0$. Equation (20) gives us

$$(\mathrm{D}^2 + 100\mathrm{D} + 10^4)Q = 100,$$

and we easily find

$$Q = \tfrac{1}{100} + e^{-50t}\,(c_1 \cos 50\sqrt{3}\,t + c_2 \sin 50\sqrt{3}\,t),$$

$$I = \frac{dQ}{dt} = e^{-50t}\,(-50\sqrt{3}\,c_1 \sin 50\sqrt{3}\,t + 50\sqrt{3}\,c_2 \cos 50\sqrt{3}\,t$$
$$-50\,c_1 \cos 50\sqrt{3}\,t - 50\,c_2 \sin 50\sqrt{3}\,t).$$

Using the initial conditions, we get

$$0 = \tfrac{1}{100} + c_1, \qquad 0 = 50\sqrt{3}\,c_2 - 50\,c_1,$$

so that

$$c_1 = -\frac{1}{100}, \qquad c_2 = -\frac{\sqrt{3}}{300},$$

and

$$Q = \frac{1}{100}\left[1 - e^{-50t}\left(\cos 50\sqrt{3}\,t + \frac{\sqrt{3}}{3}\sin 50\sqrt{3}\,t\right)\right],$$

$$I = \frac{2\sqrt{3}}{3}\,e^{-50t}\sin 50\sqrt{3}\,t.$$

We see that the frequency f of the current is $50\sqrt{3}/2\pi = 13.8$ oscillations per second, that the current rapidly damps out, and that Q rapidly approaches the steady-state value $\frac{1}{100}$ coulomb, which is that given by (16).

(e) *Physical chemistry.* We shall consider here merely a system of simultaneous equations arising in a certain type of chemical reaction. If a substance A forms an intermediate substance B, which in turn changes into a third substance C in this reaction, it is found that the respective concentrations x, y, z of the three substances obey relations of the form

$$\frac{dx}{dt} + ax = 0,$$

$$\frac{dz}{dt} = by, \tag{21}$$

$$x + y + z = c,$$

where a, b, c are constants depending upon the substances. We wish to solve these equations subject to the conditions $z = dz/dt = 0$ when $t = 0$.

Since the given initial values involve z and its first derivative, we eliminate x and y from (21) so as to get a single equation in t and z. From the last equation $y = c - x - z$; substituting in the second equation and writing D for d/dt, we get

$$bx + (D + b)z = bc. \tag{22}$$

Operating on (22) with $(D + a)$, and using the first of equations (21), we find

$$(D + a)(D + b)z = abc. \tag{23}$$

We have to distinguish two cases, according as $a \neq b$ or $a = b$. If $a \neq b$, we get from (23)

$$z = c + c_1 e^{-at} + c_2 e^{-bt},$$

whence

$$\frac{dz}{dt} = -ac_1 e^{-at} - bc_2 e^{-bt}.$$

From the initial conditions we then have

$$0 = c + c_1 + c_2, \qquad 0 = -ac_1 - bc_2,$$

so that

$$c_1 = \frac{bc}{a - b}, \qquad c_2 = \frac{-ac}{a - b}, \qquad \text{and}$$

$$z = c + \frac{c}{a - b}(be^{-at} - ae^{-bt}). \tag{24_1}$$

From the second of equations (21), there is then found

$$y = \frac{1}{b}\frac{dz}{dt} = \frac{ac}{a-b}(e^{-bt} - e^{-at}), \tag{24_2}$$

and from the third equation,

$$x = c - y - z$$

$$= c - \frac{ac}{a-b}e^{-bt} + \frac{ac}{a-b}e^{-at} - c - \frac{bc}{a-b}e^{-at} + \frac{ac}{a-b}e^{-bt}$$

$$= ce^{-at}. \tag{24_3}$$

If $a = b$, (23) yields

$$z = c + (c_1 + c_2 t)e^{-at},$$

and consequently we have

$$\frac{dz}{dt} = (c_2 - ac_1 - ac_2 t)e^{-at}.$$

Using the initial conditions, we get

$$0 = c + c_1, \qquad 0 = c_2 - ac_1,$$

so that $c_1 = -c$, $c_2 = -ac$, and

$$z = c - c(1 + at)e^{-at}. \tag{25_1}$$

Then

$$y = \frac{1}{a}\frac{dz}{dt} = acte^{-at}, \tag{25_2}$$

and

$$x = c - acte^{-at} - c + c(1 + at)e^{-at}$$

$$= ce^{-at}. \tag{25_3}$$

Equations (24) and (25) give the required solutions for $a \neq b$ and $a = b$, respectively.

PROBLEMS

1. A particle moves with simple harmonic motion in a straight line. When $t = 0$, the acceleration is 9 ft./sec.^{2}, the velocity is 3 ft./sec., and the displacement $x = -1$ ft. Find the amplitude and period of the motion.

2. A simple pendulum consists of a weight of w lb. suspended by a string of negligible weight and length L ft. If θ (rad.) is the angular displacement of the string from the vertical at time t (sec.), and if resistance is neglected, show that

$$\frac{L}{g}\frac{d^2\theta}{dt^2} = -\sin\theta.$$

If the complete angle of swing 2α is so small that $\sin \theta$ may be replaced by θ without much error, find the period of vibration and the equation of motion when the initial conditions are $\theta = \alpha$ and $d\theta/dt = 0$ for $t = 0$.

3. A simple pendulum swings through an angle 2α which may be so large that the assumption of Problem 2 regarding the replacement of $\sin \theta$ by θ cannot be made. If the pendulum is drawn aside through an angle α and released, find its actual maximum angular velocity and show that this is never as great as the maximum obtained under the assumption of Problem 2.

4. A particle moves with simple harmonic motion in a straight line under the action of a force located at the origin $x = 0$. If it starts at $x = -4$ ft. with a velocity $dx/dt = 8$ ft./sec., and if it reaches an extreme position at $x = 4\sqrt{2}$ ft., at what speed does it pass through the origin?

5. One end of a rubber band is fixed at a point A. A 1-lb. weight, attached to the other end, stretches the rubber band vertically to the point B. The length AB is 6 in. greater than the natural length of the band. If the weight is released from a point 3 in. above B, what will be its velocity when it passes B?

6. A cubical block of wood 6 in. on an edge and weighing 4 lb. floats in water (62.4 lb./ft.^{3}). If it is depressed so that its upper face lies in the water surface and is then released, find its period of vibration and equation of motion. Neglect resistance.

7. A cylinder 18 in. in diameter floats with its axis vertical in water (62.4 lb./ft.^{3}). When the cylinder is depressed slightly and released, the period of vibration is found to be 0.86 sec. Neglecting resistance, find the weight of the cylinder.

8. The attraction of a spherical mass on a particle within the mass is directed toward the center of the sphere and is proportional to the distance from the center. Suppose a straight tube bored through the center of the earth and a particle of weight w lb. to be dropped into the tube. If the radius of the earth is 3960 miles, find how long it will take (a) to pass through the tube; (b) to drop halfway to the center. Neglect resistance.

9. A 10-lb. weight is suspended by a spring which is stretched 2 in. by the weight. Assume a resistance whose magnitude (lb.) is $40/\sqrt{g}$ times the speed (ft./sec.). If the weight is drawn down 3 in. below its equilibrium position and released, find the equation of motion of the weight.

10. A 10-lb. weight suspended from a spring vibrates freely, the resistance (lb.) being numerically equal to twice the speed (ft./sec.) at any instant. If the period of the motion is to be 4 sec., find the suitable spring constant (lb./ft.).

11. A body executes damped vibrations, its motion being represented by an equation of the form $(D^2 + 2aD + b^2)x = 0$, where $D = d/dt$. If the period is 1.25 sec. and the damping factor decreases by 25% in 8.2 sec., find a and b.

12. A weight w (lb.) is suspended by a spring whose constant is 20 lb./ft. The motion of the weight is subject to a resistance (lb.) numerically equal to twice the velocity (ft./sec.). If the motion is to be oscillatory with period 1.00 sec., find the two possible values w may have.

13. A 4-lb. weight suspended from a spring causes an elongation of 2 in. It is set vibrating and the period is measured as 0.5236 sec. Assuming resistance proportional to the velocity, find the time required for the damping factor to decrease by 75%.

14. A certain damped free vibration has a period of 1 sec., in which time the damping factor decreases by 99%. If the period is made 10% greater by changing the damping, what will be the value of the damping factor at the end of the first new cycle?

15. A weight, hung on a spring and vibrating with negligible damping, has a period of 1 sec. Next it is set vibrating with a practically weightless damping vane attached to it, thereby causing a resistance proportional to the speed, and the period is then found to be 1.5 sec. Determine the differential equation corresponding to the damped vibrations.

16. The damped vibrations of a weight suspended from a spring have a period of 1 sec., and the damping factor decreases by half in 5 sec. Find the acceleration of the weight when it is 3 in. below its equilibrium position and is moving upwards with a speed of 2 in./sec.

17. A body weighing $g = 32.17$ lb. is suspended from a spring which is stretched $g/12$ ft. by the weight. Assume a resistance (lb.) equal to 7 times the speed (ft./sec.) at any instant. The body is displaced 2 ft. below its equilibrium position and is given an initial velocity v_0 (ft./sec.) directed upward. (a) Find the value of v_0 which will bring the body into equilibrium position in 1 sec. (b) Find the numerically smallest value of v_0 which will prevent the body from reaching its equilibrium position in any finite time.

18. A container weighing 1 lb. is half filled with 5 lb. of mercury and is hung on the end of a spring which is thereby stretched 1 in. The period of oscillation is found to 0.350 sec. When 5 lb. more of mercury are added, the period becomes 0.454 sec. Determine whether the resistance can be proportional to the velocity under these conditions.

19. The small oscillations of a simple pendulum with period 2 sec. are subjected to a resistance producing an angular deceleration equal to 0.10 times the angular velocity. If the pendulum is released from rest at an angular displacement of 1°, find the displacement at the end of 2 complete vibrations.

20. An 8-lb. weight, of specific gravity 2, stretches a spring 3 in. when immersed in water. Because of resistance proportional to the velocity, the period of vibration is 0.017 sec. longer than it would be without damping. By what percentage will the damping factor be decreased in 1 sec.?

21. A 5-lb. weight is to be supported by a spring and made to execute damped vibrations in which the resistance is proportional to the velocity. If the damping factor is to decrease by 90% in half a cycle, and if the period is to be 0.30 sec. more than it would be if there were no resistance, find the amount by which the weight should stretch the spring.

22. A weight of 32.17 lb. is suspended from a spring whose constant is 6 lb./ft. There is a resistance (lb.) equal to 5 times the velocity (ft./sec.) at any instant. The weight is drawn down 6 in. below its equilibrium position and then released. (a) Find the equation of the ensuing motion, and sketch its graph. (b) Determine the displacement from equilibrium position when $\frac{1}{4}$ sec. has elapsed.

23. A particle moves along the x-axis in accordance with the equation $(D^2 + 10D + 9)x = 0$, where $D = d/dt$. At time $t = 0$, the particle is 2 ft. to the right of the origin and is projected toward the left at the rate of 20 ft./sec. Find (a) the time required for the particle to reach its leftmost position; (b) the total distance traveled by the particle at the end of 1 sec.

24. A particle moves along the x-axis in accordance with the equation $(4D^2 + 4D + 1)x = 0$, where $D = d/dt$. If it starts from a point 2 ft. to the right of the origin with a speed of 3 ft./sec. directed toward the left, find the time t when the speed is zero and the displacement x at that time.

25. A body executes damped forced vibrations given by the equation $(D^2 + 2aD + b^2)x = Ce^{-at} \sin \omega t$, where the impressed force is damped by a factor

e^{-at} equal to the damping factor for the natural vibrations. Find a particular integral for this equation if (a) $\omega \neq \sqrt{b^2 - a^2}$; (b) $\omega = \sqrt{b^2 - a^2}$.

26. A 10-lb. weight is hanging at rest on a spring which is stretched 3 in. by the weight. If the upper end of the spring is given the motion $y = \sin \omega t$ (ft.) and if resistance is neglected, find the equation of motion of the weight when (a) $\omega = \sqrt{2g}$ rad./sec.; (b) $\omega = 2\sqrt{g}$ rad./sec. For both (a) and (b) find also the displacement of the weight from its equilibrium position when $t = \pi/\sqrt{g}$ sec.

27. Solve Problem 26(a) assuming a resistance whose magnitude in pounds is equal to $20/\sqrt{g}$ times the velocity in feet per second.

28. A body weighing 32.17 lb. is supported by a spring whose constant is 36 lb./ft. Assume a resistance (lb.) equal to 13 times the speed (ft./sec.) at any instant, and take the downward direction as positive. The body is displaced x_0 ft. from its equilibrium position and released, while at the same instant the upper end of the spring is given the motion $y = \sin 6t$ (ft.). If the body then executes simple harmonic motion, determine whether the initial displacement x_0 was above or below the equilibrium position, and its amount.

29. A weight of $g = 32.17$ lb. is suspended from a spring which is stretched $g/25$ ft. by the weight. At a given instant an external vertical force, which is proportional to the function $\cos 5t$, is applied to the weight. The motion of the weight is subjected to a resistance (lb.) equal to 6 times the velocity (ft./sec.) of the weight. If the weight is 0.1 in. below its equilibrium position at the end of $\pi/2$ sec., what was the initial external force?

30. A body weighing $g = 32.17$ lb. is hanging at rest on a spring which is stretched $g/41$ ft. by the weight. Assume a resistance (lb.) equal to 8 times the speed (ft./sec.) at any instant of the motion of the weight, imparted by giving the upper end of the spring the motion $y = \sin \omega t$ (ft.). After the transient motion, represented by the complementary function, has died down, the displacement x (ft.) of the weight will be given by the particular integral x_P. (a) Find the amplitude of x_P when the period $2\pi/\omega$ of the external force is equal to the natural period of vibration of the weight. (b) Find the amplitude of x_P when $\omega = 3$ rad./sec. (c) Discuss the relative values of the two amplitudes from the standpoint of resonance.

31. A weight of $g = 32.17$ lb. is hanging at rest on a spring which is stretched 3 in. by the weight. The upper end of the spring is given the motion $y = \sin 2\sqrt{g}\, t$ (ft.), and the resistance (lb.) is K times the velocity (ft./sec.). (a) Find K such that any smaller value would make the transient motion (represented by the complementary function) of the weight oscillatory. (b) Using the value of K found in (a), find the equation of motion of the weight.

32. A particle undergoes vibratory motion in accordance with the equation $(D^2 + 0.4D + 13)x = 0$, where x (ft.) is the displacement at time t (sec.) and $D = d/dt$. If the velocity at a certain time is 1 ft./sec., find the velocity one period later.

33. A 2-lb. weight is hanging at rest on a spring which is stretched $g/25$ ft. by the weight ($g = 32.17$). The upper end of the spring is given the motion $y = 1 - e^{-5t}$ (ft.) and the resulting motion of the weight is subjected to a resistance (lb.) equal to $20/g$ times the velocity (ft./sec.). Find the displacement of the weight from equilibrium position at the end of 1 sec.

34. A particle undergoes non-vibratory motion in accordance with the equation $(D^2 + 2aD + b^2)x = 0$, where x (ft.) is the displacement at time t (sec.), $D = d/dt$, and $a > b$. At time $t = 0$, $x = x_0 > 0$ and $Dx = v_0$ (ft./sec.). Show that the particle remains to the right of the origin if $v_0 \geq -x_0(a + \sqrt{a^2 - b^2})$, but that it passes through the origin, reverses its direction of motion, and ultimately approaches $x = 0$ from the left if $v_0 < -x_0(a + \sqrt{a^2 - b^2})$.

35. Discuss the motion of a particle satisfying the equation $(D^2 + 2aD + a^2)x = 0$ and the initial conditions $x = x_0 > 0$, $Dx = v_0$, for $t = 0$. (Cf. Problem 34.)

36. A coil of inductance 1 henry and negligible resistance is connected in series with a capacitance 10^{-6} farad and an e.m.f. E volts. Taking $Q = I = 0$ for $t = 0$, find the charge Q and current I when $t = 0.001$ sec. if (a) $E = 100$; (b) $E = 100 \sin 500t$; (c) $E = 100 \sin 1000t$.

37. An inductance of 1 henry, a resistance of 1600 ohms, and a capacitance of 10^{-6} farad are connected in series with an e.m.f. $100 \sin 600t$ volts. If the charge and current are both zero when $t = 0$, find the current when $t = 0.001$ sec.

38. An inductance of 1 henry, a resistance of 1200 ohms, and a capacitance of 10^{-6} farad are connected in series with an e.m.f. $100 \sin 1000t$ volts. The charge and current are both zero initially. For $t = 0.001$ sec., determine whether the transient current or the steady-state current value is numerically the larger.

39. Using the data of Problem 38, find the ratio of the current actually flowing to that which would be obtained if there were no resistance, when $t = 0.001$ sec.

40. An inductance of 1 henry, a resistance of 3000 ohms, and a capacitance of 5×10^{-7} farad are connected in series with an e.m.f. of $100e^{-1000t}$ volts. If the charge and current are both zero when $t = 0$, find the current when $t = 0.001$ sec.

41. An inductance L henries, a resistance R ohms, and a capacitance C farads are connected in series with an e.m.f. $E_0 \sin \omega t$ volts. If the charge Q and current I are both zero for $t = 0$, and if $4L > R^2C$, find expressions for Q and I at any time t. For convenience, let $a = R/2L$, $\omega_1 = \sqrt{4LC - R^2C^2}/2LC$, $X = L\omega - 1/C\omega$, $Z^2 = R^2 + X^2$. What value of ω will produce resonance?

42. Solve Problem 41 if $4L = R^2C$.

43. Solve Problem 41 if $4L < R^2C$. (Here let $\omega_2 = \sqrt{R^2C^2 - 4LC}/2LC$.)

44.* The primary of a transformer has inductance L_1 henries and resistance R_1 ohms, the secondary has inductance L_2 henries and resistance R_2 ohms, and the mutual inductance is M henries, where $L_1L_2 > M^2$. The free oscillations in the two circuits are then given by

$$L_1DI_1 + MDI_2 + R_1I_1 = 0,$$

$$MDI_1 + L_2DI_2 + R_2I_2 = 0,$$

where I_1 and I_2 are the currents in primary and secondary, respectively, and $D = d/dt$. (a) Show that I_1 and I_2 numerically diminish as t increases. (b) If L_1, L_2, and M are 1, 2, and 1 henries, respectively, R_1 and R_2 are 5 and 24 ohms, respectively, and $I_1 = 1$ amp., $I_2 = 2$ amp. when $t = 0$, find I_1 and I_2 when $t = 0.1$ sec.

45. A condenser of capacitance C farads and an e.m.f. $E_0 \sin \omega t$ are connected in series with the primary of Problem 44 and the secondary is short-circuited, so that the equations for I_1 and I_2 become

$$L_1DI_1 + MDI_2 + R_1I_1 + \frac{1}{C} \int I_1 \, dt = E_0 \sin \omega t,$$

$$MDI_1 + L_2DI_2 + R_2I_2 = 0.$$

* The differential equations of Problems 44–46 can be derived by the methods of Art. 109, Chap. XI.

By what amount must the inductance L_1 of the primary be changed if the forced oscillations, represented by particular integrals, are to be the same when the condenser is short-circuited as they are here? *Hint:* Take the particular integral for I_1 in the form $A \sin(\omega t + \alpha)$.

46. When the primary and secondary circuits of the transformer of Problem 44 contain capacitances C_1 and C_2, respectively, and the resistances R_1 and R_2 are negligible, the currents I_1 and I_2 are given by

$$L_1 D^2 I_1 + M D^2 I_2 + I_1/C_1 = E_0 \omega \cos \omega t,$$

$$M D^2 I_1 + L_2 D^2 I_2 + I_2/C_2 = 0.$$

Find the steady-state current values represented by the particular integrals. Show also that the complementary functions represent periodic oscillations when $L_1 L_2 > M^2$.

47. Tank A contains 100 gal. of brine in which 100 lb. of salt are dissolved. Tank B contains 100 gal. of water. Water flows into A at the rate of 3 gal./min., and the mixture flows into B at the rate of 4 gal./min. From B, the solution is pumped back into A at the rate of 1 gal./min. and also flows into a third tank at the rate of 3 gal./min. Find the maximum amount of salt in tank B.

48. A body falls from rest in a liquid whose density is one-third that of the body. If the liquid offers resistance proportional to the velocity, and the velocity approaches a limiting value of 40 ft./sec., find the distance fallen in 1 sec.

49. A projectile of weight w lb. is fired from a gun at the origin O. If the initial velocity is v_0 ft./sec. in a direction making an angle α with the horizontal x-axis, show that when resistance is neglected the path is a parabola, and find the maximum height and the range of the projectile on a horizontal plane through O.

50. If resistance proportional to the velocity is taken into account, find the parametric equations of the path of the projectile of Problem 49. Find also the maximum height reached.

51. Two bodies, each of weight 1 lb., slide freely in horizontal grooves perpendicular to each other, and are connected by a spring 1 ft. long and with a 50-lb./ft. constant. If the weights are placed 9 in. from the point of intersection of their grooves and released, find their equations of motion.

52. A particle lies on the line connecting two centers of equal attraction. If each attractive force is proportional to the distance of the particle from the corresponding center, and if the particle is released from rest at a point nearer one center than the other, show that the resulting motion is simple harmonic.

53. If the particle of Problem 52 starts with velocity v_0 along a line perpendicular to the line connecting the centers of attraction, show that the path of the particle is an ellipse.

54. A particle slides freely in a tube which rotates in a vertical plane about its midpoint with constant angular velocity ω. If x is the distance of the particle from the midpoint of the tube at time t, and if the tube is horizontal when $t = 0$, show that the motion of the particle along the tube is given by $D^2 x - \omega^2 x = -g \sin \omega t$, where $D = d/dt$ and g is the gravitation constant. Solve this equation if $x = x_0$, $Dx = v_0$ when $t = 0$. For what values of x_0 and v_0 is the motion simple harmonic?

55. A particle of unit mass is attracted toward a fixed point O by a force F. If (r, θ) are the polar coordinates of the particle at any instant, and if $u = 1/r$, then the motion of the particle is given by the equation $(D^2 + 1)u = F/h^2 u^2$, where $D = d/d\theta$ and h is a constant representing twice the areal velocity. Given that $\theta = Du = 0$ when $u = 1/r_0$, solve this equation if (a) $F = ku^2$; (b) $F = ku^3$. In (a), where the force varies inversely as the square of the distance r, show that the path is a conic.

56. (a) For steady heat flow through the wall of a hollow cylindrical steam pipe, whose inner and outer radii are r_1 and r_2, respectively, show that the temperature u at a radial distance r ($r_1 < r < r_2$) from the axis of the cylinder is given by $r\mathrm{D}^2u + \mathrm{D}u = 0$, where $\mathrm{D} = d/dr$. (b) If u_1 and u_2 are, respectively, the temperatures at the inner and outer surfaces of the pipe, find u as a function of r. (c) If $r_1 = 6$ cm., $r_2 = 8$ cm., $u_1 = 100°$ C., $u_2 = 90°$ C., find u for $r = 7$ cm.

57. (a) For steady heat flow through the wall of a hollow sphere of inner and outer radii r_1 and r_2, respectively, show that the temperature u at a distance r ($r_1 < r < r_2$) from the center of the sphere is given by $r\mathrm{D}^2u + 2\mathrm{D}u = 0$, where $\mathrm{D} = d/dr$. (b) If u_1 and u_2 are the temperatures at the inner and outer surfaces of the shell, find u in terms of r. (c) If $r_1 = 6$ cm., $r_2 = 8$ cm., $u_1 = 100°$ C., $u_2 = 90°$ C., find u for $r = 7$ cm.

58. The small oscillations of a certain system with two degrees of freedom are given by the equations

$$\mathrm{D}^2x + 3x - 2y = 0, \qquad \mathrm{D}^2x + \mathrm{D}^2y - 3x + 5y = 0,$$

where $\mathrm{D} = d/dt$. If $x = 0$, $y = 0$, $\mathrm{D}x = 3$, $\mathrm{D}y = 2$ when $t = 0$, find x and y when $t = \frac{1}{2}$.

59. A weight w_1 (lb.) is suspended by a spring whose upper end is fastened to a second weight w_2 (lb.). The weight w_2 is in turn supported by a second spring, the upper end of which is fixed. A force $A \sin \omega t$ (lb.) is applied to w_1. Show that the displacements x_1 and x_2 (ft.) from equilibrium positions of w_1 and w_2, respectively, are given by

$$(w_1/g)\mathrm{D}^2x_1 = -k_1(x_1 - x_2) + A \sin \omega t,$$

$$(w_2/g)\mathrm{D}^2x_2 = k_1(x_1 - x_2) - k_2x_2,$$

where k_1 and k_2 are the spring constants and $\mathrm{D} = d/dt$. Find the forced vibrations represented by the particular integrals for x_1 and x_2. For how many values of ω does resonance occur?

60. If the external force is removed, the elastic double pendulum of Problem 59 executes free oscillations. Take $w_1 = g/100$ lb., $w_2 = g/50$ lb., $k_1 = 2$ lb./ft., and $k_2 = 4$ lb./ft., and suppose the equilibrium positions of the two weights to be 1 ft. apart. If $x_1 = 4$ in., $x_2 = 2$ in., $\mathrm{D}x_1 = 0$, and $\mathrm{D}x_2 = 0$ when $t = 0$, how far apart are the two weights when $t = 0.1$ sec.?

61. For small displacements, the motion of the bob of a gyrostatic pendulum is given by the equations

$$\mathrm{D}^2x + 2a\mathrm{D}y + b^2x = 0,$$

$$\mathrm{D}^2y - 2a\mathrm{D}x + b^2y = 0,$$

where a and b are positive constants and $\mathrm{D} = d/dt$. (a) Show that the solution of this system is

$$x = c_1 \cos (\omega_1 t + \alpha) + c_2 \cos (\omega_2 t + \beta),$$

$$y = c_1 \sin (\omega_1 t + \alpha) - c_2 \sin (\omega_2 t + \beta),$$

where $\omega_1 = \sqrt{a^2 + b^2} + a$, $\omega_2 = \sqrt{a^2 + b^2} - a$, and c_1, c_2, α, and β are arbitrary constants. (b) If $a = 3$ and $b = 4$, discuss the motion when the initial conditions are (i) $x = 2$, $y = 0$, $\mathrm{D}x = 0$, $\mathrm{D}y = -4$ for $t = 0$; (ii) $x = 0$, $y = 1$, $\mathrm{D}x = 8$, $\mathrm{D}y = 0$ for $t = 0$.

62. In Thomson's experimental determination of the ratio m/e of the mass to the charge of an electron, in which the electrons were subjected to an electric field of intensity E and a magnetic field of intensity H, the equations

$$mD^2x + HeDy = Ee, \qquad mD^2y - HeDx = 0,$$

where $D = d/dt$, were employed.* If $x = y = Dx = Dy = 0$ for $t = 0$, show that the path is a cycloid whose parametric equations are

$$x = \frac{Em}{H^2e}\left(1 - \cos\frac{Het}{m}\right), \qquad y = \frac{Em}{H^2e}\left(\frac{Het}{m} - \sin\frac{Het}{m}\right).$$

63. A cantilever beam of length L in. and weighing w lb./in. is subjected to a horizontal compressive force of P lb. applied at the free end. Taking the origin at the free end and the y-axis positive upwards, the differential equation of the elastic curve is $EIy'' = -Py - \frac{1}{2}wx^2$. (a) Show that the maximum deflection is given by the formula

$$y_L = \frac{wEI}{P^2}\left(1 - \frac{\theta^2}{2} - \sec\theta + \theta\tan\theta\right),$$

where $\theta = L\sqrt{P/EI}$. (b) Find the maximum deflection of a wooden beam 2 in. by 4 in. by 10 ft., with $E = 15 \times 10^5$ lb./in.^{2} and weighing 40 lb./ft.^{3}, if the 2-in. side is horizontal and $P = 500$ lb.

* See *Phil. Mag.*, Vol. 48, p. 547, 1899.

CHAPTER II

Hyperbolic Functions

15. Introductory remarks. Hyperbolic functions are useful in a variety of physical problems. The hyperbolic functions, hyperbolic sine, hyperbolic cosine, etc., are connected with a hyperbola in a manner analogous to that in which the circular functions, sine, cosine, etc., are connected with a circle. Corresponding to the formulas of ordinary

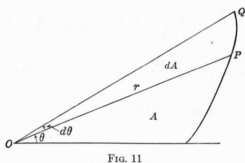

Fig. 11

trigonometry, a dual set of formulas can be developed in hyperbolic trigonometry. In order to exhibit this duality, the idea of sector area, rather than angle, is fundamental.

We recall from calculus that a sector element of area POQ (Fig. 11) is

$$dA = \tfrac{1}{2}r^2 \, d\theta,$$

or, in rectangular coordinates, since

$$r^2 = x^2 + y^2, \qquad d\theta = d\left(\tan^{-1}\frac{y}{x}\right) = \frac{x \, dy - y \, dx}{x^2 + y^2},$$

we have

$$dA = \tfrac{1}{2}(x \, dy - y \, dx),$$

where x, y are the rectangular coordinates of the point P.

16. Definitions of the six hyperbolic functions. Now consider a unit circle and a unit equilateral hyperbola (Fig. 12).

Representing by u the sector area $OPAP'$, with $OA = 1$, we shall express the rectangular coordinates x, y of P in terms of u. As the sector opens out, P moves to Q and P' to Q'. Thus the differential of the sector area u is twice the area of the sector element POQ, that is,

$$du = x\,dy - y\,dx.$$

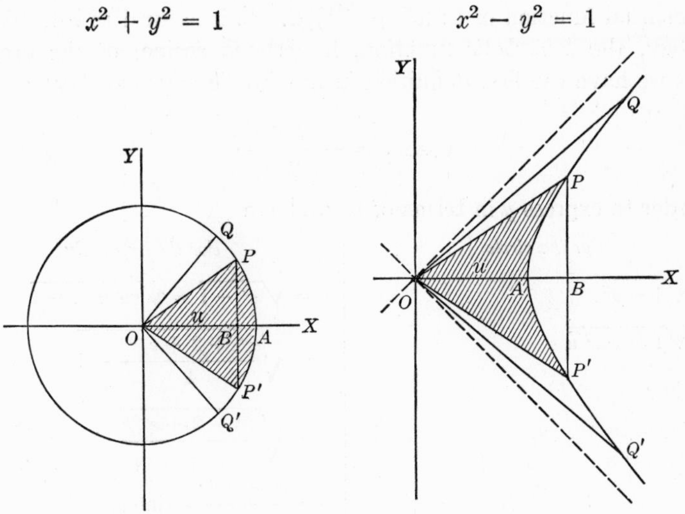

$$x^2 + y^2 = 1 \qquad\qquad x^2 - y^2 = 1$$

Fig. 12

Substituting first the value of y from the equation of the circle, then the value of y from the equation of the hyperbola, we have:

For the circle

$$du = x\,d\sqrt{1 - x^2} - \sqrt{1 - x^2}\,dx$$

$$= \left(\frac{-x^2}{\sqrt{1 - x^2}} - \sqrt{1 - x^2}\right)dx$$

$$= \frac{-dx}{\sqrt{1 - x^2}},$$

$$u = \int_1^x \frac{-dx}{\sqrt{1 - x^2}} = \cos^{-1} x,$$

$$x = \cos u.$$

For the hyperbola

$$du = x\,d\sqrt{x^2 - 1} - \sqrt{x^2 - 1}\,dx$$

$$= \left(\frac{x^2}{\sqrt{x^2 - 1}} - \sqrt{x^2 - 1}\right)dx$$

$$= \frac{dx}{\sqrt{x^2 - 1}},$$

$$u = \int_1^x \frac{dx}{\sqrt{x^2 - 1}} = \ln(x + \sqrt{x^2 - 1}),$$

$$e^u = x + \sqrt{x^2 - 1},$$

$$e^{2u} - 2xe^u + x^2 = x^2 - 1,$$

$$x = \frac{e^u + e^{-u}}{2} = \cosh u.$$

Thus, in order to express x in terms of u, we are led in the case of the circle to the familiar *circular* function, cosine. Usually we think of a cosine as being the cosine of an angle, but we could just as well think of it as being the cosine of the number representing an area. For instance, if $OA = 1$ in., the number of square inches in the circular sector u equals the number of radians in the angle POA, so that the length OB in the circle can be regarded as the cosine of either number. In the case of the hyperbola we arrive at the fact that x is a particular exponential function of u: $(e^u + e^{-u})/2$. It is natural to call this, by analogy, the *hyperbolic* function, hyperbolic cosine, of the area u. Thus we have the first definition in hyperbolic trigonometry:

$$\cosh u = \frac{e^u + e^{-u}}{2}. \tag{1}$$

In order to express y in terms of u, we have

For the circle

$$y = \sqrt{1 - x^2}$$
$$= \sqrt{1 - \cos^2 u}$$
$$= \sin u.$$

For the hyperbola

$$y = \sqrt{x^2 - 1} = \sqrt{\cosh^2 u - 1}$$
$$= \sqrt{\frac{e^{2u} + 2 + e^{-2u}}{4} - 1}$$
$$= \sqrt{\frac{e^{2u} - 2 + e^{-2u}}{4}}$$
$$= \frac{e^u - e^{-u}}{2} = \sinh u.$$

The second definition in hyperbolic trigonometry is

$$\sinh u = \frac{e^u - e^{-u}}{2}. \tag{2}$$

Hence we have the first derived formula in hyperbolic trigonometry:

$$\cosh^2 u - 1 = \sinh^2 u.$$

The other four hyperbolic functions, hyperbolic tangent, hyperbolic cotangent, hyperbolic secant, hyperbolic cosecant, we define as follows, by analogy to the circular functions:

$$\tanh u = \frac{\sinh u}{\cosh u}, \tag{3}$$

$$\coth u = \frac{1}{\tanh u}, \tag{4}$$

$$\operatorname{sech} u = \frac{1}{\cosh u}, \tag{5}$$

$$\operatorname{csch} u = \frac{1}{\sinh u}. \tag{6}$$

We regard these six definitions as defining the six hyperbolic functions also when u is negative.

17. Some formulas of hyperbolic trigonometry. Following are twenty-three of the formulas of hyperbolic trigonometry, some of which we proceed to derive.

$$\cosh^2 u - \sinh^2 u = 1, \tag{1}$$

$$\text{sech}^2 u = 1 - \tanh^2 u, \tag{2}$$

$$\text{csch}^2 u = \coth^2 u - 1, \tag{3}$$

$$\sinh(-u) = -\sinh u, \tag{4}$$

$$\cosh(-u) = \cosh u, \tag{5}$$

$$\tanh(-u) = -\tanh u, \tag{6}$$

$$\text{sech}(-u) = \text{sech } u, \tag{7}$$

$$\text{csch}(-u) = -\text{csch } u, \tag{8}$$

$$\coth(-u) = -\coth u, \tag{9}$$

$$\sinh(u+v) = \sinh u \cosh v + \cosh u \sinh v, \tag{10}$$

$$\sinh(u-v) = \sinh u \cosh v - \cosh u \sinh v, \tag{11}$$

$$\cosh(u+v) = \cosh u \cosh v + \sinh u \sinh v, \tag{12}$$

$$\cosh(u-v) = \cosh u \cosh v - \sinh u \sinh v, \tag{13}$$

$$\sinh 2u = 2 \sinh u \cosh u, \tag{14}$$

$$\cosh 2u = \cosh^2 u + \sinh^2 u, \tag{15}$$

$$\frac{d}{du} \sinh u = \cosh u, \tag{16}$$

$$\frac{d}{du} \cosh u = \sinh u, \tag{17}$$

$$\int \sinh u \, du = \cosh u, \tag{18}$$

$$\int \cosh u \, du = \sinh u, \tag{19}$$

$$\sinh u = u + \frac{u^3}{3!} + \frac{u^5}{5!} + \frac{u^7}{7!} + \cdots, \tag{20}$$

$$\cosh u = 1 + \frac{u^2}{2!} + \frac{u^4}{4!} + \frac{u^6}{6!} + \cdots, \tag{21}$$

$$\sinh iu = i \sin u, \tag{22}$$

$$\cosh iu = \cos u. \tag{23}$$

Formula (1) was obtained in Art. 16. To obtain (2) from the definitions, we have

$$1 - \tanh^2 u = 1 - \left(\frac{e^u - e^{-u}}{e^u + e^{-u}}\right)^2 = \frac{4}{(e^u + e^{-u})^2} = \operatorname{sech}^2 u.$$

To obtain (4) from definition (2) of Art. 16, we have

$$\sinh(-u) = \frac{e^{-u} - e^u}{2} = -\sinh u.$$

To obtain (10) we first add and subtract (1) and (2) of Art. 16:

$$e^u = \cosh u + \sinh u,$$
$$e^{-u} = \cosh u - \sinh u. \tag{24}$$

Then, from (2), Art. 16,

$$\sinh(u + v) = \tfrac{1}{2}[e^{u+v} - e^{-(u+v)}] = \tfrac{1}{2}(e^u e^v - e^{-u} e^{-v}).$$

Hence, from (24),

$$\sinh(u + v) = \tfrac{1}{2}[(\cosh u + \sinh u)(\cosh v + \sinh v)$$
$$- (\cosh u - \sinh u)(\cosh v - \sinh v)]$$
$$= \sinh u \cosh v + \cosh u \sinh v.$$

To obtain (16) and (19), we have

$$\frac{d}{du} \sinh u = \frac{d}{du} \frac{e^u - e^{-u}}{2} = \frac{e^u + e^{-u}}{2} = \cosh u,$$

and therefore

$$\int \cosh u \, du = \sinh u.$$

To obtain (20), (21), (22), (23), we have

$$\sinh u = \tfrac{1}{2}(e^u - e^{-u})$$
$$= \frac{1}{2}\left[\left(1 + u + \frac{u^2}{2!} + \frac{u^3}{3!} + \cdots\right) - \left(1 - u + \frac{u^2}{2!} - \frac{u^3}{3!} + \cdots\right)\right]$$
$$= u + \frac{u^3}{3!} + \frac{u^5}{5!} + \cdots,$$
$$\cosh u = \frac{1}{2}(e^u + e^{-u}) = 1 + \frac{u^2}{2!} + \frac{u^4}{4!} + \cdots.$$

We may regard these series as defining the functions $\sinh u$, $\cosh u$, when u is imaginary. Letting $u = iv$, we have,

$$\sinh (iv) = iv + \frac{i^3 v^3}{3!} + \frac{i^5 v^5}{5!} + \cdots = i\left(v - \frac{v^3}{3!} + \frac{v^5}{5!} - \cdots\right) = i \sin v$$

$$\cosh (iv) = 1 + \frac{i^2 v^2}{2!} + \frac{i^4 v^4}{4!} + \cdots = 1 - \frac{v^2}{2!} + \frac{v^4}{4!} - \cdots = \cos v.$$

From (22) and (23), we obtain

$$\sin v = \frac{1}{i} \sinh (iv) = \frac{1}{2i}(e^{iv} - e^{-iv}),$$

$$\cos v = \cosh (iv) = \tfrac{1}{2}(e^{iv} + e^{-iv}), \tag{25}$$

the exponential expressions for the sine and cosine. By adding and subtracting the second of equations (25) and i times the first, we obtain the Euler relation

$$e^{\pm iv} = \cos v \pm i \sin v. \tag{26}$$

PROBLEMS

1. Derive all the formulas (1)–(23) which are not derived in the text.

2. Find the values of $\sinh 0$, $\cosh 0$, $\tanh 0$, $\sinh^{-1} 0$, $\cosh^{-1} 1$, $\tanh^{-1} 0$, $\lim_{x \to \infty} \tanh x$, $\lim_{x \to \infty} (\sinh^{-1} x - \ln x)$.

3. Draw graphs of the equations $y = \sinh x$, $y = \cosh x$, $y = \tanh x$, $y = \coth x$, $y = \operatorname{sech} x$, $y = \operatorname{csch} x$.

4. Find the derivatives with respect to x of the six inverse hyperbolic functions: $\sinh^{-1} x$, $\cosh^{-1} x$, $\tanh^{-1} x$, $\coth^{-1} x$, $\operatorname{sech}^{-1} x$, $\operatorname{csch}^{-1} x$.

5. Show that, for $a > 0$,

$$\sinh^{-1}\frac{x}{a} = \ln \frac{x + \sqrt{x^2 + a^2}}{a}, \qquad \cosh^{-1}\frac{x}{a} = \pm \ln \frac{x + \sqrt{x^2 - a^2}}{a},$$

$$\tanh^{-1}\frac{x}{a} = \frac{1}{2}\ln \frac{a + x}{a - x}, \qquad \operatorname{csch}^{-1}\frac{x}{a} = \ln \frac{a \pm \sqrt{a^2 + x^2}}{x} \quad (x \gtrless 0).$$

6. Show that

$$\sin (x + iy) = \sin x \cosh y + i \cos x \sinh y,$$

$$\cos (x + iy) = \cos x \cosh y - i \sin x \sinh y,$$

$$\sinh (x + iy) = \sinh x \cos y + i \cosh x \sin y,$$

$$\cosh (x + iy) = \cosh x \cos y + i \sinh x \sin y.$$

7. A tangent line is drawn to the curve $y = \sinh^{-1} x$ at a point on the curve where $x = \frac{4}{3}$. Find the distance from the origin to the point where the tangent line cuts the x-axis.

8. A tangent line is drawn to the curve $y = \tanh^{-1} x$ at a point on the curve where $x = \frac{1}{2}$. Find the coordinates of the points in which the tangent line cuts the asymptotes to the curve.

9. Find the area in the first quadrant between the curves $y = \sinh x$ and $y = \cosh x$.

10. Transform $(1 + \tanh x)/(1 - \tanh x)$ into $\cosh 2x + \sinh 2x$.

18. Rectilinear motion with acceleration proportional to displacement.

In Art. 14(a), Chapter I, we obtained the general solutions of the following differential equations:

$$\frac{d^2x}{dt^2} = -k^2x. \quad \text{General solution: } x = A_1 \cos kt + B_1 \sin kt, \quad (1)$$

$$\frac{d^2x}{dt^2} = k^2x. \quad \text{General solution: } x = c_1 e^{kt} + c_2 e^{-kt}, \quad (2)$$

in which A_1, B_1, c_1, c_2 are arbitrary constants. These equations (1) and (2) represent respectively rectilinear motion of a particle under attractive and repulsive forces proportional to the displacement.

In order to exhibit the analogy between the solutions (1) and (2) we replace the exponentials by their hyperbolic equivalents as given by equations (24), Art. 17:

$$c_1 e^{kt} + c_2 e^{-kt} = c_1 (\cosh kt + \sinh kt) + c_2 (\cosh kt - \sinh kt)$$

$$= A_2 \cosh kt + B_2 \sinh kt,$$

where A_2 and B_2 are arbitrary constants related to the original constants by the equations, $A_2 = c_1 + c_2$, $B_2 = c_1 - c_2$. Instead of (2) we may then write

$$\frac{d^2x}{dt^2} = k^2x. \quad \text{General solution: } x = A_2 \cosh kt + B_2 \sinh kt. \quad (3)$$

For an attractive force we have the solution (1) expressed by circular functions; for repulsion we have the analogous solution (3) expressed by hyperbolic functions.

Consider two particles each starting from rest at a distance a from centers of attraction and repulsion respectively, the accelerations being numerically equal in both cases at $x = a$. We have for the two cases:

Attraction	Repulsion
$\dfrac{d^2x}{dt^2} = -k^2x,$	$\dfrac{d^2x}{dt^2} = k^2x,$
$x = A_1 \cos kt + B_1 \sin kt,$	$x = A_2 \cosh kt + B_2 \sinh kt,$
$a = A_1, \quad (x = a, \quad t = 0)$	$a = A_2, \quad (x = a, \quad t = 0)$
$\dfrac{dx}{dt} = -ak \sin kt + B_1 k \cos kt,$	$\dfrac{dx}{dt} = ak \sinh kt + B_2 k \cosh kt,$
$0 = B_1, \quad \left(\dfrac{dx}{dt} = 0, \quad t = 0\right)$	$0 = B_2, \quad \left(\dfrac{dx}{dt} = 0, \quad t = 0\right)$
$x = a \cos kt.$	$x = a \cosh kt.$

The displacement is a circular function of the time for the attractive force, and the corresponding hyperbolic function of the time for the repulsive force.

If t_1 and t_2 are respectively the times required by the particles to travel the first $a/2$ units of distance, let us find the ratio t_1/t_2. We have

$$\frac{k\,t_1}{k\,t_2} = \frac{\cos^{-1} 0.5}{\cosh^{-1} 1.5}, \qquad \frac{t_1}{t_2} = \frac{1.0472}{0.9625} = 1.09.$$

19. Motion under resistance. Suppose that a body falls from rest in a medium offering resistance proportional to the square of the velocity, and that the limiting velocity (when the acceleration becomes zero) is V (ft./sec.). If w (lb.) is the weight of the body and we measure y positive downwards from the starting position, we have for the differential equation of the motion

$$\frac{w}{g}\frac{d^2y}{dt^2} = w - \lambda\left(\frac{dy}{dt}\right)^2,$$

where λ is a constant of proportionality to be determined, and $g = 32.17$ ft./sec.^{2} Replacing dy/dt, the velocity, by v, we have

$$\frac{w}{g}\frac{dv}{dt} = w - \lambda v^2,$$

and, since $v = V$ when $dv/dt = 0$, $w - \lambda V^2 = 0$, or $\lambda = w/V^2$, so that the equation becomes

$$\frac{dv}{dt} = g\left(1 - \frac{v^2}{V^2}\right).$$

Separating the variables, we obtain

$$\frac{V^2\,dv}{V^2 - v^2} = g\,dt,$$

which, upon integration, yields

$$V\tanh^{-1}\frac{v}{V} = gt + c.$$

Since $v = 0$ when $t = 0$, we find $c = 0$, so that

$$v = V\tanh\frac{gt}{V}. \tag{1}$$

Replacing v by dy/dt and integrating again, we have

$$y = \frac{V^2}{g}\ln\cosh\frac{gt}{V}, \tag{2}$$

the constant of integration again being 0, since $y = 0$ when $t = 0$.

We may eliminate t from equations (1) and (2) as follows:

$$\cosh \frac{gt}{V} = \frac{1}{\operatorname{sech} \dfrac{gt}{V}} = \frac{1}{\sqrt{1 - \tanh^2 \dfrac{gt}{V}}} = \frac{1}{\sqrt{1 - \dfrac{v^2}{V^2}}} = \frac{V}{\sqrt{V^2 - v^2}}.$$

Substituting in (2) we have

$$y = \frac{V^2}{g} \ln \frac{V}{\sqrt{V^2 - v^2}}. \tag{3}$$

Equations (1), (2), (3) give the v, t relation, the y, t relation and the y, v relation, respectively for this problem.

20. The tractrix. A heavy particle P is dragged along a rough horizontal plane by a string PQ of length a (Fig. 13). Find the path of

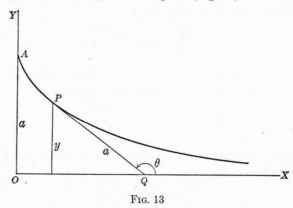

Fɪɢ. 13

P if Q moves along the x-axis and starts at the origin when P is on the y-axis at a distance of a from the origin.

The equivalent geometric problem is: Find the curve the length of whose tangent, from point of tangency to x-axis, is constant. The curve is called the *tractrix*.

Denoting by θ the inclination of the tangent line PQ to the positive x-axis, we have

$$\frac{dy}{dx} = \tan \theta = - \frac{y}{\sqrt{a^2 - y^2}}.$$

Separating the variables,

$$dx = - \frac{\sqrt{a^2 - y^2}}{y} dy.$$

Integrating (Peirce, 130, fn.),

$$x = - \sqrt{a^2 - y^2} + a \operatorname{sech}^{-1} \frac{y}{a} + c.$$

Since $y = a$ when $x = 0$, $c = 0$, and we have for the equation of the tractrix,

$$x = -\sqrt{a^2 - y^2} + a \cosh^{-1} \frac{a}{y}. \tag{1}$$

Denoting by s the length of the arc AP, positive in the direction AP, we have, since s increases as y decreases,

$$ds = -\sqrt{1 + \left(\frac{dx}{dy}\right)^2}\, dy = -\sqrt{1 + \frac{a^2 - y^2}{y^2}}\, dy = -\frac{a}{y}\, dy.$$

Then for the length AP we have

$$s = -a \int_a^y \frac{dy}{y} = a \ln \frac{a}{y}. \tag{2}$$

21. Schiele's pivot. Consider a vertical shaft rotating in a bearing (Fig. 14), which is to be so constructed that the vertical wear between pivot and bearing is to be uniform at all points.

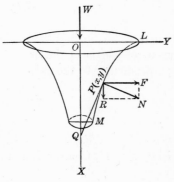

Let R (lb./in.^{2}) be the vertical pressure per unit horizontal area, W (lb.) the weight of the shaft, and A (in.^{2}) the horizontal projection of the rubbing surface; then $R = W/A$ = const. Let N (lb./in.^{2}) be the normal pressure exerted on the bearing by an area of pivot whose horizontal projection is a unit area; let F (lb./in.^{2}) be the corresponding horizontal thrust on the bearing. Then F and R are the components of N.

FIG. 14

Taking the x- and y-axes as shown in the figure, if PQ is the tangent from the point P of the curve LM of the pivot, to the x-axis, we have by similar triangles $PQ/y = N/R$; hence PQ is proportional to Ny, since R is constant. But the wear is proportional to the work done by friction in one revolution, viz., $\mu N \cdot 2\pi y$, where μ is the coefficient of friction; since this wear is to be constant, it follows that PQ is of constant length and the curve LM is a tractrix, equation (1) Art. 20,

$$x = -\sqrt{a^2 - y^2} + a \cosh^{-1} \frac{a}{y},$$

where $a = PQ = OL$ is the radius of the shaft. The pivot so constructed is known as *Schiele's pivot*.

22. A cantilever beam problem. Suppose that a cantilever beam of length L in. and weighing w lb./in. is subjected to a horizontal tensile force of P lb. applied at the free end (Fig. 15). Taking the origin at

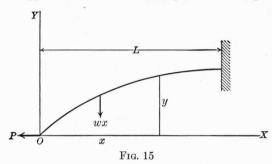

FIG. 15

the free end and the y-axis positive upwards, we have for the differential equation of the beam:

$$EIy'' = Py - \frac{wx^2}{2},$$

where E (lb./in.^{2}) is the modulus of elasticity and I (in.^{4}) is the moment of inertia of the area of a cross-section about a horizontal line perpendicular to the axis of the beam. Then

$$(D^2 - a^2)y = -\frac{wa^2}{2P} \cdot x^2,$$

where $D = d/dx$, $a = \sqrt{P/EI}$. The general solution of this equation is, by Art. 11, Chapter I, and Art. 18, Chapter II,

$$y = A \cosh ax + B \sinh ax + \frac{w}{2P}x^2 + \frac{w}{Pa^2}.$$

Since $y = 0$ when $x = 0$, $A = -w/Pa^2$, and

$$y' = -\frac{w}{Pa}\sinh ax + Ba \cosh ax + \frac{wx}{P}.$$

Since $y' = 0$ when $x = L$,

$$B = \frac{\dfrac{w}{Pa}\sinh aL - \dfrac{wL}{P}}{a \cosh aL},$$

and the equation of the curve of the beam becomes

$$y = -\frac{w}{Pa^2}\cosh ax + \left(\frac{w}{Pa^2}\sinh aL - \frac{wL}{Pa}\right)\frac{\sinh ax}{\cosh aL} + \frac{w}{2P}x^2 + \frac{w}{Pa^2}.$$

The maximum deflection is

$$y\Big]_{x=L} = -\frac{w}{Pa^2}\cosh aL + \left(\frac{w}{Pa^2}\sinh aL - \frac{wL}{Pa}\right)\tanh aL + \frac{wL^2}{2P} + \frac{w}{Pa^2}$$

$$= \frac{w}{Pa^2}\left[1 + \frac{a^2L^2}{2} + \sinh aL \tanh aL - \cosh aL - aL \tanh aL\right]$$

$$= \frac{w}{Pa^2}\left[1 + \frac{a^2L^2}{2} - \operatorname{sech} aL - aL \tanh aL\right],$$

or

$$y\Big]_{x=L} = \frac{wEI}{P^2}\left(1 + \frac{\theta^2}{2} - \operatorname{sech}\theta - \theta\tanh\theta\right),$$

where $\theta = aL = L\sqrt{P/EI}$.

If P had been a compressive force instead of a tensile force, the differential equation of the beam would have been

$$EIy'' = -Py - \frac{wx^2}{2}.$$

Since this is like the first differential equation except that $-P$ replaces P, we can immediately deduce the expression for the maximum deflection in the new case by changing P into $-P$ in the above result. We then have $\theta = L\sqrt{-P/EI} = i\theta'$, where $\theta' = L\sqrt{P/EI}$ and $i = \sqrt{-1}$, whence *

$$y\Big]_{x=L} = \frac{wEI}{P^2}\left(1 - \frac{\theta'^2}{2} - \sec\theta' + \theta'\tan\theta'\right),$$

since $\operatorname{sech} i\theta' = \sec\theta'$ and $\tanh i\theta' = i\tan\theta'$.

This is another instance of the advantages of dealing with hyperbolic functions as such, instead of with their equivalent exponential expressions. Analogies between two related physical problems whose differential equations are of nearly the same form, the difference involved being that of an algebraic sign in a key term, can often be emphasized when circular functions on the one hand and hyperbolic functions on the other are suitably utilized in the respective solutions of the differential equations. Moreover, it is then frequently possible to avoid the necessity of solving both differential equations separately; the solution obtained for one of them can be transformed, as was done here, into the corresponding solution of the other. Additional examples of such analogies will be found in the following problems.

* Cf. Problem 63 following Art. 14.

PROBLEMS

1. A body falls from rest in a medium offering resistance proportional to the square of the velocity. If the limiting velocity is 32.17 ft./sec., find (a) the velocity at the end of 1 sec.; (b) the distance fallen at the end of 1 sec.; (c) the distance fallen when the velocity is half the limiting velocity; (d) the time required to fall 200 ft.

2. A body falls from rest against resistance proportional to the square of the velocity at any instant. If the limiting velocity is 160 ft./sec., find the time required to attain half that speed.

3. A body falls from rest in a medium offering resistance proportional to the square of the speed. The limiting speed is 120 ft./sec. Find the speed attained after falling 50 ft. and the time required to reach that velocity.

4. If a body falling from rest encounters an air resistance proportional to the square of the velocity, and acquires a velocity of 110 ft./sec. in falling a distance of 300 ft., find the time elapsed and the limiting velocity.

5. The downward acceleration of a falling body is equal to $32 - \frac{1}{2}v^2$, where v is velocity (ft./sec.). If the initial velocity is zero, find the velocity and distance from the starting point at the end of 1 sec.

6. A body falls in a medium offering resistance proportional to the square of the velocity. If the motion starts with an initial velocity of 5 ft./sec., and if the limiting speed is 20 ft./sec., find the distance fallen in 0.1 sec.

7. If motion under resistance proportional to the square of the velocity starts with a speed v_0 (ft./sec.), and if the limiting speed is V (ft./sec.), show that the distance fallen in t sec. is

$$y = \frac{V^2}{g} \ln \left(\cosh \frac{gt}{V} + \frac{v_0}{V} \sinh \frac{gt}{V} \right).$$

8. A body falls into a liquid which offers resistance proportional to the square of the speed. If the limiting speed is 10 ft./sec., and if the body attains a speed of 8 ft./sec. 0.1 sec. after entering the liquid, what was the speed at entrance?

9. A body falls in a medium offering resistance proportional to the square of the speed. If the initial speed is 1 ft./sec., and if the limiting speed is 20 ft./sec., find the time necessary for the body to acquire a speed equal to one-third of its limiting value.

10. A body weighing $\frac{1}{2}g = 16.1$ lb., suspended from a spring whose constant is 32 lb./ft., is put into motion by giving the upper end of the spring the displacement $y = \frac{1}{2} \sinh 8t$ (ft.), where t (sec.) is time. Find the displacement and velocity of the body $\frac{1}{8}$ sec. after the motion starts.

11. A body weighing $g = 32.17$ lb. is repelled from a point O by a force (lb.) numerically equal to the distance x (ft.) of the body from that point. This motion is retarded by another force (lb.) numerically equal to the function $e^t - e^{-t}$, where t (sec.) is time. If the body starts from rest when $t = 0$ at $x = 2$ ft., find the distance it has traveled and its velocity when $t = \frac{3}{2}$ sec.

12. If a particle is acted upon by a force varying inversely as the square of the distance from a point O, the differential equation of motion is $d^2x/dt^2 = -k^2/x^2$ for an attractive force and $d^2x/dt^2 = k^2/x^2$ for a force of repulsion. Assume that the force has the same magnitude for both motions when $x = a$, so that the same k applies in both instances, and that the particle starts from rest at $x = a$ in each case. (a) Solve the differential equations, using the substitutions $x = a \cos^2 \theta$ and

$x = a \cosh^2 u$, respectively, and hence show that the two x, t relations may be written as

$$t = \frac{1}{k} \sqrt{\frac{a}{2}} \left[\sqrt{x(a - x)} + a \cos^{-1} \sqrt{\frac{x}{a}} \right],$$

$$t = \frac{1}{k} \sqrt{\frac{a}{2}} \left[\sqrt{x(x - a)} + a \cosh^{-1} \sqrt{\frac{x}{a}} \right].$$

(b) Find the ratio of the time intervals required to travel the first $a/2$ units of distance in the two motions.

13. For the tractrix, if the length of the tangent PQ is 1 ft., how far have P and Q traveled from their initial positions if (a) P is 4 in. from the x-axis; (b) P is 4 in. from the y-axis?

14. If a particle is moving along the tractrix with a constant x-component of velocity, $dx/dt = u$, find the value of y when the speed along the path is $2u$.

15. If the upper radius and length of Schiele's pivot are 2 and 1 in., respectively, find the lower radius.

16. A wooden cantilever beam 2 in. by 4 in. by 10 ft., with $E = 15 \times 10^5$ lb./in.^{2}, and weighing 40 lb./ft.^{3}, is subjected to a horizontal tension of 500 lb. Find the deflection of the free end if the 4-in. side is horizontal.

17. Find the deflection of the free end of the beam of Art. 22 to which a vertical load of Q lb. has also been applied at the free end.

18. The replacement of k by ik in one of the differential equations of Problem 12 produces the other. Show that this replacement in either of the x, t relations obtained in Problem 12(a) likewise transforms it into the second, so that only one half of that problem need be solved, the other then being immediately deducible.

19. Establish the relations

$$A \cosh u + B \sinh u = \sqrt{B^2 - A^2} \sinh [u + \tanh^{-1}(A/B)], \quad |B| > |A|,$$

$$A \cosh u + B \sinh u = \sqrt{A^2 - B^2} \cosh [u + \tanh^{-1}(B/A)], \quad |A| > |B|,$$

(a) by using formulas (10) and (12) of Art. 17; (b) by transforming the trigonometric identities cited on page 52.

23. The suspended cable.
We now consider a uniform flexible cable suspended from two points and hanging under its own weight (Fig. 16). Let W (lb.) be the weight of a portion of the cable measured toward the right from the lowest point A to any point P, T (lb.) the tension in the direction of the tangent at the point P, θ the acute angle which this tangent makes with the horizontal, and H (lb.) the horizontal tension at the lowest point A. Then, resolving vertically and horizontally the forces acting on the portion AP of the cable, we have

$$T \sin \theta = W,$$

$$T \cos \theta = H.$$

Division gives

$$\tan \theta = \frac{W}{H}.$$

Taking the y-axis positive upwards and the x-axis positive to the right (although we have not yet located the origin), $\tan \theta = dy/dx$; also, letting w (lb./ft.) denote the weight per unit length of the cable and s (ft.) the length of arc AP, $W = ws$; hence

$$\frac{dy}{dx} = \frac{w}{H} \cdot s.$$

This is the differential equation of the cable, but it contains three variables x, y, s. In order to eliminate s we differentiate with respect to x and replace ds/dx by $\sqrt{1 + (dy/dx)^2}$; then

$$\frac{d^2y}{dx^2} = \frac{w}{H}\sqrt{1 + \left(\frac{dy}{dx}\right)^2}.$$

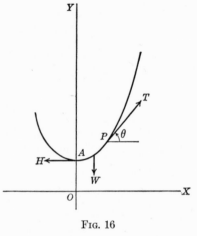

Fig. 16

To solve this differential equation, write $dy/dx = p$, $d^2y/dx^2 = dp/dx$ (Art. 6), and separate the variables:

$$\frac{dp}{\sqrt{1 + p^2}} = \frac{w}{H}\,dx.$$

Integrating, we have

$$\sinh^{-1} p = \frac{w}{H}x + c_1.$$

We now choose the y-axis through the point A so that $p = dy/dx = 0$ when $x = 0$, and $c_1 = 0$. Then

$$\frac{dy}{dx} = \sinh \frac{w}{H}x.$$

Integrating again, we have

$$y = \frac{H}{w}\cosh \frac{w}{H}x + c_2.$$

Now choose the x-axis through a point at a distance H/w below A, so that when $y = H/w$, $x = 0$, and $c_2 = 0$. Writing $a = H/w$, we have for the equation of the cable

$$y = a \cosh \frac{x}{a}, \tag{1}$$

which is the standard equation of a *catenary*; x and y are now the coordinates of any point P, referred to the origin which is at a distance a ft. below A. The length of the arc AP is

$$s = \int_0^x \sqrt{1 + y'^2}\, dx = \int_0^x \sqrt{1 + \sinh^2 \frac{x}{a}}\, dx$$

$$= \int_0^x \cosh \frac{x}{a}\, dx = a \sinh \frac{x}{a}.$$

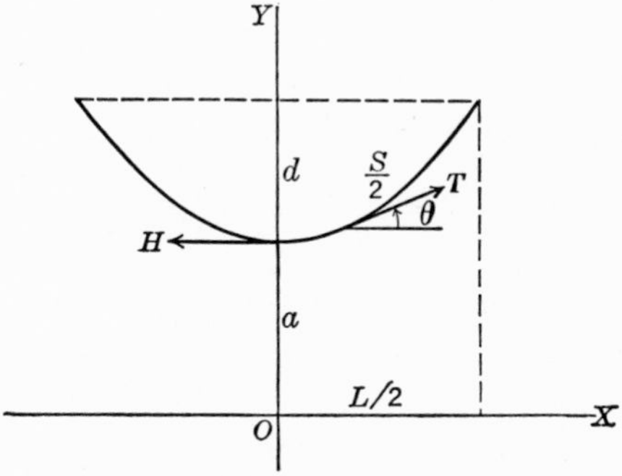

Fig. 17

Let d (ft.) be the dip of the cable suspended from two points at the same level, L (ft.) the span, and S (ft.) the length of the cable (Fig. 17). Then

$$S = 2a \sinh \frac{L}{2a}, \tag{2}$$

$$d = y\Big]_{x=L/2} - a = a \left(\cosh \frac{L}{2a} - 1 \right). \tag{3}$$

The tension at any point is

$$T = H \sec \theta = H\sqrt{1 + y'^2} = H \cosh \frac{x}{a} = wy. \tag{4}$$

Example.   A wire is fastened at the same level to two posts 100 ft. apart and the dip is 25 ft. (a) Find the length of the wire. (b) Find the tension at the lowest point if the weight of the wire is $w = 0.10$ lb./ft.

(a) From equation (3),

$$25 = a \left(\cosh \frac{50}{a} - 1 \right)$$

or

$$\frac{\lambda}{2} + 1 = \cosh \lambda, \qquad \text{where } \lambda = \frac{50}{a}.$$

We solve this equation by *trial and error*, using the table on page 125 (Peirce).

λ	$\lambda/2 + 1$	$\cosh \lambda$
1.0	1.500	1.543
0.9	1.450	1.433
0.930	1.465	1.465

$$\lambda = 0.930, \qquad a = 50/0.930.$$

Substituting in equation (2),

$$S = \frac{100}{0.930} \sinh (0.930) = \frac{107.0}{0.930} = 115 \text{ ft., the length of the wire.}$$

(b) From $a = \dfrac{H}{w}$, $H = \dfrac{5}{0.930} = 5.37$ lb., the tension at the lowest point.

24. The capillary curve; one vertical plate. We first state the two laws of capillarity on which the derivation of the equation of the capillary curve is based:

I. At the bounding surface separating a gas from a liquid, there is a surface tension which is the same at every point and in every direction.

II. At the bounding surface of a gas and a liquid with a solid, the surface of the liquid is inclined to the surface of the solid at a definite angle depending only on the nature of the solid, liquid and gas.

Given a flat vertical plate MN partially immersed in a liquid. In Fig. 18, OA represents a vertical line in the plate. We take the y-axis

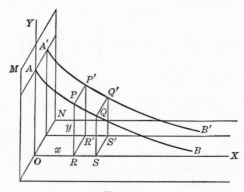

Fig. 18

along OA and the x-axis perpendicular to the plate and in the distant horizontal surface of the liquid. The xy-plane cuts the surface of the liquid in the capillary curve AB, whose equation we proceed to find.

Take a strip $ABA'B'$ of the liquid surface whose width $AA' = 1$ cm. Cut out a small element $PQP'Q'$ of the strip, whose dimensions are $PQ = \Delta s$, $PP' = 1$, and whose area is therefore Δs cm.[2]   Consider the

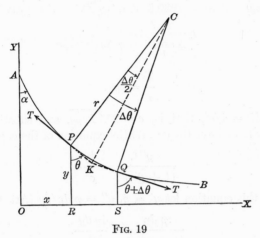

Fig. 19

column of liquid $PQP'Q'RSR'S'$ capped by this surface element. Referring to Fig. 19, let

T (dynes/cm.) = surface tension = force tangential to liquid surface per unit length of cut.

θ = acute angle between tangent and vertical at any point P.

α = fixed angle of contact between liquid surface and plate, as given by the second law.

r (cm.) = radius of curvature, PC, of curve AB at point P.

ρ (gr./cm.[3]) = density of liquid.

By the first law the surface tension T will be the same on both edges of the surface element. Due to these tensions the resultant force normal to the surface element will be

$$2 \cdot T \cos \angle PKC = 2T \sin \angle PCK = 2T \sin \frac{\Delta\theta}{2},$$

and the limiting resultant normal force on the surface element $PQP'Q'$, per unit area, will be

$$\lim_{\Delta\theta \to 0} \frac{2T \sin \dfrac{\Delta\theta}{2}}{\Delta s} = \lim_{\Delta\theta \to 0} \frac{T}{r} \cdot \frac{\sin \dfrac{\Delta\theta}{2}}{\dfrac{\Delta\theta}{2}} = \frac{T}{r}.$$

The vertical component of the normal force on the surface element, namely $(T/r) \, \Delta s \cdot \sin \theta$, holds up the column of liquid $PQP'Q'RSR'S'$, of height y and cross-section area $\Delta s \cdot \sin \theta$, and hence of weight $y \cdot \Delta s \sin \theta \cdot \rho g$, where g (980.5 cm./sec.^{2}) is the gravity constant. Therefore

$$\frac{T}{r} \, \Delta s \sin \theta = y \, \Delta s \sin \theta \cdot \rho g,$$

or

$$\frac{T}{r} = \rho g y.$$

Letting $\rho g / T = 4/c^2$, that is, $c = 2\sqrt{T/\rho g}$, and substituting $(1 + y'^2)^{3/2}/y''$ for r, we have the differential equation of the capillary curve:

$$\frac{y''}{(1 + y'^2)^{3/2}} = \frac{4y}{c^2}. \tag{1}$$

To solve this equation let $y' = p$, $y'' = p \, dp/dy$ (Art. 6); then

$$\frac{p \, dp}{(1 + p^2)^{3/2}} = \frac{4y \, dy}{c^2}.$$

Integration gives

$$-\frac{1}{\sqrt{1 + p^2}} = \frac{2y^2}{c^2} + c_1.$$

Since $p = dy/dx = 0$ when $y = 0$, $c_1 = -1$; hence

$$\frac{1}{\sqrt{1 + p^2}} = \frac{c^2 - 2y^2}{c^2}. \tag{2}$$

Before continuing with the solution of equation (2), suppose that we let h_0 represent the height to which the liquid rises on the plate, i.e., the value of y when $x = 0$. At $x = 0$ we also have $p = -\cot \alpha$. Substitution of these values in equation (2) yields a formula for h_0:

$$\sin \alpha = \frac{c^2 - 2h_0^2}{c^2},$$

$$h_0 = c \sqrt{\frac{1 - \sin \alpha}{2}} = c \sin \left(45° - \frac{\alpha}{2} \right). \tag{3}$$

Returning to equation (2), we have, squaring the reciprocals of both sides,

$$1 + p^2 = \frac{c^4}{(c^2 - 2y^2)^2}, \qquad p^2 = \frac{4y^2(c^2 - y^2)}{(c^2 - 2y^2)^2},$$

$$p = \frac{dy}{dx} = -\frac{2y\sqrt{c^2 - y^2}}{c^2 - 2y^2},$$

choosing the negative sign when extracting the square root, since the slope of the curve is negative.

Separating the variables, we have

$$dx = \frac{2y^2 - c^2}{2y\sqrt{c^2 - y^2}}\,dy = \frac{y\,dy}{\sqrt{c^2 - y^2}} - \frac{c^2}{2}\frac{dy}{y\sqrt{c^2 - y^2}}.$$

Integrating, we have

$$x + c_2 = -\sqrt{c^2 - y^2} + \frac{c}{2}\operatorname{sech}^{-1}\frac{y}{c}.$$

Since $y = h_0$ when $x = 0$, $c_2 = -\sqrt{c^2 - h_0^2} + \frac{c}{2}\operatorname{sech}^{-1}\frac{h_0}{c}$. Hence we have for the equation of the capillary curve

$$x - \sqrt{c^2 - h_0^2} + \frac{c}{2}\operatorname{sech}^{-1}\frac{h_0}{c} = -\sqrt{c^2 - y^2} + \frac{c}{2}\operatorname{sech}^{-1}\frac{y}{c},$$

or

$$x + \sqrt{c^2 - y^2} - \sqrt{c^2 - h_0^2} = \frac{c}{2}\left(\cosh^{-1}\frac{c}{y} - \cosh^{-1}\frac{c}{h_0}\right), \quad (4)$$

where h_0 is given by (3), and $c = 2\sqrt{T/\rho g}$.

25. The rotating shaft. Consider a horizontal shaft (Fig. 20) of length $2L$ (ft.) and weight w (lb./ft.). Set it rotating with angular

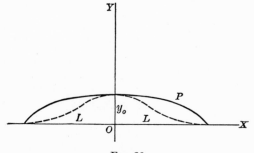

Fig. 20

velocity ω (rad./sec.). If the rotation is slow and the shaft is jarred out of line the elastic forces will overbalance the centrifugal force and restore the shaft to its original position. But if ω is gradually increased, it will reach a critical value such that if the shaft is displaced out of line the distortion will persist and the shaft will form a curve revolving about the axis which was its original position. We say that the shaft will buckle at this critical angular velocity ω_c. Take the x-axis in the original position of the shaft, the y-axis through the middle point of the shaft, and measure x and y in feet. Denote by y_0 the maximum displacement of the shaft, that is, the distance of its middle point from the x-axis. We shall find the critical angular velocity ω_c and the corresponding equation of the curve of the shaft.

The differential equation of the curve of the shaft is the same as that of a beam with varying load per unit length (Art. 7(f), equation (31′)). Here the load per unit length at any point $P(x, y)$ is the centrifugal load, $w\omega^2 y/g$, so that the differential equation for the shaft is

$$EIy^{iv} = \frac{w}{g}\omega^2 y, \tag{1}$$

where E is measured in pounds per square foot, I in feet to the fourth power, and $g = 32.17$ ft./sec.[2] Writing D for d/dx, the differential equation becomes

$$(D^4 - k^4)y = 0, \tag{2}$$

where

$$k^4 = \frac{w\omega^2}{gEI}. \tag{3}$$

The general solution of the differential equation (2) is (Art. 18, and Art. 10, Chapter I)

$$y = c_1 \cosh kx + c_2 \sinh kx + c_3 \cos kx + c_4 \sin kx. \tag{4}$$

We have four arbitrary constants to determine, but two of them can be disposed of by consideration of symmetry with respect to the y-axis. For, since y must remain unchanged when x is changed to $-x$, we have

$$y = c_1 \cosh kx - c_2 \sinh kx + c_3 \cos kx - c_4 \sin kx;$$

then, subtracting this equation from (4) gives

$$c_2 \sinh kx + c_4 \sin kx \equiv 0.$$

Since this expression is identically zero for all values of x from $-L$ to L, it follows that $c_2 = c_4 = 0$. Equation (4) then becomes

$$y = c_1 \cosh kx + c_3 \cos kx. \tag{5}$$

Differentiation of (5) gives

$$y' = k(c_1 \sinh kx - c_3 \sin kx), \tag{6}$$

$$y'' = k^2(c_1 \cosh kx - c_3 \cos kx). \tag{7}$$

The condition that the shaft is horizontal at its midpoint, i.e., $y' = 0$ when $x = 0$, is seen by equation (6) to be satisfied. We now distinguish two cases.

Case I. Flexible bearings. Suppose the bearings to be constructed so that they can swing about and allow the shaft at its ends to make an angle with the horizontal (heavy line of Fig. 20). We have the two conditions $y = 0$ when $x = L$, and $y'' = 0$ when $x = L$, the second arising from the fact that the curvature of the shaft is zero at the ends. These conditions substituted in (5) and (7) give

$$c_1 \cosh kL + c_3 \cos kL = 0, \qquad (8)$$

$$c_1 \cosh kL - c_3 \cos kL = 0. \qquad (9)$$

Adding equations (8) and (9) we have $c_1 \cosh kL = 0$, and since $\cosh kL \neq 0$, it follows that $c_1 = 0$.

Subtracting (9) from (8), we have $c_3 \cos kL = 0$. Then, either $c_3 = 0$ so that equation (5) becomes $y = 0$, and the shaft remains straight, or $\cos kL = 0$, and the smallest value of k producing this effect is $\pi/2L$. Hence ω_c, the critical value of ω, is obtained by substituting $k = \pi/2L$ in equation (3):

$$\omega_c = \frac{\pi^2}{4L^2} \sqrt{\frac{gEI}{w}}. \qquad (10)$$

Substituting $c_1 = 0$ and $k = \pi/2L$ in equation (5), it becomes $y = c_3 \cos (\pi x/2L)$. When $x = 0$, $y = y_0$, so that $c_3 = y_0$, and the equation of the curve of the shaft is

$$y = y_0 \cos \frac{\pi x}{2L}. \qquad (11)$$

Case II. Fixed bearings. In this case the bearings are constructed so that the shaft remains horizontal at the ends (dotted line of Fig. 20). We have the two conditions $y = 0$ when $x = L$, and $y' = 0$ when $x = L$. These conditions substituted in (5) and (6) give

$$c_1 \cosh kL + c_3 \cos kL = 0, \qquad (12)$$

$$c_1 \sinh kL - c_3 \sin kL = 0. \qquad (13)$$

These equations form a system of two homogeneous linear equations in the two unknowns c_1 and c_3. They have the obvious solution $c_1 = c_3 = 0$, which makes $y = 0$, in which case the shaft remains straight. The only condition under which equations (12) and (13) have a solution other than $c_1 = c_3 = 0$ is when the determinant of the coefficients vanishes, that is

$$\begin{vmatrix} \cosh kL & \cos kL \\ \sinh kL & -\sin kL \end{vmatrix} = 0,$$

or

$$\tan kL + \tanh kL = 0. \qquad (14)$$

Solving this equation by trial and error gives $kL = 2.365$. Hence ω_c', the critical value of ω, is obtained by substituting $k = 2.365/L$ in equation (3):

$$\omega_c' = \left(\frac{2.365}{L}\right)^2 \sqrt{\frac{gEI}{w}}. \tag{15}$$

The ratio of the critical angular velocity with fixed ends to the critical angular velocity with flexible ends is, from (10) and (15),

$$\frac{\omega_c'}{\omega_c} = \frac{(2.365)^2}{\pi^2/4} = \left(\frac{4.73}{\pi}\right)^2 = 2.27.$$

Solving (12) for c_1 and substituting in (5) gives

$$y = c_3 \left(\cos kx - \frac{\cos kL}{\cosh kL} \cosh kx\right)$$

$$= \frac{c_3(\cosh kL \cos kx - \cos kL \cosh kx)}{\cosh kL}.$$

When $x = 0$, $y = y_0$, so that $c_3 = \dfrac{y_0 \cosh kL}{\cosh kL - \cos kL}$, and the equation of the curve of the shaft is

$$y = y_0 \cdot \frac{\cosh kL \cos kx - \cos kL \cosh kx}{\cosh kL - \cos kL}, \tag{16}$$

where k is given by (14), i.e., $k = 2.365/L$.

In the derivation of the differential equation (1), y'' was used as an approximation for the curvature, which is justifiable only for small displacements. Hence equations (11) and (16) should be used as equations for the shaft only for small displacements. As ω is increased beyond the critical value the shaft is bowed out further from its original position until the equations (11) and (16) no longer furnish valid approximations as equations of the respective curves.

26. Voltage and current relations in a uniform transmission line under steady-state d-c. conditions. Consider an underground insulated

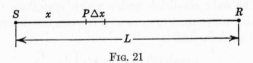

Fig. 21

cable of length L (mi.), S and R denoting, respectively, the sending and receiving ends (Fig. 21). Let P be any point on the cable at distance x from S, and Δx the corresponding small piece of cable. Let

r (ohms/mi.) = resistance of cable;
g (mhos/mi.) = leakance between conductor and sheath;
e, E_1, E_2 (volts) respectively = potential at P, S, R;
i, I_1, I_2 (amp.) respectively = current at P, S, R.

It is assumed that r, g, E_1, E_2, I_1, and I_2 are constant, and that steady-state conditions prevail, so that e and i vary only with x and not with time.

We apply Ohm's law to get the changes in potential e and current i across the small piece Δx. These changes are given approximately by

$$\Delta e = -ir\,\Delta x,$$
$$\Delta i = -eg\,\Delta x. \tag{1}$$

The minus sign in the first equation indicates a drop in potential across Δx due to resistance; the minus sign in the second equation indicates a decrease in current due to leakance. Dividing by Δx, passing to the limit as Δx approaches zero, and using D to denote d/dx, we get the differential equations

$$De + ri = 0,$$
$$ge + Di = 0. \tag{2}$$

We have here a system of first-order differential equations with constant coefficients. The method of solution (Art. 13, Chapter I) is to eliminate one of the variables and solve for the other. First multiply the first equation by D, the second by r, and subtract; then multiply the first equation by g, the second by D, and subtract; we obtain

$$(D^2 - rg)e = 0,$$
$$(D^2 - rg)i = 0. \tag{3}$$

Thus e and i satisfy the same differential equation of second order, but the constants of integration which appear in the solution will be different in the two equations owing to different end conditions.

The general solutions of equations (3) are, respectively,

$$e = A \cosh \sqrt{rg}\,x + B \sinh \sqrt{rg}\,x,$$
$$i = A' \cosh \sqrt{rg}\,x + B' \sinh \sqrt{rg}\,x. \tag{4}$$

But equations (4) with A, B, A', B' arbitrary do not represent the general solution of equations (2); the relations tying up the four constants A, B, A', B' must be found by substituting the values of e and i from (4) in one of the equations (2), say the first; we have

$$A\sqrt{rg} \sinh \sqrt{rg}\, x + B\sqrt{rg} \cosh \sqrt{rg}\, x + A'r \cosh \sqrt{rg}\, x$$
$$+ B'r \sinh \sqrt{rg}\, x = 0.$$

Equating to zero the coefficients of $\cosh \sqrt{rg}\, x$ and $\sinh \sqrt{rg}\, x$, we find

$$A' = -B \sqrt{\frac{g}{r}}, \qquad B' = -A \sqrt{\frac{g}{r}}.$$

Substituting these values of A' and B' in equations (4), we have the general solution of equations (2):

$$e = A \cosh \sqrt{rg}\, x + B \sinh \sqrt{rg}\, x,$$
$$i = -B \sqrt{\frac{g}{r}} \cosh \sqrt{rg}\, x - A \sqrt{\frac{g}{r}} \sinh \sqrt{rg}\, x. \tag{5}$$

To determine the values of A and B we make use of the end conditions:

At $S\,(x = 0)$, $e = E_1$, $i = I_1$; hence $E_1 = A$, $I_1 = -B\sqrt{g/r}$, and we have

$$e = E_1 \cosh \sqrt{rg}\, x - I_1 \sqrt{\frac{r}{g}} \sinh \sqrt{rg}\, x,$$
$$i = I_1 \cosh \sqrt{rg}\, x - E_1 \sqrt{\frac{g}{r}} \sinh \sqrt{rg}\, x. \tag{6}$$

These equations (6) give the values of the potential and current at any point P of the cable at a distance x from the sending end.

We may wish, however, to tie up the values of potential and current at S, and potential and current at R, with the length of the cable, L. For this purpose we make use of the other end conditions:

At $R\,(x = L)$, $e = E_2$, $i = I_2$. Substituting in (6),

$$E_2 = E_1 \cosh \sqrt{rg}\, L - I_1 \sqrt{\frac{r}{g}} \sinh \sqrt{rg}\, L,$$
$$I_2 = I_1 \cosh \sqrt{rg}\, L - E_1 \sqrt{\frac{g}{r}} \sinh \sqrt{rg}\, L. \tag{7}$$

These equations (7) give the potential and current at the receiving end in terms of the potential and current at the sending end and the length of the cable.

We may solve equations (7) for E_1 and I_1 in terms of E_2, I_2, and L. We solve by determinants, first writing equations (7) in the form

$$E_1 \cosh \sqrt{rg}\, L - I_1 \sqrt{\frac{r}{g}} \sinh \sqrt{rg}\, L = E_2,$$

$$-E_1 \sqrt{\frac{g}{r}} \sinh \sqrt{rg}\, L + I_1 \cosh \sqrt{rg}\, L = I_2.$$

We note that the determinant of the coefficients is unity, namely

$$\begin{vmatrix} \cosh \sqrt{rg}\, L & -\sqrt{\frac{r}{g}} \sinh \sqrt{rg}\, L \\ -\sqrt{\frac{g}{r}} \sinh \sqrt{rg}\, L & \cosh \sqrt{rg}\, L \end{vmatrix} = 1,$$

by virtue of relation (1), Art. 17. Hence

$$E_1 = E_2 \cosh \sqrt{rg}\, L + I_2 \sqrt{\frac{r}{g}} \sinh \sqrt{rg}\, L,$$

$$I_1 = I_2 \cosh \sqrt{rg}\, L + E_2 \sqrt{\frac{g}{r}} \sinh \sqrt{rg}\, L. \qquad (8)$$

These equations (8) give the values of the potential and current at the sending end in terms of the potential and current at the receiving end and the length of the cable.

Special cases of equations (8):

(a) If the receiving end is open, $I_2 = 0$, and

$$E_1 = E_2 \cosh \sqrt{rg}\, L,$$

$$I_1 = E_2 \sqrt{\frac{g}{r}} \sinh \sqrt{rg}\, L. \qquad (9)$$

(b) If the receiving end is grounded, $E_2 = 0$, and

$$E_1 = I_2 \sqrt{\frac{r}{g}} \sinh \sqrt{rg}\, L,$$

$$I_1 = I_2 \cosh \sqrt{rg}\, L. \qquad (10)$$

27. Ionization of a gas. Suppose a volume V (cm.^{3}) of a gas to be subjected to an ionizing agent, such as X-rays, and placed in an electric field. It has been found by experiment that a current will then flow through the gas, the variation of current with potential being that shown in Fig. 22. For a small potential E (statvolts), the current I (statamp.) is approximately proportional to E. As the potential is increased, the current increases more slowly than E until a stage is reached at which there is no appreciable increase of current with increased potential; the current is then said to be saturated. When E has been increased sufficiently to produce additional ionization, a second stage is reached during which I increases very rapidly with increase in potential.

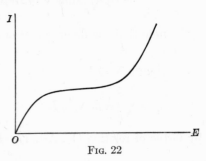

Fig. 22

For a given ionizing agent, let there be produced, in 1 cm.^{3} of the gas, Q positive and Q negative ions per second, and let e (statcoulombs) denote the charge on an ion. If a current I is flowing across the field between two plates, I/e positive ions are driven against the negative electrode, and I/e negative ions against the positive electrode, in 1 sec.; that is, I/e positive and I/e negative ions are taken out of the gas in 1 sec. by the current. Since the number of ions taken out cannot exceed the number produced in the same time interval, we have $I/e \leqq QV$, or $I \leqq QeV$. Consequently the saturation current I_s has the value $I_s = QeV$.

Now let P and N, respectively, denote the number of free positive and free negative ions in 1 cm.^{3} of the gas at time t. These free ions will tend to recombine owing to collisions between them, the number of collisions per second between positive and negative ions being proportional to the product PN. If some of these collisions result in the formation of a neutral system, the number of positive (also the number of negative) ions which disappear per second in 1 cm.^{3} will be equal to αPN, where the constant of proportionality α is called the coefficient of recombination. This number α will depend upon the pressure of the gas, its temperature, and other physical properties of the system, but will be independent of P and N.

We then have the relation

$$\frac{dP}{dt} = Q - \alpha PN = \frac{dN}{dt}, \tag{1}$$

whence

$$P - N = \text{const.} \tag{2}$$

Now, if the gas is initially uncharged, as many positive as negative ions will be present at time t. Making this assumption, and setting

$n = P = N$, we obtain the single differential equation

$$\frac{dn}{dt} = Q - \alpha n^2$$
$$= \alpha(k^2 - n^2), \tag{3}$$

where $k^2 = Q/\alpha$.

Evidently (3) is of the same form as the differential equation of motion under a resistance proportional to the square of the velocity (Art. 19). Solving (3), we get

$$\frac{dn}{k^2 - n^2} = \alpha \, dt,$$

$$\frac{1}{k} \tanh^{-1} \frac{n}{k} = \alpha t + c.$$

Since $n = 0$ when $t = 0$, $c = 0$, and therefore

$$n = k \tanh k\alpha t. \tag{4}$$

As t becomes infinite, $\tanh k\alpha t$ will approach unity, so that the steady-state value of n will be

$$n_0 = k = \sqrt{Q/\alpha}. \tag{5}$$

Using the above-mentioned empirical results and relation (4) Rümelin * performed the following experiment for the determination of α. A gas was exposed continuously to an ionizing agent, and an electric field applied intermittently by use of a rotating sector, the field being zero during part of the revolution of the sector and large enough to produce complete saturation during the remainder of the revolution. The resultant current over a complete cycle of this periodic process was measured by an electrometer.

Let T (sec.) be the time of revolution of the sector, T_1 the part of this time during which the gas is not exposed to the field, and $T_2 = T - T_1$ the time during which the field acts. Then the number of ions in 1 cm.[3] when the field is first applied is $n_1 = k \tanh k\alpha T_1$, so that the total charge to the electrometer for the time T_1 is

$$n_1 e V = k e V \tanh k\alpha T_1.$$

During the time T_2, saturation prevails, so that the total charge to the electrometer for this interval is

$$I_s T_2.$$

* For a discussion of various ways of finding α, see J. J. and G. P. Thomson, "Conduction of Electricity through Gases," Vol. 1. Rümelin's results are given in detail in his papers; see *Physikalische Zeitschrift*, 1908, and *Annalen der Physik*, 1914.

Hence the current I as measured by the electrometer is given by

$$IT = keV \tanh k\alpha T_1 + I_s T_2.$$

Now $e = I_s/QV = I_s/k^2\alpha V$, so that

$$IT = \frac{I_s}{k\alpha} \tanh k\alpha T_1 + I_s T_2.$$

Finally, let $T_2 = rT$, where $r < 1$, so that $T_1 = (1 - r)T$, and let $x = k\alpha T_1$. Then we have

$$(I - rI_s)T = \frac{I_s T_1}{x} \tanh x = \frac{I_s(1 - r)T}{x} \tanh x,$$

and

$$\frac{I - rI_s}{(1 - r)I_s} x = \tanh x. \tag{6}$$

Consequently, if I, I_s, and r are known, x may be found by trial and error from (6). Then, knowing the values of e and V, we get $Q = I_s/eV$, and, since $x = k\alpha T_1 = T_1 \cdot \sqrt{Q\alpha}$, there is found

$$\alpha = \frac{x^2}{QT_1^2} = \frac{eVx^2}{I_s T_1^2}. \tag{7}$$

PROBLEMS

1. A cable has its ends fastened at the same level to two posts 30 ft. apart. (a) Find the dip in the cable if it is 40 ft. long. (b) How long is the cable if the dip is 10 ft.? (c) Find the tension at the lowest point, and at a point of suspension, of the cable of part (b) if the weight is 1.5 lb./ft.

2. A cable 20 ft. long is suspended from two supports at the same level. If it dips 3 ft., find the distance between supports.

3. A cable, suspended from two vertical poles 25 ft. apart, has the equation $y = 10 \cosh(x/10)$ referred to an x-axis passing through the feet of the poles. Guy wires, attached to the tops of the poles, are perpendicular to the cable at its end points and run down to the ground. Find the distance between the lower ends of the guy wires.

4. Show that the right member of equation (4), Art. 24, is the length of the arc AP of the capillary curve.

5. Show that the length of the tangent of the capillary curve, drawn from P to the x-axis, approaches a limiting value $\sqrt{T/\rho g}$ as P moves out on the curve, and that the area under the curve is $(T/\rho g) \cos \alpha$.

6. A vertical glass plate is partly immersed in water. If the surface tension is 74 dynes/cm. and the contact angle is $25° 30'$, find (a) the maximum height of the water above the distant horizontal surface; (b) the distance from the plate at which the water is half the maximum height above the horizontal surface.

7. Show that an alternative form of equation (16), Art. 25, is

$$y = y_0 \frac{\sinh kL \cos kx + \sin kL \cosh kx}{\sinh kL + \sin kL}.$$

8. Find the coordinates of the points of inflection on the curve of the rotating shaft with fixed bearings.

9. Given a rotating steel shaft 1 in. in diameter and 3 ft. long, weighing 480 lb./ft.^{3}, with $E = 3 \times 10^7$ lb./in.^{2} (a) Find the critical angular velocity for the shaft with flexible bearings and for the shaft with fixed bearings. (b) For each shaft, find the deflection at the quarter point in terms of the deflection at the center.

10. Given a conductor 150 mi. long, $r = 10$ ohms/mi., $g = 10^{-7}$ mho/mi. (a) If the receiving end is open and the potential there is to be 100 volts, find the impressed potential and the current necessary at the source. (b) If the receiving end is grounded and the current there is to be 0.1 amp., find the potential and current at the source.

11. A cable 100 mi. long has a resistance $r = 1$ ohm/mi. and a leakance $g = 10^{-6}$ mho/mi. The potentials at source and load are, respectively, 500 and 440 volts. Find the current through the load.

12. A conductor for which $r = 4$ ohms/mi. and $g = 10^{-6}$ mho/mi. is 200 mi. long. The potential at the receiving end is 220 volts, and a current of 0.5 amp. is flowing through a load. (a) Find the necessary potential and current at the source. (b) With the same data as in (a), except for length of conductor, find how long the conductor must be if the impressed e.m.f. is 400 volts. (c) Determine the length if the current at the source is to be 1 amp.

13. In an ionization experiment similar to Rümelin's, suppose that the current to the electrometer is 0.0600 statamp., the saturation current is 0.0675 statamp., and the time of revolution of the sector is 0.840 sec. when 300 cm.^{3} of air is subjected to an ionizing agent and to a saturating electric field during one-tenth the revolution of the sector. Find the coefficient of recombination, given that the charge on an ion is 4.77×10^{-10} statcoulomb.

14. A particle moves toward a center of attraction O with an acceleration proportional to the function $\operatorname{sech}^2 t$, where t (sec.) is time. When $t = 0$, the particle is 10 ft. from O, and its speed and acceleration are numerically equal to 1 ft./sec. and 5 ft./sec.^{2}, respectively, directed toward O. Find the velocity and position of the particle 2 sec. later.

15. An inductance of 1 henry and a variable resistance R are connected in series with an e.m.f. of $10 \sinh kt$ volts. If $R = k \tanh kt$ (ohms) at time t (sec.), and if the current $I = 0$ when $t = 0$, find the value of k in order that the current be 5 amp. when $t = 1$ sec.

16. For a certain curve, the length of the radius of curvature at any point P is numerically equal to the length of the normal drawn from P to the x-axis. (a) Show that the differential equation has one of the forms $1 + y'^2 = \pm y y''$. (b) Explain the significance of the positive and negative signs, and show that one choice of sign leads to a family of catenaries whereas the other choice leads to a family of circles.

17. A particle starts from rest at the point $(4, 0)$ and moves thereafter subject to the equations $D^2 x = y$, $D^2 y = x$, where $D = d/dt$. Obtain parametric equations of the path of the particle in terms of trigonometric and hyperbolic functions of time t, and find the position (x, y) of the particle at the end of 1 sec.

18. A particle starts from rest at the point $(-1, 0)$ and moves thereafter in accordance with the equations $D^2x = 2y$, $D^2y = -2x$, where $D = d/dt$. (a) Obtain parametric equations of the path of the particle in terms of trigonometric and hyperbolic functions of time t. (b) Plot the path up to the point where it crosses the x-axis, and find the coordinates of its maximum point.

19. A beam $2L$ in. long, lying on an elastic foundation, is subjected to a concentrated load of P lb. at its center, which causes the entire beam to be depressed below its original position. Suppose that the load P causes a depression of y_0 in. at the center of the beam, and that P is so large that the weight of the beam may be neglected. Assuming the elastic force due to the foundation to be proportional to the displacement of the beam at any point, we have, taking the y-axis positive downward, $EIy^{iv} = -ky$. (a) Taking the origin at the center of the beam, find the elastic curve equation and the relation connecting P, E, I, k, y_0, and L. (b) For a steel rod $\frac{1}{2}$ in. by $\frac{1}{2}$ in. by 24 in., with $E = 3 \times 10^7$ lb./in.^{2}, $P = 100$ lb., and $y_0 = \frac{1}{2}$ in., find the value of k and the depression of the ends of the rod.

CHAPTER III

Elliptic Integrals

28. Rectification of the ellipse. In the calculus, the student encountered the problem of finding the length of an arc of a given curve, and was able to rectify a wide variety of curves by the evaluation of familiar integrals. He may have noticed, however, that one of the commonest curves, the ellipse, was not considered. If he asked about that curious omission, he was probably told that this apparently simple problem leads to a new kind of function, different from the "elementary" functions dealt with in a first course in calculus.

Let us now undertake the solution of the problem previously ignored, and investigate the new function we thus obtain. For later convenience, and in order to avoid subsequent transformations and manipulations, we shall deal with a pair of parametric equations for the ellipse, rather than the rectangular equation

$$\frac{x^2}{a^2} + \frac{y^2}{b^2} = 1, \tag{1}$$

in which $a = OA$, the semi-major axis, and $b = OB$, the semi-minor axis (Fig. 23). Let OP' be any radius of the circle with center at the origin O and radius a, and take as parameter ϕ the angle between OP' and the positive direction of the y-axis. From P' drop a perpendicular $P'Q$ onto the x-axis, cutting the ellipse at $P(x, y)$. Then from the figure we get

$$x = OQ = a \sin \phi,$$

and

$$y = PQ = \frac{b}{a} \sqrt{a^2 - x^2} = b \cos \phi, \tag{2}$$

by equation (1). Measuring arc length s from the upper extremity B of the minor axis, we therefore have

$$\widehat{BP} = \int ds = \int \sqrt{dx^2 + dy^2}$$

$$= \int_0^\phi \sqrt{a^2 \cos^2 \phi + b^2 \sin^2 \phi} \, d\phi,$$

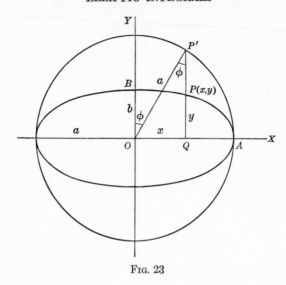

Fig. 23

since $dx = a \cos \phi \, d\phi$ and $dy = -b \sin \phi \, d\phi$, and where the upper limit is the value of ϕ corresponding to the point $P(x, y)$. Replacing $\cos^2 \phi$ by $1 - \sin^2 \phi$, we then have

$$s = \widehat{BP} = \int_0^\phi \sqrt{a^2 - (a^2 - b^2) \sin^2 \phi} \, d\phi$$

$$= a \int_0^\phi \sqrt{1 - \frac{a^2 - b^2}{a^2} \sin^2 \phi} \, d\phi,$$

$$s = a \int_0^\phi \sqrt{1 - k^2 \sin^2 \phi} \, d\phi, \tag{3}$$

where $k = \sqrt{a^2 - b^2}/a$ is the eccentricity of the ellipse, and is evidently less than unity.

We may search in vain for a method whereby the integral (3) may be evaluated in finite form in terms of the elementary functions of ϕ.* It has, in fact, been conclusively proved that no such evaluation is possible. The integral of equation (3) therefore does define a new function, denoted by $E(k, \phi)$:

$$E(k, \phi) \equiv \int_0^\phi \sqrt{1 - k^2 \sin^2 \phi} \, d\phi \qquad (0 < k < 1), \tag{4}$$

which, because of its origin, is called an *elliptic integral*. It is to be noted that $E(k, \phi)$, as is indicated by the functional notation employed,

---

* Algebraic, trigonometric, inverse trigonometric, exponential, and logarithmic functions.

is a function of two arguments: the number k, which is called the *modulus* of the elliptic integral, and which here represents the eccentricity of the ellipse; and the upper limit ϕ, called the *amplitude* of the elliptic integral.

The French mathematician Legendre was the first to make a systematic and thorough study of the integrals called elliptic, the name obviously arising from the connection of the integral (4) with the ellipse, as we have seen. Researches subsequent to Legendre's, notably those of Abel and Jacobi, have resulted in the present-day classification, according to which the function $E(k, \phi)$ is called the *elliptic integral of the second kind*, that of the first kind being the function considered later in this chapter.

It is evident from the figure and equation (3) that the total length of the ellipse will be

$$L = 4a \int_0^{\pi/2} \sqrt{1 - k^2 \sin^2 \phi} \, d\phi$$

$$= 4aE \left(k, \frac{\pi}{2} \right). \tag{5}$$

This particular elliptic integral with upper limit ϕ equal to $\pi/2$ is called the *complete elliptic integral of the second kind* and is denoted by $E(k)$, or simply by E:

$$E \equiv E(k) \equiv \int_0^{\pi/2} \sqrt{1 - k^2 \sin^2 \phi} \, d\phi \qquad (0 < k < 1). \tag{6}$$

In the next chapter we shall show how it is possible to evaluate the integrals (4) and (6) by use of infinite series, and so construct tables of the elliptic integrals just as tables of the logarithmic function are formed. On pages 121 and 123 of Peirce's "Tables" the student will find values of $E(k)$ and $E(k, \phi)$ for various values of k and ϕ.

Example. Given the ellipse $x^2 + 3y^2 = 6$; find (a) its entire length; (b) the length of arc from $x = 1$ to $x = 1.5$.

(a) Here the semi-axes of the ellipse are $a = \sqrt{6}$, $b = \sqrt{2}$. Consequently

$$k = \frac{\sqrt{a^2 - b^2}}{a} = \frac{\sqrt{6}}{3} = 0.8165,$$

and the total length is

$$L = 4aE(k) = 4\sqrt{6} \, E(0.8165).$$

Referring to Peirce's "Tables," page 121, we see that the values of E there given correspond to values of $\sin^{-1} k$ in steps of $1°$, rather than to values of k itself. Hence we get, from tables of trigonometric functions, $\sin^{-1} 0.8165 = 54° \, 44'$.

Now $E(\sin 54°) = 1.2681$, and $E(\sin 55°) = 1.2587$; by interpolation we then have $E(\sin 54° 44') = 1.2612$, and

$$L = 4\sqrt{6} \times 1.2612 = 12.4.$$

(b) To find the length of arc from $x = 1$ to $x = 1.5$, we have

$$s\Big]_{x=1}^{x=1.5} = s\Big]_{x=0}^{x=1.5} - s\Big]_{x=0}^{x=1}.$$

Now since $x = a \sin \phi$,

$$\phi\Big]_{x=1} = \sin^{-1}\frac{\sqrt{6}}{6} = 24° 6',$$

and

$$\phi\Big]_{x=1.5} = \sin^{-1}\frac{\sqrt{6}}{4} = 37° 46'.$$

Therefore

$$s\Big]_{x=1}^{x=1.5} = \sqrt{6}\,[E(0.8165, 37° 46') - E(0.8165, 24° 6')].$$

To evaluate these two elliptic integrals requires double interpolation from the table on page 123 of Peirce. To this end it will be found convenient to arrange the work as shown below, where we interpolate first with regard to $\alpha = \sin^{-1} k$ and then with regard to ϕ.*

ϕ \ α	45°	54° 44′	60°
35°	0.5928	0.5866	0.5833
37° 46′		0.6285	
40°	0.6715	0.6624	0.6575

ϕ \ α	45°	54° 44′	60°
20°	0.3456	0.3444	0.3438
24° 6′		0.4124	
25°	0.4296	0.4273	0.4261

We then have

$$s\Big]_{x=1}^{x=1.5} = \sqrt{6}\,(0.6285 - 0.4124) = 0.529.$$

29. The pendulum. We turn now to a physical problem, which will introduce the elliptic integral of the first kind. The problem we are to consider is again a familiar one, and one which could, without elliptic integrals, be only approximately solved in elementary mechanics. Let there be given a pendulum (Fig. 24) in which the weight w (lb.) may be considered concentrated at a point distant L (ft.) from the pivot, swinging through an angle 2α. We suppose the pendulum to be

---

* Interpolation in the reverse order would do as well. The student should try this alternative method also.

rigid, so that its center of gravity describes a circle arc, of radius L, for which α may have any value between $0°$ and $180°$. Take the pivot A at the point $(0, L)$, the coordinate axes being situated as shown. Let the weight w be, at any arbitrary time t (sec.), at the point $P(x, y)$ of the arc, and let θ denote the angle between AP and the y-axis; evidently we have $-\alpha \leqq \theta \leqq \alpha$. If s represents the arc length OP

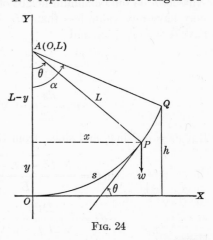

measured from O, the accelera-tion d^2s/dt^2 along the arc will be produced by the tangential com-ponent, of magnitude $w \sin \theta$, of the force w acting downward. Now if the body is in the first quadrant and is moving upwards, s is increasing, and ds/dt is positive but decreasing, so that d^2s/dt^2 is negative; again, if the motion is downwards, then s is decreasing, and ds/dt is negative and increasing in $magnitude$, that is, ds/dt is $algebraically$ decreas-ing, whence d^2s/dt^2 is negative as

FIG. 24

before. Thus d^2s/dt^2 is negative whenever θ is positive; the student may show in the same manner that d^2s/dt^2 is positive when θ is nega-tive. Hence, equating the product of mass and acceleration to the force, we have

$$\frac{w}{g}\frac{d^2s}{dt^2} = -w \sin \theta, \tag{1}$$

where g is the gravity constant (32.17 ft./sec.^{2}).

In elementary mechanics it is usual to assume the angle of swing 2α so small that $\sin \theta$ may be replaced by θ without much error. Then since $s = L\theta$, equation (1) reduces to a linear differential equation, and the pendulum is found to oscillate with simple harmonic motion, the period being $2\pi\sqrt{L/g}$, which is independent of α. We shall not make that assumption here, but shall try to solve the non-linear equation arising from (1). Letting $v = ds/dt$ denote the velocity of the body in its path, we have $d^2s/dt^2 = dv/dt = v(dv/ds)$. Also, $\sin \theta = dy/ds$, so that (1) becomes

$$v\frac{dv}{ds} = -g\frac{dy}{ds}.$$

Multiplying both sides of this equation by ds, we see that we have a simple first-order differential equation in the variables y and v. Integrating this, we have at once,

$$\frac{v^2}{2} = -gy + c_1.$$

Now let h be the maximum height of point P above the x-axis; here h may have any value less than $2L$. Then since $v = 0$ for $y = h$, we have $0 = -gh + c_1$, and

$$\frac{v^2}{2} = g(h - y),$$

$$v = \frac{ds}{dt} = \pm \sqrt{2g(h - y)}.$$

But $ds = dy/\sin \theta$, and since, from the figure,

$$\sin \theta = \frac{\sqrt{L^2 - (L - y)^2}}{L},$$

$$ds = \frac{L \, dy}{\sqrt{2Ly - y^2}}.$$

Hence

$$dt = \pm \frac{L}{\sqrt{2g}} \frac{dy}{\sqrt{h - y}\sqrt{2Ly - y^2}}.$$

Now if the body is moving upward so that dy is positive, we take the plus sign in the preceding equation, and write

$$t \Big]_{y=y_1}^{y=y_2} = \frac{L}{\sqrt{2g}} \int_{y_1}^{y_2} \frac{dy}{\sqrt{h - y}\sqrt{2Ly - y^2}}$$

for the time required to go from $P_1(x_1, y_1)$ to $P_2(x_2, y_2)$. If, on the other hand, the body is moving in the opposite direction, dy will be negative, and we should take the minus sign in the expression for dt, whence

$$t \Big]_{y=y_2}^{y=y_1} = -\frac{L}{\sqrt{2g}} \int_{y_2}^{y_1} \frac{dy}{\sqrt{h - y}\sqrt{2Ly - y^2}}$$

$$= \frac{L}{\sqrt{2g}} \int_{y_1}^{y_2} \frac{dy}{\sqrt{h - y}\sqrt{2Ly - y^2}},$$

as before. That is,

$$t \Big]_{y=y_1}^{y=y_2} = t \Big]_{y=y_2}^{y=y_1},$$

so that the direction of motion is immaterial, the two intervals of time required for the same arc to be traversed in opposite directions being equal. The student may feel that this fact is obvious on the grounds of physical intuition, but it is well to notice that such physical sensibilities should be logically verifiable.

In particular, the time required to go from O to any point $P\ (x,\ y)$, (or from P to O), will be

$$t = \frac{L}{\sqrt{2g}} \int_0^y \frac{dy}{\sqrt{h - y}\sqrt{2Ly - y^2}}.$$

Now if we let

$$y = h \sin^2 \phi, \tag{2}$$

we have $dy = 2h \sin\phi \cos\phi \, d\phi$, $\sqrt{h - y} = \sqrt{h}\cos\phi$, and

$$t = \frac{L}{\sqrt{2g}} \int_0^\phi \frac{2h \sin\phi \cos\phi \, d\phi}{\sqrt{h}\cos\phi \sqrt{2Lh \sin^2\phi - h^2 \sin^4\phi}}$$

$$= \frac{2L}{\sqrt{2g}} \int_0^\phi \frac{d\phi}{\sqrt{2L - h \sin^2\phi}}$$

$$= \sqrt{\frac{L}{g}} \int_0^\phi \frac{d\phi}{\sqrt{1 - \frac{h}{2L} \sin^2\phi}}$$

$$= \sqrt{\frac{L}{g}} \int_0^\phi \frac{d\phi}{\sqrt{1 - k^2 \sin^2\phi}},$$

where $k = \sqrt{h/2L} < 1$, and the upper limit ϕ corresponds to the point $P(x,\ y)$.* The integral in this expression is the function called the *elliptic integral of the first kind*, and denoted by $F(k,\ \phi)$:

$$F(k,\ \phi) \equiv \int_0^\phi \frac{d\phi}{\sqrt{1 - k^2 \sin^2\phi}} \qquad (0 < k < 1). \tag{3}$$

Thus we have

$$t \Big]_{y=0}^{y=y} = \sqrt{\frac{L}{g}} \, F(k,\ \phi), \tag{4}$$

and

$$t \Big]_{y=y_1}^{y=y_2} = t \Big]_{\phi=\phi_1}^{\phi=\phi_2} = \sqrt{\frac{L}{g}} \, [F(k,\ \phi_2) - F(k,\ \phi_1)],$$

where $y_1 = h \sin^2 \phi_1$ and $y_2 = h \sin^2 \phi_2$.

---

* That is, ϕ corresponds to y in virtue of the relation (2). The angle ϕ introduced as a parameter should not be confused with the angular displacement θ corresponding to y; the relation between ϕ and θ is given by equation (6).

To interpret the modulus k and the amplitude ϕ in this problem, we note from the figure that $h = L(1 - \cos \alpha)$. Hence

$$k = \sqrt{\frac{h}{2L}} = \sqrt{\frac{1 - \cos \alpha}{2}} = \sin \frac{\alpha}{2}, \tag{5}$$

and

$$\sin \phi = \sqrt{\frac{y}{h}} = \sqrt{\frac{1 - \cos \theta}{1 - \cos \alpha}} = \frac{\sin \dfrac{\theta}{2}}{\sin \dfrac{\alpha}{2}}. \tag{6}$$

If we denote by T the period of the pendulum, we have

$$T = 4t \Big]_{y=0}^{y=h} = 4 \sqrt{\frac{L}{g}} \int_0^{\pi/2} \frac{d\phi}{\sqrt{1 - k^2 \sin^2 \phi}}$$

$$= 4 \sqrt{\frac{L}{g}} F\left(k, \frac{\pi}{2}\right).$$

When, as here, the upper limit ϕ of the integral (3) is equal to $\pi/2$, the function is called the *complete elliptic integral of the first kind*, and is denoted by $K(k)$, or merely K:

$$K \equiv K(k) \equiv \int_0^{\pi/2} \frac{d\phi}{\sqrt{1 - k^2 \sin^2 \phi}} \qquad (0 < k < 1). \tag{7}$$

Thus we have

$$T = 4 \sqrt{\frac{L}{g}} K(k). \tag{8}$$

The elliptic integrals (3) and (7) have likewise been tabulated; Peirce, pages 121 and 122, gives values of these functions for certain values of k and ϕ.

Example. A seconds pendulum is one taking 1 sec. to swing from one end of its arc to the other, so that its period is 2 sec. Find (*a*) the length of a seconds pendulum that swings through an angle of 120°; (*b*) the time required by this pendulum to descend through 30° of arc from its highest point.

(*a*) Here $\alpha = 60°$, $T = 2$ sec. Consequently $k = \sin(\alpha/2) = \frac{1}{2}$, and we get from (8)

$$2 = 4\sqrt{\frac{L}{g}} K\left(\frac{1}{2}\right),$$

whence

$$\sqrt{\frac{L}{g}} = \frac{1}{2K(\frac{1}{2})} = \frac{1}{2 \times 1.6858},$$

$$L = \frac{32.17}{(2 \times 1.6858)^2} = 2.83 \text{ ft.}$$

(b) When $\theta = 60°$, ϕ is evidently $90°$; when $\theta = 30°$, we have, also by equation (6),

$$\sin \phi = \frac{\sin \dfrac{\theta}{2}}{\sin \dfrac{\alpha}{2}} = \frac{\sin 15°}{\sin 30°} = \frac{0.2588}{0.5000} = 0.5176,$$

$$\phi = 31° \; 10'.$$

Therefore equation (4) gives us

$$t \Big]_{\theta = 60°}^{\theta = 30°} = t \Big]_{\theta = 30°}^{\theta = 60°} = \sqrt{\frac{L}{g}} \left[K\!\left(\frac{1}{2}\right) - F\!\left(\frac{1}{2}, 31° \; 10'\right) \right]$$

$$= 0.5000 - \frac{0.5505}{2 \times 1.6858} = 0.337 \text{ sec.}$$

30. Discussion of elliptic integrals and functions. If, in equation (3), Art. 29, which is known as Legendre's form, we make the substitution $x = \sin \phi$, we get as another (Jacobi's) form of the elliptic integral of the first kind,

$$F(k, \phi) \equiv F_1(k, x) \equiv \int_0^x \frac{dx}{\sqrt{(1 - x^2)(1 - k^2 x^2)}} \qquad (0 < k < 1), \quad (1)$$

where F_1 is the function obtained from F by our substitution. Likewise, setting $x = \sin \phi$ in equation (4), Art. 28 (Legendre's form), we have as alternative (Jacobi's) form of the elliptic integral of the second kind,

$$E(k, \phi) \equiv E_1(k, x) \equiv \int_0^x \sqrt{\frac{1 - k^2 x^2}{1 - x^2}} \, dx$$

$$\equiv \int_0^x \frac{(1 - k^2 x^2) \, dx}{\sqrt{(1 - x^2)(1 - k^2 x^2)}} \qquad (0 < k < 1). \qquad (2)$$

We notice that in each of the expressions (1) and (2) the integrand is a rational function of x and the square root of a quartic expression in x, that is, each integral is of the form

$$\int R(x, \sqrt{a_0 x^4 + a_1 x^3 + a_2 x^2 + a_3 x + a_4}) \, dx, \qquad (3)$$

where R denotes a rational function of its two arguments. Some integrals of the type (3) may be evaluated in terms of elementary functions; for example,

$$\int \frac{4a_0 x^3 + 3a_1 x^2 + 2a_2 x + a_3}{\sqrt{a_0 x^4 + a_1 x^3 + a_2 x^2 + a_3 x + a_4}} \, dx$$

can obviously be so integrated. In general, however, (3) will include in its expression the two functions (1) and (2) and the *elliptic integral of the third kind,*

$$\mathrm{II}_1(n, k, x) \equiv \int_0^x \frac{dx}{(1 + nx^2)\sqrt{(1 - x^2)(1 - k^2x^2)}} \qquad (0 < k < 1), \quad (4)$$

where n is any constant. Specifically, if, in the integral (3), the coefficients a_0 and a_1 are both zero (and for certain other functions, as in the above example), the integral may be expressed in terms of elementary functions alone, while if a_0, a_1, or both are different from zero, the elementary functions augmented by the functions (1), (2), and (4) will surely suffice for the expression of any such integral. The discussion of this problem, as well as of the elliptic integral of the third kind (4), will be omitted in this book since we shall have no occasion to make use of these topics in our applications.*

Let us now inspect the graphs (Fig. 25) of the integrands of the elliptic integrals of the first and second kinds as functions of ϕ,

$$y = \frac{1}{\sqrt{1 - k^2 \sin^2 \phi}}, \qquad y = \sqrt{1 - k^2 \sin^2 \phi}.$$

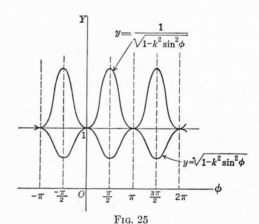

Fig. 25

We see that the first function is periodic with period π, with axes of symmetry at $\phi = 0$, $\pm\pi/2$, $\pm\pi$, $\cdots$, and that it oscillates between its minimum value, unity, and its maximum value, depending upon the value of the modulus k. Similarly, the function $y = \sqrt{1 - k^2 \sin^2 \phi}$ is periodic with period π, with axes of symmetry at $\phi = 0$, $\pm\pi/2$, $\pm\pi$, $\cdots$, but has unity as its maximum value, the minimum value

* See, for example, Goursat-Hedrick, "Mathematical Analysis," Vol. I.

depending upon k. Because of the periodicity and symmetry exhibited by each graph, and since the elliptic integrals $F(k, \phi)$ and $E(k, \phi)$ are represented geometrically by the areas under portions of the respective curves, it is necessary to tabulate $F(k, \phi)$ and $E(k, \phi)$ only for values of ϕ between $0°$ and $90°$.

Just as in elementary work it is often necessary or desirable to deal with the inverses of the trigonometric functions, and with the two functions inverse to each other, the exponential and logarithmic functions, so we sometimes speak of the function inverse to the elliptic integral of the first kind. Suppose the modulus k fixed, and consider the integral (3), Art. 29, as a function of its upper limit ϕ:

$$u \equiv u(\phi) \equiv \int_0^\phi \frac{d\phi}{\sqrt{1 - k^2 \sin^2 \phi}}.$$

Since ϕ is the amplitude of u, we call the inverse of u by this name, and denote it by

$$\phi = \operatorname{am} u, \tag{5}$$

or, sometimes, when the modulus k is to be brought into evidence,

$$\phi = \operatorname{am}(u, \bmod k).$$

Also, since ϕ may be regarded as an angle, we sometimes deal with the trigonometric functions of ϕ; in particular, we use the notations

$$\sin \phi \equiv \sin \operatorname{am} u \equiv \operatorname{sn} u, \tag{6}$$

$$\cos \phi \equiv \sqrt{1 - \operatorname{sn}^2 u} \equiv \cos \operatorname{am} u \equiv \operatorname{cn} u, \tag{7}$$

$$\sqrt{1 - k^2 \sin^2 \phi} \equiv \Delta \phi \equiv \operatorname{dn} u. \tag{8}$$

The functions (6), (7), (8) we call elliptic functions of u. They are connected by formulas somewhat similar to the trigonometric formulas.*

PROBLEMS

1. Show that $K(k)$ continually increases, whereas $E(k)$ continually decreases, as k varies from 0 to 1. By examining the integrals defining K and E, for $k = 0$ and $k = 1$, find the maximum and minimum values possessed by the two complete elliptic integrals.

2. The integral

$$\int_0^\phi \frac{d\phi}{\sqrt{1 - k^2 \sin^2 \phi}}$$

was defined as the elliptic integral of the first kind when $0 < k < 1$. If $k > 1$,

* See, for example, Peirce, "Tables," 705–734.

this integral may also be expressed in terms of an elliptic integral. By means of the substitution $k \sin \phi = \sin x$, show that

$$\int_0^\phi \frac{d\phi}{\sqrt{1 - k^2 \sin^2 \phi}} = \frac{1}{k} F\left(\frac{1}{k}, x\right) \qquad (k > 1),$$

where the amplitude x is evaluated from the upper limit of integration as $x = \sin^{-1} (k \sin \phi)$, and the integral has a real value when $k \sin \phi \leqq 1$.

3. Express the integral

$$\int_0^\phi \frac{\sin^2 \phi \, d\phi}{\sqrt{1 - k^2 \sin^2 \phi}} \qquad (0 < k < 1)$$

in terms of elliptic integrals. What is the result when the upper limit of integration has the value $\pi/2$?

4. Show that

$$\int_0^\phi \frac{\cos^2 \phi \, d\phi}{\sqrt{1 - k^2 \sin^2 \phi}} = \left(1 - \frac{1}{k^2}\right) F(k, \phi) + \frac{1}{k^2} E(k, \phi),$$

when $0 < k < 1$, and evaluate the result for $k = \frac{1}{2}$, $\phi = 1$.

5. The integral

$$\int_0^\phi \sqrt{1 - k^2 \sin^2 \phi} \, d\phi$$

was defined as the elliptic integral of the second kind when $0 < k < 1$. If $k > 1$, this integral may also be expressed in terms of elliptic integrals. By means of the substitution $k \sin \phi = \sin x$, show that

$$\int_0^\phi \sqrt{1 - k^2 \sin^2 \phi} \, d\phi = \left(\frac{1}{k} - k\right) F\left(\frac{1}{k}, x\right) + kE\left(\frac{1}{k}, x\right) \qquad (k > 1),$$

where the amplitude x is evaluated from the upper limit of integration as $x = \sin^{-1} (k \sin \phi)$, and the integral has a real value when $k \sin \phi \leqq 1$.

6. Using the same notation and substitution as in Problem 5, show that

$$\int_0^\phi \frac{\sin^2 \phi \, d\phi}{\sqrt{1 - k^2 \sin^2 \phi}} = \frac{1}{k}\left[F\left(\frac{1}{k}, x\right) - E\left(\frac{1}{k}, x\right)\right] \qquad (k > 1).$$

7. By means of the transformation $x = \pi/2 - y$, show that

$$\int_0^{\pi/2} \frac{dx}{\sqrt{\sin x}} = \int_0^{\pi/2} \frac{dy}{\sqrt{\cos y}}.$$

Hence, by letting $\cos y = \cos^2 z$, show that these integrals are elliptic, and find their common value.

8. Using the identity $\cos x = 2 \cos^2 (x/2) - 1$, and then letting $x/2 = \pi/2 - y$, show that the integral

$$\int_0^\phi \frac{dx}{\sqrt{c - \cos x}} \qquad (c > 1)$$

is elliptic and evaluate it for $c = 7$, $\phi = \pi/2$.

9. Show that the integral

$$\int_0^{\pi/4} \frac{dx}{\sqrt{3 + \cos x}}$$

is elliptic, and compute its value.

10. By means of the substitution $x = \frac{1}{2}a(1 - \sin \theta)$, show that

$$\int_0^{a/2} \frac{dx}{\sqrt{2ax - x^2}\sqrt{a^2 - x^2}} = \frac{2}{3a} K\left(\frac{1}{3}\right).$$

11. As an alternative derivation of equation (3), Art. 28, begin with the rectangular equation (1), and show that the integral for the length of elliptical arc is of the form (2), Art. 30, whence the result follows.

12. Given the ellipse $x^2 + 4y^2 = 4$, find (a) the length of arc from $x = 1$ to $x = 2$; (b) the abscissa of the point bisecting the quadrantal arc.

13. An ellipse of eccentricity $\frac{1}{2}$ and a circle have the same area. Find the ratio of their circumferences.

14. Given the curve $y = \sin x$, find (a) the length of one arch; (b) the coordinates of the points trisecting the arc from $x = \pi/2$ to $x = 3\pi/2$.

15. The length of a certain ellipse of eccentricity $\frac{1}{2}\sqrt{2}$ is twice that of one arch of the curve $y = \sin x$. Find the length of arc in the first quadrant between the points on the ellipse with abscissas $\frac{1}{2}$ and 1, respectively.

16. Find the period of a pendulum 2 ft. long oscillating through an angle of 40°. By what percentage must the length be changed if the period is to be the same but the angle of swing is doubled?

17. A pendulum, swinging through an arc of 60°, has a period of 1 sec. Find the time required to fall from the highest point of its swing through an arc of 10°.

18. A pendulum 9 in. long has a period of 1 sec. Find (a) the angle through which the pendulum swings; (b) the time required to descend through the first quarter of its swing from an extreme position.

19. A pendulum bob, swinging through an angle of 240°, starts from its extreme position, which is 3 ft. above its lowest level. Find how long it takes the bob to acquire a velocity of 13.27 ft./sec.

20. Two pendulums, of equal length, swing through angles of 160° and 80°, respectively. Find the ratio of the times required to fall through the first quarter of the respective swings, from the corresponding highest points.

21. A pendulum is 8.04 ft. long. Determine the vertical distance through which the bob must fall to its lowest position if it starts from rest and if the time necessary to fall the first half of that distance is 0.404 sec.

22. Find the area bounded by the curve $y^2(1 - 2\sin^2 x) = 1$ and the lines $x = \pm c$. What is the limit of this area as c approaches $\pi/4$? *Hint:* See Problem 2.

23. Find the area enclosed by one loop of the curve $3y^2 - 3 + 4\sin^2 x = 0$.

24. A particle, starting from rest, slides from the edge to the bottom of a smooth hemispherical bowl of radius r (ft.). (a) If θ (rad.) is the angular displacement in time t (sec.), show that the differential equation of motion is $r\mathrm{D}^2\theta = g \cos \theta$, where $\mathrm{D} = d/dt$ and $g = 32.17$ ft./sec.[2] (b) If $r = 2$ ft., find the time of descent.

25. A bowl, 2 ft. in diameter and 1 ft. deep, is in the form of a paraboloid of revolution. Find the time required for a particle, starting from rest, to slide from the edge to the bottom of the bowl.

26. Given the lemniscate $\rho^2 = \cos 2\theta$, find (a) its entire length; (b) the length of the arc from $\theta = 0$ to $\theta = \pi/6$.

27. (a) Find the length of one leaf of the rose curve $\rho = \sin n\theta$. (b) Using the result of part (a), find the entire length of each of the curves $\rho = \sin 2\theta$, $\rho = \sin 3\theta$.

28. The center of a sphere of radius a lies on the surface of a right circular cylinder of diameter $a/2$. Find (a) the surface area of the cylinder intercepted by the sphere; (b) the surface area of the sphere intercepted by the cylinder.

29. Establish each of the following relations. (Cf. Peirce: 530, 532, 534, 536.)

(a) $\displaystyle \int_x^1 \frac{dx}{\sqrt{(1 - x^2)(x^2 - k^2)}} = F\left(\sqrt{1 - k^2},\ \sin^{-1}\sqrt{\frac{1 - x^2}{1 - k^2}}\right),\ 0 < k < x < 1;$

(b) $\displaystyle \int_0^x \frac{dx}{\sqrt{x(1 - x)(1 - k^2 x)}} = 2F(k,\ \sin^{-1}\sqrt{x}),\qquad 0 < k < 1,\ 0 < x < 1;$

(c) $\displaystyle \int_x^1 \frac{dx}{\sqrt{x(1 - x)(x - k^2)}} = 2F\left(\sqrt{1 - k^2},\ \sin^{-1}\sqrt{\frac{1 - x}{1 - k^2}}\right),\ 0 < k^2 < x < 1;$

(d) $\displaystyle \int_0^x \frac{dx}{\sqrt{(a^2 - x^2)(b^2 - x^2)}} = \frac{1}{a} F\left(\frac{b}{a},\ \frac{x}{b}\right),\ 0 < x < b < a.$

31. A mechanical brake problem.

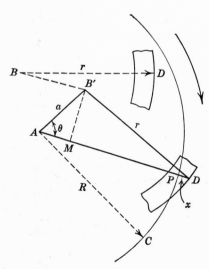

FIG. 26

We consider now a mechanical type of brake,* a portion of which is shown diagrammatically in Fig. 26. A rigid cylindrical shell C, of inner radius R (ft.), rotates about a fixed axis A. A second cylindrical shell, on part of which the brake lining is mounted, is inside C, and has its center originally at B; we suppose the brake lining to be an elastic strip obeying Hooke's law. Let r (ft.) be the distance from the center B to the outer surface of the undeformed lining.

Now suppose the brake to be applied, thereby moving the point B to B', and let a (ft.) denote the distance AB'. Let P be any point

*An analysis of this problem was given by I. Opatowski, *Am. Math. Monthly*, p. 443, Aug.–Sept., 1941.

of contact of the lining with the surface C, and let θ (rad.) denote the variable angle PAB'. If the constraining surface C were not present, the point P would be situated at D', where $B'D' = r$. Thus the deformation of the elastic strip at P, measured along the line AD', is $x = PD'$ (ft.). From the figure we get for the deformation,

$$x = PD' = AM + MD' - AP$$

$$= a \cos \theta + \sqrt{r^2 - a^2 \sin^2 \theta} - R. \tag{1}$$

Now the radial force Δf acting on an element of arc $R\,\Delta\theta$ is, by Hooke's law, $cx\,\Delta\theta$ (lb.), where c is a constant of proportionality. Consequently, if μ is the coefficient of friction between the brake lining and the surface C, the force of friction is $\Delta F = \mu\,\Delta f = \mu cx\,\Delta\theta$ (lb.), and the torque exerted by the braking action is $\Delta T = R\,\Delta F = R\mu cx\,\Delta\theta$ (ft-lb.). Therefore, if α and β are the values of θ corresponding to the extreme positions of the contact point P, the resultant torque is

$$T = R\mu c \int_{\alpha}^{\beta} (a \cos \theta + \sqrt{r^2 - a^2 \sin^2 \theta} - R)\,d\theta$$

$$= R\mu c[a\,(\sin \beta - \sin \alpha) - R(\beta - \alpha)]$$

$$+ R\mu c r \int_{\alpha}^{\beta} \sqrt{1 - (a^2/r^2) \sin^2 \theta}\,d\theta. \tag{2}$$

If, in particular, $r = a$, (2) reduces to

$$T = R\mu c[2a\,(\sin \beta - \sin \alpha) - R(\beta - \alpha)]. \tag{3}$$

If $a/r < 1$, the last integral in (2) is an elliptic integral of the second kind, and we have

$$T = R\mu c[a\,(\sin \beta - \sin \alpha) - R(\beta - \alpha) + rE(a/r, \beta)$$

$$- rE(a/r, \alpha)]. \tag{4}$$

Finally, if $a/r > 1$, the integral appearing in (2) can be expressed in terms of elliptic integrals of both the first and second kinds. (See Problem 5 following Art. 30.)

32. Capillarity: two parallel vertical plates. In Chapter II, Art. 24, we discussed the theory of capillarity, and derived the differential equation of the capillary curve in the form

$$\frac{y''}{(1 + y'^2)^{3/2}} = \frac{\rho g}{T} y = \frac{4}{c^2} y, \tag{1}$$

where ρ is the specific gravity (gr./cm.³) of the liquid, g the gravity constant (980.5 cm./sec.^{2}), T the surface tension of the liquid (dynes/cm.), and $c = 2\sqrt{T/\rho g}$. We also solved the differential equation (1) subject to the conditions prevailing when a single vertical plate is partly immersed in a large expanse of the liquid, and found that the height to which the liquid rises on the plate, measured from the distant horizontal surface of the liquid, is given by

$$h_0 = c\sqrt{\frac{1 - \sin \alpha}{2}}, \tag{2}$$

where α is the contact angle between liquid and plate.

Let us suppose now that we have two parallel vertical plates AC and BD immersed in the liquid at a distance $2a$ (cm.) apart (Fig. 27); we

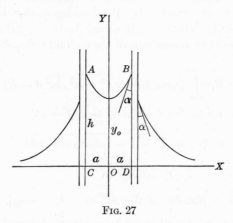

Fig. 27

wish to find the equation of the capillary curve AB between the plates. We may do this by again solving the differential equation (1), subject now to the new physical conditions imposed by the present problem. We choose the x-axis lying in the distant (outside) horizontal surface of the liquid and the y-axis midway between the plates. Let the y-intercept of the capillary curve be y_0 and let h be the maximum height to which the liquid rises between the plates.

As before, let $y' = p$, $y'' = p\,dp/dy$, so that equation (1) becomes

$$\frac{p\,dp}{(1 + p^2)^{3/2}} = \frac{4}{c^2}\,y\,dy,$$

whence, by integration, we have again

$$-\frac{1}{\sqrt{1 + p^2}} = \frac{2y^2}{c^2} + c_1,$$

where c_1 is the constant of integration. Since now $p = dy/dx = 0$ when $y = y_0$, we find $c_1 = -1 - (2y_0^2/c^2)$, and consequently

$$\frac{1}{\sqrt{1 + p^2}} = 1 - \frac{2}{c^2}(y^2 - y_0^2).$$

We note here, for later use, that since $p = \cot \alpha$ when $y = h$,

$$\sin \alpha = 1 - \frac{2}{c^2}(h^2 - y_0^2),$$

and

$$h^2 - y_0^2 = c^2 \frac{1 - \sin \alpha}{2} = h_0^2 \qquad (3)$$

by equation (2). Thus h, the maximum height to which the liquid rises between the plates, is always greater than the capillary rise h_0 outside the plates, provided y_0 is not zero.

Solving now for p, we get

$$1 + p^2 = \frac{c^4}{[c^2 - 2(y^2 - y_0^2)]^2},$$

$$\frac{dy}{dx} = \frac{\sqrt{c^4 - [c^2 - 2(y^2 - y_0^2)]^2}}{c^2 - 2(y^2 - y_0^2)}$$

$$= \frac{\sqrt{4c^2(y^2 - y_0^2) - 4(y^2 - y_0^2)^2}}{c^2 - 2(y^2 - y_0^2)},$$

and

$$dx = \frac{c^2 - 2(y^2 - y_0^2)}{2\sqrt{c^2(y^2 - y_0^2) - (y^2 - y_0^2)^2}} \, dy.$$

In extracting the square root, we have chosen the positive sign for dy/dx. This means merely that we are confining our attention to the right-hand half of the capillary curve, which is certainly permissible in view of the symmetry of our figure with respect to the y-axis.

To integrate the last equation above, make the substitution $y^2 - y_0^2 = c^2 \cos^2 \phi$, whence

$$y = \sqrt{y_0^2 + c^2 \cos^2 \phi}. \qquad (4)$$

Then

$$y \, dy = -c^2 \cos \phi \sin \phi \, d\phi,$$

$$\sqrt{c^2(y^2 - y_0^2) - (y^2 - y_0^2)^2} = c^2 \cos \phi \sin \phi,$$

and

$$dx = \frac{c^2 - 2c^2 \cos^2 \phi}{2c^2 \cos \phi \sin \phi} \left(- \frac{c^2 \cos \phi \sin \phi \, d\phi}{\sqrt{y_0^2 + c^2 \cos^2 \phi}} \right)$$

$$= \frac{c^2 - 2c^2 \sin^2 \phi}{2\sqrt{y_0^2 + c^2 \cos^2 \phi}} \, d\phi.$$

Now let

$$k^2 = \frac{c^2}{y_0^2 + c^2} \, ; \tag{5}$$

obviously $k < 1$. We therefore have, by (5),

$$dx = \frac{c^2 - 2c^2 \sin^2 \phi}{\dfrac{2c}{k} \sqrt{1 - k^2 \sin^2 \phi}} \, d\phi$$

$$= \frac{ck}{2} \frac{d\phi}{\sqrt{1 - k^2 \sin^2 \phi}} - \frac{c}{k} \frac{1 - 1 + k^2 \sin^2 \phi}{\sqrt{1 - k^2 \sin^2 \phi}} \, d\phi$$

$$= \left(\frac{ck}{2} - \frac{c}{k} \right) \frac{d\phi}{\sqrt{1 - k^2 \sin^2 \phi}} + \frac{c}{k} \sqrt{1 - k^2 \sin^2 \phi} \, d\phi.$$

Consequently, since $\phi = \pi/2$ when $y = y_0$, or when $x = 0$, integration between limits gives us

$$\int_0^x dx = x = \left(\frac{ck}{2} - \frac{c}{k} \right) \int_{\pi/2}^{\phi} \frac{d\phi}{\sqrt{1 - k^2 \sin^2 \phi}} + \frac{c}{k} \int_{\pi/2}^{\phi} \sqrt{1 - k^2 \sin^2 \phi} \, d\phi$$

$$= \left(\frac{c}{k} - \frac{ck}{2} \right) \int_{\phi}^{\pi/2} \frac{d\phi}{\sqrt{1 - k^2 \sin^2 \phi}} - \frac{c}{k} \int_{\phi}^{\pi/2} \sqrt{1 - k^2 \sin^2 \phi} \, d\phi,$$

$$x = \frac{c}{k} \left\{ \left(1 - \frac{k^2}{2} \right) [K(k) - F(k, \phi)] - [E(k) - E(k, \phi)] \right\}. \tag{6}$$

It is seen that both k and ϕ in this expression for x depend upon y_0, which is so far unknown. But we have not as yet used the fact that the plates are a distance $2a$ apart. This means that $x = a$ when $y = h$, and therefore ϕ_1, the value of ϕ corresponding to $x = a$, is given by

$$\cos \phi_1 = \frac{\sqrt{h^2 - y_0^2}}{c} = \frac{h_0}{c} = \sqrt{\frac{1 - \sin \alpha}{2}}, \tag{7}$$

from equations (3) and (4). Hence

$$a = \left(\frac{c}{k} - \frac{ck}{2} \right) [K(k) - F(k, \phi_1)] - \frac{c}{k} [E(k) - E(k, \phi_1)]. \tag{8}$$

We may thus proceed in the following manner. We first find, by trial and error, the value of k from the implicit relation (8), in which $c = 2\sqrt{T/\rho g}$ and ϕ_1 is given by (7). Then the definition (5) of k yields y_0, and finally the equations (6) and (4) give us x and y in terms of the parameter ϕ. In particular, the maximum rise h between the plates is given by (3).

In connection with the relation (3) between the capillary rises outside and between the plates, we noted that $h > h_0$ provided $y_0 \neq 0$. Now if y_0 were zero, we should have $k = 1$ by (5). Then $K(k)$ would become infinite (see Art. 30, Problem 1), while $F(k, \phi_1)$, $E(k)$, and $E(k, \phi_1)$ all remain finite, so that by (8) we should have a infinite, contrary to supposition. Hence the liquid will always rise to a higher level between the plates than it will outside them.

33. The elastica. As another application of elliptic integrals, we consider the *elastica*, the curve assumed by a uniform elastic spring, originally straight, the ends of which are subjected to two equal and opposite compressive forces (Fig. 28). Let the x-axis be taken through

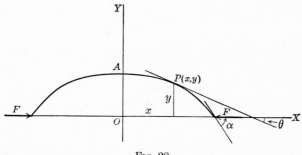

FIG. 28

the ends of the spring and the y-axis through its midpoint. Let the magnitude of the force applied at each end, along the x-axis, be F (lb.), and let the tangent at any point $P(x, y)$ of the curve make an angle θ with the negative direction of the x-axis, x and y being measured in inches. Then the bending moment equation [Chapter I, Art. 7(f)] gives us

$$\frac{EI}{R} = M = -Fy, \tag{1}$$

where E (lb./in.^{2}) is the modulus of elasticity, I (in.^{4}) is the moment of inertia of the cross-sectional area of the spring with respect to a line perpendicular to the xy-plane and through the neutral section, and R (in.) is the radius of curvature at the point P.

If s (in.) is the arc length AP, we have

$$\frac{1}{R} = -\frac{d\theta}{ds} = -\frac{dy}{ds}\frac{d\theta}{dy} = \sin\theta\,\frac{d\theta}{dy}\,;$$

hence (1) may be written

$$EI \sin\theta\,d\theta = -Fy\,dy,$$

or, letting $c^2 = EI/F$,

$$y\,dy = -c^2 \sin\theta\,d\theta. \qquad (2)$$

Integration yields

$$\frac{y^2}{2} = c^2 \cos\theta + c_1.$$

Denoting by α the value of θ at the end of the spring where $y = 0$, we find $c_1 = -c^2 \cos\alpha$, and therefore

$$y = \sqrt{2}\,c\,\sqrt{\cos\theta - \cos\alpha}. \qquad (3)$$

Replacing $\sin\theta$ by $-dy/ds$ in (2), we obtain

$$ds = c^2\frac{d\theta}{y} = \frac{c}{\sqrt{2}}\frac{d\theta}{\sqrt{\cos\theta - \cos\alpha}}.$$

Substituting $\cos\theta = 1 - 2\sin^2(\theta/2)$, $\cos\alpha = 1 - 2\sin^2(\alpha/2)$, this becomes

$$ds = \frac{c}{2}\frac{d\theta}{\sqrt{\sin^2\dfrac{\alpha}{2} - \sin^2\dfrac{\theta}{2}}}.$$

Letting $k = \sin(\alpha/2)$ and $\sin(\theta/2) = k\sin\phi$, whence

$$\cos\frac{\theta}{2}\frac{d\theta}{2} = k\cos\phi\,d\phi$$

and

$$d\theta = \frac{2k\cos\phi\,d\phi}{\sqrt{1 - k^2\sin^2\phi}},$$

we have

$$s = c\int_0^\phi \frac{d\phi}{\sqrt{1 - k^2\sin^2\phi}} = cF(k,\phi),$$

and (3) reduces to

$$y = 2c\sqrt{\sin^2\frac{\alpha}{2} - \sin^2\frac{\theta}{2}} = 2ck\cos\phi.$$

To find x in terms of ϕ, we have

$$dx = \cos \theta \cdot ds = (1 - 2k^2 \sin^2 \phi) \frac{c \, d\phi}{\sqrt{1 - k^2 \sin^2 \phi}},$$

$$x = c \int_0^\phi \frac{2(1 - k^2 \sin^2 \phi) - 1}{\sqrt{1 - k^2 \sin^2 \phi}} \, d\phi = c[2E(k, \phi) - F(k, \phi)].$$

Summarizing, we have for the parametric equations of the elastica,

$$x = c[2E(k, \phi) - F(k, \phi)], \tag{4}$$

$$y = 2ck \cos \phi, \tag{5}$$

and for the arc length AP,

$$s = cF(k, \phi), \tag{6}$$

where

$$c = \sqrt{\frac{EI}{F}}, \qquad k = \sin \frac{\alpha}{2}, \qquad \phi = \sin^{-1} \frac{\sin (\theta/2)}{\sin (\alpha/2)}.$$

If $2a$, b, and L, measured in inches, are, respectively, the distance between the ends of the spring, the maximum deflection, and the length of the spring, we have, since $\phi = \pi/2$ when $\theta = \alpha$ and $\phi = 0$ when $\theta = 0$,

$$a = c[2E(k) - K(k)], \tag{4'}$$

$$b = 2ck, \tag{5'}$$

$$L = 2cK(k). \tag{6'}$$

Equation (6') is also of particular interest in that it indicates a critical value for L. For, the function $K(\sin \alpha/2)$ must be greater than $\pi/2$ (see Art. 30, Problem 1), and therefore L must be greater than πc to produce the supposed bent form; if $L < \pi c$, we have simple compression without bending. An equivalent statement is that, for a given value of L, the number $c = \sqrt{EI/F}$ must be sufficiently small if bending is to result; this may be brought about by decreasing E or I, or more simply by increasing the force F.

34. The swinging cord. Our next problem is the determination of the curve assumed by a skipping rope (Fig. 29). Consider a uniform cord or chain rotating about a horizontal axis to which the ends are fixed at two points a distance $2a$ (ft.) apart. Let ω (rad./sec.) denote the constant angular velocity of rotation, which we suppose so large that centrifugal force predominates over the gravitational force due to the small weight of the cord; we accordingly consider only the former force. Let w (lb./ft.) be the weight per foot of cord, and let t (pdl.)

be the tension at any point $P(x, y)$ of the curve. Take the x-axis through the two ends of the cord, the origin O being at the left-hand end, and let θ be the angle of inclination of the tension t.* If s (ft.) is the arc length measured from O, consider a second point Q at a distance Δs along the curve from P. The three forces acting on the arc Δs are then the two tensions t and $t + \Delta t$ at P and Q, respectively, and the centrifugal force $F = w\,\Delta s\,\omega^2 y_1$ (pdl.), where y_1 (ft.) is some

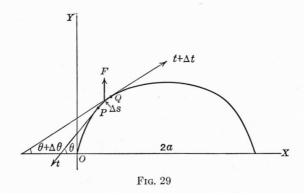

Fig. 29

ordinate between y and $y + \Delta y$. Since the element Δs must be in equilibrium under these three forces, we have, by resolving the forces into their horizontal and vertical components,

$$(t + \Delta t)\cos(\theta + \Delta\theta) = t\cos\theta, \tag{1}$$

$$(t + \Delta t)\sin(\theta + \Delta\theta) = t\sin\theta - w\,\Delta s\,\omega^2 y_1. \tag{2}$$

Now the first of these equations tells us that the horizontal component of tension must everywhere be the same. Let T denote this constant force, so that $t\cos\theta = T$; it is seen that T must be the thrust in poundals in the axis of rotation due to the pull of the cord. Dividing (2) by (1), we have

$$\tan(\theta + \Delta\theta) = \tan\theta - \frac{w\,\Delta s\,\omega^2 y_1}{T},$$

or

$$\frac{\tan(\theta + \Delta\theta) - \tan\theta}{\Delta s} = -\frac{w\omega^2 y_1}{T}.$$

The limiting value of the left member of this equation, as Δs approaches zero, is $d(\tan\theta)/ds = (\sec^2\theta)(d\theta/ds)$; also, since y_1 approaches

* We confine the discussion to the left half of the cord; points on the right half may be dealt with by consideration of symmetry in the line $x = a$.

y, we get, as the differential equation of the left half of the cord,

$$\sec^2 \theta \, \frac{d\theta}{ds} + \frac{w\omega^2 y}{T} = 0.$$

Now $d\theta/ds$ is the curvature, $y''/(1 + y'^2)^{3/2}$, and $\sec^2 \theta = 1 + \tan^2 \theta = 1 + y'^2$. Hence the differential equation takes the form

$$\frac{y''}{\sqrt{1 + y'^2}} + \frac{w\omega^2 y}{T} = 0. \tag{3}$$

Since the independent variable x is lacking, we set $y' = p$, $y'' = p(dp/dy)$ (Art. 6), whence we have

$$\frac{p \, dp}{\sqrt{1 + p^2}} + \frac{w\omega^2 y \, dy}{T} = 0.$$

Let the maximum value of y be b, so that $p = 0$ for $y = b$. Then integration between limits yields

$$\sqrt{1 + p^2} \, \Big]_0^p + \frac{w\omega^2}{2T} y^2 \, \Big]_b^y = 0,$$

$$\sqrt{1 + p^2} - 1 + c(y^2 - b^2) = 0, \tag{4}$$

where

$$c = \frac{w\omega^2}{2T}. \tag{5}$$

Therefore

$$\sqrt{1 + p^2} = 1 + c(b^2 - y^2),$$

$$1 + p^2 = 1 + 2c(b^2 - y^2) + c^2(b^2 - y^2)^2,$$

$$p^2 = c(b^2 - y^2)[2 + c(b^2 - y^2)].$$

Now let

$$y = b \sin \phi, \tag{6}$$

so that $p = (b \cos \phi)(d\phi/dx)$. Then

$$b^2 \cos^2 \phi \left(\frac{d\phi}{dx} \right)^2 = b^2 c (\cos^2 \phi)(2 + b^2 c \cos^2 \phi),$$

$$\left(\frac{d\phi}{dx} \right)^2 = c(2 + b^2 c - b^2 c \sin^2 \phi)$$

$$= c(2 + b^2 c) \left(1 - \frac{b^2 c}{2 + b^2 c} \sin^2 \phi \right).$$

If we write, for simplicity,

$$k^2 = \frac{b^2 c}{2 + b^2 c} = \frac{b^2 w \omega^2}{4T + b^2 w \omega^2}, \tag{7}$$

by (5), then $k < 1$ and $c(2 + b^2 c) = b^2 c^2 / k^2$. Consequently

$$\left(\frac{d\phi}{dx}\right)^2 = \frac{b^2 c^2}{k^2} (1 - k^2 \sin^2 \phi),$$

$$dx = \frac{k}{bc} \frac{d\phi}{\sqrt{1 - k^2 \sin^2 \phi}}.$$

Integrating between limits, we have, since $x = 0$ when $y = 0$,

$$\int_0^x dx = \frac{k}{bc} \int_0^\phi \frac{d\phi}{\sqrt{1 - k^2 \sin^2 \phi}},$$

$$x = \frac{k}{bc} F(k, \phi). \tag{8}$$

Equations (6) and (8) are the parametric equations of the left half of our curve, c and k being given by (5) and (7), respectively.

Now, from (4) and (6),

$$\frac{ds}{dx} = \sqrt{1 + p^2} = 1 + c(b^2 - y^2) = 1 + b^2 c \cos^2 \phi$$

$$= 1 + b^2 c - b^2 c \sin^2 \phi.$$

But, from (7), $b^2 c = 2k^2 / (1 - k^2)$, and therefore

$$\frac{ds}{dx} = 1 + \frac{2k^2}{1 - k^2} - \frac{2k^2}{1 - k^2} \sin^2 \phi$$

$$= \frac{1 + k^2 - 2k^2 \sin^2 \phi}{1 - k^2}$$

$$= \frac{k^2 - 1 + 2(1 - k^2 \sin^2 \phi)}{1 - k^2}$$

$$= -1 + \frac{2}{1 - k^2} (1 - k^2 \sin^2 \phi).$$

Dividing this by the expression for $d\phi/dx$ given above, we get

$$\frac{ds}{d\phi} = -\frac{k}{bc\sqrt{1 - k^2 \sin^2 \phi}} + \frac{2k}{bc(1 - k^2)} \sqrt{1 - k^2 \sin^2 \phi},$$

$$ds = -\frac{k}{bc} \frac{d\phi}{\sqrt{1 - k^2 \sin^2 \phi}} + \frac{b}{k} \sqrt{1 - k^2 \sin^2 \phi}\, d\phi,$$

$$s = \frac{b}{k} E(k, \phi) - \frac{k}{bc} F(k, \phi). \tag{9}$$

Consequently, if the total length of the cord is L, we have also the relation

$$L = 2s\Big]_{y=b} = 2s\Big]_{\phi=\pi/2},$$

$$L = \frac{2b}{k} E(k) - \frac{2k}{bc} K(k). \tag{10}$$

It may be shown by the calculus of variations that the cord will take the form which, with given length L, has the maximum moment of inertia about the axis of revolution.

35. Field intensity due to a circular current. As an application of elliptic integrals to electrical theory, we shall take the problem of computing the magnetic field intensity at any point of the plane of a circular loop in which current is flowing. The basis of our analysis is Ampère's law,* which states that the magnetic field intensity at any point P is

$$dH = \frac{I \sin \alpha\, ds}{r^2} \tag{1}$$

dynes per unit pole,† or, conventionally, lines per square centimeter, where ds (cm.) is a circuit element carrying a current I (abamp.), r (cm.) is the radius vector from P to ds, and α is the angle between r and ds. The direction of dH is at right angles to both r and ds.

Suppose that the current I is flowing in a circular loop of radius a (cm.) and that the point P, at which the field intensity is desired, is distant b (cm.) from the center O of the loop. We have to consider two cases, according as P is within or without the circle.

(a) In the first case (Fig. 30), let P be inside the circle, so that $b < a$. Let θ denote the angle between the radius vector r from P to any point Q of the circle and the line through O and P. If $\Delta s = QA$

---

* Also variously called Laplace's law or the Biot-Savart relation.
† We shall use c.g.s. units throughout this article.

is an arc of the circular loop, angle APQ will be $\Delta\theta$. With P as center and radius r describe a circle arc cutting PA at B, and let β be the angle between QB and Δs. Since QB is perpendicular to r, and α is the angle between r and Δs, we have $\alpha = 90° - \beta$. Hence $\Delta s \cdot \sin \alpha$ $= \Delta s \cdot \cos \beta$. But $\Delta s \cdot \cos \beta$ is approximately equal to $r \, \Delta\theta$. Thus

$$\Delta H_1 = \frac{I \, \Delta\theta}{r}$$

is an approximate expression for the field intensity at P due to the arc Δs. If we sum up all such expressions around the circle, and take the

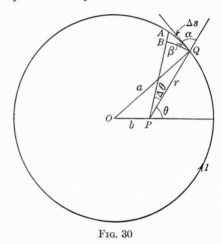

Fɪɢ. 30

limit as the number of such arcs becomes infinite while each Δs approaches zero, we have *exactly*

$$H_1 = I \int_0^{2\pi} \frac{d\theta}{r}. \tag{2}$$

Now from the triangle OPQ, we have by the law of cosines

$$a^2 = b^2 + r^2 - 2br \cos (180° - \theta) = b^2 + r^2 + 2br \cos \theta.$$

If we solve this quadratic equation for r, we get

$$r = -b \cos \theta \pm \sqrt{b^2 \cos^2 \theta + a^2 - b^2}$$

$$= -b \cos \theta \pm \sqrt{a^2 - b^2 \sin^2 \theta}.$$

Since r is positive, we must choose the plus sign; inserting this value of r in (2), we find

$$H_1 = I \int_0^{2\pi} \frac{d\theta}{\sqrt{a^2 - b^2 \sin^2 \theta} - b \cos \theta}.$$

Multiplying numerator and denominator of the integrand by $(\sqrt{a^2 - b^2 \sin^2 \theta} + b \cos \theta)$ so as to rationalize the denominator, we obtain

$$H_1 = \frac{I}{a^2 - b^2} \int_0^{2\pi} (\sqrt{a^2 - b^2 \sin^2 \theta} + b \cos \theta)\, d\theta$$

$$= \frac{I}{a^2 - b^2} \int_0^{2\pi} \sqrt{a^2 - b^2 \sin^2 \theta}\, d\theta,$$

since $\int_0^{2\pi} \cos \theta\, d\theta = 0$. Moreover, because of the symmetry of the graph of $y = \sqrt{a^2 - b^2 \sin^2 \theta}$,* we may write

$$H_1 = \frac{4I}{a^2 - b^2} \int_0^{\pi/2} \sqrt{a^2 - b^2 \sin^2 \theta}\, d\theta,$$

$$= \frac{4Ia}{a^2 - b^2} \int_0^{\pi/2} \sqrt{1 - k_1^2 \sin^2 \theta}\, d\theta,$$

where $k_1 = b/a < 1$, and therefore, dividing numerator and denominator of the coefficient of the integral by a^2, we have finally

$$H_1 = \frac{4I}{a} \frac{E(k_1)}{1 - k_1^2}. \tag{3}$$

For $k_1 = 0$, i.e., when the point P is at the center of the circle, there is found, since $E(0) = \pi/2$, the familiar formula

$$H_1 = \frac{2\pi I}{a}.$$

As k_1 approaches unity, which occurs when the point P gets closer to the current-carrying conductor, $E(k_1)$ approaches unity, and H_1 becomes infinite, as may be expected from Ampère's law (1).

(b) In the second case (Fig. 31), P is outside the circle, and $b > a$. As before, let θ denote the angle OPQ, $\Delta s = \widehat{QA}$, $\Delta \theta$ = angle APQ, and let the arc QB of radius r be drawn. Since $\Delta s \sin \alpha = \Delta s \cos (\alpha - 90°)$ $= r\, \Delta \theta$ approximately, we have again

$$\Delta H_2 = \frac{I\, \Delta \theta}{r}$$

* Cf. Art. 30.

as the approximate expression for the field intensity at P due to Δs,

and since $\lim\limits_{\Delta\theta \to 0} \dfrac{\Delta H_2}{\Delta\theta} = \dfrac{dH_2}{d\theta}$,

$$dH_2 = I\,\frac{d\theta}{r}. \tag{4}$$

So far our work has been exactly analogous to that of the first case. Now, however, if E and F are the two points in which the line OP produced cuts the circle, and D is the point of contact of the tangent line to the circle from P, we have two expressions for the radius vector

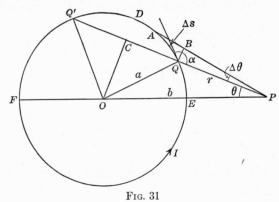

Fig. 31

r, according as the point on the circle is between D and E, as Q, or between D and F, as Q'.* If OC is perpendicular to r, we have $OC = b\sin\theta$, $PC = b\cos\theta$, $QC = Q'C = \sqrt{a^2 - b^2\sin^2\theta}$. Consequently we get for the position Q,

$$r = PC - QC = b\cos\theta - \sqrt{a^2 - b^2\sin^2\theta},$$

and for the position Q',

$$r = PC + Q'C = b\cos\theta + \sqrt{a^2 - b^2\sin^2\theta}.$$

Also, since $\sin OPD = a/b$, the angle θ varies only between $\pm\arcsin(a/b)$; hence, substituting for r in (4) and summing up around the circle, we get, letting $\theta_1 = \arcsin(a/b)$, for convenience,

$$H_2 = I\left[\int_0^{\theta_1}\frac{d\theta}{b\cos\theta - \sqrt{a^2 - b^2\sin^2\theta}} + \int_{\theta_1}^0\frac{d\theta}{b\cos\theta + \sqrt{a^2 - b^2\sin^2\theta}}\right.$$

$$\left. + \int_0^{-\theta_1}\frac{d\theta}{b\cos\theta + \sqrt{a^2 - b^2\sin^2\theta}} + \int_{-\theta_1}^0\frac{d\theta}{b\cos\theta - \sqrt{a^2 - b^2\sin^2\theta}}\right].$$

---

* We have a similar distinction when the lower half of the circle is considered, but because of the symmetry of our figure with respect to the line OP, no additional discussion is necessary.

We next rationalize the denominators, change θ into $-\theta$ in the third and fourth integrals, and reverse the order of integration in the second and fourth integrals. There is obtained

$$H_2 = \frac{I}{b^2 - a^2} \left[\int_0^{\theta_1} (b \cos \theta + \sqrt{a^2 - b^2 \sin^2 \theta}\,) \, d\theta \right.$$

$$- \int_0^{\theta_1} (b \cos \theta - \sqrt{a^2 - b^2 \sin^2 \theta}\,) \, d\theta$$

$$- \int_0^{\theta_1} (b \cos \theta - \sqrt{a^2 - b^2 \sin^2 \theta}\,) \, d\theta$$

$$\left. + \int_0^{\theta_1} (b \cos \theta + \sqrt{a^2 - b^2 \sin^2 \theta}\,) \, d\theta \right]$$

$$= \frac{4I}{b^2 - a^2} \int_0^{\theta_1} \sqrt{a^2 - b^2 \sin^2 \theta} \, d\theta. \tag{5}$$

This integral is not obviously elliptic as it stands since $b > a$. But, if we let $b \sin \theta = a \sin \phi$, we have

$$b \cos \theta \, d\theta = a \cos \phi \, d\phi,$$

$$\sqrt{a^2 - b^2 \sin^2 \theta} = a \cos \phi,$$

and

$$H_2 = \frac{4I}{b^2 - a^2} \int_0^{\pi/2} \frac{a \cos \phi \cdot a \cos \phi \, d\phi}{b \cos \theta}$$

$$= \frac{4I}{b(b^2 - a^2)} \int_0^{\pi/2} \frac{a^2 - a^2 \sin^2 \phi}{\sqrt{1 - \dfrac{a^2}{b^2} \sin^2 \phi}} \, d\phi.$$

Finally, let $k_2 = a/b < 1$, whence

$$H_2 = \frac{4I}{b(1 - k_2^2)} \int_0^{\pi/2} \frac{k_2^2 - k_2^2 \sin^2 \phi}{\sqrt{1 - k_2^2 \sin^2 \phi}} \, d\phi$$

$$= \frac{4I}{b(1 - k_2^2)} \int_0^{\pi/2} \frac{k_2^2 - 1 + 1 - k_2^2 \sin^2 \phi}{\sqrt{1 - k_2^2 \sin^2 \phi}} \, d\phi$$

$$= \frac{4I}{b} \left[\frac{1}{1 - k_2^2} \int_0^{\pi/2} \sqrt{1 - k_2^2 \sin^2 \phi} \, d\phi \right.$$

$$\left. - \int_0^{\pi/2} \frac{d\phi}{\sqrt{1 - k_2^2 \sin^2 \phi}} \right],$$

$$H_2 = \frac{4I}{a} \left[\frac{k_2 E(k_2)}{1 - k_2^2} - k_2 K(k_2) \right]. \tag{6}$$

As k_2 approaches zero, so that the point P recedes indefinitely from O, equation (6) shows that H_2 approaches zero, as we should expect. As k_2 approaches unity, the expression (6) becomes indeterminate, but it is easy to see from (5) that H_2 will become infinite, as would naturally be the case as the point P approaches the circle.

PROBLEMS

1. In the brake problem of Art. 31, take $r = 2a$, $R = 5a/2$, and $\alpha = 30°$. Find the angle β for which the torque has its maximum value, and determine the value of β, to the nearest degree, for which the torque has half its maximum value.

2. Two parallel vertical glass plates are partly immersed in water. The surface tension is 74.0 dynes/cm., and the contact angle is $25° 30'$. (a) Find the distance between the plates when the maximum height to which the water rises between the plates is 0.5 cm. above the outside horizontal surface. (b) Find the minimum height of the curve above the outside horizontal surface when the maximum height of the capillary curve is 0.5 cm. (c) Find the maximum height of the capillary curve when the plates are 1 cm. apart.

3. A flexible strip of length L in. is bent into an elastica in which the two ends touch. Find (a) the angle α; (b) the maximum ordinate in terms of L.

4. Find the maximum breadth of the elastica of Problem 3.

5. A strip of steel for which $E = 3 \times 10^7$ lb./in.^{2} is $\frac{1}{2}$ in. wide, $\frac{1}{64}$ in. thick, and 10 in. long. Find (a) the thrust at the ends which will produce a maximum deflection of 1 in.; (b) the maximum deflection produced by a thrust of 1 lb. at the ends.

6. A strip of steel for which $E = 3 \times 10^7$ lb./in.^{2} is $\frac{1}{2}$ in. wide and $\frac{1}{64}$ in. thick. Find the thrust at the ends which will produce a maximum deflection of 1 in. when the ends are brought 5 in. apart.

7. A strip of steel 7 in. long is deflected by applying at each end a force of F lb. such that $c = \sqrt{EI/F} = 2$ in. Find (a) the distance between supports; (b) the maximum deflection; (c) the deflection at a point P on the arc one-quarter of the horizontal distance from one support to the other; (d) the length of the curve from its midpoint to P.

8. A strip of steel 10 in. long is deflected into the form of an elastica, the thrust being such that the maximum deflection is equal to the distance between the ends of the strip. Find the maximum deflection.

9. A strip of steel for which $E = 3 \times 10^7$ lb./in.^{2} is $\frac{1}{2}$ in. wide, $\frac{1}{64}$ in. thick, and 20 in. long. It is bent by means of a string connecting the ends so that the steel is perpendicular to the string at the ends. Find the tension in the string and the maximum deflection.

10. A swinging cord weighing 1 lb./ft. rotates at an angular velocity of 20 rad./sec. The distance between the ends is 2 ft. (a) If the horizontal thrust at each end is 200 pdl., find the maximum displacement and the displacement at a horizontal distance of 6 in. from an end. (b) If the maximum displacement from the axis is 2 ft. find the horizontal thrust at the ends and the length of the cord.

11. A current I abamp. is flowing in a circular loop of radius a cm. A point P_1 in the plane of the circle is at distance $b < a$ from the center. If H_1 is the magnetic field intensity at P_1, plot values of $aH_1/4I$ against values of $k_1 = b/a$, taking $\sin^{-1} k_1$ in $15°$ steps. From the graph determine the value of k_1 for which H_1 has twice its value at the center of the circle; using this value of k_1 as a first approximation, obtain a more accurate value by use of tables.

12. If H_2 is the intensity at distance $b > a$ from the center of the loop of Problem 11, plot values of $aH_2/4I$ against values of $k_2 = a/b$. From the graph determine the value of k_2 for which H_2 has ten times its value for $k_2 = \frac{1}{2}$, and then get k_2 more accurately by use of tables.

13. A particle moves along the x-axis from $x = 0$ to $x = \frac{1}{2}$ under the action of a force $F = 10\sqrt{2\cos 2x - 1}$. Find the work done by the force.

14. In the flow of water through a pipe, the mean hydraulic radius (m.h.r.) is defined as the ratio of the area of the cross-section of the stream to the wetted perimeter. Calculate the m.h.r. for an elliptical pipe flowing full, the axes of the ellipse being 4 in. and 3 in., and find its ratio to the m.h.r. for a circular pipe of the same cross-sectional area.

15. A sphere of radius 6 in. floats half submerged in water. Neglecting the resistance of the water, find the period of vibration of the sphere if it is pressed down so as to be tangent to the water surface and then released.

CHAPTER IV

Infinite Series

36. Introduction. In this chapter, we shall investigate some of the properties of infinite series, paying particular attention to power series, and shall consider two powerful methods for the solution of ordinary differential equations by means of infinite series. Our purpose in studying this topic is twofold: first, infinite series in themselves make possible the numerical solution of many important physical problems which would otherwise be extremely difficult to handle; secondly, some knowledge of the behavior of infinite series will be necessary for the treatment of topics discussed later in this book. We shall give in this chapter several examples and problems illustrating the use of infinite series, and refer to them again in subsequent chapters; in particular, the topic of Fourier series will be reserved for Chapters V and VII.

37. Definitions. We begin by reviewing a few definitions and facts concerning infinite series.*

Let u_1, u_2, $\cdots$, u_n, $\cdots$ be any unending sequence of functions of a variable x (or of numbers in the special case in which each u is independent of x). Then the symbol

$$\sum_{n=1}^{\infty} u_n(x) \equiv u_1(x) + u_2(x) + \cdots + u_n(x) + \cdots \qquad (1)$$

is called an *infinite series*. In order that this symbol shall have some significance, it is first of all necessary to know the law of formation of the successive u's, or, what is equivalent, to know the manner in which the general term u_n depends upon its position as nth term in the series. In what follows we suppose this information given.

Let $s_n(x)$ denote the sum of the first n terms of (1),

$$s_n(x) = u_1(x) + u_2(x) + \cdots + u_n(x). \qquad (2)$$

For some particular value of x for which the u's are defined, say $x = x_0$, the sequence of numbers $s_1(x_0)$, $s_2(x_0)$, $\cdots$, $s_n(x_0)$, $\cdots$ may or may not approach a limit as n becomes infinite. By a limit is meant a number,

---

* The student will be aided in making this review by referring to a textbook on calculus in which fuller discussions and proofs may be found.

depending in general upon the value $x = x_0$, so that it may be denoted by $s(x_0)$, such that, for n sufficiently large, the difference between $s_n(x_0)$ and $s(x_0)$ may be made numerically as small as we please. More precisely, we say that $s(x_0)$ is the limit of $s_n(x_0)$ as n becomes infinite, if, given a positive number ϵ, however small, there exists a positive number $N(x_0, \epsilon)$ such that

$$\left| s(x_0) - s_n(x_0) \right| < \epsilon$$

for every n greater than $N(x_0, \epsilon)$. Here we are employing functional notation for the number $N(x_0, \epsilon)$ to emphasize the fact that its value depends, in general, on both the value x_0 of x and ϵ.

Thus, the sequence of numbers 3.1, 3.01, 3.001, $\cdots$, $3 + 10^{-n}$, $\cdots$ approaches the limit 3; for, given any $\epsilon > 0$, the quantity $\left| 3 - (3 + 10^{-n}) \right| = 10^{-n}$ can evidently be made less than ϵ by taking $n > N(\epsilon)$, where $10^{-N(\epsilon)} = \epsilon$, i.e., $N(\epsilon) = -(\ln \epsilon)/(\ln 10)$.

Now, if the sequence $s_1(x_0)$, $s_2(x_0)$, $\cdots$, $s_n(x_0)$, $\cdots$ does approach a limit $s(x_0)$, we say that the series (1) *converges* for $x = x_0$, and we call $s(x_0)$ the *sum* of the series when $x = x_0$; if the sequence does not approach a limit, the series (1) is said to *diverge* for $x = x_0$.

It should be noted that, for a sequence of functions of x, the definitions of convergence and divergence involve the value x_0 of the variable x. That is, given the number $\epsilon > 0$, the quantity $N(x, \epsilon)$ in the definition of limit will in general be different for various values of x. We shall discuss in Art. 39 the situation arising when the series is such that an $N(\epsilon)$, independent of x, exists.

When, as occurs most frequently, we are dealing with merely real values of x, we shall have as a range of values of x, an interval, say from $x = x_1$ to $x = x_2$; sometimes the interval will include one of the end points x_1, x_2, sometimes both, and sometimes neither. If, however, it becomes necessary to consider x as a complex variable, our range of values will be a two-dimensional region of the complex plane; again, a region may or may not include one or more of its boundary points. We shall use the letter R to denote the range under consideration, whether this be an interval of the real x-axis or a region of the complex plane, and speak of R in either case as a *region*.

Now a series (1) may converge for every value of x of a certain region R and diverge for every x not in R; then R is called the *region of convergence* of the series.

Let x_0 be in R, so that the series

$$\sum_{n=1}^{\infty} u_n(x_0) \equiv u_1(x_0) + u_2(x_0) + \cdots + u_n(x_0) + \cdots \qquad (3)$$

converges. If, when we replace the terms in (3) by their absolute values, the resulting series

$$\sum_{n=1}^{\infty} |u_n(x_0)| \equiv |u_1(x_0)| + |u_2(x_0)| + \cdots + |u_n(x_0)| + \cdots \quad (4)$$

also converges, then (3) is said to be *absolutely convergent*. If (4) is convergent, then (3) must also converge.

We state two frequently employed tests for convergence, the comparison test and the ratio test.

Comparison test. Let

$$a_1 + a_2 + \cdots + a_n + \cdots$$

be a given series of positive numbers. If we can find a convergent series of numbers,

$$c_1 + c_2 + \cdots + c_n + \cdots,$$

such that $a_n \leq c_n$ for every n from a certain point on in the series, the given series must converge. If, on the other hand, we can find a divergent series of numbers,

$$D_1 + D_2 + \cdots + D_n + \cdots,$$

such that $a_n \geq D_n$ for every n sufficiently large, the given series must diverge.

Two series frequently useful in applying the comparison test are the geometric series,

$$a + ar + ar^2 + \cdots + ar^n + \cdots,$$

which converges and has as sum $a/(1 - r)$ when $|r| < 1$ and diverges when $|r| \geq 1$, and the p-series,

$$1 + \frac{1}{2^p} + \frac{1}{3^p} + \cdots + \frac{1}{n^p} + \cdots,$$

which is convergent for $p > 1$ and divergent for $p \leq 1$.

Cauchy's ratio test. Let there be given a series of continuous functions.

$$\sum_{n=1}^{\infty} u_n \equiv u_1 + u_2 + \cdots + u_n + \cdots,$$

and form the ratio u_{n+1}/u_n. If the limit of $|u_{n+1}/u_n|$ as n becomes infinite exists and is less than unity, the given series converges absolutely; if this limit does not exist, or if it is greater than unity, the given series diverges; if the limit is equal to unity, the test gives no information.

By a *power series* is meant a series of the form

$$\sum_{n=0}^{\infty} a_n x^n \equiv a_0 + a_1 x + a_2 x^2 + \cdots + a_n x^n + \cdots, \qquad (5)$$

where the coefficients a_0, a_1, a_2, $\cdots$ are constants, independent of x. The ratio test given above is particularly valuable in determining the region of absolute convergence of a power series.

A series of real constants whose terms are alternately positive and negative is called an *alternating series*. If, after a certain point, the terms of an alternating series decrease in numerical value, and the nth term approaches zero, the series is convergent. Of particular importance in gauging the accuracy of numerical work with a convergent alternating series is the fact that the sum of the first n terms of such a series differs numerically from the sum of the series by less than the absolute value of the $(n + 1)$th term.

A function $f(x)$ possessing derivatives of all orders at a point $x = x_0$ may be expanded in a *Taylor's series*,

$$f(x) = f(x_0) + f'(x_0)(x - x_0) + \frac{f''(x_0)}{2!}(x - x_0)^2 + \cdots$$

$$+ \frac{f^{(n)}(x_0)}{n!}(x - x_0)^n + \cdots, \qquad (6)$$

convergent for $|x - x_0|$ sufficiently small. If $x_0 = 0$, (6) reduces to *Maclaurin's series*,

$$f(x) = f(0) + f'(0)x + \frac{f''(0)}{2!}x^2 + \cdots + \frac{f^{(n)}(0)}{n!}x^n + \cdots. \qquad (7)$$

This is a power series of the form (5), with $a_n = f^{(n)}(0)/n!$.

For convenience, in the following article we shall deal with Maclaurin's series, the generalization to Taylor's series offering no difficulty.

38. Theorems on power series. We collect here some theorems regarding power series. The proofs of these theorems belong properly to a course in the theory of functions, rather than in a book on engineering mathematics, as some of the proofs are rather difficult and require considerable background. Consequently we shall omit all proofs,* giving merely statements of the theorems useful to us, with

---

* The interested reader may find proofs in K. Knopp's "Theory and Application of Infinite Series," or L. L. Smail's "Elements of the Theory of Infinite Processes."

simple illustrations to bring out concretely the meanings and applications of the theorems.

THEOREM I. *If, for the power series*

$$a_0 + a_1x + a_2x^2 + \cdots + a_nx^n + \cdots,$$

we have

$$\lim_{n \to \infty} \left| \frac{a_{n-1}}{a_n} \right| = r,$$

then the series is absolutely convergent for $|x| < r$ *and divergent for* $|x| > r$. *The behavior of the series for* $|x| = r$ *must be determined by other means.*

This theorem may be easily proved by applying Cauchy's ratio test. As an illustration of the theorem consider the series

$$x - \frac{x^2}{2} + \frac{x^3}{3} - \cdots + (-1)^n \frac{x^{n+1}}{n+1} + \cdots;$$

we find

$$\left| \frac{a_{n-1}}{a_n} \right| = \left| \frac{n}{n-1} \right| = \left| \frac{1}{1 - \frac{1}{n}} \right|,$$

and

$$\lim_{n \to \infty} \left| \frac{a_{n-1}}{a_n} \right| = 1,$$

so that the given series converges for $|x| < 1$ and diverges for $|x| > 1$. For $x = 1$, the series becomes

$$1 - \frac{1}{2} + \frac{1}{3} - \cdots + (-1)^n \frac{1}{n+1} + \cdots,$$

which is an alternating series whose successive terms decrease numerically, with the nth term approaching zero, so that we have convergence for $x = 1$. For $x = -1$, we get

$$-1 - \frac{1}{2} - \frac{1}{3} - \cdots - \frac{1}{n+1} - \cdots,$$

which is the negative of the p-series with $p = 1$ and therefore diverges. Hence we have, finally, convergence for $-1 < x \leqq 1$, and divergence for all other real values of x.

THEOREM II. *Let $f(x)$ be represented by a power series*

$$f(x) = a_0 + a_1x + a_2x^2 + \cdots + a_nx^n + \cdots,$$

convergent for $|x| < r_1$, and let $g(x)$ be given by a second power series

$$g(x) = b_0 + b_1x + b_2x^2 + \cdots + b_nx^n + \cdots,$$

convergent for $|x| < r_2$. Let r be the smaller of the two numbers r_1 and r_2, so that both series converge for $|x| < r$. Then the sum $f(x) + g(x)$ is represented by the power series

$$f(x) + g(x) = (a_0 + b_0) + (a_1 + b_1)x + \cdots + (a_n + b_n)x^n + \cdots,$$

convergent at least for $|x| < r$. That is, two power series may be added term by term, and the resulting series is valid for those values of x for which both of the given series converge.

As an example, let

$$f(x) = e^x = 1 + x + \frac{x^2}{2!} + \cdots + \frac{x^n}{n!} + \cdots,$$

and

$$g(x) = e^{-x} = 1 - x + \frac{x^2}{2!} - \cdots + (-1)^n \frac{x^n}{n!} + \cdots.$$

Then

$$e^x + e^{-x} = 2\left[1 + 0 \cdot x + \frac{x^2}{2!} + \cdots + \frac{1 + (-1)^n}{2}\frac{x^n}{n!} + \cdots\right]$$

$$= 2\cosh x.$$

Here, since the series for e^x and e^{-x} converge for all values of x, the series for their sum, $2\cosh x$, converges likewise for all x, as may be readily checked by means of the ratio test.

THEOREM III. *If*

$$f(x) = a_0 + a_1x + a_2x^2 + \cdots + a_nx^n + \cdots$$

and

$$g(x) = b_0 + b_1x + b_2x^2 + \cdots + b_nx^n + \cdots$$

both converge for $|x| < r$, the product $f(x) \cdot g(x)$ is given by the power series

$$f(x) \cdot g(x) = a_0b_0 + (a_0b_1 + a_1b_0)x + (a_0b_2 + a_1b_1 + a_2b_0)x^2 + \cdots,$$

which also converges at least for $|x| < r$. Thus, one power series may be multiplied by another to obtain the expansion of the product of the two functions, the coefficients being formed just as in the multiplication of two polynomials, and the product series converges whenever the two given series are convergent.

To illustrate this theorem, consider the series

$$\sinh x = x + \frac{x^3}{3!} + \frac{x^5}{5!} + \cdots + \frac{x^{2n-1}}{(2n-1)!} + \cdots,$$

$$\cosh x = 1 + \frac{x^2}{2!} + \frac{x^4}{4!} + \cdots + \frac{x^{2n-2}}{(2n-2)!} + \cdots.$$

We then have

$$\sinh x \cosh x = x + \left(\frac{1}{2!} + \frac{1}{3!}\right)x^3 + \left(\frac{1}{4!} + \frac{1}{3!2!} + \frac{1}{5!}\right)x^5 + \cdots$$

$$= x + \tfrac{2}{3}x^3 + \tfrac{2}{15}x^5 + \cdots$$

$$= \frac{1}{2}\left[2x + \frac{(2x)^3}{3!} + \frac{(2x)^5}{5!} + \cdots\right]$$

$$= \tfrac{1}{2}\sinh 2x.$$

Again, each of the original series converges for all x, as does the product series.

THEOREM IV. *If*

$$f(x) = a_0 + a_1 x + a_2 x^2 + \cdots + a_n x^n + \cdots$$

and

$$g(x) = b_0 + b_1 x + b_2 x^2 + \cdots + b_n x^n + \cdots$$

both converge, and if, in addition, $b_0 \neq 0$, then the quotient $f(x)/g(x)$ is represented by the series

$$\frac{f(x)}{g(x)} = \frac{a_0}{b_0} + \frac{a_1 b_0 - a_0 b_1}{b_0^2}x + \frac{a_2 b_0^2 - a_1 b_0 b_1 + a_0 b_1^2 - a_0 b_0 b_2}{b_0^3}x^2 + \cdots,$$

obtained by dividing the series for $f(x)$ by that for $g(x)$. The resulting quotient series must itself be examined to determine its region of convergence, since no conclusion can be drawn from knowledge of the regions of convergence of $f(x)$ and $g(x)$.

To illustrate, consider the series

$$\sin x = x - \frac{x^3}{3!} + \frac{x^5}{5!} - \cdots + \frac{(-1)^{n-1}x^{2n-1}}{(2n-1)!} + \cdots,$$

$$\cos x = 1 - \frac{x^2}{2!} + \frac{x^4}{4!} - \cdots + \frac{(-1)^{n-1}x^{2n-2}}{(2n-2)!} + \cdots.$$

Then we find by division,

$$\frac{\sin x}{\cos x} = x + \frac{x^3}{3} + \frac{2x^5}{15} + \cdots = \tan x.$$

Although the series for $\sin x$ and $\cos x$ converge for all values of x, that for $\tan x$ is convergent only for $|x| < \pi/2$.

If, in the expansion of $g(x)$, $b_0 = 0$, we may sometimes obtain a power series as quotient. For example, suppose that $g(x) = x$, so that its series is finite rather than an infinite one, together with $f(x) = \sin x = x - x^3/3! + x^5/5! - \cdots$. Then we get the power series

$$\frac{\sin x}{x} = 1 - \frac{x^2}{3!} + \frac{x^4}{5!} - \cdots + (-1)^{n-1}\frac{x^{2n-2}}{(2n-1)!} + \cdots.$$

In this case, the series for $\sin x$ and for x (x itself) converge for all values of x, and the series for $(\sin x)/x$ does likewise. On the other hand, although the quotient may not be a power series when $b_0 = 0$, the infinite series may be obtainable and useful for various purposes. Thus, if

$$f(x) = \cos x = 1 - \frac{x^2}{2!} + \frac{x^4}{4!} - \cdots, \qquad g(x) = x,$$

we have

$$\frac{\cos x}{x} = \frac{1}{x} - \frac{x}{2!} + \frac{x^3}{4!} - \cdots + (-1)^{n-1}\frac{x^{2n-3}}{(2n-2)!} + \cdots.$$

This is not a power series because of the presence of the term $1/x$, but since the power series beginning with the second term is convergent for all values of x, the above infinite series may be used for any x other than $x = 0$.

THEOREM V. *Let*

$$z = a_0 + a_1 y + a_2 y^2 + \cdots + a_n y^n + \cdots$$

converge for $|y| < r_1$, *and let*

$$y = b_0 + b_1 x + b_2 x^2 + \cdots + b_n x^n + \cdots,$$

converge for $|x| < r_2$. *If* $|b_0| < r_1$, *we may substitute for y in the first series its value in terms of x from the second series so as to obtain z as a power series in x, convergent for* $|x|$ *sufficiently small. In particular, if the given series for z converges for all values of y, the series for z in terms of x may then always be found, and this will converge for* $|x| < r_2$.

For example, let

$$z = e^y = 1 + y + \frac{y^2}{2!} + \frac{y^3}{3!} + \cdots + \frac{y^{n-1}}{(n-1)!} + \cdots,$$

and

$$y = \tan x = x + \frac{x^3}{3} + \frac{2x^5}{15} + \cdots.$$

Here the series for e^y converges for every y, and consequently we get

$$e^{\tan x} = 1 + x + \frac{x^2}{2} + \frac{x^3}{2} + \frac{3x^4}{8} + \frac{37x^5}{120} + \cdots,$$

which converges for $|x| < \pi/2$ since the series for $\tan x$ has this region of convergence.

THEOREM VI. *If*

$$f(x) = a_0 + a_1x + a_2x^2 + \cdots + a_nx^n + \cdots$$

converges for $|x| < r$, *the derivative of* $f(x)$ *may be obtained by term-by-term differentiation of the series,*

$$\frac{d}{dx}f(x) = a_1 + 2a_2x + \cdots + na_nx^{n-1} + \cdots,$$

and the resulting series also is convergent for $|x| < r$.

As a simple example, let

$$f(x) = \sin x = x - \frac{x^3}{3!} + \frac{x^5}{5!} - \cdots + (-1)^{n-1}\frac{x^{2n-1}}{(2n-1)!} + \cdots,$$

whence

$$\frac{d}{dx}\sin x = 1 - \frac{x^2}{2!} + \frac{x^4}{4!} - \cdots + (-1)^{n-1}\frac{x^{2n-2}}{(2n-2)!} + \cdots$$

$$= \cos x.$$

Here the series for $\sin x$ converges for every x, and that for $\cos x$ does likewise.

THEOREM VII. *If*

$$f(x) = a_0 + a_1x + a_2x^2 + \cdots + a_nx^n + \cdots$$

converges for $|x| < r$, *the integral of* $f(x)$ *may be found by integrating the series term by term,*

$$\int f(x)\, dx = c + a_0x + \frac{a_1}{2}x^2 + \frac{a_2}{3}x^3 + \cdots + \frac{a_n}{n+1}x^{n+1} + \cdots,$$

where c *is an arbitrary constant, and the integral series converges for* $|x| < r$.

To illustrate, let

$$f(x) = \frac{1}{1 + x^2} = 1 - x^2 + x^4 - \cdots + (-1)^{n-1}x^{2n-2} + \cdots,$$

whence

$$\int \frac{dx}{1 + x^2} = c + x - \frac{x^3}{3} + \frac{x^5}{5} - \cdots + (-1)^{n-1}\frac{x^{2n-1}}{2n - 1} + \cdots$$

$$= \arctan x + c.$$

Since the series for $1/(1 + x^2)$ converges for $|x| < 1$, the series for arctan x has the same region of convergence.

THEOREM VIII. *If two power series* $\displaystyle\sum_{n=0}^{\infty} a_n x^n$ *and* $\displaystyle\sum_{n=0}^{\infty} b_n x^n$ *are equal for every* $|x| < r$, *the coefficients of like powers in the two series must be equal, i.e.,* $a_0 = b_0$, $a_1 = b_1$, $a_2 = b_2$, $\cdots$. *Thus, if a function is expanded in a power series by two different methods, the series obtained must be identical.*

For example, consider the function $f(x) = 1/(1 - x)$. By Maclaurin's formula (7), Art. 37, we have

$$f(x) = (1 - x)^{-1} \qquad\qquad f(0) = 1,$$

$$f'(x) = (1 - x)^{-2}, \qquad\qquad f'(0) = 1,$$

$$f''(x) = 2(1 - x)^{-3}, \qquad\qquad f''(0) = 2!,$$

$$f'''(x) = 3 \cdot 2(1 - x)^{-4}, \qquad\qquad f'''(0) = 3!,$$

$$\cdots \cdots \cdots \cdots \cdots \cdots \cdots \cdots \cdots \cdots,$$

$$f^{(n)}(x) = n!(1 - x)^{-n-1}, \qquad f^{(n)}(0) = n!,$$

$$\frac{1}{1 - x} = 1 + x + x^2 + \cdots + x^n + \cdots,$$

convergent for $|x| < 1$. Alternatively, if we divide 1 by $(1 - x)$, we have

$$
\begin{array}{r}
1 + x + x^2 + \cdots \\
\hline
1 - x \overline{)\, 1} \\
\underline{1 - x} \\
x \\
\underline{x - x^2} \\
x^2 \\
\cdots
\end{array}
$$

which is the same expansion. We might also obtain our series by use of the binomial formula,

$$(a + b)^n = a^n + na^{n-1}b + \frac{n(n-1)}{2!} a^{n-2}b^2 + \cdots,$$

with $a = 1$, $b = -x$, $n = -1$, since this formula holds for every n when $\left| b/a \right| < 1$, but this is not essentially different, the binomial series itself being obtainable from equation (7), Art. 37.

THEOREM IX. *Let $y = f(x)$, where $y_0 = f(x_0)$, be expanded in a Taylor's series,*

$$y = y_0 + a_1(x - x_0) + a_2(x - x_0)^2 + \cdots + a_n(x - x_0)^n + \cdots,$$

convergent for $\left| x - x_0 \right|$ sufficiently small. Then the inverse function $x = g(y)$ is obtainable as a power series,

$$x = x_0 + b_1(y - y_0) + b_2(y - y_0)^2 + \cdots + b_n(y - y_0)^n + \cdots,$$

where

$$b_1 = \frac{1}{a_1}, \qquad b_2 = -\frac{a_2}{a_1^3}, \qquad b_3 = \frac{2a_2^2 - a_1 a_3}{a_1^5}, \cdots,$$

convergent for $\left| y - y_0 \right|$ sufficiently small, provided only that $a_1 \neq 0$.

Thus, if

$$y = \ln (1 + x) = x - \frac{x^2}{2} + \frac{x^3}{3} - \cdots + (-1)^{n-1}\frac{x^n}{n} + \cdots,$$

this theorem yields, by *reversion*,

$$x = y + \frac{y^2}{2!} + \frac{y^3}{3!} + \cdots + \frac{y^n}{n!} + \cdots = e^y - 1.$$

39. Other types of infinite series. We have seen in the preceding article that power series have many of the properties of polynomials; this fact enables us to make use of such series in a number of problems encountered in engineering work. However, it sometimes happens that a given problem is more naturally or more conveniently investigated by the aid of other types of infinite series. Thus, we shall find in Chapter V that various functions not representable by power series valid throughout the entire range of values of our variable can nevertheless be easily represented by certain forms of trigonometric series. Moreover, when solving certain types of partial differential equations, useful solutions are obtained in the form of infinite series of functions other than power functions.

It therefore becomes desirable to inquire into the properties of more general types of infinite series. As in Art. 38, we shall omit proofs * of the theorems stated, but shall give illustrations of their content.

For a proper understanding of the theorems of this article, we must first discuss the concept of *uniform convergence*. It was pointed out in Art. 37 that, in the definition of limit there given, upon which rested in turn the definitions of convergence and divergence, the number N corresponding to the stipulated ϵ depends in general upon the value of the variable x appearing in the terms of the series. To illustrate, consider the series

$$x + x(1 - x) + x(1 - x)^2 + \cdots + x(1 - x)^{n-1} + \cdots,$$

which converges for all values of x in the interval $0 \leqq x \leqq 1$. Using the formula for the sum of a geometric progression, we find

$$s_n(x) = 1 - (1 - x)^n,$$

and for any x between 0 and 1, and for $x = 1$, we have

$$s(x) = \lim_{n \to \infty} s_n(x) = 1.$$

Hence

$$\left| s_n(x) - s(x) \right| = (1 - x)^n.$$

Now, if we examine this series from the standpoint of our fundamental definitions, we see from the foregoing that, for a given $\epsilon > 0$, n must be such that $(1 - x)^n < \epsilon$, or

$$n > \frac{\ln \epsilon}{\ln (1 - x)}.$$

Suppose, for definiteness, that we are given $\epsilon = \frac{1}{100}$, so that we must have $n > -(\ln 100)/\ln (1 - x)$. It is evident that $N(x, \epsilon)$ will depend upon x. Thus, if $x = \frac{1}{10}$, we may take $N(\frac{1}{10}, \epsilon) = -(\ln 100)/\ln \frac{9}{10}$ $= 43.7$ approximately; similarly, $N(\frac{1}{100}, \epsilon) = 459$, $N(\frac{1}{1000}, \epsilon) = 4603$, and so on. The smaller the value of x, the greater $N(x, \epsilon)$ must be.

It frequently happens, however, that an N may be chosen which will serve for a given ϵ whatever the value of x. Thus consider the series

$$\frac{1}{1 + x^2} - \frac{1}{2 + x^2} + \frac{1}{3 + x^2} - \cdots + \frac{(-1)^{n-1}}{n + x^2} + \cdots,$$

which converges for any real x. Since, for any real x, the series is alternating,

$$\left| s_n(x) - s(x) \right| < \frac{1}{n + 1 + x^2},$$

---

* Proofs may be found in the textbooks by Knopp and Smail, previously cited.

whence we must have

$$\frac{1}{n + 1 + x^2} < \epsilon,$$

or

$$n > \frac{1}{\epsilon} - 1 - x^2.$$

It is seen that we may put $N = 1/\epsilon - 1$ here, no matter what value x may have.

The difference in the behavior of the above two series is due to the possession or non-possession of the property of uniform convergence. We frame the following definition:

The series of functions

$$\sum_{n=1}^{\infty} u_n(x) \equiv u_1(x) + u_2(x) + \cdots + u_n(x) + \cdots,$$

convergent in some region, and representing the function $s(x)$ in its region of convergence, is said to be *uniformly convergent* over a region R if, given any $\epsilon > 0$, there exists a positive number $N(\epsilon)$, depending upon ϵ but *independent of x*, such that $\left| s_n(x) - s(x) \right| < \epsilon$ for every $n > N(\epsilon)$ and for every x in R.

Thus, the first series $\sum_{n=1}^{\infty} x(1 - x)^{n-1}$ is not uniformly convergent over the interval $0 \leq x \leq 1$; the second series $\sum_{n=1}^{\infty} \frac{(-1)^{n-1}}{n + x^2}$ is uniformly convergent over any interval. Note, however, that the former series is uniformly convergent over some intervals, e.g., the interval $\frac{1}{2} \leq x \leq 1$.

It should also be remarked that the function defined by the series $\sum_{n=1}^{\infty} x(1 - x)^{n-1}$ is discontinuous at $x = 0$. For the value of the function when $x = 0$ is 0, whereas, as we have seen, the series converges to the value 1 for $0 < x \leq 1$. But the function is continuous over any interval, such as $\frac{1}{2} \leq x \leq 1$, for which the series is uniformly convergent; in fact, if a series of functions continuous throughout a region R is uniformly convergent over R, the function represented by the series is always continuous in R.

Although some series may be easily tested for uniform convergence by means of the definition given above, it is usually simpler to employ the following test.

Theorem I. *Weierstrass's M-test.* *Let*

$$\sum_{n=1}^{\infty} u_n(x) \equiv u_1(x) + u_2(x) + \cdots + u_n(x) + \cdots$$

be a given series of functions defined in a region R. If the series of positive constants

$$M_1 + M_2 + \cdots + M_n + \cdots$$

is convergent, and if $\left| u_n(x) \right| \leqq M_n$ *for every n and for all values of x in R, the given series is uniformly convergent in R. Moreover, the series of u's is absolutely convergent in R.*

To illustrate the use of the M-test, consider first the power series

$$x + \frac{x^2}{2^3} + \frac{x^3}{3^3} + \cdots + \frac{x^n}{n^3} + \cdots.$$

Now, since $\left| x^n/n^3 \right| \leqq 1/n^3$ for $\left| x \right| \leqq 1$, and since the series

$$1 + \frac{1}{2^3} + \frac{1}{3^3} + \cdots + \frac{1}{n^3} + \cdots$$

is convergent, we may use the latter series as our M-series, whence it follows that the given series is uniformly and absolutely convergent for $\left| x \right| \leqq 1$. The absolute convergence of $\sum_{n=1}^{\infty} \frac{x^n}{n^3}$ for $\left| x \right| < 1$ may, of course, be readily established by means of Cauchy's ratio test.

As a second example, consider the series

$$\cos x + \frac{\cos 2x}{2^2} + \frac{\cos 3x}{3^2} + \cdots + \frac{\cos nx}{n^2} + \cdots.$$

Since $\left| \cos nx \right| \leqq 1$ for all values of x and for any n, we may take as M-series the series

$$1 + \frac{1}{2^2} + \frac{1}{3^2} + \cdots + \frac{1}{n^2} + \cdots,$$

and consequently the trigonometric series is absolutely and uniformly convergent for every x. We shall meet trigonometric series of this sort in Chapter V; thus this example is particularly pertinent as an illustration of the use of Weierstrass's M-test.

The first example, $\sum_{n=1}^{\infty} \frac{x^n}{n^3}$, being a power series, suggests a question as to the possible uniform convergence of power series in general. The next theorem we cite serves as an answer to this question.

THEOREM II. *If the power series*

$$\sum_{n=0}^{\infty} a_n x^n \equiv a_0 + a_1 x + a_2 x^2 + \cdots + a_n x^n + \cdots$$

is convergent for $|x| < r$, *it is uniformly convergent for* $|x| \leq r'$, *where* r' *is any positive number less than* r.

The property of uniform convergence is of importance in connection with the integration or differentiation of series.

THEOREM III. *Let the series of continuous functions*

$$\sum_{n=1}^{\infty} u_n(x) \equiv u_1(x) + u_2(x) + \cdots + u_n(x) + \cdots$$

converge uniformly to a function $s(x)$ *in a closed interval* $a \leq x \leq b$. *Then if* x_1 *and* x_2 *are any two numbers between* a *and* b, *i.e., if* $a < x_1 < b$ *and* $a < x_2 < b$, *the series may be integrated term by term between the limits* x_1 *and* x_2, *and the series of integrals will represent the integral of* $s(x)$ *over this subinterval:*

$$\int_{x_1}^{x_2} s(x)\, dx = \int_{x_1}^{x_2} u_1(x)\, dx + \int_{x_1}^{x_2} u_2(x)\, dx + \cdots + \int_{x_1}^{x_2} u_n(x)\, dx + \cdots.$$

As an example, consider the series

$$\cos x + \frac{\cos 3x}{3^2} + \frac{\cos 5x}{5^2} + \cdots + \frac{\cos (2n-1)x}{(2n-1)^2} + \cdots.$$

Here each term is a continuous function of x, and, by Theorem I, with $M_n = 1/(2n-1)^2$, the series converges uniformly in any interval. By the theory given in Chapter V, this series represents the function $\pi^2/8 - \pi|x|/4$ in the interval $-\pi \leq x \leq \pi$. (Cf. Example 2, Art. 45.) Hence, if we take, say, $x_1 = 0$, $x_2 = \pi/2$, we may write

$$\int_0^{\pi/2} \left(\frac{\pi^2}{8} - \frac{\pi x}{4} \right) dx = \int_0^{\pi/2} \cos x\, dx + \int_0^{\pi/2} \frac{\cos 3x}{3^2}\, dx + \cdots$$

$$+ \int_0^{\pi/2} \frac{\cos (2n-1)x}{(2n-1)^2}\, dx + \cdots,$$

$$\left[\frac{\pi^2 x}{8} - \frac{\pi x^2}{8} \right]_0^{\pi/2} = \left[\sin x + \frac{\sin 3x}{3^3} + \cdots + \frac{\sin (2n-1)x}{(2n-1)^3} + \cdots \right]_0^{\pi/2},$$

and

$$\frac{\pi^3}{32} = 1 - \frac{1}{3^3} + \frac{1}{5^3} - \frac{1}{7^3} + \cdots + \frac{(-1)^{n-1}}{(2n-1)^3} + \cdots.$$

We have thus deduced a convergent series of constants from which π may be evaluated.

THEOREM IV.   *Let the series*

$$\sum_{n=1}^{\infty} u_n(x) \equiv u_1(x) + u_2(x) + \cdots + u_n(x) + \cdots$$

represent a function $s(x)$ in a closed interval $a \leqq x \leqq b$. If each term possesses a derivative, $u'_n(x) = du_n(x)/dx$, and if the derived series

$$u'_1(x) + u'_2(x) + \cdots + u'_n(x) + \cdots$$

is uniformly convergent in the interval (a, b), then this derived series represents the function $ds(x)/dx$ in that interval.

As a simple example, take the series

$$x + \frac{x^3}{3!} + \frac{x^5}{5!} + \cdots + \frac{x^{2n-1}}{(2n-1)!} + \cdots,$$

which represents the function $\sinh x$ in any closed interval. Each term obviously possesses a derivative for every x, and we get from term-by-term differentiation

$$1 + \frac{x^2}{2!} + \frac{x^4}{4!} + \cdots + \frac{x^{2n-2}}{(2n-2)!} + \cdots.$$

Now, this power series, absolutely convergent for every x, is, by Theorem II, uniformly convergent in any closed interval. Hence it must represent the function $d(\sinh x)/dx = \cosh x$, which it evidently does.

On the other hand, consider the series

$$2\left[\sin x - \frac{1}{2} \sin 2x + \frac{1}{3} \sin 3x - \cdots + \frac{(-1)^{n-1}}{n} \sin nx + \cdots \right].$$

It will be shown later (Chapter V, Art. 45), that this series represents the function $s(x) = x$ in the interval $-\pi < x < \pi$, and therefore in any closed interval lying within this range. Each term of the series possesses a derivative, so that term-by-term differentiation gives us

$$2[\cos x - \cos 2x + \cos 3x - \cdots + (-1)^{n-1} \cos nx + \cdots].$$

But this series does not converge for any value of x, much less converge uniformly. Hence we cannot draw the conclusion that the derived series represents $ds(x)/dx = 1$. In fact, since it does not converge at all, it cannot represent any function.

40. Applications. As stated before, we shall have occasion to apply infinite series to a variety of problems in later chapters. We give here merely a few of the ways in which series may be used in computational problems.

(a) One of the most common uses of power series is in the evaluation of definite integrals. For example, consider the integral

$$\int_0^1 \frac{\sin x}{x}\, dx.$$

Now the indefinite integral of the function $(\sin x)/x$ cannot be expressed in terms of a finite number of the elementary functions, and consequently we are forced to evaluate the above definite integral by other means. We have

$$\sin x = x - \frac{x^3}{3!} + \frac{x^5}{5!} - \cdots + (-1)^{n-1} \frac{x^{2n-1}}{(2n-1)!} + \cdots,$$

so that

$$\frac{\sin x}{x} = 1 - \frac{x^2}{3!} + \frac{x^4}{5!} - \cdots + (-1)^{n-1} \frac{x^{2n-2}}{(2n-1)!} + \cdots.$$

This power series is absolutely convergent for every value of x, and hence, by Theorem VII, Art. 38, we are justified in integrating term by term. We therefore get

$$\int_0^1 \frac{\sin x}{x}\, dx = \int_0^1 \left(1 - \frac{x^2}{3!} + \frac{x^4}{5!} - \frac{x^6}{7!} + \cdots \right) dx$$

$$= \left[x - \frac{x^3}{3\cdot 3!} + \frac{x^5}{5\cdot 5!} - \frac{x^7}{7\cdot 7!} + \cdots \right]_0^1$$

$$= 1 - \frac{1}{3\cdot 3!} + \frac{1}{5\cdot 5!} - \frac{1}{7\cdot 7!} + \cdots.$$

By taking sufficient terms of this series, we may evaluate our integral to any desired degree of accuracy. Moreover, since the series is an alternating one, we have a definite criterion as to the maximum possible error introduced by breaking off the series at any given point.

(b) Infinite series may also be used to find the numerical values of a function for different values of the variable. Thus, from series expansions for the trigonometric, exponential, and logarithmic functions, tables of these functions may be evolved. To evaluate $e^{0.1}$, we may use the Maclaurin expansion

$$e^x = 1 + x + \frac{x^2}{2!} + \cdots + \frac{x^{n-1}}{(n-1)!} + \cdots,$$

whence

$$e^{0.1} = 1 + \tfrac{1}{10} + \tfrac{1}{200} + \tfrac{1}{6000} + \cdots.$$

If, however, we wish to find the value of $e^{2.1}$, say, the Maclaurin series may not converge sufficiently rapidly for accurate and rapid computation. We should therefore expand e^x in a series of powers of $(x - 2)$ by Taylor's formula,

$$e^x = e^2 \left[1 + (x - 2) + \frac{(x - 2)^2}{2!} + \cdots + \frac{(x - 2)^{n-1}}{(n - 1)!} + \cdots \right],$$

so that we get

$$e^{2.1} = e^2 (1 + \tfrac{1}{10} + \tfrac{1}{200} + \tfrac{1}{6000} + \cdots).$$

If we have found $e^{0.1}$ by a previous computation, we should of course write $e^{2.1} = e^2 \cdot e^{0.1}$, which is equivalent to the preceding equation.

As a particular problem in evaluating a function for tabulating purposes, we return now to the elliptic integrals discussed in Chapter III. Consider the elliptic integral of the first kind,

$$F(k, \phi) \equiv \int_0^\phi \frac{d\phi}{\sqrt{1 - k^2 \sin^2 \phi}} \qquad (0 < k < 1).$$

In this integral, the function $(1 - k^2 \sin^2 \phi)^{-\frac{1}{2}}$ may be expanded into a series by means of the binomial formula,

$$(a + b)^n = a^n + na^{n-1}b + \frac{n(n - 1)}{2!} a^{n-2}b^2 + \cdots,$$

the expansion being valid for any n if $|b/a| < 1$. For, since $k < 1$, and $\sin \phi \leqq 1$, we have here $|b/a| = |k^2 \sin^2 \phi| < 1$. Then we get the series

$$(1 - k^2 \sin^2 \phi)^{-\frac{1}{2}} = 1 + \frac{k^2}{2} \sin^2 \phi + \frac{3k^4}{8} \sin^4 \phi + \cdots, \qquad (1)$$

which holds certainly for $k < 1$ and for any value of ϕ. In particular, if we put $\phi = \pi/2$, we get the convergent series

$$1 + \frac{k^2}{2} + \frac{3k^4}{8} + \frac{5k^6}{16} + \cdots. \qquad (2)$$

Now since $|\sin \phi| \leqq 1$, the terms of series (1) are less than or at most equal to the corresponding terms of series (2). Hence, by Weierstrass's M-test (Theorem I, Art. 39), series (1) is uniformly convergent in any ϕ-interval, and consequently (Theorem III, Art. 39) we may integrate term by term. In this way the function $F(k, \phi)$ may be evaluated for any specified values of k and ϕ, the integration being performed by means of recursion formulas for $\int \sin^n x \, dx$ (Peirce, 263).

In dealing with the complete elliptic integral of the first kind,

$$K(k) \equiv \int_0^{\pi/2} \frac{d\phi}{\sqrt{1 - k^2 \sin^2 \phi}} \qquad (0 < k < 1),$$

we may materially shorten the work by making use of Wallis's formula (Peirce, 483). We then have, from (1),

$$K = \int_0^{\pi/2} \left(1 + \frac{k^2}{2} \sin^2 \phi + \frac{3k^4}{8} \sin^4 \phi + \frac{5k^6}{16} \sin^6 \phi + \cdots \right) d\phi$$

$$= \frac{\pi}{2} \left[1 + \left(\frac{1}{2} \right)^2 k^2 + \left(\frac{1 \cdot 3}{2 \cdot 4} \right)^2 k^4 + \left(\frac{1 \cdot 3 \cdot 5}{2 \cdot 4 \cdot 6} \right)^2 k^6 + \cdots \right]. \qquad (3)$$

If, for example, $k = \sin 10°$, equation (3) gives us

$$K = \frac{\pi}{2} (1 + 0.00754 + 0.00009 + \cdots) = 1.5828,$$

which checks with the value given in Peirce's "Tables."

(c) As an engineering application of infinite series, we consider next the problem of designing a proportional-flow weir, such as the Sutro weir,* for which the discharge of water is proportional to the head. Such a weir is of use as a control for a grit-chamber outlet, as a control for a float-regulated closing device, and as a flow meter.

Let the weir opening be bounded by the vertical edges $DR = a$ (ft.) and $CE = a + h$ (ft.), the horizontal crest $CD = b$ (ft.), and the curve RS whose equation relative to the axes shown (Fig. 32) is desired. Let the total discharge of water through the weir in 1 sec. be Q (ft.^{3}/sec.), and suppose that the line MN, placed for conveni-

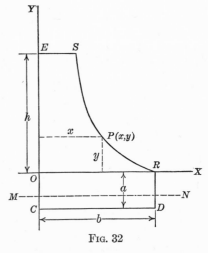

Fig. 32

* See E. A. Pratt, "Another Proportional-Flow Weir; Sutro Weir," *Engineering News*, p. 462, August 27, 1914; E. Soucek, H. E. Howe, and F. T. Mavis, "Sutro Weir Investigations Furnish Discharge Coefficients," *Engineering News-Record*, p. 679, November 12, 1936.

ence of calculation and of actual operation at a distance $a/3$ (ft.) above the crest, is taken as datum line, so that we are to have

$$Q = k\left(h + \frac{2a}{3}\right), \tag{4}$$

where k is some constant of proportionality whose value is to be found.

Now the theoretical discharge in cubic feet per second through a rectangular strip of area $w\,dz$ (ft.²) a distance z (ft.) below the water surface is given approximately by $\sqrt{2gz}\,w\,dz$,* where $g = 32.17$ ft./sec.² Hence the discharge Q_1 through the rectangular opening $CDRO$ is

$$Q_1 = b\sqrt{2g}\int_h^{a+h} \sqrt{z}\,dz$$

$$= \tfrac{2}{3}b\sqrt{2g}\,[(a+h)^{3/2} - h^{3/2}], \tag{5}$$

and that through the opening $ORSE$ is

$$Q_2 = \sqrt{2g}\int_0^h \sqrt{h-y}\,x\,dy. \tag{6}$$

Equating Q to the sum of Q_1 and Q_2, we get

$$k\left(h + \frac{2a}{3}\right) = \frac{2}{3}b\sqrt{2g}\,[(a+h)^{3/2} - h^{3/2}] + \sqrt{2g}\int_0^h \sqrt{h-y}\,x\,dy. \tag{7}$$

This relation is to hold for all non-negative values of h. Setting $h = 0$, we have

$$\frac{2ak}{3} = 2b\sqrt{2g}\,\frac{a^{3/2}}{3},$$

whence

$$k = b\sqrt{2ga}. \tag{8}$$

Substitution of this value of k in (7) yields

$$a^{1/2}b\sqrt{2g}\left(h + \frac{2a}{3}\right) = \frac{2}{3}b\sqrt{2g}[(a+h)^{3/2} - h^{3/2}] + \sqrt{2g}\int_0^h \sqrt{h-y}\,x\,dy,$$

$$\int_0^h \sqrt{h-y}\,x\,dy = b[a^{1/2}h + \tfrac{2}{3}a^{3/2} - \tfrac{2}{3}(a+h)^{3/2} + \tfrac{2}{3}h^{3/2}]$$

$$= \tfrac{2}{3}b[a^{3/2} + \tfrac{3}{2}a^{1/2}h + h^{3/2} - (a+h)^{3/2}]. \tag{9}$$

* See any textbook on hydraulics.

We wish to find x as a function of y such that the relation (9) is satisfied for all positive values of a and h. Since the character of the functional relationship between x and y is unpredictable, it is natural to assume for x an infinite series involving y and to determine, if possible, the coefficients such that (9) is fulfilled. This procedure requires that the right-hand member of (9) be expressed in series form, and we here have two possible choices, namely those given by the two expansions

$$(a + h)^{3/2} = a^{3/2} + \tfrac{3}{2}a^{1/2}h + \tfrac{3}{8}a^{-1/2}h^2 - \cdots, \qquad \left| h/a \right| < 1,$$

$$(h + a)^{3/2} = h^{3/2} + \tfrac{3}{2}h^{1/2}a + \tfrac{3}{8}h^{-1/2}a^2 - \cdots, \qquad \left| a/h \right| < 1.$$

Since in practice $h > a$, it would seem that the second series should be chosen. But it turns out * that a series of ascending powers of y, when substituted for x, will not produce a series in descending powers of h, while a series of descending powers of y, when multiplied term-by-term by $\sqrt{h - y}$ and integrated between the limits 0 and h, produces a divergent result.

We therefore write (9) as

$$\int_0^h \sqrt{h - y}\, x\, dy = \tfrac{2}{3}b(h^{3/2} - \tfrac{3}{8}a^{-1/2}h^2 + \tfrac{1}{16}a^{-3/2}h^3$$

$$- \tfrac{3}{128}a^{-5/2}h^4 + \cdots). \quad (9')$$

Now we have, for $y \geqq 0$,

$$\int_0^h y^m \sqrt{h - y}\, dy = \int_0^h y^m (h^{1/2} - \tfrac{1}{2}h^{-1/2}y + \tfrac{1}{8}h^{-3/2}y^2 - \cdots)\, dy$$

$$= \left[\frac{h^{1/2}y^{m+1}}{m + 1} - \frac{h^{-1/2}y^{m+2}}{2(m + 2)} + \frac{h^{-3/2}y^{m+3}}{8(m + 3)} - \cdots \right]_0^h$$

$$= (\text{const.})h^{m+3/2},$$

so that the first term in the right member of (9') can be obtained from a constant term in the series for x, and other terms in (9') by taking m half an odd integer. Consequently we assume

$$x = A_1 + A_2 y^{1/2} + A_3 y^{3/2} + A_4 y^{5/2} + \cdots. \qquad (10)$$

* Verification is left to the student.

Substituting in the left member of (9′), and using formulas 214 and 218 of Peirce, we get, since $\left[\sqrt{hy - y^2} \right]_0^h = 0$,

$$\int_0^h (A_1\sqrt{h - y} + A_2\sqrt{hy - y^2} + A_3y\sqrt{hy - y^2}$$

$$+ A_4y^2\sqrt{hy - y^2} + \cdots)\, dy$$

$$= \left[-\frac{2A_1}{3}(h - y)^{3/2} + \frac{A_2h^2}{8}\sin^{-1}\frac{2y - h}{h} \right.$$

$$+ \frac{A_3h}{2} \cdot \frac{h^2}{8}\sin^{-1}\frac{2y - h}{h}$$

$$\left. + \frac{5A_4h}{8} \cdot \frac{h^3}{16}\sin^{-1}\frac{2y - h}{h} + \cdots \right]_0^h$$

$$= \frac{2A_1h^{3/2}}{3} + \frac{\pi A_2h^2}{8} + \frac{\pi A_3h^3}{16} + \frac{5\pi A_4h^4}{128} + \cdots. \quad (11)$$

We must therefore have, from (9′) and (11),

$$A_1 = b, \quad A_2 = -\frac{2}{\pi}a^{-1/2}b, \quad A_3 = \frac{2}{3\pi}a^{-3/2}b, \quad A_4 = -\frac{2}{5\pi}a^{-5/2}b, \cdots,$$

whence

$$x = b\left[1 - \frac{2}{\pi}\left(\frac{y^{1/2}}{a^{1/2}} - \frac{y^{3/2}}{3a^{3/2}} + \frac{y^{5/2}}{5a^{5/2}} - \cdots\right)\right]. \quad (12)$$

But

$$\tan^{-1}u = u - \frac{u^3}{3} + \frac{u^5}{5} - \frac{u^7}{7} + \cdots, \quad |u| < 1,$$

whence we infer

$$x = b\left(1 - \frac{2}{\pi}\tan^{-1}\sqrt{\frac{y}{a}}\right), \quad |y/a| < 1. \quad (13)$$

There are two reasons for looking askance at the result (13). In the first place, we have inferred the inverse tangent of $\sqrt{y/a}$ from merely the first few terms of the series (12). Secondly, even if we were to show that the series (12) is the expansion of the function given in (13), we should at best be assured of the correctness of our result when $|y/a| < 1$, whereas we should like a functional relation between x and y valid for all positive values of y. That (13) is indeed a correct and sufficiently general solution of our problem may be shown by direct substitution of (13) in (9); this task is left to the student in Problem 15, below.

PROBLEMS

1. Expand each of the following functions in a power series by a direct application of Maclaurin's formula. Also obtain each series by another method, and determine the region of convergence in each case, making use of the theorems of Art. 38.

(a) $x \cos x$;   (b) $\sin x^2$;

(c) $e^x \cos x$;   (d) $e^{\sinh x}$;

(e) $\tanh^{-1} x$;   (f) $\cosh (e^x - 1)$.

2. Evaluate the following definite integrals, citing the theorems on which each step is based.

(a) $\displaystyle\int_0^1 e^{-x^2}\, dx$;   (b) $\displaystyle\int_0^1 \frac{\sin x}{\sqrt{x}}\, dx$;

(c) $\displaystyle\int_0^x \frac{\ln (1 + x)}{x}\, dx$;   (d) $\displaystyle\int_0^{1/4} e^{\sin x}\, dx$;

(e) $\displaystyle\int_0^1 \sin x^2\, dx$;   (f) $\displaystyle\int_0^{0.2} \frac{\cosh x}{\sqrt{1 - x}}\, dx \cdot$

3. Using Theorem IX, Art. 38, find the inverse of each of the following functions by reversion of series.

(a) $y = x - \dfrac{x^3}{3!} + \dfrac{x^5}{5!} - \cdots$;

(b) $y = x - \dfrac{x^2}{2^2} + \dfrac{x^3}{3^2} - \dfrac{x^4}{4^2} + \cdots$.

4. Find the area bounded by the curve $xy = \sin x$, the lines $x = 1$ and $x = 2$, and the x-axis.

5. Find the centroid of the area of Problem 4.

6. Find the area bounded by the curve $xy = \sinh x$, the line $x = 1$, and the coordinate axes.

7. Find the area bounded by the curve $y = \sqrt{8 - x^3}$, the line $x = 1$, and the coordinate axes.

8. If $(1 - x)\, dy/dx = e^{-x}$, and $y = -0.1$ when $x = 0$, find the value of y when $x = \frac{1}{3}$.

9. A rectilinear motion is given by the equation

$$\frac{dv}{dt} = e^{-t} + \frac{2v}{1 + t},$$

where t (sec.) is time and v (ft./sec.) is velocity. If $v = 0$ when $t = 0$, find the velocity when $t = 0.1$ sec.

10. Evaluate $\displaystyle\int_0^\pi \frac{dx}{(4 - \cos x)^2}$ by expanding $(1 - \frac{1}{4}\cos x)^{-2}$ in an infinite series and integrating term by term. Use Wallis's formula (Peirce, 483).

11. Obtain a power series in k representing the complete elliptic integral of the second kind $E(k)$, and use this series to compute $E(\frac{1}{2})$ correct to four significant figures.

12. Compute the value of the elliptic integral

$$\int_0^{31°} \frac{d\phi}{\sqrt{1 - k^2 \sin^2 \phi}}, \quad \text{where } k = \sin 8°,$$

(a) by use of series; (b) by double interpolation with the tables.

13. A particle moves from rest at a distance 1 ft. towards a center of attraction O in accordance with the equation $d^2x/dt^2 = -2x^3$, where x (ft.) is the displacement from O at time t (sec.). Find the time required to travel from the halfway point to the center O.

14. According to Planck's radiation law, the radiation density ψ is

$$\psi = \frac{8\pi h}{c^3} \int_0^\infty \nu^3 (e^{h\nu/KT} - 1)^{-1} \, d\nu,$$

where ν = frequency (sec.$^{-1}$), T = temperature (deg. abs.), h = Planck's constant = 6.554×10^{-27} erg sec., c = velocity of light = 2.998×10^{10} cm./sec., and K = Boltzmann's constant = 1.372×10^{-16} erg/deg. By expanding the binomial expression in the integrand and integrating term by term, show that the above formula reduces to the Stefan-Boltzmann law, $\psi = aT^4$. Compute a, and specify the units in which it is measured.

15. By direct substitution and integration, show that the functional relation (13), Art. 40, satisfies equation (9) identically for all positive values of a and h.

16. (a) If the upper and lower horizontal dimensions of the Sutro weir are to be 1.5 in. and 6 in., respectively, and the desired theoretical discharge is to be 2 ft.^{3}/sec., find the vertical dimensions a and h. (b) If the height h of the weir and the lower horizontal dimension b are to be 24 in. and 12 in., respectively, and the theoretical discharge is to be 3 ft.^{3}/sec., find the upper horizontal dimension.

17. A transition spiral, used in highway engineering, is defined as a curve whose curvature varies directly as the arc length. Let the initial point of this spiral be the origin O, and let the tangent at O be the x-axis. (a) Show that parametric equations of the spiral can be written as

$$x = k \int_0^\phi \frac{\cos \theta}{\sqrt{\theta}} \, d\theta, \qquad y = k \int_0^\phi \frac{\sin \theta}{\sqrt{\theta}} \, d\theta,$$

where k is a constant. (b) Evaluate the ratio x/y for $\phi = \pi/4$.

41. Picard's method.
We shall devote the remainder of this chapter to a discussion of two methods of solving ordinary differential equations by means of infinite series. The methods given in Chapter I apply only to certain standard forms of differential equations, and aim at the determination of solutions in finite form. Frequently, however, the differential equations arising in a physical problem do not fall into one of the familiar types, and it may not be possible to find solutions in terms of a finite number of the elementary functions. It is natural, then, to attempt a solution in the form of an infinite series, or to try for an approximate solution when we are concerned primarily with numerical computations.

One method of getting a numerical approximation is that known as Picard's method of successive approximations, after the French mathe-

matician who evolved it.   Although the method is useful only for those
equations for which the successive integrations can be easily performed,
it has great theoretical value in that it also provides a proof of the existence of solutions of differential equations of very broad type.   We do
not, in this book, consider the problem of the existence theorem,* but
confine ourselves to the application of Picard's method to numerical
approximations.

Consider the equation of first order,

$$\frac{dy}{dx} = f(x, y), \tag{1}$$

and suppose that we desire a solution of this equation such that $y = b$
when $x = a$; that is, we are seeking not the general solution of (1),
containing an arbitrary constant, but a particular solution satisfying
the additional condition $y\big]_{x=a} = b$.   If we multiply (1) by dx and
formally integrate between limits, we get

$$\int_b^y dy = \int_a^x f(x, y)\, dx,$$

or

$$y = b + \int_a^x f(x, y)\, dx. \tag{2}$$

This is an integral equation equivalent to the differential equation (1)
together with the boundary condition, the unknown function y appearing now under the integral sign instead of in a derivative.   If we replace y in $f(x, y)$ by b, and perform the indicated integration in relation (2), we get a first approximation to the desired solution,

$$y_1 = b + \int_a^x f(x, b)\, dx.$$

Now replace y in the right-hand member of (2) by y_1, thereby obtaining a second approximation,

$$y_2 = b + \int_a^x f(x, y_1)\, dx.$$

We continue this process, replacing y in the function $f(x, y)$ of (2) by
the nth approximation y_n to obtain the $(n + 1)$th approximation,

$$y_{n+1} = b + \int_a^x f(x, y_n)\, dx. \tag{3}$$

---

* Such proofs may be found in H. T. H. Piaggio's "Differential Equations" or
E. L. Ince's "Ordinary Differential Equations."

We thus obtain a sequence of functions of x, namely, y_1, y_2, $\cdots$, y_n, y_{n+1}, $\cdots$ as approximations to the solution of equation (1), and for each of these functions we have, by (3), $y_{n+1}\big]_{x=a} = b$. The theory of Picard's method shows that the sequence y_1, y_2, $\cdots$ tends to a limiting function Y as n becomes infinite, and that this limiting function is the solution of equation (1) which satisfies the given condition,

$$\lim_{n \to \infty} y_n = Y, \qquad \frac{dY}{dx} \equiv f(x, Y), \qquad Y\big]_{x=a} = b,$$

whenever the function $f(x, y)$ of equation (1) obeys certain restrictions which we shall not state but which are met in all the cases with which we have to deal.

A simple example will serve to illustrate the method. Let there be given the differential equation

$$\frac{dy}{dx} = 2xy - 2x, \tag{4}$$

and suppose that we require that solution of (4) which takes on the value 2 when $x = 0$. The integral equation corresponding to (4) is then

$$y = 2 + \int_0^x (2xy - 2x)\, dx. \tag{5}$$

Putting $y = 2$ in the right-hand member of (5) and integrating, we get

$$y_1 = 2 + \int_0^x (4x - 2x)\, dx$$
$$= 2 + x^2.$$

Setting $y = 2 + x^2$ in (5) and integrating again, we find

$$y_2 = 2 + \int_0^x (4x + 2x^3 - 2x)\, dx$$
$$= 2 + x^2 + \frac{x^4}{2}.$$

Continuing in this fashion, we easily obtain the following successive approximations,

$$y_3 = 2 + x^2 + \frac{x^4}{2} + \frac{x^6}{6},$$

$$y_4 = 2 + x^2 + \frac{x^4}{2} + \frac{x^6}{6} + \frac{x^8}{24}.$$

In this particular example (but not in general), the successive approximations are all polynomials in x, each one containing precisely the same terms as the preceding approximation but with one additional power term. A little study of the first few approximations may therefore enable us to infer the form of the nth approximation,

$$y_n = 2 + x^2 + \frac{x^4}{2!} + \frac{x^6}{3!} + \cdots + \frac{x^{2n}}{n!}. \tag{6}$$

That this inference is correct is easily proved by mathematical induction, for we have, supposing (6) correct for $n = n$,

$$y_{n+1} = 2 + \int_0^x \left(2x + 2x^3 + \cdots + \frac{2x^{2n+1}}{n!} \right) dx$$

$$= 2 + x^2 + \frac{x^4}{2!} + \cdots + \frac{x^{2n+2}}{(n+1)!},$$

which is of the same form as (6) with $n + 1$ replacing n. It follows that the limit function Y can therefore be obtained; we have, in fact,

$$Y = \lim_{n \to \infty} y_n = 2 + x^2 + \frac{x^4}{2!} + \frac{x^6}{3!} + \cdots + \frac{x^{2n}}{n!} + \cdots$$

$$= 1 + \left[1 + x^2 + \frac{(x^2)^2}{2!} + \frac{(x^2)^3}{3!} + \cdots + \frac{(x^2)^n}{n!} + \cdots \right]$$

$$= 1 + e^{x^2}.$$

It is easily seen that this function does satisfy equation (4) identically in x, and that $Y\Big]_{x=0} = 2$ as required. Here Y was not only obtained but could be recognized as a function expressible in finite form; actually, of course, Picard's method was not needed in this case since equation (4) is a linear equation of the first order which may be solved directly by the method of Art. 5, Chapter I.

In a more complicated problem we should probably not be so fortunate as to be able to deduce the nth approximation. But if we wanted to find the value of y corresponding to a given value of x, say $x = c$, we could find in turn $y_1\Big]_{x=c}$, $y_2\Big]_{x=c}$, $\cdots$, proceeding until the desired accuracy is obtained; for example, if a numerical result correct to three significant figures were required, we should continue the process until further approximations appeared to yield refinements only in the fourth figure.

42. Method of Frobenius. The second method of which we make use is one due to Frobenius. This process is applicable to homogeneous linear differential equations of any order, with variable coefficients, and also plays a large part in the theory of such equations.* It consists, in its full generality, of assuming a solution in the form of a series,

$$y = x^c(a_0 + a_1 x + \cdots + a_n x^n + \cdots), \tag{1}$$

where the numbers c, a_0, a_1, $\cdots$, a_n, $\cdots$ are to be determined by substituting (1) in the given differential equation and setting the complete coefficient of each power of x equal to zero. It should be emphasized that this method is a tentative one,† in that certain linear differential equations possess no solution of the form (1). For example, the equation

$$x^4 \frac{d^2y}{dx^2} + 2x^3 \frac{dy}{dx} - y = 0$$

has no solution of type (1) since its general solution is $y = c_1 e^{1/x} + c_2 e^{-1/x}$, and the functions $e^{1/x}$ and $e^{-1/x}$ cannot be expressed in series of ascending powers of x

As a special case of the Frobenius method, we sometimes assume a solution in the form of a Maclaurin series,

$$y = a_0 + a_1 x + \cdots + a_n x^n + \cdots, \tag{2}$$

to which (1) reduces if $c = 0$, since it is easier to deal with series (2) than with series (1). Then if our efforts to find a solution of the type (2) fail, or if the solution so obtained is not sufficiently general for our purpose, we may assume a solution of the form (1).

As an example, consider the equation

$$4x \frac{d^2y}{dx^2} + 2 \frac{dy}{dx} - y = 0, \tag{3}$$

and let us seek a solution of the form (2). Differentiating (2) twice and substituting in (3), we get the relation

$$8a_2 x + 24a_3 x^2 + \cdots + 4n(n-1)a_n x^{n-1} + \cdots$$

$$+ 2a_1 + 4a_2 x + 6a_3 x^2 + \cdots + 2na_n x^{n-1} + \cdots$$

$$-a_0 - a_1 x - a_2 x^2 - \cdots - a_{n-1} x^{n-1} - \cdots = 0. \tag{4}$$

---

* See, for example, the books of Piaggio and Ince, previously cited.

† That is, in the absence of knowledge of the theory of linear differential equations. The Frobenius theory enables one to determine the conditions under which a given linear equation will have a solution of the postulated form.

This equation will be satisfied identically in x if the complete coefficients of the successive powers of x are set equal to zero. Hence we have the further relations

$$2a_1 - a_0 = 0, \qquad 12a_2 - a_1 = 0, \qquad 30a_3 - a_2 = 0, \; \cdots,$$

$$2n(2n-1)a_n - a_{n-1} = 0, \; \cdots,$$

whence

$$a_1 = \frac{a_0}{2}, \qquad a_2 = \frac{a_1}{12} = \frac{a_0}{24}, \qquad a_3 = \frac{a_2}{30} = \frac{a_0}{720}, \; \cdots,$$

$$a_n = \frac{a_{n-1}}{2n(2n-1)}, \; \cdots. \tag{5}$$

As a matter of fact, only the relation between a_n and a_{n-1} is actually needed, since this holds for $n = 1, 2, \cdots$. Replacing n by $n-1$ in the latter, we have

$$a_{n-1} = \frac{a_{n-2}}{(2n-2)(2n-3)},$$

so that

$$a_n = \frac{a_{n-2}}{2n(2n-1)(2n-2)(2n-3)}.$$

Proceeding in this way, we ultimately find

$$a_n = \frac{a_0}{(2n)!}, \tag{6}$$

which is checked for $n = 1, 2, 3$ by the first three of relations (5). Substituting for $a_1, a_2, \cdots$ their values as given by (6) in series (2), we therefore get the series solution

$$y = a_0 \left[1 + \frac{x}{2!} + \frac{x^2}{4!} + \frac{x^3}{6!} + \cdots + \frac{x^n}{(2n)!} + \cdots \right], \tag{7}$$

where a_0 is arbitrary. Inspection of (7) shows that the series in brackets is merely the expansion of the function $\cosh \sqrt{x}$, so that a solution of the given differential equation (3) is

$$y = a_0 \cosh \sqrt{x}. \tag{8}$$

That this is indeed a solution may be easily checked by direct substitution. Our tentative method has therefore been successful in that we have found a solution of (3) containing one arbitrary constant. In a sense, however, it has not been completely successful, for we have, so to speak, only half the general solution, this latter involving two arbitrary constants. It so happens in this particular example that the general solution would have been obtained had we assumed a series solution of the more general form (1) instead of the Maclaurin series (2). (See Problem 7 at the end of this chapter.)

When employing the general Frobenius method, involving the series (1), we assume, as we evidently may without loss of generality, that $a_0 \neq 0$. After substituting (1) and its successive derivatives in the given differential equation, we are again led to an infinite system of relations similar to (5) in the constants $c, a_0, a_1, \cdots$. The first of these equations, obtained by setting equal to zero the coefficient of the lowest power of x in the series which is to vanish identically, is called the *indicial equation* since it serves to determine the index c. If the differential equation under investigation is of order m, the indicial equation will in general be an algebraic equation of degree m. Thus it may happen that m distinct possible values of c can be found from the indicial equation, whence we shall get m distinct * solutions of our differential equation. When this occurs, we have the general solution as a linear combination of the m distinct functions with arbitrary constants as coefficients.

If we wish to make use of the series solutions obtained by the Frobenius method, we should, of course, examine each series for convergence to determine the region of its validity. The series (7) found in our example, for instance, is convergent for all values of x, and hence may be used in computation.

PROBLEMS

1. Using Picard's method of successive approximations, obtain a solution of the equation $dy/dx = y + x$ such that $y = 1$ when $x = 0$. Carry out the work through the fourth approximation, and check your result by finding the exact particular solution.

2. Given the equation $dy/dx = 1 + 2xy - 2x^2$. If $y = 1$ when $x = 0$, use Picard's method to find the value of y when $x = \frac{1}{2}$.

3. A 10-lb. weight starts its motion with an initial velocity of 5 ft./sec. and moves thereafter subject to a force of $20\sqrt{t}$ lb., where t (sec.) is time, acting in the direction of the initial velocity. The motion is opposed by a resisting force numerically equal to $10v/g$ lb., where v is velocity (ft./sec.) and $g = 32.17$ ft./sec.^{2} Using Picard's method, find the velocity when $t = \frac{1}{4}$ sec.

4. Tank A contains 100 gal. of brine in which are dissolved 50 lb. of salt. Tank B contains 100 gal. of water. Water runs into A at the rate of 3 gal./min ,

* By distinct we mean here linearly independent; for a precise discussion of this concept, see the textbooks on differential equations referred to previously.

and the mixture, kept uniform by stirring, runs into B at the rate of 2 gal./min. If the resulting solution, likewise kept uniform by stirring, then runs out of B at the rate of 2 gal./min., find the amount of salt in B at the end of 20 min. (a) by direct use of a series; (b) by Picard's method.

5. Apply Picard's method to the equation $dy/dx = 2y - 2x^2 - 3$, where $y = 2$ for $x = 0$. From the first few approximations, infer that $y_n = 2 + x + x^2 - 2^n x^{n+1}/(n+1)! - 2^{n+1} x^{n+2}/(n+2)!$ Hence deduce that the solution is $y = 2 + x + x^2$, and verify this result.

6. Apply Picard's method to the equation $dy/dx = 1 + 2xy - 2x^2$, where $y = 1$ for $x = 0$. From the first few approximations, infer that $y_n = 1 + x + x^2 + x^4/2! + \cdots + x^{2n}/n! - 2^n x^{2n+1}/1 \cdot 3 \cdot 5 \cdots (2n+1)$. Hence deduce that the solution is $y = x + e^{x^2}$, and verify this result. (Cf. Problem 2.)

7. Find the complete solution of the example of Art. 42 by the method of Frobenius, using the more general series (1).

8. Using the method of Frobenius, find the general solution of the differential equation $2x(1 - x) \, d^2y/dx^2 + (1 + x) \, dy/dx - y = 0$.

9. Find the general solution of the differential equation $x(1 - x) \, d^2y/dx^2 + 2(1 - 2x) \, dy/dx - 2y = 0$.

10. Find the general solution of the differential equation $2x(1 - 2x) \, d^2y/dx^2 + (1 + 4x^2) \, dy/dx - (1 + 2x)y = 0$.

11. Using the method of Frobenius, obtain two independent solutions of the equation $2x(1 - x) \, d^2y/dx^2 + (1 - x) \, dy/dx + 3y = 0$: one, the irrational algebraic function $y_1 = (1 - x)\sqrt{x}$; the other, in the form of the series $y_2 = 1 - 3x + x^2 + \cdots + 3x^{n+1}/(2n + 1)(2n - 1) + \cdots$. Show that the latter series is the expansion of the transcendental function

$$y_2 = 1 - \frac{3}{2}x - \frac{3}{4}(1 - x)\sqrt{x}\ln\frac{1 + \sqrt{x}}{1 - \sqrt{x}}.$$

12. A particle moves from rest at a distance 10 ft. towards a center of attraction, the force varying inversely as the distance. If the initial acceleration is numerically equal to 5 ft./sec.^{2}, find the time required to traverse the first two-thirds of the distance to the center.

13. A particle moves from rest at a distance 10 ft. towards a center of attraction, the force varying directly as the square of the distance. If the initial acceleration is numerically equal to 1 ft./sec.^{2}, find the time required to travel from the halfway point to the center.

14. The following formulas give the maximum deflection y_L of a cantilever beam of length L (in.) and weight w (lb./in.) subjected to a horizontal force P (lb.) at the free end.

Compressive force P (Problem 63, Art. 14):

$$y_L = \frac{wEI}{P^2}\left(1 - \frac{\theta^2}{2} - \sec\theta + \theta\tan\theta\right).$$

Tensile force P (Art. 22):

$$y_L = \frac{wEI}{P^2}\left(1 + \frac{\theta^2}{2} - \operatorname{sech}\theta - \theta\tanh\theta\right).$$

Show that these formulas may be written, respectively:

$$y_L = \frac{wEI}{P^2} \left(\frac{\theta^4}{8} + \frac{7\theta^6}{144} + \frac{113\theta^8}{5760} + \cdots \right),$$

$$y_L = \frac{wEI}{P^2} \left(\frac{\theta^4}{8} - \frac{7\theta^6}{144} + \frac{113\theta^8}{5760} - \cdots \right),$$

which are convenient for computation when $\theta = L\sqrt{P/EI}$ is small.

A wooden cantilever beam 2 in. by 4 in. by 10 ft., with $E = 15 \times 10^5$ lb./in.^{2} and weighing 40 lb./ft.^{3} is subjected to a horizontal force of 100 lb. at the free end. If the 2-in. side is horizontal, find the maximum deflection when the force is (a) compressive; (b) tensile.

15. Tank A contains 100 gal. of brine in which 100 lb. of salt are dissolved. Tank B contains 100 gal. of water. Brine flows from A to B at the rate of 2 gal./min., the mixture is pumped from B back to A at the rate of 1 gal./min., and 1 gal./min. also flows from B into a third tank. Let x and y (lb.) denote the salt content of tanks A and B, respectively, at time t (min.). Formulate the differential equations of the system, and eliminate y to obtain a second-order linear equation for x. For convenience, introduce a new independent variable, $u = 100 - t$, to get

$$100u^2 \frac{d^2x}{du^2} - 2u(100 + u) \frac{dx}{du} + 2(100 + u)x = 0.$$

Apply the method of Frobenius to this equation, and hence show that

$$x = \tfrac{1}{2}(100 - t)(1 + e^{-t/50}), \qquad y = 50 - (50 - t)e^{-t/50}.$$

CHAPTER V

Fourier Series

43. Introduction. In Chapter IV we discussed certain properties of infinite series in general, and gave particular attention to power series because of their wide applicability and frequent occurrence. In some types of problems, however, it is impractical or otherwise undesirable to deal with power series, and we often find a more natural approach to a required result through an infinite series of trigonometric functions. Because of the periodicity of the trigonometric functions, it may be correctly supposed that such series would be useful in the investigation of various periodic physical phenomena. In addition, we shall see in Chapter VII that many partial differential equations arising in physics and engineering are most conveniently solved by means of such series of trigonometric terms whereas series of power functions would be awkward to use.

44. Definitions and formulas. By a trigonometric series we shall mean a series of the form

$$\frac{a_0}{2} + \sum_{n=1}^{\infty} (a_n \cos nx + b_n \sin nx), \tag{1}$$

where the a's and b's are constants. The constant term in (1) is written as $a_0/2$ rather than as a_0 for later convenience, for we shall see that the formula we obtain for a_n will then hold for $n = 0$ as well as for $n = 1$, 2, $\cdots$.

Whether a series of the form (1) will converge for any value of x, and if so, what manner of function it will represent, will of course depend upon the numbers a_n and b_n. But if it converges in any closed interval of length 2π, say $c \leqq x \leqq c + 2\pi$, it must, because of the periodicity of the functions $\sin nx$ and $\cos nx$, converge for every real value of x, and consequently will represent a function defined for all values of x and periodic with period 2π. We therefore need deal with merely the interval $c \leqq x \leqq c + 2\pi$, the behavior of our series for other values of x being completely known when its properties for this interval are determined.

In order to investigate the nature and behavior of a series of the type (1), we shall make use of the following formulas, where m and n are any positive integers or zero, except for the restrictions stipulated:

(I) $\displaystyle\int_c^{c+2\pi} \sin nx\, dx = \left[-\frac{1}{n}\cos nx\right]_c^{c+2\pi} = 0, \qquad n \neq 0,$

(II) $\displaystyle\int_c^{c+2\pi} \cos nx\, dx = \left[\frac{1}{n}\sin nx\right]_c^{c+2\pi} = 0, \qquad n \neq 0,$

(III) $\displaystyle\int_c^{c+2\pi} \sin mx \cos nx\, dx$

$$= \tfrac{1}{2}\int_c^{c+2\pi} [\sin (m-n)x + \sin (m+n)x]\, dx = 0,$$

(IV) $\displaystyle\int_c^{c+2\pi} \sin mx \sin nx\, dx$

$$= \tfrac{1}{2}\int_c^{c+2\pi} [\cos (m-n)x - \cos (m+n)x]\, dx = 0, \qquad m \neq n,$$

(V) $\displaystyle\int_c^{c+2\pi} \cos mx \cos nx\, dx$

$$= \tfrac{1}{2}\int_c^{c+2\pi} [\cos (m-n)x + \cos (m+n)x]\, dx = 0, \qquad m \neq n,$$

(VI) $\displaystyle\int_c^{c+2\pi} \sin^2 nx\, dx = \tfrac{1}{2}\int_c^{c+2\pi} (1 - \cos 2nx)\, dx = \pi, \qquad n \neq 0,$

(VII) $\displaystyle\int_c^{c+2\pi} \cos^2 nx\, dx = \tfrac{1}{2}\int_c^{c+2\pi} (1 + \cos 2nx)\, dx = \pi, \qquad n \neq 0.$

We are now ready to prove

THEOREM I. *If the series*

$$\frac{a_0}{2} + a_1 \cos x + a_2 \cos 2x + \cdots + a_n \cos nx + \cdots$$

$$+ b_1 \sin x + b_2 \sin 2x + \cdots + b_n \sin nx + \cdots \quad (1)$$

is uniformly convergent in the closed interval $c \leqq x \leqq c + 2\pi$, *and has the sum* $f(x)$, *then for* $n = 0, 1, 2, \cdots$ *we have*

$$a_n = \frac{1}{\pi}\int_c^{c+2\pi} f(x) \cos nx\, dx, \qquad b_n = \frac{1}{\pi}\int_c^{c+2\pi} f(x) \sin nx\, dx. \quad (2)$$

First of all, we note that since the series (1) is uniformly convergent for $c \leqq x \leqq c + 2\pi$, and because of the periodicity of the functions $\sin nx$ and $\cos nx$, we have (1) uniformly convergent over every real x

interval, and therefore this series may be integrated term by term (Theorem III, Art. 39). We therefore find

$$
\int_c^{c+2\pi} f(x)\,dx = \int_c^{c+2\pi} \frac{a_0}{2}\,dx
$$
$$
+ \int_c^{c+2\pi} a_1 \cos x\,dx + \cdots + \int_c^{c+2\pi} a_n \cos nx\,dx + \cdots
$$
$$
+ \int_c^{c+2\pi} b_1 \sin x\,dx + \cdots + \int_c^{c+2\pi} b_n \sin nx\,dx + \cdots
$$
$$
= a_0\pi
$$

by formulas (I) and (II). Thus a_0 is given by the first of equations (2) with $n = 0$.

Now let

$$
s_n(x) = \frac{a_0}{2} + a_1 \cos x + a_2 \cos 2x + \cdots + a_n \cos nx
$$
$$
+ b_1 \sin x + b_2 \sin 2x + \cdots + b_n \sin nx.
$$

Then by definition of uniform convergence, we have, given any $\epsilon > 0$,

$$
\left| f(x) - s_n(x) \right| < \epsilon
$$

for n sufficiently large and for any x. If we multiply (1) by $\cos nx$, the resulting series is also uniformly convergent. For, we have, since $\left| \cos nx \right| \leqq 1$,

$$
\left| f(x) \cos nx - s_n(x) \cos nx \right| \leqq \left| f(x) - s_n(x) \right| < \epsilon
$$

for any x. Consequently the new series may likewise be integrated term by term; doing this, we get

$$
\int_c^{c+2\pi} f(x) \cos nx\,dx = \int_c^{c+2\pi} \frac{a_0}{2} \cos nx\,dx
$$
$$
+ \int_c^{c+2\pi} a_1 \cos x \cos nx\,dx + \cdots
$$
$$
+ \int_c^{c+2\pi} a_n \cos^2 nx\,dx + \cdots
$$
$$
+ \int_c^{c+2\pi} b_1 \sin x \cos nx\,dx + \cdots
$$
$$
+ \int_c^{c+2\pi} b_n \sin nx \cos nx\,dx + \cdots
$$
$$
= a_n\pi
$$

by formulas (II), (III), (V), (VII), and therefore we have the first of equations (2) for $n = 1, 2, \cdots$.

Finally, if we multiply (1) by $\sin nx$, which will similarly give us another uniformly convergent series, and integrate, we find

$$\int_c^{c+2\pi} f(x) \sin nx \, dx = \int_c^{c+2\pi} \frac{a_0}{2} \sin nx \, dx$$

$$+ \int_c^{c+2\pi} a_1 \cos x \sin nx \, dx + \cdots$$

$$+ \int_c^{c+2\pi} a_n \cos nx \sin nx \, dx + \cdots$$

$$+ \int_c^{c+2\pi} b_1 \sin x \sin nx \, dx + \cdots$$

$$+ \int_c^{c+2\pi} b_n \sin^2 nx \, dx + \cdots$$

$$= b_n \pi$$

by formulas (I), (III), (IV), (VI). This gives us the expression for b_n stated in the theorem.

In the above discussion we have regarded the trigonometric series as the given thing, and supposed it uniformly convergent with some sum function $f(x)$. It has then been shown that the coefficients of the given series are related to the function $f(x)$ represented, by the relations (2). Now ordinarily we start with a given function $f(x)$ and attempt to find a series representing it. On the basis of the foregoing derivation, we should naturally compute numbers a_n and b_n associated with $f(x)$, by means of equations (2), and thus *formally construct* the series (1). A series so constructed from $f(x)$ is called a *Fourier series* belonging to $f(x)$. We then have hope, but, in general, no assurance, that the Fourier series for $f(x)$ will converge and that it will represent $f(x)$. Indeed, for a function arbitrarily given, neither of these hopes may be fulfilled.*

Fortunately, however, a very wide class of functions will possess Fourier series that do converge and represent them. Every function defined for an interval $c < x < c + 2\pi$ and possessing a Taylor series expansion valid in this interval will certainly possess a Fourier series representing it, and in addition many functions for which no Taylor development over the interval exists may nevertheless be expanded in a

---

* It is not even true that all continuous functions are representable by their Fourier series.

Fourier series. It is this wide applicability of Fourier series that furnishes one reason for their importance and usefulness.

It is beyond the scope of this book to discuss conditions under which a function will be represented by its Fourier series.* We merely state Fourier's theorem, which applies to all the functions that normally arise in physical and engineering applications.

THEOREM II. *Any single-valued function $f(x)$, continuous except possibly for a finite number of finite discontinuities in an interval of length 2π, and having only a finite number of maxima and minima in this interval, possesses a convergent Fourier series representing it.*

By a finite discontinuity at a point $x = x_0$ we mean, roughly speaking, a finite "jump" in the graph of the function, as shown in Fig. 33. More precisely, if $\lim_{h \to 0^+} f(x_0 - h)$

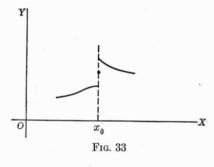

and $\lim_{h \to 0^+} f(x_0 + h)$ both exist but are different numbers, we say that $f(x)$ has a finite discontinuity at $x = x_0$. It turns out that, when $f(x)$ has a finite discontinuity at $x = x_0$, the Fourier series yields the arithmetic mean of the two limits given above when we set $x = x_0$ in the series.

FIG. 33

45. Examples. We proceed to consider a few concrete functions to exemplify the manner in which Fourier series are obtained.

Example 1. Consider the function $f(x)$ defined by the relations (Fig. 34)

$$f(x) = 1, \qquad 0 < x < \pi;$$
$$f(x) = 2, \qquad \pi < x < 2\pi. \tag{1}$$

Here we are dealing with an interval of length 2π, for which $c = 0$. We have

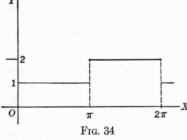

FIG. 34

not defined $f(x)$ at the midpoint of our interval, but the statement at the close of Art. 44 indicates that the resulting series will yield $f(\pi) = \frac{3}{2}$. Moreover, the series, because of its periodic character, will define $f(x)$ for every x not in our interval, whence we should expect to get $f(0) = f(2\pi) = \frac{3}{2}$ also. This we shall verify.

It may be mentioned, in passing,

* See, for example, Goursat-Hedrick, "Mathematical Analysis," Vol. I.

that there is nothing strange about defining our function in the two halves of the interval by means of two different equations; we shall have frequent occasion to deal with such functions in our applications. As a matter of fact, we can by a slightly artificial device define the above function over the given range by means of a single equation if desired, namely

$$f(x) = \frac{3}{2} + \frac{x - \pi}{2 \mid x - \pi \mid},$$

but this is not necessary.

Now by formulas (2), Art. 44, we have

$$a_0 = \frac{1}{\pi} \int_0^{2\pi} f(x)\, dx = \frac{1}{\pi} \int_0^{\pi} 1 \cdot dx + \frac{1}{\pi} \int_\pi^{2\pi} 2 \cdot dx = 1 + 2 = 3,$$

$$a_n = \frac{1}{\pi} \int_0^{2\pi} f(x) \cos nx\, dx = \frac{1}{\pi} \int_0^{\pi} 1 \cdot \cos nx\, dx + \frac{1}{\pi} \int_\pi^{2\pi} 2 \cdot \cos nx\, dx$$

$$= \left[\frac{1}{\pi n} \sin nx \right]_0^{\pi} + \left[\frac{2}{\pi n} \sin nx \right]_\pi^{2\pi} = 0, \qquad n = 1, 2, \cdots,$$

$$b_n = \frac{1}{\pi} \int_0^{2\pi} f(x) \sin nx\, dx = \frac{1}{\pi} \int_0^{\pi} \sin nx\, dx + \frac{1}{\pi} \int_\pi^{2\pi} 2 \sin nx\, dx$$

$$= \left[-\frac{1}{\pi n} \cos nx \right]_0^{\pi} + \left[-\frac{2}{\pi n} \cos nx \right]_\pi^{2\pi}$$

$$= -\frac{\cos n\pi}{\pi n} + \frac{1}{\pi n} - \frac{2}{\pi n} + \frac{2}{\pi n} \cos n\pi$$

$$= \frac{1}{\pi n} (\cos n\pi - 1), \qquad n = 1, 2, \cdots.$$

For this function, therefore, all the a's with the exception of a_0 vanish, and all the b's with even subscript do likewise since the cosine of an even multiple of π is unity. Substituting $n = 1, 3, 5, \cdots$ in the expression for b_n, we get

$$b_1 = -\frac{2}{\pi}, \ b_3 = -\frac{2}{3\pi}, \ b_5 = -\frac{2}{5\pi}, \cdots,$$

and we have the Fourier series

$$f(x) = \frac{3}{2} - \frac{2}{\pi} \left(\sin x + \frac{1}{3} \sin 3x + \frac{1}{5} \sin 5x + \cdots \right). \tag{2}$$

Since the function defined by equations (1) satisfies the conditions of Theorem II, Art. 44, the series (2) will represent $f(x)$. We see also that we do get from (2), as predicted,

$$f(0) = f(\pi) = f(2\pi) = \tfrac{3}{2}.$$

Moreover, an interesting by-product may be obtained from series (2). Setting $x = \pi/2$, we get, since $f(\pi/2) = 1$,

$$1 = \frac{3}{2} - \frac{2}{\pi} \left(1 - \frac{1}{3} + \frac{1}{5} - \frac{1}{7} + \cdots \right),$$

or

$$\frac{\pi}{4} = 1 - \frac{1}{3} + \frac{1}{5} - \frac{1}{7} + \cdots. \tag{3}$$

Thus we have found from the Fourier expansion an alternating convergent series representing the number $\pi/4$.

Example 2. Let a function be defined as follows (Fig. 35):

$$f(x) = -x, \qquad -\pi < x \leqq 0,$$
$$f(x) = x, \qquad 0 < x < \pi. \tag{4}$$

This time we take the initial point of our interval at $-\pi$. Again, the series we

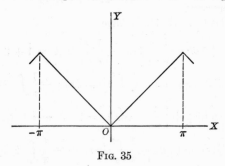

Fig. 35

obtain will yield a value of $f(x)$ for every x, but now the series function will be continuous everywhere,* as indicated by the graph. We find here

$$a_0 = \frac{1}{\pi} \int_{-\pi}^{\pi} f(x)\, dx = \frac{1}{\pi} \int_{-\pi}^{0} (-x)\, dx + \frac{1}{\pi} \int_{0}^{\pi} x\, dx$$

$$= \frac{\pi}{2} + \frac{\pi}{2} = \pi,$$

$$a_n = \frac{1}{\pi} \int_{-\pi}^{\pi} f(x) \cos nx\, dx = \frac{1}{\pi} \int_{-\pi}^{0} (-x) \cos nx\, dx + \frac{1}{\pi} \int_{0}^{\pi} x \cos nx\, dx$$

$$= -\frac{1}{\pi} \left[\frac{x \sin nx}{n} + \frac{\cos nx}{n^2} \right]_{-\pi}^{0} + \frac{1}{\pi} \left[\frac{x \sin nx}{n} + \frac{\cos nx}{n^2} \right]_{0}^{\pi}$$

$$= -\frac{1}{\pi n^2} + \frac{\cos n\pi}{\pi n^2} + \frac{\cos n\pi}{\pi n^2} - \frac{1}{\pi n^2} = \frac{2}{\pi n^2} (\cos n\pi - 1),$$

$$b_n = \frac{1}{\pi} \int_{-\pi}^{\pi} f(x) \sin nx\, dx = \frac{1}{\pi} \int_{-\pi}^{0} (-x) \sin nx\, dx + \frac{1}{\pi} \int_{0}^{\pi} x \sin nx\, dx$$

$$= -\frac{1}{\pi} \left[-\frac{x \cos nx}{n} + \frac{\sin nx}{n^2} \right]_{-\pi}^{0} + \frac{1}{\pi} \left[-\frac{x \cos nx}{n} + \frac{\sin nx}{n^2} \right]_{0}^{\pi}$$

$$= \frac{\cos n\pi}{n} - \frac{\cos n\pi}{n} = 0.$$

Consequently we get the series

$$f(x) = \frac{\pi}{2} - \frac{4}{\pi} \left[\cos x + \frac{1}{3^2} \cos 3x + \frac{1}{5^2} \cos 5x + \cdots \right]. \tag{5}$$

* Note, however, that this function does not possess a derivative at $x = 0$, $\pm\pi$, $\pm 2\pi$, $\cdots$.

If we substitute $x = 0$ in (5), we find another interesting series involving π,

$$0 = \frac{\pi}{2} - \frac{4}{\pi}\left[1 + \frac{1}{3^2} + \frac{1}{5^2} + \frac{1}{7^2} + \cdots\right],$$

$$\frac{\pi^2}{8} = 1 + \frac{1}{3^2} + \frac{1}{5^2} + \frac{1}{7^2} + \cdots. \tag{6}$$

Since the positive roots of $\cos x = 0$ are $x = \pi/2,\ 3\pi/2,\ 5\pi/2,\ \cdots$, series (6) gives us the curious result that the sum of the squares of the reciprocals of the positive zeros of $\cos x$ is equal to $\frac{1}{2}$ (cf. the analogous result concerning the zeros of the Bessel function $J_0(x)$, Art. 76, Chapter VII).

Example 3. As a final example, we take the function defined by

$$f(x) = x, \qquad -\pi < x < \pi. \tag{7}$$

This function (Fig. 36) coincides with that of Example 2 in the right-hand half of the interval, but differs in the left-hand half.

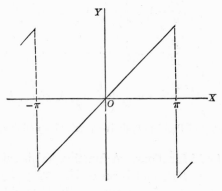

Fig. 36

We find in this case

$$a_0 = \frac{1}{\pi}\int_{-\pi}^{\pi} f(x)\,dx = \frac{1}{\pi}\int_{-\pi}^{\pi} x\,dx = 0,$$

$$a_n = \frac{1}{\pi}\int_{-\pi}^{\pi} f(x)\cos nx\,dx = \frac{1}{\pi}\int_{-\pi}^{\pi} x\cos nx\,dx = 0,$$

$$b_n = \frac{1}{\pi}\int_{-\pi}^{\pi} f(x)\sin nx\,dx = \frac{1}{\pi}\int_{-\pi}^{\pi} x\sin nx\,dx = -\frac{2}{n}\cos n\pi,$$

whence

$$f(x) = 2(\sin x - \tfrac{1}{2}\sin 2x + \tfrac{1}{3}\sin 3x - \cdots). \tag{8}$$

Substitution of $x = \pi/2$ in (8) again yields the alternating series (3) for $\pi/4$. For $x = -\pi$ or $x = \pi$ we find $f(x) = 0$, which is the midpoint of the break at each discontinuity of (8).

PROBLEMS

Expand each of the functions in Problems 1–7 in a Fourier series, and examine each series at the points of discontinuity when such exist.

1. $f(x) = x, 0 < x < \pi; f(x) = 0, \pi < x < 2\pi$.
2. $f(x) = x^2, 0 < x < \pi; f(x) = -x^2, \pi < x < 2\pi$.
3. $f(x) = e^x, -\pi < x < \pi$.
4. $f(x) = x \sin x, 0 < x < 2\pi$.
5 $f(x) = \sqrt{1 - \cos x}, -\pi < x < \pi$.
6. $f(x) = \cos ax, -\pi < x < \pi$ $(a \neq 0, \pm1, \pm2, \cdots)$.
7. $f(x) = |\sin x|, -\pi < x < \pi$.

8. Expand the function $f(x) = \sin x$ for $0 < x \leq \pi$, $f(x) = 0$ for $\pi < x < 2\pi$, and show that the result checks when $x = 0$ and when $x = \pi/2$.

9. Obtain the Fourier series for the function $f(x) = x^2$, $-\pi < x < \pi$, and from it deduce the relations

$$\frac{\pi^2}{6} = 1 + \frac{1}{2^2} + \frac{1}{3^2} + \frac{1}{4^2} + \cdots,$$

$$\frac{\pi^2}{12} = 1 - \frac{1}{2^2} + \frac{1}{3^2} - \frac{1}{4^2} + \cdots,$$

$$\frac{\pi^2}{8} = 1 + \frac{1}{3^2} + \frac{1}{5^2} + \frac{1}{7^2} + \cdots.$$

10. From the result of Problem 3, derive a series for $\pi/\sinh \pi$.

46. Even and odd functions. A function $f(x)$ is said to be an even function if $f(-x) \equiv f(x)$, and is an odd function if $f(-x) \equiv -f(x)$. Examples of an even function are x^2, $\cos x$; of an odd function, x and $\sin x$. If a Maclaurin series contains only even powers of x, it is an even function; and if it contains only odd powers, it is an odd function. The geometric characteristic of the graph of an even function is its symmetry with respect to the y-axis; for the graph of an odd function, we have symmetry with respect to the origin.

Example 2 of Art. 45 evidently has to do with an even function, whereas in Example 3 we have an odd function, as may be seen from the graphs. Now it turned out in Example 2 that every b_n vanished, the series (5) containing only the constant and cosine terms. On the other hand, the a's of Example 3 were all found to be equal to zero, and the series (8) involved only sine terms.

These occurrences were not accidents, but might have been foretold. We have in this connection the following theorem.

THEOREM. *When an even function $f(x)$ is expanded in a Fourier series over the interval from $-\pi$ to π, the coefficients of the series will be given by*

$$a_n = \frac{2}{\pi} \int_0^\pi f(x) \cos nx \, dx, \qquad b_n = 0. \qquad (1)$$

When an odd function is developed in this interval, we have

$$a_n = 0, \qquad b_n = \frac{2}{\pi} \int_0^\pi f(x) \sin nx \, dx. \qquad (2)$$

It is easy on geometric grounds to see the truth of this theorem. We shall, however, give an analytical proof of the first part of the theorem, the second half being capable of similar treatment. Let $f(x)$ be even, so that $f(-x) \equiv f(x)$. We have

$$a_n = \frac{1}{\pi} \int_{-\pi}^\pi f(x) \cos nx \, dx = \frac{1}{\pi} \int_{-\pi}^0 f(x) \cos nx \, dx + \frac{1}{\pi} \int_0^\pi f(x) \cos nx \, dx.$$

Now in the first integral of the last expression, replace x by $-x$. Remembering that $\cos nx$ is an even function, we then get

$$a_n = \frac{1}{\pi} \int_\pi^0 f(x) \cos nx(-dx) + \frac{1}{\pi} \int_0^\pi f(x) \cos nx \, dx.$$

If in the first of these integrals we change the order of integration and at the same time change the sign of the integral, we see that it becomes a duplicate of the second integral, whence the first of equations (1) follows. Likewise, we have

$$b_n = \frac{1}{\pi} \int_{-\pi}^\pi f(x) \sin nx \, dx = \frac{1}{\pi} \int_{-\pi}^0 f(x) \sin nx \, dx + \frac{1}{\pi} \int_0^\pi f(x) \sin nx \, dx$$

$$= \frac{1}{\pi} \int_\pi^0 f(x) \sin (-nx)(-dx) + \frac{1}{\pi} \int_0^\pi f(x) \sin nx \, dx$$

$$= -\frac{1}{\pi} \int_0^\pi f(x) \sin nx \, dx + \frac{1}{\pi} \int_0^\pi f(x) \sin nx \, dx$$

$$= 0,$$

whence the second of equations (1) holds.

This theorem materially shortens the computation when we have to find the Fourier series of either an even or an odd function for the interval $-\pi < x < \pi$.

47. Half-range series. In some problems we are concerned with an interval of length π instead of length 2π. In addition, we may be forced by the conditions of the problem to expand a given function in a series of sines alone or a series of cosines alone. Suppose that we are given a function $f(x)$ defined for $0 < x < \pi$. It follows from the discussion of Art. 46 that we may find an expansion valid over this interval, in either sine terms alone or cosine terms alone. For, if we wish a sine expansion, say, we may create a function $F(x)$ which is identical with $f(x)$ for $0 < x < \pi$ but equal to $-f(-x)$ for $-\pi < x < 0$:

$$F(x) = f(x), \qquad 0 < x < \pi,$$
$$F(x) = -f(-x), \qquad -\pi < x < 0. \tag{1}$$

Then $F(x)$ will be an odd function for the interval $-\pi < x < \pi$, and will accordingly possess a Fourier series involving only sine terms. Since we are concerned with only the range $0 < x < \pi$, and since $F(x)$ coincides with $f(x)$ there, we shall have the desired expansion of $f(x)$ in this half-range. Likewise, if we desire a cosine expansion for $f(x)$, we may define a new function $F(x)$ equal to $f(x)$ for $0 < x < \pi$, as before, but equal to $f(-x)$ for $-\pi < x < 0$:

$$F(x) = f(x), \qquad 0 < x < \pi,$$
$$F(x) = f(-x), \qquad -\pi < x < 0. \tag{2}$$

Hence $F(x)$ will be even and therefore will be expressible in a cosine series.

Thus a function $f(x)$ defined over the interval $0 < x < \pi$ is capable of these two distinct types of series. Since these two series are valid over the half-range $0 < x < \pi$, we call them half-range series.

An example will render the procedure clear. Let $f(x) = x + 1$, $0 < x < \pi$, and suppose first that we require a sine expansion. We define the function $F(x)$ by means of equations (1),

$$F(x) = x + 1, \qquad 0 < x < \pi,$$
$$F(x) = x - 1, \qquad -\pi < x < 0.$$

From the graph (Fig. 37), we see that $F(x)$ is an odd function. Hence we need compute only the b's, as follows.

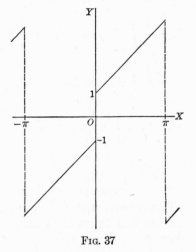

Fig. 37

$$b_n = \frac{2}{\pi} \int_0^\pi (x + 1) \sin nx \, dx = \frac{2}{\pi} \left[-\frac{x \cos nx}{n} + \frac{\sin nx}{n^2} - \frac{\cos nx}{n} \right]_0^\pi$$

$$= \frac{2}{\pi n} (1 - \cos n\pi - \pi \cos n\pi).$$

Consequently we get

$$f(x) = \frac{2}{\pi} \left[(\pi + 2) \sin x - \frac{\pi}{2} \sin 2x + \frac{1}{3} (\pi + 2) \sin 3x - \frac{\pi}{4} \sin 4x + \cdots \right].$$

As a check, we have

$$f\left(\frac{\pi}{2}\right) = \frac{2(\pi + 2)}{\pi} \left(1 - \frac{1}{3} + \frac{1}{5} - \frac{1}{7} + \cdots \right) = \frac{2(\pi + 2)}{\pi} \cdot \frac{\pi}{4} = \frac{\pi}{2} + 1,$$

by relation (3) of Art. 45.

For the cosine expansion, we find from equations (2),

$$F(x) = x + 1, \qquad 0 < x < \pi,$$
$$F(x) = -x + 1, \qquad -\pi < x < 0.$$

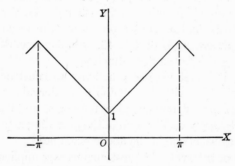

FIG. 38

For this even function (Fig. 38), we have

$$a_0 = \frac{2}{\pi} \int_0^\pi (x + 1) \, dx = \frac{2}{\pi} \left[\frac{x^2}{2} + x \right]_0^\pi = \pi + 2,$$

$$a_n = \frac{2}{\pi} \int_0^\pi (x + 1) \cos nx \, dx = \frac{2}{\pi} \left[\frac{x \sin nx}{n} + \frac{\cos nx}{n^2} + \frac{\sin nx}{n} \right]_0^\pi$$

$$= \frac{2}{\pi n^2} (\cos n\pi - 1),$$

whence

$$f(x) = \frac{\pi}{2} + 1 - \frac{4}{\pi} \left(\cos x + \frac{1}{3^2} \cos 3x + \frac{1}{5^2} \cos 5x + \cdots \right).$$

To check, we get, as we should expect,

$$f(0) = \frac{\pi}{2} + 1 - \frac{4}{\pi}\left(1 + \frac{1}{3^2} + \frac{1}{5^2} + \cdots\right) = \frac{\pi}{2} + 1 - \frac{4}{\pi} \cdot \frac{\pi^2}{8} = 1,$$

$$f(\pi) = \frac{\pi}{2} + 1 + \frac{4}{\pi}\left(1 + \frac{1}{3^2} + \frac{1}{5^2} + \cdots\right) = \frac{\pi}{2} + 1 + \frac{\pi}{2} = \pi + 1,$$

by equation (6), Art. 45, and

$$f\left(\frac{\pi}{2}\right) = \frac{\pi}{2} + 1.$$

For the above illustration we chose a function which is neither even nor odd. If the given function were odd, for example, $F(x)$ would be given by the same expression in x in the two relations (1), and the half-range sine series would be also the full-range series for $-\pi < x < \pi$. Thus, in the case $f(x) = x$, we should automatically get the sine series (8) of Art. 45, valid for $-\pi < x < \pi$. But when finding the half-range cosine series for an odd function $f(x)$, we should get different expressions for $F(x)$ from (2), and a series representing the negative of $f(x)$ for $-\pi < x < 0$, as series (5) of Art. 45. Similar remarks apply to the two half-range series for an even function.

In practice, it is not necessary actually to construct the function $F(x)$, for it coincides with $f(x)$ in the half-interval, $0 < x < \pi$, with which we are concerned, and its values for $-\pi < x < 0$ are immaterial. We need merely apply the theorem of the preceding article to the given function $f(x)$, as was done in the above examples.

48. Change of interval. In most engineering applications of trigonometric series, we require an expansion of a given function over an interval of length different from π or 2π. To this end, we might obtain a development over the interval from $-\pi$ to π, say, and then stretch or compress this interval by means of a transformation of variable to suit the circumstances.

Suppose that we have given a function $f(x)$ defined for the interval $-L < x < L$, where L is any positive number. We regard this interval as the result of elongating (or compressing) the interval from $-\pi$ to π in the ratio L/π. Thus, if we denote by z the variable referring to the latter interval, we must have $x/z = L/\pi$, or

$$z = \frac{\pi x}{L}. \tag{1}$$

Now $f(x) = f(Lz/\pi)$, regarded as a function of z, may be represented by a Fourier series,

$$f\left(\frac{Lz}{\pi}\right) = \frac{a_0}{2} + a_1 \cos z + a_2 \cos 2z + \cdots + a_n \cos nz + \cdots$$
$$+ b_1 \sin z + b_2 \sin 2z + \cdots + b_n \sin nz + \cdots, \quad (2)$$

valid for $-\pi < z < \pi$, which, under the transformation (1) becomes

$$f(x) = \frac{a_0}{2} + a_1 \cos \frac{\pi x}{L} + a_2 \cos \frac{2\pi x}{L} + \cdots + a_n \cos \frac{n\pi x}{L} + \cdots$$
$$+ b_1 \sin \frac{\pi x}{L} + b_2 \sin \frac{2\pi x}{L} + \cdots + b_n \sin \frac{n\pi x}{L} + \cdots, \quad (3)$$

valid for $-L < x < L$. However, we need not go through the intermediate step of developing the z-series (2), but may compute the coefficients a_n and b_n of (3) directly. For we have

$$a_n = \frac{1}{\pi} \int_{-\pi}^{\pi} f\left(\frac{Lz}{\pi}\right) \cos nz \, dz = \frac{1}{L} \int_{-L}^{L} f(x) \cos \frac{n\pi x}{L} \, dx,$$
$$b_n = \frac{1}{\pi} \int_{-\pi}^{\pi} f\left(\frac{Lz}{\pi}\right) \sin nz \, dz = \frac{1}{L} \int_{-L}^{L} f(x) \sin \frac{n\pi x}{L} \, dx. \qquad (4)$$

As an example, let it be required to expand the function

$$f(x) = 0, \qquad -2 < x < 0,$$
$$f(x) = k, \qquad 0 < x < 2,$$

where k is any constant different from zero (Fig. 39). We get from formulas (4), with $L = 2$,

$$a_0 = \tfrac{1}{2} \int_{-2}^{0} 0 \cdot dx + \tfrac{1}{2} \int_{0}^{2} k \cdot dx = k,$$

$$a_n = \frac{1}{2} \int_{-2}^{0} 0 \cdot \cos \frac{n\pi x}{2} \, dx + \frac{1}{2} \int_{0}^{2} k \cdot \cos \frac{n\pi x}{2} \, dx$$
$$= \left[\frac{k}{n\pi} \sin \frac{n\pi x}{2} \right]_{0}^{2} = 0, \qquad n = 1, 2, \cdots,$$

$$b_n = \frac{1}{2} \int_{-2}^{0} 0 \cdot \sin \frac{n\pi x}{2} \, dx + \frac{1}{2} \int_{0}^{2} k \cdot \sin \frac{n\pi x}{2} \, dx$$
$$= \left[-\frac{k}{n\pi} \cos \frac{n\pi x}{2} \right]_{0}^{2} = \frac{k}{n\pi} (1 - \cos n\pi).$$

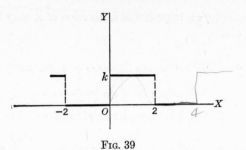

FIG. 39

Hence, substituting in (3), we have

$$f(x) = \frac{k}{2} + \frac{2k}{\pi}\left(\sin\frac{\pi x}{2} + \frac{1}{3}\sin\frac{3\pi x}{2} + \frac{1}{5}\sin\frac{5\pi x}{2} + \cdots\right).$$

Half-range series for the interval $0 < x < L$ may be obtained in similar fashion. For the half-range sine series, we find

$$f(x) = b_1 \sin\frac{\pi x}{L} + b_2 \sin\frac{2\pi x}{L} + \cdots + b_n \sin\frac{n\pi x}{L} + \cdots, \qquad (5)$$

where

$$b_n = \frac{2}{L}\int_0^L f(x)\sin\frac{n\pi x}{L}\,dx, \qquad (6)$$

and for the half-range cosine series, we get

$$f(x) = \frac{a_0}{2} + a_1 \cos\frac{\pi x}{L} + a_2 \cos\frac{2\pi x}{L} + \cdots + a_n \cos\frac{n\pi x}{L} + \cdots, \qquad (7)$$

where

$$a_n = \frac{2}{L}\int_0^L f(x)\cos\frac{n\pi x}{L}\,dx. \qquad (8)$$

For example, let it be required to expand the function (Fig. 40)

$$f(x) = 1, \qquad 0 < x < \frac{a}{2},$$

$$f(x) = -1, \qquad \frac{a}{2} < x < a, \qquad (9)$$

in a cosine series. From (8) we then get

$$a_0 = \frac{2}{a}\int_0^{a/2} 1\cdot dx + \frac{2}{a}\int_{a/2}^a (-1)\,dx = 1 - 1 = 0,$$

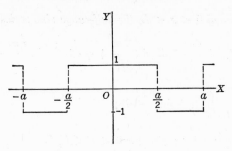

FIG. 40

and for $n = 1, 2, \cdots$,

$$a_n = \frac{2}{a} \int_0^{a/2} 1 \cdot \cos \frac{n\pi x}{a}\, dx + \frac{2}{a} \int_{a/2}^a (-1) \cos \frac{n\pi x}{a}\, dx$$

$$= \left[\frac{2}{n\pi} \sin \frac{n\pi x}{a} \right]_0^{a/2} - \left[\frac{2}{n\pi} \sin \frac{n\pi x}{a} \right]_{a/2}^a$$

$$= \frac{2}{n\pi} \sin \frac{n\pi}{2} + \frac{2}{n\pi} \sin \frac{n\pi}{2} = \frac{4}{n\pi} \sin \frac{n\pi}{2}.$$

Therefore, by (7),

$$f(x) = \frac{4}{\pi} \left(\cos \frac{\pi x}{a} - \frac{1}{3} \cos \frac{3\pi x}{a} + \frac{1}{5} \cos \frac{5\pi x}{a} - \cdots \right). \tag{10}$$

In particular, since (10) represents an even function, we have

$$1 = \frac{4}{\pi} \left(\cos \frac{\pi x}{a} - \frac{1}{3} \cos \frac{3\pi x}{a} + \frac{1}{5} \cos \frac{5\pi x}{a} - \cdots \right), \tag{11}$$

valid for $-a/2 < x < a/2$. We shall make use of this series in connection with a diffusion problem in Chapter VII.

For convenience, we bring together the relationships embodied in equations (3)–(8) in the form of a theorem.

THEOREM. *The Fourier series belonging to a function $f(x)$, defined in the interval $-L < x < L$, is given by*

$$f(x) = \frac{a_0}{2} + a_1 \cos \frac{\pi x}{L} + a_2 \cos \frac{2\pi x}{L} + \cdots + a_n \cos \frac{n\pi x}{L} + \cdots$$

$$+ b_1 \sin \frac{\pi x}{L} + b_2 \sin \frac{2\pi x}{L} + \cdots + b_n \sin \frac{n\pi x}{L} + \cdots,$$

where

$$a_n = \frac{1}{L} \int_{-L}^L f(x) \cos \frac{n\pi x}{L}\, dx, \qquad b_n = \frac{1}{L} \int_{-L}^L f(x) \sin \frac{n\pi x}{L}\, dx.$$

For the half-interval $0 < x < L$, the half-range sine series for $f(x)$ is

$$f(x) = b_1 \sin \frac{\pi x}{L} + b_2 \sin \frac{2\pi x}{L} + \cdots + b_n \sin \frac{n\pi x}{L} + \cdots,$$

where

$$b_n = \frac{2}{L} \int_0^L f(x) \sin \frac{n\pi x}{L}\, dx;$$

and the half-range cosine series, for $0 < x < L$, is

$$f(x) = \frac{a_0}{2} + a_1 \cos \frac{\pi x}{L} + a_2 \cos \frac{2\pi x}{L} + \cdots + a_n \cos \frac{n\pi x}{L} + \cdots,$$

where

$$a_n = \frac{2}{L} \int_0^L f(x) \cos \frac{n\pi x}{L}\, dx.$$

PROBLEMS

1. Find sine and cosine half-range series for the function $f(x) = x^2$, $0 < x < \pi$. Why do these results differ from the result of Problem 2 following Art. 45?

2. Find sine and cosine half-range series for the function $f(x) = e^x$, $0 < x < \pi$. Why do these results differ from the result of Problem 3 following Art. 45?

3. Find sine and cosine half-range series for the function $f(x) = x$, $0 < x \leqq \pi/2$, $f(x) = \pi - x$, $\pi/2 < x < \pi$.

4. Find the Fourier series for the function $f(x) = -1$, $-2 < x \leqq -1$, $f(x) = x$, $-1 < x \leqq 1$, $f(x) = 1$, $1 < x < 2$.

5. Find sine and cosine half-range expansions of the function $f(x) = 2x - 1$, in the interval $0 < x < 1$.

6. Find an expansion for the function $f(x) = 1 + \sin x$, in the interval $-1 < x < 1$. By setting $x = \pi/4$, obtain a series for csc 1.

7. Find an expansion in a series of sines and cosines for the function $f(x) = 2$, $-2 < x < 0$, $f(x) = x$, $0 < x < 2$.

8. Find the half-range cosine series for the function $f(x) = 1 - x$, $0 < x \leqq 2$, $f(x) = x - 3$, $2 < x < 4$.

9. Find the half-range sine expansion for the function $f(x) = x^2 - 2$, in the interval $0 < x < 2$. Using this series, obtain a numerical series for π^3.

10. Find the half-range cosine expansion for the function of Problem 9.

11. Obtain the half-range sine series for the function $f(x) = 2x^2 - 4x$, $0 < x < 2$.

12. Find the half-range cosine series for the function of Problem 11.

13. Find the half-range sine expansion for the function $f(x) = (x - 1)^2$, in the interval $0 < x < 1$.

14. Find the half-range cosine series for the function of Problem 13. Using this series, obtain a numerical series for π^2.

15. Show that a linear substitution of the form $z = mx + k$ will transform any interval $a \leqq z \leqq b$ into any other interval $c \leqq x \leqq d$. Using the proper linear substitution, transform the sine series for unity in the interval $0 < z < \pi$ into the cosine series (11) of Art. 48.

49. Combination of series. It is often necessary to obtain a half-range sine or cosine series, for a given half-range $0 < x < L$, of a linear or quadratic function of x. Instances of such needs will arise in our work with partial differential equations in Chapter VII.

Instead of deriving such series by the application of the theorem of Art. 48, we may conveniently combine known half-range series for 1, x, and x^2. In this connection, formulas 808–812 of Peirce's "Tables" will be found useful, as illustrated in the following example.

Let it be required to find a sine series and a cosine series for the function

$$f(x) = 3x - 9, \qquad 0 < x < 6.$$

To get a sine series for this function, we combine the sine series for x (Peirce, 809) and the sine series for unity (Peirce, 808), using the value $c = 6$ for the maximum value in the x-range. We then get, multiplying the former by 3, the latter by -9, and adding,

$$3x - 9 = 3 \cdot \frac{2 \cdot 6}{\pi}\left[\sin\frac{\pi x}{6} - \frac{1}{2}\sin\frac{2\pi x}{6} + \frac{1}{3}\sin\frac{3\pi x}{6} - \cdots\right]$$

$$- 9 \cdot \frac{4}{\pi}\left[\sin\frac{\pi x}{6} \qquad\qquad + \frac{1}{3}\sin\frac{3\pi x}{6} + \cdots\right].$$

Evidently the terms involving odd multiples of $\pi x/6$ cancel, and the result is

$$3x - 9 = -\frac{18}{\pi}\left(\sin\frac{\pi x}{3} + \frac{1}{2}\sin\frac{2\pi x}{3} + \frac{1}{3}\sin\frac{3\pi x}{3} + \cdots\right),$$

$$0 < x < 6.$$

The cosine series may be similarly found. Multiply Peirce's formula 810 by 3, setting $c = 6$, and subtract 9 from the result. Then we get

$$3x - 9 = -\frac{72}{\pi^2}\left(\cos\frac{\pi x}{6} + \frac{1}{3^2}\cos\frac{3\pi x}{6} + \frac{1}{5^2}\cos\frac{5\pi x}{6} + \cdots\right),$$

$$0 < x < 6.$$

50. R.m.s. value of a function. In a number of physical applications, particularly in connection with alternating-current theory,[*] we have occasion to deal with the concept of root-mean-square (r.m.s.) or effec-

---

[*] See, for example, Art. 75, Chapter VII.

P305

tive value of a function. The r.m.s. value of $y = f(x)$ over an interval from $x = a$ to $x = b$ is defined as

$$\bar{\bar{y}} = \sqrt{\frac{\int_a^b y^2 \, dx}{b - a}}. \tag{1}$$

If, in particular, our interval is of length 2π, say $c < x < c + 2\pi$, equation (1) gives us

$$\bar{y}^2 = \frac{1}{2\pi} \int_c^{c+2\pi} y^2 \, dx. \tag{2}$$

Now suppose $y = f(x)$ is expanded in a Fourier series,

$$y = f(x) = \frac{a_0}{2} + \sum_{n=1}^{\infty} (a_n \cos nx + b_n \sin nx), \tag{3}$$

for $c < x < c + 2\pi$. Then the mean square value, i.e., the square of the r.m.s. value, of y over the given interval is

$$\bar{y}^2 = \frac{a_0^2}{4} + \frac{1}{2} \sum_{n=1}^{\infty} (a_n^2 + b_n^2). \tag{4}$$

To obtain this formula, we shall merely substitute series (3) in equation (2), carrying out the necessary operations formally; that the resulting series (4) converges may be proved without difficulty.[*] When we square $f(x)$, we get terms of the following types:

$$\frac{a_0^2}{4}, \ b_n^2 \sin^2 nx, \ a_n^2 \cos^2 nx, \ a_0 b_n \sin nx, \ a_0 a_n \cos nx,$$

$$2a_n b_m \sin mx \cos nx, \ 2b_m b_n \sin mx \sin nx, \ 2a_m a_n \cos mx \cos nx.$$

Now the integrals, from c to $c + 2\pi$, of the last five of these expressions vanish, by formulas (I)–(V) of Art. 44, whereas

$$\int_c^{c+2\pi} \frac{a_0^2}{4} \, dx = \frac{\pi a_0^2}{2},$$

$$\int_c^{c+2\pi} b_n^2 \sin^2 nx \, dx = \pi b_n^2,$$

$$\int_c^{c+2\pi} a_n^2 \cos^2 nx \, dx = \pi a_n^2,$$

* See K. Knopp, "Infinite Series," p. 361.

by formulas (VI), (VII). Consequently

$$\bar{y}^2 = \frac{1}{2\pi}\left[\frac{\pi a_0^2}{2} + \pi a_1^2 + \pi a_2^2 + \cdots + \pi a_n^2 + \cdots \right.$$
$$\left. + \pi b_1^2 + \pi b_2^2 + \cdots + \pi b_n^2 + \cdots \right],$$

whence equation (4) follows.

As an illustration of the use of equation (4), suppose that we have an alternating-current wave represented by the series

$$i = I_1 \sin (\omega t + \alpha_1) + I_3 \sin (3\omega t + \alpha_3) + I_5 \sin (5\omega t + \alpha_5) + \cdots, \quad (5)$$

where i denotes the instantaneous current at time t; ω is 2π times the fundamental frequency; $I_1, I_3, \cdots$ are the amplitudes of the fundamental, third harmonic, etc.; and $\alpha_1, \alpha_3, \cdots$ are angles representing phase displacements. If we expand each term of the above series by the trigonometric addition formula, we get the current i expressed in the form

$$i = A_1 \cos \omega t + A_3 \cos 3\omega t + A_5 \cos 5\omega t + \cdots$$
$$+ B_1 \sin \omega t + B_3 \sin 3\omega t + B_5 \sin 5\omega t + \cdots,$$

where $A_n = I_n \sin \alpha_n$, $B_n = I_n \cos \alpha_n$. Hence we have from (4)

$$\bar{i}^2 = \tfrac{1}{2}(A_1^2 + B_1^2 + A_3^2 + B_3^2 + A_5^2 + B_5^2 + \cdots)$$
$$= \tfrac{1}{2}(I_1^2 + I_3^2 + I_5^2 + \cdots), \quad (6)$$

which is the square of the effective value of the current. Similarly, if the impressed voltage e is given by

$$e = E_1 \sin (\omega t + \beta_1) + E_3 \sin (3\omega t + \beta_3) + E_5 \sin (5\omega t + \beta_5) + \cdots, \quad (7)$$

the effective voltage will be

$$\bar{e} = \sqrt{\frac{E_1^2 + E_3^2 + E_5^2 + \cdots}{2}}. \quad (8)$$

As a second application of equation (4), we derive a series involving π, of which we shall make use in Art. 52. Consider the function $f(x) = x^2$, $-\pi < x < \pi$, whose Fourier series is readily found by the methods explained earlier in the chapter to be (cf. Problem 9, Art. 45)

$$x^2 = \frac{\pi^2}{3} - 4\left(\cos x - \frac{1}{2^2}\cos 2x + \frac{1}{3^2}\cos 3x - \cdots\right). \quad (9)$$

Now on the one hand, equation (2) gives us as the mean square value of our function

$$\frac{1}{2\pi} \int_{-\pi}^{\pi} x^4 \, dx = \frac{1}{\pi} \int_{0}^{\pi} x^4 \, dx = \frac{\pi^4}{5}. \tag{10}$$

Moreover, from the Fourier expansion (9) we get by equation (4) the series

$$\frac{\pi^4}{9} + 8\left(1 + \frac{1}{2^4} + \frac{1}{3^4} + \cdots\right) \tag{11}$$

as a second expression for the mean square value of x^2 over the interval. Equating the two results, we find the relation

$$\frac{\pi^4}{90} = 1 + \frac{1}{2^4} + \frac{1}{3^4} + \frac{1}{4^4} + \cdots. \tag{12}$$

51. Harmonic analysis. If we have given the values of an unknown function $f(x)$ corresponding to a set of values of the variable x, as in the case of a group of physical measurements, we can gain visual knowledge of the variation of $f(x)$ over the given range by inspection of a graph. It is sometimes desirable to find an equation which will "fit" the graph, i.e., an equation whose graph varies but little from that obtained from our numerical table.

There are a number of ways in which this curve-fitting may be attempted, including polynomial approximation and harmonic analysis.* The main difficulties in a particular problem are usually to choose the most useful type of functional relation which may be assumed to fit, and then to estimate the proper number of constants, coefficients or exponents, which may or should be determined.

We give here one form of harmonic analysis which may be easily and rapidly applied. We shall discuss it merely in connection with a range of values of the variable x from 0 to 2π, since the extension of the method to problems involving other ranges may be made without difficulty, following the procedure outlined for a change of interval given in Art. 48. The following theorem gives the relations upon which the analysis is based.

* See J. Lipka, "Graphical and Mechanical Computation," and Carse and Shearer, "Fourier Analysis and Periodogram Analysis." The method of least squares, applied to curve-fitting, is considered in Chapter IX, Art. 90, of this book.

Theorem. *If the equation of a given curve for the interval $0 \leqq x < 2\pi$ is expressed in a Fourier expansion,*

$$f(x) = \frac{a_0}{2} + a_1 \cos x + a_2 \cos 2x + \cdots + a_n \cos nx + \cdots$$
$$+ b_1 \sin x + b_2 \sin 2x + \cdots + b_n \sin nx + \cdots, \quad (1)$$

then

$$2m(a_m + a_{3m} + a_{5m} + \cdots) = f(0) - f\left(\frac{\pi}{m}\right)$$
$$+ f\left(\frac{2\pi}{m}\right) - \cdots - f\left(\frac{2m-1}{m}\pi\right), \quad (2)$$

and

$$2m(b_m - b_{3m} + b_{5m} - \cdots) = f\left(\frac{\pi}{2m}\right) - f\left(\frac{3\pi}{2m}\right)$$
$$+ f\left(\frac{5\pi}{2m}\right) - \cdots - f\left(\frac{4m-1}{2m}\pi\right), \quad (3)$$

for $m = 1, 2, 3, \cdots$.

To prove this, we use the Euler relations,

$$e^{nix} = \cos nx + i \sin nx,$$
$$e^{-nix} = \cos nx - i \sin nx, \quad (4)$$

where i denotes $\sqrt{-1}$, from which we get, by addition and subtraction,

$$\cos nx = \frac{e^{nix} + e^{-nix}}{2}, \qquad \sin nx = \frac{e^{nix} - e^{-nix}}{2i}. \quad (5)$$

Substituting these expressions in series (1), we have

$$f(x) = \frac{a_0}{2} + \sum_{n=1}^{\infty} (a_n \cos nx + b_n \sin nx)$$

$$= \frac{a_0}{2} + \sum_{n=1}^{\infty} \left[\left(\frac{a_n}{2} + \frac{b_n}{2i}\right) e^{nix} + \left(\frac{a_n}{2} - \frac{b_n}{2i}\right) e^{-nix} \right]$$

$$= \frac{a_0}{2} + \sum_{n=1}^{\infty} \left[\frac{a_n - ib_n}{2} e^{nix} + \frac{a_n + ib_n}{2} e^{-nix} \right].$$

For simplicity, let

$$\alpha_n = \frac{a_n - ib_n}{2}, \qquad \beta_n = \frac{a_n + ib_n}{2},$$

whence

$$a_n = \alpha_n + \beta_n, \qquad b_n = i(\alpha_n - \beta_n), \qquad (6)$$

and

$$f(x) = \frac{a_0}{2} + \sum_{n=1}^{\infty} (\alpha_n e^{nix} + \beta_n e^{-nix}). \qquad (7)$$

Now since $1 = \cos 2n\pi + i \sin 2n\pi = e^{2ni\pi}$, where n is any positive integer, we have on extraction of the $(2m)$th root, $1^{1/2m} = e^{ni\pi/m}$. Let $r_n = e^{ni\pi/m}$ $(n = 1, 2, \cdots, 2m)$ denote the $2m$ distinct $(2m)$th roots of unity; evidently $r_m = -1$ and $r_{2m} = 1$. Then from (7) we find

$$f(0) = \frac{a_0}{2} + \sum_{n=1}^{\infty} (\alpha_n + \beta_n),$$

$$f\left(\frac{\pi}{m}\right) = \frac{a_0}{2} + \sum_{n=1}^{\infty} (\alpha_n r_n + \beta_n r_n^{-1})$$

$$f\left(\frac{2\pi}{m}\right) = \frac{a_0}{2} + \sum_{n=1}^{\infty} (\alpha_n r_n^2 + \beta_n r_n^{-2}),$$

$$\cdots \cdots \cdots \cdots \cdots \cdots \cdots \cdots,$$

$$f\left(\frac{2m-1}{m}\pi\right) = \frac{a_0}{2} + \sum_{n=1}^{\infty} (\alpha_n r_n^{2m-1} + \beta_n r_n^{-2m+1}).$$

Hence

$$f(0) - f\left(\frac{\pi}{m}\right) + f\left(\frac{2\pi}{m}\right) - \cdots - f\left(\frac{2m-1}{m}\pi\right)$$

$$= \sum_{n=1}^{\infty} [\alpha_n (1 - r_n + r_n^2 - \cdots - r_n^{2m-1})$$

$$+ \beta_n (1 - r_n^{-1} + r_n^{-2} - \cdots - r_n^{-2m+1})]. \qquad (8)$$

But for $n = 1, 2, \cdots, m-1, m+1, \cdots, 2m$, we have

$$1 - r_n + r_n^2 - \cdots - r_n^{2m-1} = \frac{1 - (-r_n)^{2m}}{1 + r_n} = \frac{1 - r_n^{2m}}{1 + r_n} = 0,$$

$$1 - r_n^{-1} + r_n^{-2} - \cdots - r_n^{-2m+1} = \frac{1 - (-r_n)^{-2m}}{1 + r_n^{-1}} = \frac{1 - r_n^{-2m}}{1 + r_n^{-1}} = 0,$$

since by the definition of r_n, $r_n \neq -1$ and $r_n^{2m} = 1$ for these values of n, while

$$1 - r_m + r_m^2 - \cdots - r_m^{2m-1} = 1 + 1 + 1 + \cdots + 1 = 2m,$$

$$1 - r_m^{-1} + r_m^{-2} - \cdots - r_m^{-2m+1} = 1 + 1 + 1 + \cdots + 1 = 2m.$$

Moreover, since $e^{i\pi(2rm+s)/m} = e^{si\pi/m}$ when r and s are integers, the above four relations are repeated in the group containing $\alpha_{2m+1}, \cdots,$ α_{4m} and in the group involving $\beta_{2m+1}, \cdots \beta_{4m}$, and so on in the subsequent groups.   Therefore we have

$$f(0) - f\left(\frac{\pi}{m}\right) + f\left(\frac{2\pi}{m}\right) - \cdots - f\left(\frac{2m-1}{m}\pi\right)$$

$$= 2m(\alpha_m + \beta_m + \alpha_{3m} + \beta_{3m} + \alpha_{5m} + \beta_{5m} + \cdots)$$

$$= 2m(a_m + a_{3m} + a_{5m} + \cdots)$$

by the first of equations (6).   This proves relation (2).

Next let $\rho_n = e^{ni\pi/2m}(n = 1, 2, \cdots, 4m)$ be the $(4m)$th roots of unity; then $\rho_m = i, \rho_{2m} = -1, \rho_{3m} = -i, \rho_{4m} = 1$, and $\rho_n^2 = r_n$ for any n. We now have

$$f\left(\frac{\pi}{2m}\right) = \frac{a_0}{2} + \sum_{n=1}^{\infty}(\alpha_n\rho_n + \beta_n\rho_n^{-1}),$$

$$f\left(\frac{3\pi}{2m}\right) = \frac{a_0}{2} + \sum_{n=1}^{\infty}(\alpha_n\rho_n^3 + \beta_n\rho_n^{-3}),$$

$$f\left(\frac{5\pi}{2m}\right) = \frac{a_0}{2} + \sum_{n=1}^{\infty}(\alpha_n\rho_n^5 + \beta_n\rho_n^{-5}),$$

$$\cdots\cdots\cdots\cdots\cdots\cdots\cdots\cdots,$$

$$f\left(\frac{4m-1}{2m}\pi\right) = \frac{a_0}{2} + \sum_{n=1}^{\infty}(\alpha_n\rho_n^{4m-1} + \beta_n\rho_n^{-4m+1}).$$

It follows that

$$f\left(\frac{\pi}{2m}\right) - f\left(\frac{3\pi}{2m}\right) + f\left(\frac{5\pi}{2m}\right) - \cdots - f\left(\frac{4m-1}{2m}\pi\right)$$

$$= \sum_{n=1}^{\infty}[\alpha_n\rho_n(1 - \rho_n^2 + \rho_n^4 - \cdots - \rho_n^{4m-2})$$

$$+ \beta_n\rho_n^{-1}(1 - \rho_n^{-2} + \rho_n^{-4} - \cdots - \rho_n^{-4m+2})].$$

Again, for $n = 1, 2, \cdots, m-1, m+1, \cdots, 2m$, we have

$$1 - \rho_n^2 + \rho_n^4 - \cdots - \rho_n^{4m-2} = 1 - r_n + r_n^2 - \cdots - r_n^{2m-1} = 0,$$

$$1 - \rho_n^{-2} + \rho_n^{-4} - \cdots - \rho_n^{-4m+2} = 1 - r_n^{-1} + r_n^{-2} - \cdots - r_n^{-2m+1} = 0,$$

while

$$1 - \rho_m^2 + \rho_m^4 - \cdots - \rho_m^{4m-2} = 1 - r_m + r_m^2 - \cdots - r_m^{2m-1} = 2m,$$

$$1 - \rho_m^{-2} + \rho_m^{-4} - \cdots - \rho_m^{-4m+2} = 1 - r_m^{-1} + r_m^{-2} - \cdots - r_m^{-2m+1} = 2m.$$

Hence, from the first $2m$ terms of the preceding summation, we get merely $2m\alpha_m\rho_m + 2m\beta_m\rho_m^{-1} = 2mi(\alpha_m - \beta_m)$ since $\rho_m = i$ and $\rho_m^{-1} = -i$, which in turn is equal to $2mb_n$ by the second of equations (6). Likewise, from the next $2m$ terms of our summation, we get only $2m\alpha_{3m}\rho_{3m} + 2m\beta_{3m}\rho_{3m}^{-1} = -2mi(\alpha_{3m} - \beta_{3m}) = -2mb_{3m}$. Again, since

$$e^{i\pi(4rm+s)/2m} = e^{si\pi/2m},$$

we have cyclic repetition, whence equation (3) follows.

Relations (2) and (3) may now be used for curve-fitting as follows. Our first step is to judge, from the appearance of the curve, how many terms of a Fourier series will serve to fit the graph adequately. In the absence of relevant information, only experience will aid in making this initial judgment; however, as we shall see, the present method gives us a basis on which our judgment may be confirmed. Suppose, then, that we decide that we need compute no a's and b's with subscript greater than ten, or, in other words, that we may assume all such coefficients equal to zero. From equations (2) and (3) we then have, since $a_{30} = a_{50} = \cdots = b_{30} = b_{50} = \cdots = 0$,

$$20a_{10} = f(0) - f\left(\frac{\pi}{10}\right) + f\left(\frac{\pi}{5}\right) - \cdots - f\left(\frac{19\pi}{10}\right),$$

$$20b_{10} = f\left(\frac{\pi}{20}\right) - f\left(\frac{3\pi}{20}\right) + f\left(\frac{\pi}{4}\right) - \cdots - f\left(\frac{39\pi}{20}\right).$$

From the curve we measure the necessary ordinates, whence a little addition and subtraction yield numerical values of a_{10} and b_{10}. Now if both these numbers are close to zero, our supposition that coefficients with subscripts greater than ten are negligible is borne out, at least until $a_9, a_8, \cdots$ and $b_9, b_8, \cdots$ are computed. But if either a_{10} or b_{10} is large in comparison with, say, the maximum absolute value of $f(x)$, it may appear advisable to start farther out in the series, and compute, for example, a_{15} and b_{15}.

If, to make our procedure definite, we find a_{10} and b_{10} both small numerically, we can next compute a_9 and b_9, a_8 and b_8, etc. These are all found individually until we reach a_3 and b_3, where we must use the values of a_9 and b_9 previously obtained, since we have

$$6(a_3 + a_9) = f(0) - f\left(\frac{\pi}{3}\right) + \cdots - f\left(\frac{5\pi}{3}\right),$$

$$6(b_3 - b_9) = f\left(\frac{\pi}{6}\right) - f\left(\frac{\pi}{2}\right) + \cdots - f\left(\frac{11\pi}{6}\right).$$

Likewise, the computations of a_2, b_2, a_1, b_1 involve coefficients already determined. Finally, $a_0/2$ may be found from the relation

$$f(0) = \frac{a_0}{2} + a_1 + a_2 + \cdots + a_{10}.$$

When a large number of curves are to be analyzed harmonically, a mechanical device may be used which shortens the labor of computation.*

PROBLEMS

1. Using the sine series for $f(x) = x$, $0 < x < \pi$, apply the method of Art. 50 to show that

$$\frac{\pi^2}{6} = 1 + \frac{1}{2^2} + \frac{1}{3^2} + \frac{1}{4^2} + \cdots.$$

2. From the cosine series for $f(x) = x$, $0 < x < \pi$, deduce the relation

$$\frac{\pi^4}{96} = 1 + \frac{1}{3^4} + \frac{1}{5^4} + \frac{1}{7^4} + \cdots.$$

3. From the sine series for $f(x) = 1$, $0 < x < \pi$, obtain the relation

$$\frac{\pi^2}{8} = 1 + \frac{1}{3^2} + \frac{1}{5^2} + \frac{1}{7^2} + \cdots.$$

4. From the cosine series for $f(x) = (2x - 1)^2$, $0 < x < 1$, obtain the relation

$$\frac{\pi^4}{90} = 1 + \frac{1}{2^4} + \frac{1}{3^4} + \cdots.$$

5. Using the table of values given below, plot accurately the curve $y = f(x)$ and analyze it harmonically, starting with the computation of a_5 and b_5.

x	y		x	y
0	1.98		π	-0.22
$\pi/9$	1.69		$10\pi/9$	-0.61
$2\pi/9$	1.70		$11\pi/9$	-0.58
$\pi/3$	2.15		$4\pi/3$	-0.31
$4\pi/9$	2.79		$13\pi/9$	0.13
$5\pi/9$	3.11		$14\pi/9$	0.73
$2\pi/3$	2.77		$5\pi/3$	1.43
$7\pi/9$	1.82		$16\pi/9$	1.98
$8\pi/9$	0.67		$17\pi/9$	2.17
			2π	1.98

* See W. Koenig, "Mechanical Analysis of Waves," *Bell Laboratories Record.* Vol. XIII, No. 9, p. 258, May, 1935.

52. The use of trigonometric series in beam and bridge problems.
For the application of this subject to the theory of suspension bridges
we give two references: S. Timoshenko, "The Stiffness of Suspension
Bridges," *Am. Soc. C. E. Trans.*, Vol. 94 (1930), page 377; G. C.
Priester, "Application of Trigonometric Series to Cable Stress Analysis
in Suspension Bridges," *Univ. of Mich. Engineering Research Bulletin* 12.
We shall consider here only an introduction to the subject, namely, the
application of trigonometric series to a simple beam carrying a concentrated load or a uniform load.

Suppose that we have a beam of length L ft. simply supported at
its ends and carrying a concentrated load of P lb. at $x = c$, the origin

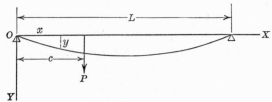

FIG. 41

being taken at the left end (Fig. 41). This problem appeared as Problem 69 following Art. 7 of Chapter I. Solving it by the regular methods,
two different equations were obtained for the curve of the beam, one
holding to the left of P and the other holding to the right of P. Now
we have found that such a function may, by means of trigonometric
series, be represented by a single series throughout the whole interval;
it seems natural, therefore, to try to obtain a trigonometric series
representing the curve of the beam throughout the interval $0 \leq x \leq L$.

We take the y-axis positive downwards and represent the curve of
the beam by a series of sines vanishing at $x = 0$ and $x = L$, namely

$$y = b_1 \sin \frac{\pi x}{L} + b_2 \sin \frac{2\pi x}{L} + \cdots + b_n \sin \frac{n\pi x}{L} + \cdots. \tag{1}$$

We have to determine the b's so that this series will represent the curve
of the beam in the interval $0 \leq x \leq L$.

Let us now obtain the potential energy, W, of the beam represented
by (1). We have, from equation (28), Art. 7(f):

$$W = \frac{EI}{2} \int_0^L y''^2 \, dx. \tag{2}$$

Differentiating (1) twice, we have

$$y'' = -\frac{\pi^2}{L^2}\left(b_1 \sin \frac{\pi x}{L} + b_2 2^2 \sin \frac{2\pi x}{L} + \cdots + b_n n^2 \sin \frac{n\pi x}{L} + \cdots\right).$$

We now square this value of y'', substitute in (2), and integrate, but it will not be necessary to include the cross-product terms, since

$$\int_0^L \sin\frac{m\pi x}{L} \sin\frac{n\pi x}{L}\,dx = 0 \qquad (m \neq n).$$

Furthermore, $\int_0^L \sin^2\frac{n\pi x}{L}\,dx = \frac{L}{2}$, so that

$$W = \frac{EI}{2}\frac{\pi^4}{L^4} \int_0^L \sum_{n=1}^{\infty} b_n^2 n^4 \sin^2\frac{n\pi x}{L}\,dx,$$

or

$$W = \frac{EI\pi^4}{4L^3} \sum_{n=1}^{\infty} b_n^2 n^4. \tag{3}$$

This potential energy, W, is imparted to the beam by the load P acting at $x = c$ and producing the deflection y_c at that point, where

$$y_c = \sum_{n=1}^{\infty} b_n \sin\frac{n\pi c}{L}. \tag{4}$$

If, now, we consider the load P as acting through an infinitesimal displacement dy_c it will do an amount of work $P\,dy_c$ equal to the infinitesimal increase, dW, in the potential energy of the beam and expressible in terms of the infinitesimal changes, db_n, in the b's. We have, then, from (3) and (4),

$$\frac{EI\pi^4}{4L^3} \sum_{n=1}^{\infty} 2n^4 b_n\,db_n = P \sum_{n=1}^{\infty} \sin\frac{n\pi c}{L}\,db_n,$$

or,

$$\sum_{n=1}^{\infty} \left(\frac{EI\pi^4}{2L^3} n^4 b_n - P \sin\frac{n\pi c}{L}\right) db_n = 0.$$

This equation is satisfied, independently of the values of db_n, if and only if

$$\frac{EI\pi^4}{2L^3} n^4 b_n = P \sin\frac{n\pi c}{L},$$

that is,

$$b_n = \frac{2L^3 P}{EI\pi^4} \frac{\sin\,(n\pi c/L)}{n^4}.$$

With the b's thus determined, we substitute them in (1) and have the equation of the curve of the beam:

$$y = \frac{2L^3 P}{EI\pi^4} \sum_{n=1}^{\infty} \frac{\sin\,(n\pi c/L)}{n^4} \cdot \sin\frac{n\pi x}{L}. \tag{5}$$

Example 1. Suppose that P acts at the midpoint of the beam ($c = L/2$); find the maximum deflection.

We have, from (5),

$$y\Big]_{x=L/2} = \frac{2L^3 P}{EI\pi^4} \sum_{n=1}^{\infty} \frac{\sin^2 (n\pi/2)}{n^4}$$

$$= \frac{2L^3 P}{EI\pi^4} \left(\frac{1}{1^4} + \frac{1}{3^4} + \frac{1}{5^4} + \cdots \right). \tag{6}$$

We have shown in Art. 50 that

$$\frac{1}{1^4} + \frac{1}{2^4} + \frac{1}{3^4} + \frac{1}{4^4} + \cdots = \frac{\pi^4}{90}. \tag{7}$$

The sum of the even terms of (7) is

$$\frac{1}{2^4} \left(1 + \frac{1}{2^4} + \frac{1}{3^4} + \cdots \right) = \frac{1}{16} \cdot \frac{\pi^4}{90}.$$

Hence the sum of the odd terms of (7) is $\dfrac{15}{16} \dfrac{\pi^4}{90}$, and we have, substituting in (6),

$$y\Big]_{x=L/2} = \frac{2L^3 P}{EI\pi^4} \cdot \frac{15}{16} \frac{\pi^4}{90} = \frac{1}{48} \frac{L^3 P}{EI}.$$

Without summing the series in (6) we could use the first two terms and obtain

$$y\Big]_{x=L/2} = \frac{2L^3 P}{EI\pi^4} \cdot \frac{82}{81} = \frac{164}{81\pi^4} \frac{L^3 P}{EI},$$

a result which differs from the one obtained above by about 0.2%.

Now consider (Fig. 42) a beam of length L ft. simply supported at its ends and carrying a uniform load of w lb./ft. The weight of a small element of length dc, at distance c from 0, is $w\,dc$. Replacing P by $w\,dc$ in equation (5) and integrating with respect to c from 0 to L, we have

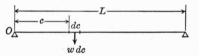

Fig. 42

$$y = \frac{2L^3 w}{EI\pi^4} \sum_{n=1}^{\infty} \frac{\sin (n\pi x/L)}{n^4} \int_0^L \sin \frac{n\pi c}{L}\, dc.$$

Since

$$\int_0^L \sin \frac{n\pi c}{L}\, dc = -\frac{L}{n\pi} \cos \frac{n\pi c}{L} \Big]_0^L$$

$$= \frac{L}{n\pi} (1 - \cos n\pi) = \begin{cases} 0 \ (n \text{ even}) \\ \dfrac{2L}{n\pi} \ (n \text{ odd}), \end{cases}$$

we have for the equation of the curve of the beam

$$y = \frac{4L^4 w}{EI\pi^5} \sum_{n=1,3,5,\cdots}^{\infty} \frac{\sin(n\pi x/L)}{n^5}.$$ (8)

Example 2. Find the maximum deflection of the beam considered above. We have

$$y\Big]_{x=L/2} = \frac{4L^4 w}{EI\pi^5}\left[\frac{1}{1^5} - \frac{1}{3^5} + \frac{1}{5^5} - \cdots\right].$$

The sum of the series in brackets is $5\pi^5/1536$ (Knopp, "Infinite Series," page 240); hence the maximum deflection of the beam is

$$y\Big]_{x=L/2} = \frac{4L^4 w}{EI\pi^5} \cdot \frac{5\pi^5}{1536} = \frac{5}{384}\frac{L^4 w}{EI}.$$

Without summing the series, we could use merely the first term and obtain

$$y\Big]_{x=L/2} = \frac{4}{\pi^5}\frac{L^4 w}{EI},$$

a result differing from the value obtained above by less than 0.4%.

The equation of a beam which is uniformly loaded and also carries a concentrated load is obtained by setting y equal to the sum of the values found in (5) and (8).

PROBLEMS

1. Derive equation (5), Art. 52, by the following alternative procedure. First express the bending moment as

$$M = -\frac{P}{L}(L - c)x, \qquad 0 \le x \le c;$$

$$M = -\frac{Pc}{L}(L - x), \qquad c \le x \le L;$$

and obtain the Fourier half-range sine series for this function in the interval $0 \le x \le L$. Using the fact that $EIy'' = M$, equate the foregoing result to EIy'' as given by equation (1), and thence find b_n.

2. In Example 1 of Art. 52 suppose that P acts at the quarter-point of the beam; find the deflection at the midpoint. Show that, if two non-vanishing terms of the series are used, the result differs by about 0.1% from that which would be obtained from the equation of Problem 69, Art. 7.

3. In Example 2 of Art. 52 find the deflection at the quarter-point. Show that if only one term of the series is used the result is too small by less than 0.4%.

4. A wooden beam 3 in. by 3 in. by 12 ft., simply supported at the ends, weighing 40 lb./ft.^{3}, and for which $E = 15 \times 10^5$ lb./in.^{2}, carries a concentrated load of 300 lb. at a distance of 2 ft. from the left end. Find the deflection at a point 5 ft. from the left end.

5. A cast-iron beam 2 in. by 2 in. by 8 ft., simply supported at the ends and weighing 450 lb./ft.^{3}, carries a concentrated load of 500 lb. at a distance of 16 in. from the right end. $E = 15 \times 10^6$ lb./in.^{2} Find the deflection at distances of 4.0 ft., 4.4 ft., and 4.8 ft. from the left end. Estimate the location of the point of maximum deflection, and check by substituting in the series for y'.

CHAPTER VI

Gamma, Bessel, and Legendre Functions

53. The factorial. The gamma function, which is useful in evaluating certain definite integrals, many of which arise in physical problems, is a generalization of the factorial. We recall the definition of factorial n, written $n!$, for n a positive integer:

$$n! = n(n - 1)(n - 2) \cdots 1. \tag{1}$$

For example, $4! = 4 \cdot 3 \cdot 2 \cdot 1 = 24$. It follows from (1) that

$$(n + 1)! = (n + 1) \cdot n!. \tag{2}$$

We may regard this formula as defining $n!$ when $n = 0$. Thus $1! = 1 \cdot 0!$, or $0! = 1$.

54. Generalization of the factorial; the gamma function. From the definition of $n!$ when $n = 0, 1, 2, 3, \cdots$, as given in the preceding paragraph, we may plot the function $n!$, getting a series of points as in Fig. 43. It is natural to wonder whether we can find a function whose graph is a smooth curve connecting these points, i.e., a function that will reduce to $n!$ when $n = 0, 1, 2, 3, \cdots$, and yield a continuous set of values for non-integral values of n.

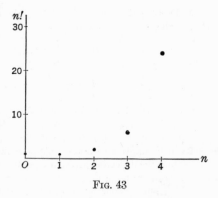

FIG. 43

In searching for such a function we might notice what happens when we integrate by parts $\int x^n e^{-x} \, dx$, with $u = x^n$, $dv = e^{-x} \, dx$, so that $du = nx^{n-1} \, dx$, $v = -e^{-x}$. We have

$$\int x^n e^{-x} \, dx = -x^n e^{-x} + n \int x^{n-1} e^{-x} \, dx. \tag{1}$$

Now we wish to choose limits of integration such that the first term on the right will vanish for both limits. Such a pair of limits is 0 and ∞

since, for any value of $n > 0$ (not necessarily an integer), $x^n e^{-x}\Big]_{x=0} = 0$;

also $x^n e^{-x}\Big]_{x \to \infty} = \dfrac{x^n}{e^x}\Big]_{x \to \infty}$, which is of the meaningless form ∞/∞ for $n > 0$, but by differentiating both numerator and denominator p times, where p is the first integer $\geqq n$, we have

$$\frac{x^n}{e^x}\bigg]_{x \to \infty} = \frac{n(n-1)(n-2)\cdots(n-p+1)}{x^{p-n}e^x}\bigg]_{x \to \infty} = 0.$$

Furthermore, both integrals in (1), taken between 0 and ∞ for $n > 0$, represent definite functions of n. Hence we have, from (1),

$$\int_0^\infty x^n e^{-x}\,dx = n\int_0^\infty x^{n-1}e^{-x}\,dx \qquad (n > 0). \qquad (2)$$

The integral on the right is a function of n which, when multiplied by n gives the same function of $n + 1$, whether n is an integer or a fraction; it reminds us of $(n - 1)!$ when n is an integer, which has this property, for, from (2), Art. 53,

$$n! = n(n-1)!;$$

it is a generalization of the factorial $(n - 1)!$—we call it the **gamma function** of n:

$$\Gamma(n) = \int_0^\infty x^{n-1}e^{-x}\,dx \qquad (n > 0). \qquad (3)$$

Then, from (2), we have

$$\Gamma(n + 1) = n\Gamma(n). \qquad (4)$$

Now if we can compute the value of the integral (3) for values of n throughout a unit interval, say $1 < n \leqq 2$, the formula (4) will give the values of the integral throughout the next unit interval, $2 < n \leqq 3$, from which in turn the values of the integral for $3 < n \leqq 4$ are determined, and so on for all positive values of $n > 1$.

Furthermore, using formula (4) in the form

$$\Gamma(n) = \frac{\Gamma(n + 1)}{n}, \qquad (4')$$

we may, from the values of the integral for $1 < n \leqq 2$, obtain the values of the integral for $0 < n \leqq 1$. Thus we can find the value of $\Gamma(n)$ for all values of $n > 0$ provided we know its value for $1 < n \leqq 2$.

We may now generalize further for negative values of n by letting the formula (4) or (4') define $\Gamma(n)$ when n is any negative number except a negative integer. For example, putting $n = -\frac{1}{2}$ in (4') we obtain $\Gamma(-\frac{1}{2})$ in terms of $\Gamma(\frac{1}{2})$. Since the numbers $0, -1, -2, -3, \cdots$ substituted in turn for n in (4') do not yield finite values for $\Gamma(n)$ we exclude these values from the domain of definition of the gamma function.

The complete definition of the gamma function defining it for all real values of n except when n is zero or a negative integer is

$$\Gamma(n) = \int_0^\infty x^{n-1}e^{-x}\,dx \qquad (n > 0),$$

$$\Gamma(n) = \frac{\Gamma(n+1)}{n} \qquad (0 > n \neq -1, -2, -3, \cdots).$$

$$(5)$$

It is possible to generalize the gamma function still further for complex values of n, obtaining the Gauss pi function $\Pi(n)$, but we shall not use this function in our subsequent work.*

A table of numerical values of $\Gamma(n)$ for $1 < n \leq 2$ is given in Peirce's "Tables." From this table the values of $\Gamma(n)$ for values of n outside the interval $1 < n \leq 2$ (except $n = 0, -1, -2, -3, \cdots$) may be found by use of the relation (4) or (4').

Example. Find the value of (a) $\Gamma(3.6)$; (b) $\Gamma(0.5)$; (c) $\Gamma(-0.5)$.

(a) $\Gamma(3.6) = 2.6\Gamma(2.6) = (2.6)(1.6)\Gamma(1.6)$, by (4).
log $\Gamma(3.6) = \log 2.6 + \log 1.6 + \log \Gamma(1.6)$
$= 0.4150 + 0.2041 + 9.9511 - 10 = 0.5702,$
$\Gamma(3.6) = 3.717.$

(b) $\Gamma(0.5) = 2\Gamma(1.5)$, by (4'),
$= 2(0.8862) = 1.772.$

(c) $\Gamma(-0.5) = \dfrac{\Gamma(0.5)}{-0.5} = -4\Gamma(1.5) = -4(0.8862) = -3.545.$

To show that $\Gamma(n)$ reduces to $(n-1)!$ when n is a positive integer, we start with
$$\Gamma(n) = (n-1)\Gamma(n-1),$$

then replace $\Gamma(n-1)$ by its value obtained from the same formula by changing n to $n-1$, namely $\Gamma(n-1) = (n-2)\Gamma(n-2)$, and so on, thus:
$$\Gamma(n) = (n-1)(n-2)\Gamma(n-2)$$
$$= (n-1)(n-2)\cdots 1 \cdot \Gamma(1).$$

* See, e.g., J. Edwards, "Integral Calculus," Vol. 2, Chapter XXIV.

But $\Gamma(1) = \int_0^\infty e^{-x}\, dx = -e^{-x}\Big]_0^\infty = 1$; hence

$$\Gamma(n) = (n-1)(n-2)\cdots 1 = (n-1)!$$

when n is a positive integer.

We may now fill in the graph of the factorial (Fig. 43) and obtain the graph of $\Gamma(n)$, as in Fig. 44.

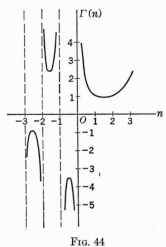

Fig. 44

It is an interesting exercise to find the exact value of $\Gamma(\tfrac{1}{2})$ by integration and compare with the value found by the tables in the preceding example.

$$\Gamma(\tfrac{1}{2}) = \int_0^\infty x^{-\frac{1}{2}} e^{-x}\, dx \qquad (\text{let } x = y^2,\ dx = 2y\, dy)$$

$$= 2\int_0^\infty e^{-y^2}\, dy = 2\int_0^\infty e^{-x^2}\, dx, \qquad \text{let } y = x \quad dy = dx$$

$$[\Gamma(\tfrac{1}{2})]^2 = 4\int_0^\infty e^{-x^2}\, dx \int_0^\infty e^{-y^2}\, dy = 4\int_0^\infty \int_0^\infty e^{-(x^2+y^2)}\, dy\, dx.$$

Changing to polar coordinates, we have

$$[\Gamma(\tfrac{1}{2})]^2 = 4\int_0^{\pi/2} \int_0^\infty e^{-\rho^2}\rho\, d\rho\, d\theta = -2\int_0^{\pi/2} e^{-\rho^2}\Big]_0^\infty d\theta$$

$$= 2\int_0^{\pi/2} d\theta = \pi.$$

Therefore

$$\Gamma(\tfrac{1}{2}) = \sqrt{\pi}. \tag{6}$$

This is the exact value of $\Gamma(\frac{1}{2})$. To four figures we have $\sqrt{\pi} = 1.772$, the value found by the tables for $\Gamma(0.5)$.

55. A useful formula. From the definition of the gamma function (5), of Art. 54, we have

$$\Gamma(m) \cdot \Gamma(n) = \int_0^\infty s^{m-1}e^{-s}\,ds \int_0^\infty t^{n-1}e^{-t}\,dt \qquad (m > 0, n > 0).$$

Letting $s = x^2$, $ds = 2x\,dx$, $t = y^2$, $dt = 2y\,dy$,

$$\Gamma(m)\Gamma(n) = \int_0^\infty 2x^{2m-1}e^{-x^2}\,dx \int_0^\infty 2y^{2n-1}e^{-y^2}\,dy$$

$$= 4\int_0^\infty \int_0^\infty x^{2m-1}y^{2n-1}e^{-(x^2+y^2)}\,dy\,dx.$$

Changing to polar coordinates,

$$\Gamma(m)\Gamma(n) = 4\int_0^{\pi/2} \int_0^\infty (\rho\cos\theta)^{2m-1}(\rho\sin\theta)^{2n-1}e^{-\rho^2}\rho\,d\rho\,d\theta$$

$$= 2\int_0^{\pi/2} \cos^{2m-1}\theta \sin^{2n-1}\theta\,d\theta \int_0^\infty \rho^{2m+2n-2}e^{-\rho^2}2\rho\,d\rho.$$

Letting $\rho^2 = z$,

$$\Gamma(m)\Gamma(n) = 2\int_0^{\pi/2} \cos^{2m-1}\theta \sin^{2n-1}\theta\,d\theta \int_0^\infty z^{m+n-1}e^{-z}\,dz$$

$$= 2\int_0^{\pi/2} \cos^{2m-1}\theta \sin^{2n-1}\theta\,d\theta \cdot \Gamma(m+n).$$

Therefore

$$\int_0^{\pi/2} \cos^{2m-1}\theta \sin^{2n-1}\theta\,d\theta = \frac{\Gamma(m)\Gamma(n)}{2\Gamma(m+n)} \qquad (m > 0, n > 0). \quad (1)$$

If we change $2m - 1$ to n, $2n - 1$ to 0, i.e., m to $\dfrac{n+1}{2}$, n to $\frac{1}{2}$ we obtain as a special case of (1):

$$\int_0^{\pi/2} \cos^n\theta\,d\theta = \frac{\Gamma\left(\dfrac{n+1}{2}\right)}{\Gamma\left(\dfrac{n}{2}+1\right)} \cdot \frac{\sqrt{\pi}}{2} = \int_0^{\pi/2} \sin^n\theta\,d\theta \qquad (n > -1),$$

the last integral being written down by symmetry—it could have been obtained by changing $2n - 1$ to n and $2m - 1$ to 0. If n is an even integer the above expression becomes

$$\frac{\dfrac{n-1}{2}\cdot\dfrac{n-3}{2}\cdots\dfrac{1}{2}\,\Gamma\!\left(\dfrac{1}{2}\right)}{\dfrac{n}{2}\cdot\dfrac{n-2}{2}\cdots\dfrac{2}{2}\,\Gamma\!\left(\dfrac{2}{2}\right)}\cdot\frac{\sqrt{\pi}}{2}=\frac{(n-1)(n-3)\cdots 1}{n(n-2)\cdots 2}\cdot\frac{\pi}{2},$$

and, if n is an odd integer, it becomes

$$\frac{\dfrac{n-1}{2}\cdot\dfrac{n-3}{2}\cdots\dfrac{2}{2}\,\Gamma\!\left(\dfrac{2}{2}\right)}{\dfrac{n}{2}\cdot\dfrac{n-2}{2}\cdots\dfrac{1}{2}\,\Gamma\!\left(\dfrac{1}{2}\right)}\cdot\frac{\sqrt{\pi}}{2}=\frac{(n-1)(n-3)\cdots 2}{n(n-2)\cdots 1}.$$

Hence we have the much-used Formula 483 of Peirce's "Tables" (Wallis's formula):

$$\int_0^{\pi/2}\sin^n\theta\,d\theta=\int_0^{\pi/2}\cos^n\theta\,d\theta$$

$$=\frac{(n-1)(n-3)\cdots 1}{n(n-2)\cdots 2}\cdot\frac{\pi}{2},\ \text{if } n \text{ is a positive even integer;}$$

$$=\frac{(n-1)(n-3)\cdots 2}{n(n-2)\cdots 1},\ \text{if } n \text{ is a positive odd integer;}$$

$$=\frac{\Gamma\!\left(\dfrac{n+1}{2}\right)}{\Gamma\!\left(\dfrac{n}{2}+1\right)}\cdot\frac{\sqrt{\pi}}{2}\qquad (n>-1). \tag{2}$$

Letting $x=\cos^2\theta$, the integral of formula (1) becomes

$$\tfrac{1}{2}\int_0^1 x^{m-1}(1-x)^{n-1}\,dx.$$

The **beta function** of m and n is defined as follows:

$$B(m,\,n)=\int_0^1 x^{m-1}(1-x)^{n-1}\,dx.$$

We then have

$$\int_0^1 x^{m-1}(1-x)^{n-1}\,dx=2\int_0^{\pi/2}\cos^{2m-1}\theta\,\sin^{2n-1}\theta\,d\theta$$

$$=B(m,\,n)=\frac{\Gamma(m)\,\Gamma(n)}{\Gamma(m+n)}, \tag{3}$$

in which $m>0$, $n>0$.

56. A problem in dynamics. A particle moves from rest at a distance a (ft.) towards a center of attraction, the force varying inversely as the distance. Find the time required to reach the center.

If x (ft.) is the distance from the center at time t (sec.), we have

$$\frac{d^2x}{dt^2} = -\frac{k}{x},$$

with $dx/dt = 0$ and $x = a$ when $t = 0$; k (ft.^{2}/sec.^{2}) is a positive constant of proportionality. Setting $v = dx/dt$, $v(dv/dx) = d^2x/dt^2$ (Art. 6), we have

$$v\frac{dv}{dx} = -\frac{k}{x},$$

whence integration yields

$$\frac{v^2}{2} = -k \ln x + c.$$

Since $v = 0$ when $x = a$, $c = k \ln a$, and therefore $v^2 = (dx/dt)^2 = 2k \ln (a/x)$. Taking the square root and using the negative sign since dx/dt is negative, we get

$$dt = -\frac{1}{\sqrt{2k}} \frac{dx}{\sqrt{\ln (a/x)}},$$

so that, if T is the time required to reach the center,

$$\int_0^T dt = T = -\frac{1}{\sqrt{2k}} \int_a^0 \frac{dx}{\sqrt{\ln (a/x)}}.$$

Now let $y = \ln (a/x)$, whence $x = ae^{-y}$ and $dx = -ae^{-y}\,dy$. Then

$$T = \frac{a}{\sqrt{2k}} \int_0^\infty y^{-\frac{1}{2}}e^{-y}\,dy = \frac{a\Gamma(\frac{1}{2})}{\sqrt{2k}} = a\sqrt{\frac{\pi}{2k}} \text{ sec.}$$

PROBLEMS

1. By substituting $y = e^{-x}$ in equation (3), Art. 54, obtain another form for $\Gamma(n)$ (Peirce's "Tables," page 140):

$$\Gamma(n) = \int_0^1 \left(\ln \frac{1}{y}\right)^{n-1} dy.$$

2. Evaluate the following integrals:

(a) $\displaystyle\int_0^\infty e^{-x^3}\,dx;$ (b) $\displaystyle\int_0^\infty xe^{-x^3}\,dx;$

(c) $\displaystyle\int_0^1 \frac{dx}{\sqrt{1-x^4}};$ (d) $\displaystyle\int_0^{\pi/2} \sqrt{\tan \theta}\,d\theta.$

3. Given the function

$$F(m, n) = \int_0^1 x^m \left(\ln \frac{1}{x} \right)^n dx,$$

show that (a) $F(m, n) = \Gamma(n + 1)/(m + 1)^{n+1}$; (b) $\partial F(m, n)/\partial m = -F(m, n + 1)$.

4. Find the area inside the oval $(1 + x^2)y^2 = 1 - x^2$.

5. Find the length of the lemniscate $\rho^2 = \cos 2\theta$.

6. Find the volume generated by rotating one loop of the curve $\rho^2 = \sin \theta$ about the polar axis.

7. Find the area of one loop of the curve $\rho^6 = \sin \theta \cos^2 \theta$.

8. Find the area bounded by the curve $y^2 = 1 - x^4$.

9. Find the area bounded by the curve $(4 - x^2)y^2 = x^5$ and its right-hand asymptote.

10. (a) Find an expression in terms of gamma functions for the area bounded by the curve $x^{2m} + y^{2n} = 1$. (b) Evaluate the result of part (a) when $m = n = \frac{1}{3}$, and check by direct computation of the area enclosed by the astroid.

11. Find the moment of inertia, with respect to the polar axis, of the area bounded by one loop of the curve $\rho^3 = \sin^2 \theta$.

12. Show that

$$B(n, n) = \frac{\sqrt{\pi}\, \Gamma(n)}{2^{2n-1}\Gamma(n + \frac{1}{2})}.$$

13. Find an expression, in terms of n, for

$$\int_0^1 \frac{dx}{\sqrt{1 - x^n}}.$$

Evaluate the result for $n = 4$.

14. Find an expression, in terms of a and n, for

$$\int_0^a \sqrt{a^n - x^n}\, dx.$$

Evaluate the result for $a = 10$, $n = 2$, and check the answer.

15. By means of the substitution $y = h^2 x^2$, show that

$$\int_0^\infty x^n e^{-h^2 x^2}\, dx = \frac{\Gamma\left(\dfrac{n + 1}{2}\right)}{2h^{n+1}} \qquad (n > -1).$$

When $n = 0$, this reduces to the relation

$$\int_0^\infty e^{-h^2 x^2}\, dx = \frac{\sqrt{\pi}}{2h},$$

which arises in connection with the probability curve (Art. 88).

16. Show that, if $c > 1$,

$$\int_0^\infty \frac{x^c}{c^x}\, dx = \frac{\Gamma(c + 1)}{(\ln c)^{c+1}}.$$

Draw and evaluate the area represented by the integral when $c = 2$, and find the coordinates of the maximum point.

17. Using four terms of a series, compute the value of the integral

$$\int_0^1 x^{3/2}(1 - x)^{1/10}\, dx,$$

and compare the result with the value obtained by using formula (3), Art. 55, and a table of gamma functions.

18. Find the distance from the pole to the centroid of the area of one loop of the curve $\rho^4 = \sin^3 \theta \cos \theta$.

19. Show that

$$\Gamma(\tfrac{1}{4})\Gamma(\tfrac{3}{4}) = 2\int_0^{\pi/2} \sqrt{\tan \theta}\, d\theta = 4\int_0^\infty \frac{x^2\, dx}{1 + x^4} = \pi\sqrt{2}.$$

20. Express the value of the integral

$$\int_0^{\pi/2} \frac{dy}{\sqrt{\cos y}}$$

in terms of gamma functions. Hence, using the result of Problem **7**, Art. 30, show that

$$K\left(\frac{\sqrt{2}}{2}\right) = \frac{\sqrt{2\pi}\ \Gamma(\tfrac{1}{4})}{4\Gamma(\tfrac{3}{4})}.$$

21. Combining the results of the preceding problem and Problem 3, Art. 30, show that

$$E\left(\frac{\sqrt{2}}{2}\right) = \frac{\sqrt{2\pi}\ \Gamma(\tfrac{1}{4})}{8\Gamma(\tfrac{3}{4})} + \frac{\sqrt{2\pi}\ \Gamma(\tfrac{3}{4})}{2\Gamma(\tfrac{1}{4})}.$$

22. Combining the results of Problems 20 and 21, show that

$$2\left[K\left(\frac{\sqrt{2}}{2}\right)\right]^2 - 4E\left(\frac{\sqrt{2}}{2}\right)K\left(\frac{\sqrt{2}}{2}\right) + \pi = 0.$$

23. An arch is in the form of an elastica (Art. 33) whose ends are perpendicular to the line joining them. Using the results of Problems 20 and 21, show that $aL = \pi c^2$, and evaluate the ratio L/a.

24. Using Maclaurin's series and gamma functions, evaluate

$$\int_0^{\pi/2} \cos\,(\sin^{1/3} x)\, dx.$$

25. Find the area in the first quadrant bounded by the curve $x^3 + y^{2/5} = 1$ and the coordinate axes.

26. In the problem of Art. 56, if the particle starts at a distance of 25 ft. from the center with an acceleration numerically equal to 8 ft./sec.^{2}, find the time required to reach the center and the time required to travel the first half of the distance to the center.

27. In the problem of Art. 56, if the particle takes 1 hr. to reach the center, find the time required to travel the first third of the distance to the center.

28. Find the time required for a particle to slide from the edge to the bottom of a smooth hemispherical bowl 2 ft. in diameter.

29. A particle starts from rest at a distance 2 ft. from a center of attraction O and moves toward O under the action of a force which varies inversely as the fourth power of the distance from O. If the initial acceleration of the particle is numerically equal to 8 ft./sec.^{2}, find the time required to reach O.

30. A particle starts from rest at a distance 10 ft. from a center of attraction, the force varying directly as the square of the distance. Initially the acceleration is numerically equal to 1 ft./sec.^{2} Using gamma functions, find the time required to reach the center.

31. A particle moves in a straight line in accordance with the law $d^2x/dt^2 = -(2 + 3x^5)/2x^3$, where x (ft.) is the displacement from the center of attraction O at time t (sec.). If it starts from rest at a distance 1 ft. from O, find (a) the time required to reach O; (b) the time required to travel the last $\frac{1}{2}$ ft.

32. A particle starts from rest at a distance 1 ft. from a center of attraction O, the motion being given by the equation $d^2x/dt^2 = -1/x^n$, where $n > 1$. Find an expression, in terms of n, for the time required to reach O. Evaluate the result for $n = 2$, and check by a direct computation.

33. A particle starts from rest at a distance 1 ft. from a center of attraction O, the motion being given by the equation $d^2x/dt^2 = -x^n$, where $n > 0$. Find an expression, in terms of n, for the time required to reach O. Evaluate the result for $n = 1$, and check by a direct computation.

34. Evaluate the triple integral

$$\iiint_V x^{a-1}y^{b-1}z^{c-1}\,dV,$$

where V is the volume cut from the first octant by the plane $x + y + z = 1$.

35. By suitably choosing values of a, b, and c, use the result of Problem 34 to compute the volume of the tetrahedron, its centroid, and its moment of inertia with respect to an edge lying along a coordinate axis.

57. The Bessel function $J_n(x)$.

Bessel functions are named after the German mathematician and astronomer Friedrich Wilhelm Bessel, who was director of the observatory at Königsberg. He obtained them in solving a differential equation connected with a problem in planetary motion. If Bessel functions applied only to this problem they would not be so useful to the engineer and physicist, but it happens that they arise in many practical problems in electrical engineering, acoustics, aeronautics, hydrodynamics, thermodynamics, and the theory of elasticity. For example, they are used in the following types of problems: loading electrical transmission lines to increase inductance; determination of eddy-current loss in the core of a solenoid; the theory of vibration of membranes as in loud speakers; problems dealing with wind-tunnel interference; and problems in heat flow. The student is referred to N. W. McLachlan's treatise, "Bessel Functions for Engineers," in which a bibliography of ninety-three references to theory and applications is given.

Bessel functions are particular solutions of the differential equation

$$x^2 \frac{d^2y}{dx^2} + x \frac{dy}{dx} + (x^2 - n^2)y = 0, \tag{1}$$

which is called Bessel's equation of order n, although the differential equation is, of course, of order 2. The number n may have any value, positive or negative, integral or fractional, or even complex. The form of the general solution of (1) depends on the character of n. We are going to obtain first a particular solution of (1) when n is a positive real number or zero, $n \geqq 0$; this particular solution will be a Bessel function.

We use the method of Frobenius. (See Chapter IV, Art. 42.) Assume a solution in the form

$$y = x^c(a_0 + a_1x + a_2x^2 + a_3x^3 + \cdots), \tag{2}$$

substitute it in the differential equation (1), and determine c and the a's so that the equation is satisfied. We should keep in mind that we are not now trying to find the most general value of y which will satisfy (1), but the simplest particular value of y, and we emphasize this by calling it y_1 and writing (2) in the form

$$y_1 = a_0x^c + a_1x^{c+1} + a_2x^{c+2} + a_3x^{c+3} + \cdots. \tag{3}$$

We now substitute y_1, dy_1/dx, d^2y_1/dx^2 for y, dy/dx, d^2y/dx^2 in (1) and arrange the result in tabular form. At the top of the table are the various powers of x which occur, at the left the terms of the equation in reverse order, with their corresponding coefficients in the body of the table.

	x^c	x^{c+1}	x^{c+2}	x^{c+3}	x^{c+4}	$\cdots$
$-n^2y_1$	$-a_0n^2$	$-a_1n^2$	$-a_2n^2$	$-a_3n^2$	$-a_4n^2$	$\cdots$
x^2y_1	$\cdots\cdots$	$\cdots\cdots$	a_0	a_1	a_2	$\cdots$
$x\dfrac{dy_1}{dx}$	a_0c	$a_1(c+1)$	$a_2(c+2)$	$a_3(c+3)$	$a_4(c+4)$	$\cdots$
$x^2\dfrac{d^2y_1}{dx^2}$	$a_0c(c-1)$	$a_1(c+1)c$	$a_2(c+2)(c+1)$	$a_3(c+3)(c+2)$	$a_4(c+4)(c+3)$	$\cdots$

Since the complete coefficient of each power of x must vanish, we write at the left the equations obtained by placing the sum of each column equal to zero; these equations will be satisfied if c and the a's have the values written at the right.

$$a_0(c^2 - n^2) = 0, \qquad c = n, \ a_0 \text{ arbitrary}$$

$$a_1[(c+1)^2 - n^2] = 0, \qquad a_1 = 0;$$

$$a_2[(c+2)^2 - n^2] + a_0 = 0, \qquad a_2 = \frac{-a_0}{2(2n+2)} \ ;$$

$$a_3[(c+3)^2 - n^2] + a_1 = 0, \qquad a_3 = 0;$$

$$a_4[(c+4)^2 - n^2] + a_2 = 0, \qquad a_4 = \frac{-a_2}{4(2n+4)} \ ;$$

. .

. .

. .

$$a_r[(c+r)^2 - n^2] + a_{r-2} = 0, \qquad a_r = \frac{-a_{r-2}}{r(2n+r)} \cdot$$

. .

. .

. .

We notice that all a's with odd subscript vanish; furthermore we may substitute in a_4 the value of a_2 previously found, then in a_6 the value of a_4, etc., thus obtaining all the a's in terms of a_0 and n:

$$a_4 = \frac{a_0}{2 \cdot 4(2n+2)(2n+4)} \ ,$$

$$a_6 = \frac{-a_0}{2 \cdot 4 \cdot 6(2n+2)(2n+4)(2n+6)} \ ,$$

and, in general, writing the even subscript r as $2k$,

$$a_{2k} = (-1)^k \frac{a_0}{2 \cdot 4 \cdot 6 \cdots 2k(2n+2)(2n+4)\cdots(2n+2k)}$$

$$= (-1)^k \frac{a_0}{2^{2k}k!(n+1)(n+2)\cdots(n+k)} \cdot$$

The general term of equation (3) then becomes

$$(-1)^k \frac{a_0 x^{n+2k}}{2^{2k}k!(n+1)(n+2)\cdots(n+k)} \cdot$$

We now choose a_0 so as to make this expression as simple as possible, since a_0 is arbitrary and we are after a particular solution. We could take a_0 equal to unity, but it is better to let

$$a_0 = \frac{1}{2^n \Gamma(n+1)};$$

this makes the power of 2 in the denominator the same as the power of x in the numerator and produces in the denominator $(n+k)(n+k-1) \cdots (n+1)\Gamma(n+1)$, which is an expanded form of $\Gamma(n+k+1)$ obtained by a repeated application of (4), Art. 54. Equation (3) may then be written

$$y_1 = \sum_{k=0}^{\infty} (-1)^k \frac{x^{n+2k}}{2^{n+2k} k! \Gamma(n+k+1)}. \tag{4}$$

We have here a function of x in the form of an infinite series which is a particular solution of the Bessel equation (1); we call it the **Bessel function $J_n(x)$**:

$$J_n(x) = \sum_{k=0}^{\infty} (-1)^k \frac{x^{n+2k}}{2^{n+2k} k! \Gamma(n+k+1)} \qquad (n \geqq 0). \tag{5}$$

This is the definition of the Bessel function of order n, where n is any positive real number, or zero. The series converges uniformly in any finite interval.

In the special case where n is a positive integer or zero,

$$\Gamma(n+k+1) = (n+k)!,$$

and

$$J_n(x) = \sum_{k=0}^{\infty} (-1)^k \frac{x^{n+2k}}{2^{n+2k} k! (n+k)!} \qquad (n = 0, 1, 2, \cdots). \tag{6}$$

One might think that $J_0(x)$ is the simplest of the J's but, at least from one point of view, $J_{1/2}(x)$ is simpler—it can be expressed in finite form. If $n = \frac{1}{2}$ in (5), we have

$$J_{1/2}(x) = \sum_{k=0}^{\infty} (-1)^k \frac{x^{2k+1/2}}{2^{2k+1/2} k! \Gamma\left(\dfrac{2k+3}{2}\right)}.$$

We now multiply inside the summation sign by $\sqrt{x/2}$ and outside by $\sqrt{2/x}$, at the same time expanding $\Gamma\left(\dfrac{2k+3}{2}\right)$ by a repeated application of (4), Art. 54; then

$$J_{\frac{1}{2}}(x) = \sqrt{\frac{2}{x}} \sum_{k=0}^{\infty} (-1)^k \frac{x^{2k+1}}{2^{2k+1}k! \dfrac{2k+1}{2} \cdot \dfrac{2k-1}{2} \cdots \dfrac{1}{2} \Gamma\left(\dfrac{1}{2}\right)}.$$

Replacing $\Gamma(\frac{1}{2})$ by its value $\sqrt{\pi}$ [equation (6), Art. 54], and cancelling a 2 from the denominator of each of the $k+1$ fractions following $k!$, i.e., cancelling 2^{k+1} into 2^{2k+1}, we get

$$J_{\frac{1}{2}}(x) = \sqrt{\frac{2}{\pi x}} \sum_{k=0}^{\infty} (-1)^k \frac{x^{2k+1}}{2^k k! (2k+1)(2k-1)\cdots 1}.$$

Now if we multiply 2^k into $k!$ by multiplying each factor of $k(k-1)\cdots 1$ by 2, we have $2k(2k-2)\cdots 2$ which, sandwiched into $(2k+1)(2k-1)\cdots 1$, produces $(2k+1)!$, so that

$$J_{\frac{1}{2}}(x) = \sqrt{\frac{2}{\pi x}} \sum_{k=0}^{\infty} (-1)^k \frac{x^{2k+1}}{(2k+1)!},$$

wherein we recognize (at least if expanded) the familiar series for $\sin x$. Therefore

$$J_{\frac{1}{2}}(x) = \sqrt{\frac{2}{\pi x}} \sin x. \tag{7}$$

58. Two differential formulas involving J_0 and J_1. Writing out the expansion for $J_0(x)$ and $J_1(x)$ we have, from (6), Art. 57,

$$J_0(x) = 1 - \frac{x^2}{2^2} + \frac{x^4}{2^4(2!)^2} - \frac{x^6}{2^6(3!)^2} + \cdots + (-1)^k \frac{x^{2k}}{2^{2k}(k!)^2} + \cdots,$$

$$J_1(x) = \frac{x}{2} - \frac{x^3}{2^3 2!} + \frac{x^5}{2^5 2! 3!} - \frac{x^7}{2^7 3! 4!} + \cdots$$

$$+ (-1)^k \frac{x^{2k+1}}{2^{2k+1}k!(k+1)!} + \cdots.$$

We notice that the derivative of the second term in $J_0(x)$ is the negative of the first term of $J_1(x)$, the derivative of the third term in $J_0(x)$ is the negative of the second term of $J_1(x)$, etc. In general, the derivative of the term containing x^{2k+2} in $J_0(x)$ is

$$\frac{d}{dx}(-1)^{k+1}\frac{x^{2k+2}}{2^{2k+2}(k+1)!^2} = -(-1)^k\frac{(2k+2)x^{2k+1}}{2^{2k+2}(k+1)!^2}$$

$$= -(-1)^k\frac{x^{2k+1}}{2^{2k+1}k!(k+1)!},$$

which is the negative of the term containing x^{2k+1} in $J_1(x)$; also, the derivative of the first term of $J_0(x)$ is zero. Hence

$$\frac{d}{dx}J_0(x) = -J_1(x). \tag{1}$$

We now multiply the series for $J_1(x)$ by x and differentiate:

$$\frac{d}{dx}[xJ_1(x)]$$

$$= \frac{d}{dx}\left[\frac{x^2}{2} - \frac{x^4}{2^3 2!} + \frac{x^6}{2^5 2!3!} - \cdots + (-1)^k\frac{x^{2k+2}}{2^{2k+1}k!(k+1)!} + \cdots\right]$$

$$= x - \frac{x^3}{2^2} + \frac{x^5}{2^4 2!^2} - \cdots + (-1)^k\frac{x^{2k+1}}{2^{2k}(k!)^2} + \cdots,$$

that is,

$$\frac{d}{dx}[xJ_1(x)] = xJ_0(x). \tag{2}$$

We shall use formulas (1) and (2) in Chapter VII.

59. The roots of $J_0(x) = 0$ and $J_1(x) = 0$. The student is familiar with the theorem in algebra which states that an equation of degree n,

$$a_0 x^n + a_1 x^{n-1} + \cdots + a_{n-1}x + a_n = 0, \qquad (a_0 \neq 0),$$

has n roots, real or complex. He may have been one of those who wondered why so much work is expended in proving a theorem which is rather obviously true. As a matter of fact it is far from obvious, and might be considered surprising, that this general equation has any root at all. Suppose that n is increased indefinitely; then according to this theorem the number of roots increases indefinitely. Is it obvious, or does it even seem likely, that the equation,

$$a_0 + a_1 x + a_2 x^2 + a_3 x^3 + \cdots = 0,$$

will have an infinite number of roots? As a matter of fact, it may have no root at all, real or complex. For example, the equation

$$1 + x + \frac{x^2}{2!} + \frac{x^3}{3!} + \cdots + \frac{x^n}{n!} + \cdots = 0$$

has no root. It is equivalent to $e^x = 0$, and no finite value of x, real or complex, satisfies this equation. When we form an equation by setting an infinite series in x equal to zero it is usually a difficult problem to determine the nature of its roots or to find them when we know their nature. The nature of the roots of $J_0(x) = 0$ and $J_1(x) = 0$, however, is known, and tables of these roots have been constructed.* The roots of $J_0(x) = 0$ are useful in certain physical problems, for example, the problem in Art. 76, Chapter VII.

The following statements † indicate the nature of the roots of $J_0(x) = 0$ and $J_1(x) = 0$. These equations have no complex roots; they each have an infinite number of distinct real roots; between two consecutive roots of either equation lies one and only one root of the other equation, i.e., the roots of the two equations separate each other; in each equation the difference between consecutive roots, as the roots become larger and larger, approaches the limiting value π, i.e., the functions $J_0(x)$ and $J_1(x)$ are "almost periodic" with (almost) period 2π — the functions behave somewhat like cos x and sin x.

Following are the first five positive roots of $J_0(x) = 0$ and $J_1(x) = 0$ to four decimal places, together with the differences between consecutive roots.

$J_0(x) = 0$		$J_1(x) = 0$	
Roots	Differences	Roots	Differences
2.4048		3.8317	
	3.1153		3.1839
5.5201		7.0156	
	3.1336		3.1579
8.6537		10.1735	
	3.1378		3.1502
11.7915		13.3237	
	3.1394		3.1469
14.9309	.	16.4706	.
.	.	.	.
.	.	.	.
.		.	

* See Jahnke-Emde, "Funktionentafeln," for values of these roots to four or five decimal places.

† For proof of these statements see Frank-v. Mises, "Differentialgleichungen der Physik."

The differences of the roots of $J_0(x) = 0$ are approaching π from below; those of $J_1(x) = 0$ are approaching π from above. The roots of $J_1(x) = 0$ fit in between the roots of $J_0(x) = 0$ to form an increasing sequence.

It is an interesting fact that the sum of the squares of the reciprocals of the positive roots of $J_0(x) = 0$ is $\frac{1}{4}$:

$$\frac{1}{2.4048^2} + \frac{1}{5.5201^2} + \frac{1}{8.6537^2} + \cdots = \frac{1}{4}.$$

This relation is obtained in Art. 76, Chapter VII. The corresponding relation for the positive roots, $\pi/2, 3\pi/2, 5\pi/2, \cdots$ of $\cos x = 0$ is

$$\frac{1}{(\pi/2)^2} + \frac{1}{(3\pi/2)^2} + \frac{1}{(5\pi/2)^2} + \cdots = \frac{4}{\pi^2}\left[1 + \frac{1}{3^2} + \frac{1}{5^2} + \cdots\right] = \frac{1}{2},$$

since the series in brackets is equal to $\pi^2/8$ by (6), Art. 45, Chapter V.

For values of $J_0(x)$ and $J_1(x)$ to four decimal places at intervals of 0.1, see Jahnke-Emde's "Tables." Fig. 45 shows the graphs of $J_0(x)$

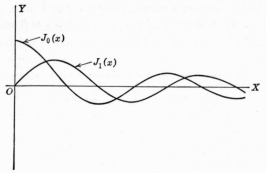

Fig. 45

and $J_1(x)$ for $x > 0$. $J_0(x)$ is an even function like $\cos x$, and $J_1(x)$ is an odd function like $\sin x$, as can be seen from the series representations of the preceding article.

60. Two integral relations involving J_0 and J_1. Using primes to denote derivatives, we may write the Bessel equation of order n, (1) Art. 57, together with its solution (5), in the form

$$x^2 y'' + xy' + (x^2 - n^2)y = 0, \qquad y = J_n(x).$$

Changing x to ax, hence y' to y'/a, y'' to y''/a^2, gives

$$x^2 y'' + xy' + (a^2 x^2 - n^2)y = 0, \qquad y = J_n(ax),$$

and, for $n = 0$,

$$xy'' + y' + a^2 xy = 0, \qquad y = J_0(ax). \tag{1}$$

Now we can get some interesting and useful results by considering two of these Bessel equations of order zero and their solutions:

$$xu'' + u' + \alpha^2 xu = 0, \qquad u = J_0(\alpha x), \tag{2}$$

$$xv'' + v' + \beta^2 xv = 0, \qquad v = J_0(\beta x). \tag{3}$$

Then

$$u(xv'' + v' + \beta^2 xv) - v(xu'' + u' + \alpha^2 xu) = 0,$$

or

$$(\beta^2 - \alpha^2)xuv = x(u''v - uv'') + (u'v - uv'). \tag{4}$$

Now the right member of equation (4) is an exact derivative: $d[x(u'v - uv')]/dx$, so that integration of (4) between $x = 0$ and $x = 1$ gives

$$(\beta^2 - \alpha^2)\int_0^1 xuv\, dx = \left[x(u'v - uv') \right]_0^1 = u'v - uv' \Big]_{x=1}. \tag{5}$$

Since $u = J_0(\alpha x)$, we have from (1), Art. 58,

$$u' = \frac{d}{dx} J_0(\alpha x) = \frac{d}{d(\alpha x)} J_0(\alpha x) \cdot \frac{d(\alpha x)}{dx} = -\alpha J_1(\alpha x).$$

Similarly $v = J_0(\beta x)$, $v' = -\beta J_1(\beta x)$, and equation (5) becomes

$$\int_0^1 xJ_0(\alpha x)J_0(\beta x)\, dx = \frac{-\alpha J_1(\alpha)J_0(\beta) + \beta J_0(\alpha)J_1(\beta)}{\beta^2 - \alpha^2}. \tag{6}$$

Now, if α and β are distinct roots of $J_0(x) = 0$, $J_0(\alpha) = 0$, $J_0(\beta) = 0$, and equation (6) reduces to

$$\int_0^1 xJ_0(\alpha x)J_0(\beta x)\, dx = 0 \qquad (\alpha \neq \beta). \tag{7}$$

However, if $\beta = \alpha$, each being a root of $J_0(x) = 0$, the right member of (6) is of the meaningless form $0/0$, and we may evaluate the limit by considering α as a root of $J_0(x) = 0$ and β as a variable approaching α. Then the right member of (6) is $-\alpha J_1(\alpha)J_0(\beta)/(\beta^2 - \alpha^2)$, and, by differentiating both numerator and denominator with respect to β, we have

$$\lim_{\beta \to \alpha} \frac{-\alpha J_1(\alpha)J_0(\beta)}{\beta^2 - \alpha^2} = \lim_{\beta \to \alpha} \frac{\alpha J_1(\alpha)J_1(\beta)}{2\beta} = \frac{1}{2} J_1^2(\alpha). \tag{8}$$

Hence we obtain from (6)

$$\int_0^1 xJ_0^2(\alpha x)\, dx = \tfrac{1}{2}J_1^2(\alpha). \tag{9}$$

The integral relations (7) and (9) will enable us in the next article to find the coefficients in the expansion of a function of x in terms of Bessel functions.

61. Expansion of $f(x)$ in terms of Bessel functions of order zero. Denote by α_1, α_2, α_3, $\cdots$ the positive roots of $J_0(x) = 0$. Then for a wide class of functions an expansion of the following form, valid for $0 < x < 1$, is possible.*

$$f(x) = A_1 J_0(\alpha_1 x) + A_2 J_0(\alpha_2 x) + \cdots + A_n J_0(\alpha_n x) + \cdots. \qquad (1)$$

To determine the A's we multiply (1) by $x J_0(\alpha_n x)$ and integrate from 0 to 1, assuming the validity of termwise integration. All integrals on the right vanish by virtue of (7), Art. 60, except the one containing A_n, and we have

$$\int_0^1 x J_0(\alpha_n x) f(x) \, dx = A_n \int_0^1 x J_0^2(\alpha_n x) \, dx$$

$$= \frac{A_n}{2} J_1^2(\alpha_n),$$

by (9), Art. 60. Therefore

$$A_n = \frac{2}{J_1^2(\alpha_n)} \int_0^1 x J_0(\alpha_n x) f(x) \, dx. \qquad (2)$$

We then have an expansion for $f(x)$ in the form (1), the coefficients being given by (2).

Example. Expand unity into a series of Bessel functions of order zero.

Here $f(x) = 1$ and $A_n = \dfrac{2}{J_1^2(\alpha_n)} \displaystyle\int_0^1 x J_0(\alpha_n x) \, dx.$

We can perform this integration by use of formula (2), Art. 58, for changing x to $\alpha_n x$ in that formula gives us

$$d[\alpha_n x J_1(\alpha_n x)] = \alpha_n x J_0(\alpha_n x) \, d(\alpha_n x),$$

or

$$d\left[\frac{x J_1(\alpha_n x)}{\alpha_n}\right] = x J_0(\alpha_n x) \, dx.$$

Hence

$$A_n = \frac{2}{J_1^2(\alpha_n)} \left[\frac{x J_1(\alpha_n x)}{\alpha_n}\right]_0^1 = \frac{2}{\alpha_n J_1(\alpha_n)},$$

and series (1) gives for the expansion of unity:

$$1 = \frac{2}{\alpha_1} \frac{J_0(\alpha_1 x)}{J_1(\alpha_1)} + \frac{2}{\alpha_2} \frac{J_0(\alpha_2 x)}{J_1(\alpha_2)} + \cdots + \frac{2}{\alpha_n} \frac{J_0(\alpha_n x)}{J_1(\alpha_n)} + \cdots. \qquad (3)$$

---

* Sufficient conditions are that the function be continuous and have a finite number of oscillations in the interval $0 \leqq x \leqq 1$.

The series is valid for $0 < x < 1$. It does not hold for $x = 1$ since the series then reduces to zero; it does, however, hold for $x = 0$, giving the relation *

$$\sum_{n=1}^{\infty} \frac{1}{\alpha_n J_1(\alpha_n)} = \frac{1}{2}.$$

62. The Bessel function $J_{-n}(x)$. If we change n to $-n$ in series (5), Art. 57, we obtain

$$\sum_{k=0}^{\infty} (-1)^k \frac{x^{-n+2k}}{2^{-n+2k}k!\Gamma(-n+k+1)}.$$

If n is not a positive integer, this series is convergent for all real values of x except zero and defines a function which we call $J_{-n}(x)$.

When n approaches a positive integer N, $\Gamma(-n+k+1)$ becomes infinite if $k = 0, 1, 2, \cdots, (N-1)$, so that for these values of k, the terms of the above series approach zero; the non-vanishing part of the series begins with $k = N$ and takes the form

$$\sum_{k=N}^{\infty} (-1)^k \frac{x^{-N+2k}}{2^{-N+2k}k!(-N+k)!}$$

$$= (-1)^N \left\{ \frac{x^N}{2^N N!} - \frac{x^{N+2}}{2^{N+2}(N+1)!} + \frac{x^{N+4}}{2^{N+4}(N+2)!2!} - \cdots \right\}$$

$$= (-1)^N J_N(x),$$

which we define as the value of $J_{-N}(x)$, where N is a positive integer. We then have for the complete definition of the Bessel function of negative order:

$$J_{-n}(x) = \sum_{k=0}^{\infty} (-1)^k \frac{x^{-n+2k}}{2^{-n+2k}k!\Gamma(-n+k+1)}$$

$$(0 \le n \ne 1, 2, 3, \cdots), \quad (1)$$

$$J_{-N}(x) = (-1)^N J_N(x) \qquad (N = 1, 2, 3, \cdots). \qquad (1')$$

When $n = 0$, (1) gives the same value for $J_0(x)$ as (1) of Art. 57.

The function $J_{-\frac{1}{2}}(x)$, like $J_{\frac{1}{2}}(x)$, can be expressed in finite form. We have, letting $n = \frac{1}{2}$ in (1) (cf. the derivation of the formula for $J_{\frac{1}{2}}(x)$ in Art. 57),

---

* This relation may be established by a more extensive analysis.

$$J_{-\frac{1}{2}}(x) = \sum_{k=0}^{\infty} (-1)^k \frac{x^{-\frac{1}{2}+2k}}{2^{-\frac{1}{2}+2k} k! \Gamma\left(\frac{2k+1}{2}\right)}$$

$$= \sqrt{\frac{2}{x}} \sum_{k=0}^{\infty} (-1)^k \frac{x^{2k}}{2^{2k} k! \frac{2k-1}{2} \cdot \frac{2k-3}{2} \cdots \frac{1}{2} \Gamma\left(\frac{1}{2}\right)}$$

$$= \sqrt{\frac{2}{\pi x}} \sum_{k=0}^{\infty} (-1)^k \frac{x^{2k}}{2^k k! (2k-1)(2k-3)\cdots 1}$$

$$= \sqrt{\frac{2}{\pi x}} \sum_{k=0}^{\infty} (-1)^k \frac{x^{2k}}{(2k)!}$$

$$= \sqrt{\frac{2}{\pi x}} \cos x. \tag{2}$$

The function $J_{-n}(x)$, when substituted for y in the Bessel equation (1), Art. 57, will satisfy it, since $J_{-n}(x)$ differs from the solution $J_n(x)$ only in the sign of n, and n appears only squared in the Bessel equation. Thus, when n is not an integer or zero, we have two independent particular solutions $y_1 = J_n(x)$ and $y_2 = J_{-n}(x)$ of Bessel's equation of order n, and the general solution is

$$y = AJ_n(x) + BJ_{-n}(x), \tag{3}$$

where A and B are arbitrary constants. For example, the general solution of Bessel's equation of order $\frac{1}{2}$,

$$x^2 \frac{d^2 y}{dx^2} + x \frac{dy}{dx} + \left(x^2 - \frac{1}{4}\right) y = 0,$$

is

$$y = AJ_{\frac{1}{2}}(x) + BJ_{-\frac{1}{2}}(x)$$

$$= A\sqrt{\frac{2}{\pi x}} \sin x + B\sqrt{\frac{2}{\pi x}} \cos x,$$

or

$$y = c_1 \frac{\sin x}{\sqrt{x}} + c_2 \frac{\cos x}{\sqrt{x}}.$$

When $n = 0$, (3) reduces to $y = (A + B)J_0(x) = CJ_0(x)$, where C is an arbitrary constant. When n is a positive integer N, (3) reduces to $y = [A + B(-1)^N]J_N(x) = KJ_N(x)$, where K is an arbitrary constant. Thus equation (3) yields only a particular solution of Bessel's equation when n is an integer or zero. To obtain the general solution in this case the functions $J_n(x)$ and $J_{-n}(x)$, which are called Bessel functions of the first kind, are not sufficient, and Bessel functions of the second kind are introduced. However, we shall not discuss these more complicated functions of the second kind, since none of the applications which we shall consider will involve them.*

63. The ber and bei functions. We now consider the following differential equation which occurs in certain problems in electrical engineering and which we shall meet in Chapter VII in connection with an eddy-current problem:

$$x \frac{d^2y}{dx^2} + \frac{dy}{dx} - ixy = 0, \tag{1}$$

where $i = \sqrt{-1}$. This is equation (1) of Art. 60, with $a^2 = -i$, so that we have as a particular solution:

$$y = J_0(ax) = J_0[(-i)^{\frac{1}{2}}x] = J_0(i^{\frac{3}{2}}x). \tag{2}$$

Now $i^{\frac{3}{2}}$ has two values, for

$$i^{\frac{3}{2}} = (-i)^{\frac{1}{2}} = e^{i(3\pi/2 + 2n\pi)/2} \qquad (n = 0, 1),$$

$$i^{\frac{3}{2}} = e^{3\pi i/4} \qquad \text{or} \qquad e^{7\pi i/4}.$$

In the particular solution (2) we choose $i^{\frac{3}{2}} = e^{3\pi i/4}$.

Substituting $i^{\frac{3}{2}}x$ for x in the series for $J_0(x)$, Art. 58, we have

$$J_0(i^{\frac{3}{2}}x) = 1 - \frac{i^3 x^2}{2^2} + \frac{i^6 x^4}{2^4(2!)^2} - \frac{i^9 x^6}{2^6(3!)^2} + \frac{i^{12} x^8}{2^8(4!)^2} - \frac{i^{15} x^{10}}{2^{10}(5!)^2} + \cdots$$

$$= 1 + \frac{ix^2}{2^2} - \frac{x^4}{2^4(2!)^2} - \frac{ix^6}{2^6(3!)^2} + \frac{x^8}{2^8(4!)^2} + \frac{ix^{10}}{2^{10}(5!)^2} - \cdots$$

$$= \left[1 - \frac{x^4}{2^2 4^2} + \frac{x^8}{2^2 4^2 6^2 8^2} - \cdots \right]$$

$$\quad + i \left[\frac{x^2}{2^2} - \frac{x^6}{2^2 4^2 6^2} + \frac{x^{10}}{2^2 4^2 6^2 8^2 10^2} - \cdots \right]$$

$$= \left[1 + \sum_{k=1}^{\infty} (-1)^k \frac{x^{4k}}{2^2 4^2 6^2 \cdots (4k)^2} \right]$$

$$\quad + i \left[-\sum_{k=1}^{\infty} (-1)^k \frac{x^{4k-2}}{2^2 4^2 6^2 \cdots (4k-2)^2} \right].$$

---

* Applications involving these functions may be found in McLachlan's "Bessel Functions for Engineers."

Thus for x real $J_0(i^{3/2}x)$ is complex. We define the ber (Bessel-real) and bei (Bessel-imaginary) functions as the series in the above brackets:

$$\text{ber } x = 1 + \sum_{k=1}^{\infty}(-1)^k \frac{x^{4k}}{2^2 4^2 6^2 \cdots (4k)^2} \; ;$$

(3)

$$\text{bei } x = -\sum_{k=1}^{\infty}(-1)^k \frac{x^{4k-2}}{2^2 4^2 6^2 \cdots (4k-2)^2} \; ;$$

so that

$$J_0(i^{3/2}x) = \text{ber } x + i \text{ bei } x.$$

(4)

We next derive two formulas connecting the ber and bei functions. If the second term of the ber series, namely $-(x^4/2^2 4^2)$, is differentiated and then multiplied by x, the result is $-(x^4/2^2 4)$; the same result with opposite sign is obtained if the first term of the bei series, namely $x^2/2^2$, is multiplied by x and then integrated from 0 to x. A similar relation may be noted between the third term of the ber series and the second term of the bei series. This suggests the following derivation, using equations (3):

$$x \text{ ber}' x = \sum_{k=1}^{\infty}(-1)^k \frac{x^{4k}}{2^2 4^2 6^2 \cdots (4k-2)^2 (4k)} = -\int_0^x x \text{ bei } x \, dx,$$

or

$$\frac{d}{dx}(x \text{ ber}' x) = -x \text{ bei } x.$$

(5)

We may notice further that identical results are obtained by multiplying any term of the ber series by x, then integrating from 0 to x, and by differentiating the corresponding term of the bei series, then multiplying by x. The general derivation follows, using again equations (3):

$$\int_0^x x \text{ ber } x \, dx = \frac{x^2}{2} + \sum_{k=1}^{\infty}(-1)^k \frac{x^{4k+2}}{2^2 \cdot 4^2 \cdot 6^2 \cdots (4k)^2 (4k+2)} .$$

Bringing the first term of the series under the summation symbol, the series appears in the form

$$-\sum_{k=1}^{\infty}(-1)^k \frac{x^{4k-2}}{2^2 \cdot 4^2 \cdot 6^2 \cdots (4k-4)^2 (4k-2)} = x \text{ bei}' x.$$

Hence

$$\frac{d}{dx}(x \text{ bei}' x) = x \text{ ber } x.$$

(6)

Tables giving numerical values of ber x, bei x, ber$'$ x, and bei$'$ x may be found in McLachlan's "Bessel Functions for Engineers," pages 177, 178. Since most of the physical applications of Bessel functions depend also on partial differential equations, we defer the discussion of such prob-

lems until the next chapter, giving here only one application to a problem in mechanics.

64. Wire clamped at lower end. Given a wire of length L (in.) and weight w (lb./in.) clamped at its lower end at a small angle $\tan^{-1} p_0$ to the vertical (Fig. 46). We wish to find the deflection due to bending and the inclination to the vertical at the upper end.

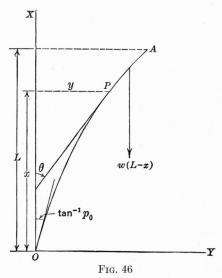

FIG. 46

We first find the differential equation of the curve of the wire. Take the x-axis vertical and the y-axis horizontal through the lower end of the wire, and let $P(x, y)$ be any point on the wire at which we consider the shear, Q, due to the weight of the portion PA of the wire above P. Equating the expression for shear found in Art. 7(f), Chapter I, to the resolved part of the weight of PA normal to the wire, we have

$$Q = EIy''' = -w(L - x) \sin \theta,$$

where E (lb./in.^{2}) is the modulus of elasticity and I (in.^{4}) is the moment of inertia of the area of a cross-section about a horizontal line perpendicular to the axis of the wire. Replacing $\sin \theta$ by $\tan \theta = y'$ for small bending, as in the derivation of the formula for Q, the differential equation of the curve of the wire is *

$$y''' + \frac{w}{EI} (L - x)y' = 0. \qquad (1)$$

Letting $y' = p$, $L - x = r$, $w/EI = c^2$, then $y''' = d^2p/dx^2 = d^2p/dr^2$, and equation (1) takes the form

$$\frac{d^2p}{dr^2} + c^2rp = 0. \qquad (2)$$

* A second method of deriving this equation is given in Problem 19, Art. 67.

To solve this equation and get p as a series in r we use the method of Frobenius, Chapter IV, Art. 42. Note that, at the free end of the wire where $r = 0$, p, the slope, is not to be zero or infinite. We therefore omit the factor preceding the series (1) of Art. 42, Chapter IV, and write

$$p = a_0 + a_1 r + a_2 r^2 + a_3 r^3 + \cdots. \tag{3}$$

Furthermore, since the curvature of the wire is zero at the upper end, A, we must have $y'' = dp/dx = 0$ when $x = L$, and hence $dp/dr = 0$ when $r = 0$, that is,

$$a_1 + 2a_2 r + 3a_3 r^2 + \cdots = 0$$

when $r = 0$, whence $a_1 = 0$. Our trial series for p thus takes the form

$$p = a_0 + a_2 r^2 + a_3 r^3 + \cdots. \tag{4}$$

Substituting this value of p in (2) and arranging the result in tabular form—at the top of the table, the various powers of r which occur, at the left, the terms of the equation with their corresponding coefficients in the body of the table—we have

	Constant	r	r^2	r^3	r^4	r^5	r^6	r^7	$\cdots$
$c^2 r p$		$c^2 a_0$		$c^2 a_2$	$c^2 a_3$	$c^2 a_4$	$c^2 a_5$	$c^2 a_6$	$\cdots$
$\dfrac{d^2 p}{dr^2}$	$2a_2$	$3 \cdot 2 a_3$	$4 \cdot 3 a_4$	$5 \cdot 4 a_5$	$6 \cdot 5 a_6$	$7 \cdot 6 a_7$	$8 \cdot 7 a_8$	$9 \cdot 8 a_9$	$\cdots$

Since the complete coefficient of each power of r must vanish, the sum of each column must equal zero. Hence

$$a_2 = a_5 = a_8 = \cdots = 0, \qquad a_4 = a_7 = a_{10} = \cdots = 0,$$

$$a_3 = -\frac{c^2 a_0}{3 \cdot 2}, \text{ with } a_0 \text{ arbitrary,}$$

$$a_6 = -\frac{c^2 a_3}{6 \cdot 5} = \frac{c^4 a_0}{6 \cdot 5 \cdot 3 \cdot 2},$$

$$a_9 = -\frac{c^2 a_6}{9 \cdot 8} = -\frac{c^6 a_0}{9 \cdot 8 \cdot 6 \cdot 5 \cdot 3 \cdot 2},$$

$$a_{3k} = (-1)^k \frac{c^{2k}a_0}{3k(3k-1)(3k-3)(3k-4)\cdots 6\cdot 5\cdot 3\cdot 2}$$

$$= (-1)^k \frac{c^{2k}a_0}{3^{2k}k!(k-\frac{1}{3})(k-\frac{4}{3})\cdots\frac{2}{3}}.$$

Substituting in (4) we have for a particular solution of (2):

$$p = a_0 \Gamma\left(\frac{2}{3}\right) \sum_{k=0}^{\infty} (-1)^k \frac{c^{2k}r^{3k}}{3^{2k}k!\Gamma(k+\frac{2}{3})}. \tag{5}$$

This reminds us of the Bessel function $J_{-\frac{1}{3}}(az)$, for if we change x to az in (1), Art. 62, with $n = \frac{1}{3}$, we have

$$J_{-\frac{1}{3}}(az) = \left(\frac{az}{2}\right)^{-\frac{1}{3}} \sum_{k=0}^{\infty} (-1)^k \frac{a^{2k}z^{2k}}{2^{2k}k!\Gamma(k+\frac{2}{3})}. \tag{6}$$

The summation in (5) will reduce to that in (6) if we let $c/3 = a/2$ and $r^3 = z^2$; and if we also take $a_0 = \dfrac{(a/2)^{-\frac{1}{3}}}{\Gamma(2/3)}\cdot A$, where A is another arbitrary constant, equation (5) reduces to

$$p = Az^{\frac{1}{3}}J_{-\frac{1}{3}}(az), \tag{7}$$

another form of the particular solution of (2), where $z = r^{\frac{3}{2}}$ and $a = \frac{2}{3}c$.

To satisfy the condition $p = p_0$ when $x = 0$, i.e., when $z = L^{\frac{3}{2}}$, we have, from (7),

$$A = \frac{p_0}{L^{\frac{1}{2}}J_{-\frac{1}{3}}(aL^{\frac{3}{2}})}.$$

Substituting the value of A in (7),

$$p = \frac{dy}{dx} = \frac{p_0 z^{\frac{1}{3}}J_{-\frac{1}{3}}(az)}{L^{\frac{1}{2}}J_{-\frac{1}{3}}(aL^{\frac{3}{2}})}. \tag{8}$$

But $x = L - z^{\frac{2}{3}}$, $dx = -\frac{2}{3}z^{-\frac{1}{3}}dz$; hence

$$dy = -\frac{2p_0 J_{-\frac{1}{3}}(az)}{3L^{\frac{1}{2}}J_{-\frac{1}{3}}(aL^{\frac{3}{2}})}dz.$$

Letting y_L be the displacement of the upper end of the wire from the vertical, and integrating from $y = 0$ to $y = y_L$ while z varies from $z = L^{\frac{3}{2}}$ to $z = 0$,

$$y_L = \frac{2p_0}{3L^{\frac{1}{2}}} \frac{\int_0^{L^{\frac{3}{2}}} J_{-\frac{1}{3}}(az)\,dz}{J_{-\frac{1}{3}}(aL^{\frac{3}{2}})}$$

$$= \frac{2p_0}{3L^{\frac{1}{2}}} \frac{\int_0^{L^{\frac{3}{2}}} \left(\frac{2}{az}\right)^{\frac{1}{3}} \sum_{k=0}^{\infty} (-1)^k \frac{(az)^{2k}}{2^{2k}k!\Gamma(k+\frac{2}{3})} az}{\left(\frac{2}{aL^{\frac{3}{2}}}\right)^{\frac{1}{3}} \sum_{k=0}^{\infty} (-1)^k \frac{(aL^{\frac{3}{2}})^{2k}}{2^{2k}k!\Gamma(k+\frac{2}{3})}}$$

$$= \frac{2p_0}{3} \cdot \frac{\int_0^{L^{\frac{3}{2}}} \left(\dfrac{z^{-\frac{1}{3}}}{\Gamma(\frac{2}{3})} - \dfrac{a^2 z^{\frac{5}{3}}}{2^2\cdot\frac{2}{3}\Gamma(\frac{2}{3})} + \dfrac{a^4 z^{\frac{11}{3}}}{2^4 2!\frac{5}{3}\cdot\frac{2}{3}\Gamma(\frac{2}{3})} - \cdots\right) dz}{\dfrac{1}{\Gamma(\frac{2}{3})} - \dfrac{a^2 L^3}{2^2\cdot\frac{2}{3}\Gamma(\frac{2}{3})} + \dfrac{a^4 L^6}{2^4 2!\frac{5}{3}\cdot\frac{2}{3}\Gamma(\frac{2}{3})} - \cdots}$$

$$= \frac{2p_0}{3} \cdot \frac{\frac{3}{2}L - \frac{3}{8}\cdot\frac{3}{8}a^2 L^4 + \frac{3}{14}\cdot\frac{9}{320}a^4 L^7 - \cdots}{1 - \frac{3}{8}a^2 L^3 + \frac{9}{320}a^4 L^6 - \cdots}$$

$$= p_0 L \cdot \frac{1 - \frac{3}{32}a^2 L^3 + \frac{9}{2240}a^4 L^6 - \cdots}{1 - \frac{3}{8}a^2 L^3 + \frac{9}{320}a^4 L^6 - \cdots}, \tag{9}$$

$$y_L = p_0 L(1 + \tfrac{9}{32}a^2 L^3 + \tfrac{729}{8960}a^4 L^6 + \cdots) \text{ in.} \tag{10}$$

This formula gives the displacement of the upper end of the wire from the vertical. Since p_0L is the displacement of the upper end of the wire when straight, the deflection due to bending is represented by the series (10), omitting the first term.

To obtain the inclination of the wire to the vertical, at the upper end, we let $r = 0$ in equation (8) and denote by p_L the corresponding value of p. Noting that the first term of the series for $r^{\frac{1}{3}}J_{-\frac{1}{3}}(ar)$ is $2^{\frac{1}{3}}/a^{\frac{1}{3}}\Gamma(\frac{2}{3})$, we get

$$p_L = \frac{2^{\frac{1}{3}}p_0}{a^{\frac{1}{3}}L^{\frac{1}{2}}\Gamma(\frac{2}{3})J_{-\frac{1}{3}}(aL^{\frac{3}{2}})}. \tag{11}$$

Then $\tan^{-1} p_L$ will be the required angle of inclination.

If L is large enough so that $J_{-\frac{1}{3}}(aL^{\frac{3}{2}}) = 0$, formula (8) breaks down. This indicates that the differential equation (1), which was set up under the assumption of small bending, is no longer valid. The smallest positive root of $J_{-\frac{1}{3}}(x) = 0$ is 1.87; we must therefore stipulate that $aL^{\frac{3}{2}} < 1.87$, that is, $L < (1.87/a)^{\frac{2}{3}}$. The approximations given by (10) and (11) become less accurate as L approaches the above critical value.

PROBLEMS

1. Compute, correct to four decimal places, the values of $J_0(2)$, $J_1(1)$, $J_{1/2}(\pi/4)$, $J_{-1/2}(\frac{1}{2})$.

2. Derive the formulas

$$\frac{d}{dx}[x^{n+1}J_{n+1}(x)] = x^{n+1}J_n(x),$$

$$\frac{d}{dx}[x^{-n}J_n(x)] = -x^{-n}J_{n+1}(x).$$

3. Eliminate $J_{n+1}(x)$ between the relations of Problem 2, and obtain Bessel's equation (1), Art. 57, with y replaced by $J_n(x)$.

4. Using relation (2), Art. 58, and the Bessel differential equation satisfied by $J_1(x)$, show that

$$xJ_1(x) - (x^2 - 1)J_1(x) = x^2 J_0'(x) + xJ_0(x).$$

Hence deduce relation (1), Art. 58.

5. Show that

$$\frac{d}{dx}J_n(x) = J_{n-1}(x) - \frac{n}{x}J_n(x) = \frac{n}{x}J_n(x) - J_{n+1}(x),$$

and hence that

$$J_n(x) = \frac{x}{2n}[J_{n-1}(x) + J_{n+1}(x)].$$

6. Show that

$$\frac{d}{dx}[xJ_0(x)J_1(x)] = x[J_0^2(x) - J_1^2(x)],$$

and hence evaluate, correct to four decimal places,

$$\int_0^1 x(J_0^2 - J_1^2)\, dx.$$

7. Show that $2J_0''(x) = J_2(x) - J_0(x)$, $4J_0'''(x) + 3J_0'(x) + J_3(x) = 0$.

8. Show that

$$\frac{d}{dx}[J_n^2(x)] = \frac{x}{2n}[J_{n-1}^2(x) - J_{n+1}^2(x)].$$

9. Show that

$$J_{3/2}(x) = \sqrt{\frac{2}{\pi x}}\left(\frac{\sin x}{x} - \cos x\right).$$

10. Obtain a finite expression for $J_{5/2}(x)$, and use it to compute $J_{5/2}(\pi/2)$.

11. Show that $y = xJ_1(x)$ is a solution of the differential equation $xy'' - y' - x^2 J_0'(x) = 0$.

12. Show that $y = x^{1/2}J_{3/2}(x)$ is a solution of the equation $x^2 y'' + (x^2 - 2)y = 0$.

13. Show that $y = xJ_n(x)$ is a solution of the equation $x^2 y'' - xy' + (1 + x^2 - n^2)y = 0$.

14. Show that $y = x^n J_n(x)$ is a solution of the equation $xy'' + (1 - 2n)y' + xy = 0$. When $n = \frac{1}{2}$, show that the general solution of this equation is $y = c_1 \sin x$

$+ c_2 \cos x$. What values must c_1 and c_2 be given to produce the proper expression for the Bessel function of order $\frac{1}{2}$?

15. Show that

$$\int x J_0^2(x) \, dx = \tfrac{1}{2} x^2 [J_0^2(x) + J_1^2(x)] + c,$$

and hence evaluate

$$\int_0^1 x J_0^2(x) \, dx.$$

16. Show that $y = x^{\frac{1}{2}} J_n(x)$ is a solution of the equation $x^2 y'' + (x^2 - n^2 + \frac{1}{4})y = 0$, and evaluate y' for $x = 1$ and $n = 1$.

17. (a) Using the method of Frobenius, find a Maclaurin series solution of the equation $x^2 y'' - xy' + (x^2 + 1)y = 0$, and identify this series as the expansion of $x J_0(x)$. (b) By direct substitution, show that $y = x J_0(x)$ satisfies the equation of part (a).

18. Show that

$$\int_0^a x(\text{ber}^2 x + \text{bei}^2 x) \, dx = a(\text{ber } a \, \text{bei}' \, a - \text{bei } a \, \text{ber}' \, a).$$

19. Using the fact that $y = \text{ber } x + i \, \text{bei } x$ is a solution of the equation $xy'' + y' - ixy = 0$, derive the relations

$$\frac{d}{dx} (x \, \text{ber}' \, x) = -x \, \text{bei } x, \qquad \frac{d}{dx} (x \, \text{bei}' \, x) = x \, \text{ber } x.$$

20. Using relations (5) and (6) of Art. 63, obtain a fourth-order linear differential equation satisfied by ber x.

21. Using relations (1) and (2) of Art. 58, together with integration by parts, obtain the reduction formula

$$\int x^n J_0(x) \, dx = x^n J_1(x) + (n - 1)x^{n-1} J_0(x) - (n - 1)^2 \int x^{n-2} J_0(x) \, dx.$$

22. Using the result of Problem 21, show that

$$\int_0^1 x^3 J_0(ax) \, dx = \frac{a^2 - 4}{a^3} J_1(a) + \frac{2}{a^2} J_0(a),$$

$$\int_0^1 x(1 - x^2) J_0(ax) \, dx = \frac{4}{a^3} J_1(a) - \frac{2}{a^2} J_0(a).$$

23. If $\alpha_1, \alpha_2, \cdots, \alpha_n, \cdots$ are the successive positive roots of $J_0(x) = 0$, show that

$$x^2 = 2 \sum_{n=1}^{\infty} \frac{\alpha_n^2 - 4}{\alpha_n^3 J_1(\alpha_n)} J_0(\alpha_n x).$$

24. Show that

$$J_0(kx) = 2 J_0(k) \sum_{n=1}^{\infty} \frac{\alpha_n J_0(\alpha_n x)}{(\alpha_n^2 - k^2) J_1(\alpha_n)},$$

where the α's are the positive roots of $J_0(x) = 0$ and k is a constant different from all the α's.

25. Show that

$$\ln x = -2 \sum_{n=1}^{\infty} \frac{J_0(\alpha_n x)}{\alpha_n^2 J_1^2(\alpha_n)},$$

where the α's are the positive roots of $J_0(x) = 0$.

26. A steel wire 5 ft. long and $\frac{1}{8}$ in. in diameter, for which the density is 480 lb./ft.^{3} and $E = 3 \times 10^7$ lb./in.^{2}, is clamped at the lower end at an angle of 1° to the vertical. Find the deflection due to bending and the inclination to the vertical at the upper end. Verify the fact that the length of the wire is less than the critical value.

27. By using the first four terms of the series for $J_{-\frac{1}{3}}(x)$, find an approximate value of the smallest positive root of $J_{-\frac{1}{3}}(x) = 0$.

28. Solve equation (1) of Art. 64 by the following alternative method. Making successively the substitutions $y' = p$, $L - x = r^{\frac{2}{3}}$, $p = r^{\frac{1}{3}}z$, $4w/9EI = a^2$, transform (1) into

$$r^2 \frac{d^2 z}{dr^2} + r \frac{dz}{dr} + \left(a^2 r^2 - \frac{1}{9} \right) z = 0.$$

Show that the general solution of this equation is

$$z = A J_{\frac{1}{3}}(ar) + B J_{-\frac{1}{3}}(ar),$$

and determine the constants A and B so that the conditions of the problem are satisfied. The particular solution may be expressed in the form

$$p = \frac{dy}{dx} = \frac{p_0 r^{\frac{1}{3}} J_{-\frac{1}{3}}(ar)}{L^{\frac{1}{2}} J_{-\frac{1}{3}}(aL^{\frac{3}{2}})},$$

from which the value of y_L, equation (10), may be found by integration.

65. Legendre functions.

Another second-order linear differential equation of considerable importance in applied mathematics is Legendre's equation,

$$(1 - x^2) \frac{d^2 y}{dx^2} - 2x \frac{dy}{dx} + n(n + 1)y = 0. \tag{1}$$

Here n is a constant, and the functions satisfying (1) are accordingly called Legendre's functions of order n. When n is zero or a positive integer, equation (1) has polynomial solutions of special interest, as we shall see.

The general method of Frobenius may be applied to Legendre's equation, just as it was to Bessel's. Setting

$$y = a_0 x^c + a_1 x^{c+1} + a_2 x^{c+2} + \cdots, \tag{2}$$

we get, by equating the total coefficient of each power of x to zero, the relations

$$a_0 c(c - 1) = 0, \tag{3}$$

$$a_1 (c + 1)c = 0, \tag{4}$$

$$a_2(c+2)(c+1) - a_0(c+1)c + n(n+1)a_0 = 0, \quad \cdots,$$

$$a_r(c+r)(c+r-1) - a_{r-2}(c+r-1)(c+r-2)$$
$$+ n(n+1)a_{r-2} = 0, \quad \cdots. \quad (5)$$

The indicial equation (3) yields two possible values of c: $c = 0$ and $c = 1$.

When $c = 0$, relation (4) is satisfied, so that a_1 as well as a_0 is arbitrary. The general relation (5) therefore gives, with $r = 2, 3, \cdots$, in turn,

$$a_2 = -\frac{n(n+1)}{2!} a_0,$$

$$a_3 = -\frac{(n-1)(n+2)}{3!} a_1,$$

$$a_4 = \frac{(n-2)n(n+1)(n+3)}{4!} a_0,$$

$$a_5 = \frac{(n-3)(n-1)(n+2)(n+4)}{5!} a_1,$$

and so on, as the student may readily verify. Hence we have, for $c = 0$, two independent solutions of Legendre's equation:

$$y_1 = a_0\left[1 - \frac{n(n+1)}{2!}x^2\right.$$
$$\left. + \frac{(n-2)n(n+1)(n+3)}{4!}x^4 - \cdots\right], \quad (6)$$

$$y_2 = a_1\left[x - \frac{(n-1)(n+2)}{3!}x^3\right.$$
$$\left. + \frac{(n-3)(n-1)(n+2)(n+4)}{5!}x^5 - \cdots\right]. \quad (7)$$

Evidently y_1 is an even function, and y_2 an odd function, of x.

When $c = 1$, (4) requires that $a_1 = 0$, whence $a_3 = a_5 = a_7 = \cdots = 0$, by (5). We also find, from (5),

$$a_2 = -\frac{(n-1)(n+2)}{3!} a_0,$$

$$a_4 = \frac{(n-3)(n-1)(n+2)(n+4)}{5!} a_0, \cdots,$$

and thus the value $c = 1$ furnishes precisely solution (7) over again. Therefore $y = y_1 + y_2$, where y_1 and y_2 are given by (6) and (7), respectively, is the general solution of Legendre's equation. Application of Theorem I, Art. 38, shows that series (6) and (7) are absolutely convergent for $|x| < 1$.

If n is zero or an even positive integer, the coefficients of all powers of x beyond x^n in (6) reduce to zero, so that y_1 becomes a polynomial of degree n. Likewise, if n is an odd positive integer, (7) becomes a polynomial of degree n. Thus, whenever n is zero or a positive integer, the general solution of Legendre's equation contains a polynomial solution, $P_n(x)$, and an infinite series solution, $Q_n(x)$. The *Legendre polynomials* $P_n(x)$ are defined as follows:

$$P_n(x) = (-1)^{n/2} \frac{1 \cdot 3 \cdot 5 \cdots (n-1)}{2 \cdot 4 \cdot 6 \cdots n} \left[1 - \frac{n(n+1)}{2!} x^2 + \cdots \right]$$

$$(n \text{ even}), \quad (8)$$

$$P_n(x) = (-1)^{(n-1)/2} \frac{1 \cdot 3 \cdot 5 \cdots n}{2 \cdot 4 \cdot 6 \cdots (n-1)} \left[x - \frac{(n-1)(n+2)}{3!} x^3 + \cdots \right]$$

$$(n \text{ odd}). \quad (9)$$

Here the coefficients a_0 and a_1 of (6) and (7), respectively, have been chosen so that we have $P_n(1) = 1$ for every positive integral value of n.

It may be shown that $Q_n(x)$, called the Legendre functions of the second kind, become infinite as x approaches ± 1; accordingly, the usefulness of these functions is restricted, and they do not arise in applied mathematics as often as the rational integral functions $P_n(x)$. The remainder of our discussion will therefore be confined to Legendre polynomials.

Although the even and odd functions (8) and (9) seem to be unlike in form, it is possible to get a single expression for $P_n(x)$. When n is even, (8) yields, compactly,

$$P_n(x) = (-1)^{n/2} \frac{1 \cdot 3 \cdots (n-1)}{2 \cdot 4 \cdots n} \sum_{k=0}^{n/2} (-1)^k \times$$

$$\frac{(n-2k+2)(n-2k) \cdots n(n+1)(n+3) \cdots (n+2k-1)}{(2k)!} x^{2k}.$$

Expanding this summation in descending powers of x, from $k = n/2$ to $k = 0$, we get

$$P_n(x) = \frac{1 \cdot 3 \cdots (n-1)}{2 \cdot 4 \cdots n} \left[\frac{2 \cdot 4 \cdots n(n+1)(n+3) \cdots (2n-1)}{n!} x^n \right.$$

$$- \frac{4 \cdots n(n+1) \cdots (2n-3)}{(n-2)!} x^{n-2}$$

$$\left. + \frac{6 \cdots n(n+1) \cdots (2n-5)}{(n-4)!} x^{n-4} - \cdots \right]$$

$$= \frac{(2n-1)(2n-3) \cdots 3 \cdot 1}{n!} \left[x^n - \frac{n(n-1)}{2(2n-1)} x^{n-2} \right.$$

$$\left. + \frac{n(n-1)(n-2)(n-3)}{2 \cdot 4(2n-1)(2n-3)} x^{n-4} - \cdots \right].$$

Likewise, when n is odd, (9) gives

$$P_n(x) = (-1)^{(n-1)/2} \frac{1 \cdot 3 \cdots n}{2 \cdot 4 \cdots (n-1)} \sum_{k=0}^{(n-1)/2} (-1)^k \times$$

$$\frac{(n-2k+1) \cdots (n-1)(n+2) \cdots (n+2k)}{(2k+1)!} x^{2k+1},$$

so that expansion in the reverse order yields

$$P_n(x) = \frac{1 \cdot 3 \cdots n}{2 \cdot 4 \cdots (n-1)} \left[\frac{2 \cdot 4 \cdots (n-1)(n+2)(n+4) \cdots (2n-1)}{n!} x^n \right.$$

$$- \frac{4 \cdots (n-1)(n+2) \cdots (2n-3)}{(n-2)!} x^{n-2}$$

$$\left. + \frac{6 \cdots (n-1)(n+2) \cdots (2n-5)}{(n-4)!} x^{n-4} - \cdots \right]$$

$$= \frac{(2n-1)(2n-3) \cdots 3 \cdot 1}{n!} \left[x^n - \frac{n(n-1)}{2(2n-1)} x^{n-2} \right.$$

$$\left. + \frac{n(n-1)(n-2)(n-3)}{2 \cdot 4(2n-1)(2n-3)} x^{n-4} - \cdots \right],$$

which has precisely the same form as for n even.   Hence, sandwiching in factorials and powers of 2 in much the same way as was done in Art. 57, we find that

$$P_n(x) = \sum_{k=0}^{N} \frac{(-1)^k (2n - 2k)!}{2^n k!(n - k)!(n - 2k)!} x^{n-2k}, \qquad (10)$$

where $N = n/2$ when n is even and $N = (n - 1)/2$ when n is odd. The first few Legendre polynomials are

$$P_0(x) = 1, \qquad P_1(x) = x, \qquad P_2(x) = \tfrac{1}{2}(3x^2 - 1),$$

$$P_3(x) = \tfrac{1}{2}(5x^3 - 3x), \qquad P_4(x) = \tfrac{1}{8}(35x^4 - 30x^2 + 3),$$

$$P_5(x) = \tfrac{1}{8}(63x^5 - 70x^3 + 15x).$$

These illustrate the fact that $P_n(1) = 1$, as was stated above.

Using (10), we may now establish an important and useful relation known as *Rodrigues's formula*. From the binomial theorem, for any positive integer n, we have

$$(x^2 - 1)^n = \sum_{k=0}^{n} \frac{(-1)^k n!}{k!(n - k)!} x^{2n-2k}.$$

To introduce the factor $(2n - 2k)!$ and to get the $(n - 2k)$th power of x, as they appear in the kth term of (10), we differentiate $(x^2 - 1)^n$ n times. Then, using the operator $D = d/dx$, we get

$$D^n(x^2 - 1)^n = \sum_{k=0}^{N} \frac{(-1)^k n!}{k!(n - k)!} \cdot \frac{(2n - 2k)!}{(n - 2k)!} x^{n-2k}.$$

Comparison with (10) shows immediately that we have

$$P_n(x) = \frac{1}{2^n n!} D^n(x^2 - 1)^n; \qquad (11)$$

this is Rodrigues's formula.

As an application of Legendre polynomials, consider the problem of determining the potential at a point P due to two electric charges, numerically equal but opposite in sign. Suppose the charges, q and $-q$, to be a distance $2a$ apart, with O as midpoint as shown in Fig. 47; let $OP = b$, and let angle $AOP = \theta$. Then the potential at P is, by definition,

$$u = \frac{q}{r} - \frac{q}{s} = q\,(r^{-1} - s^{-1}), \qquad (12)$$

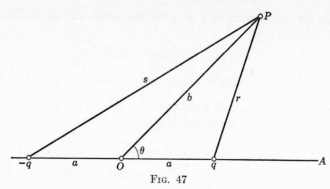

Fig. 47

where

$$r = \sqrt{a^2 + b^2 - 2ab\cos\theta},$$

$$s = \sqrt{a^2 + b^2 + 2ab\cos\theta}.$$

If $b > a$, we may write

$$r^{-1} = \frac{1}{b}\left(1 - \frac{2a\cos\theta}{b} + \frac{a^2}{b^2}\right)^{-\frac{1}{2}} = \frac{1}{b}(1 - 2xy + y^2)^{-\frac{1}{2}},$$

where $x = \cos\theta$, $y = a/b$. Since x and y are both numerically less than 1, $2xy - y^2$ also is, and therefore (Peirce, 750)

$$[1 - (2xy - y^2)]^{-\frac{1}{2}} = 1 + \sum_{r=1}^{\infty} \frac{1\cdot3\cdots(2r-1)}{2\cdot4\cdots2r}(2xy - y^2)^r$$

$$= 1 + \sum_{r=1}^{\infty} \frac{(2r)!}{2^{2r}(r!)^2}(2xy - y^2)^r.$$

But we also have, by the binomial theorem, for each positive integer r,

$$(2xy - y^2)^r = \sum_{j=0}^{r} \frac{(-1)^j r!}{j!(r-j)!} 2^{r-j} x^{r-j} y^{r+j},$$

whence

$$(1 - 2xy + y^2)^{-\frac{1}{2}} = 1 + \sum_{r=1}^{\infty} \sum_{j=0}^{r} \frac{(-1)^j(2r)! x^{r-j}}{2^{r+j} j! r!(r-j)!} y^{r+j}.$$

Now let $r + j$ have a fixed value n; as j runs through the values 0, 1, $\cdots$, k, $\cdots$, n, then r will have the corresponding values n, $n - 1$, $\cdots$, $n - k$, $\cdots$, 0, so that the total coefficient of $y^{r+j} = y^n$ will be

$$\sum_{k=0}^{N} \frac{(-1)^k(2n-2k)! x^{n-2k}}{2^n k!(n-k)!(n-2k)!} = P_n(x),$$

by (10). We therefore have the relation

$$(1 - 2xy + y^2)^{-\frac{1}{2}} = 1 + \sum_{n=1}^{\infty} P_n(x)y^n = \sum_{n=0}^{\infty} P_n(x)y^n, \qquad (13)$$

valid for $|x| < 1$, $|y| < 1$. Changing x into $-x$, we also have

$$(1 + 2xy + y^2)^{-\frac{1}{2}} = \sum_{n=0}^{\infty} P_n(-x)y^n,$$

and therefore (12) becomes

$$u = \frac{q}{b} \sum_{n=0}^{\infty} \left[P_n(\cos \theta) - P_n(-\cos \theta) \right] \left(\frac{a}{b}\right)^n, \qquad (14)$$

since $x = \cos \theta$, $y = a/b$. But, if n is even, $P_n(x)$ is an even function, so that $P_n(-\cos \theta) = P_n(\cos \theta)$, and consequently all even powers in (14) vanish. On the other hand, when n is odd, $P_n(x)$ is an odd function, whence $P_n(-\cos \theta) = -P_n(\cos \theta)$ and the odd powers in (14) are duplicated. Hence, for $b > a$,

$$u = \frac{2q}{b} \sum_{n=0}^{\infty} P_{2n+1}(\cos \theta) \left(\frac{a}{b}\right)^{2n+1}. \qquad (15)$$

When b is very large compared to a, a single term of (15) may be taken as an approximation to the exact value of u. Therefore the potential is nearly equal to

$$\frac{2q}{b} P_1(\cos \theta) \left(\frac{a}{b}\right) = \frac{2qa}{b^2} \cos \theta.$$

The quantity $2qa$ is called the dipole moment; denoting this by μ, we have, as the dipole potential,

$$u_d = \frac{\mu \cos \theta}{b^2}.$$

If $b < a$, the expression for the potential at P becomes

$$u = \frac{2q}{a} \sum_{n=0}^{\infty} P_{2n+1}(\cos \theta) \left(\frac{b}{a}\right)^{2n+1}; \qquad (16)$$

this follows at once from (15), for we have merely to interchange the letters a and b throughout, as we may since the expressions for the distances r and s are symmetric in a and b.

The foregoing application is one instance of the way in which a function may be expanded in a series of Legendre polynomials $P_n(x)$, valid for $|x| < 1$. More general types of expansions, analogous to those obtained with Bessel functions, are also obtainable as follows. From Rodrigues's formula (11), we have, for k any positive integer or zero,

$$x^k P_n(x) = \frac{1}{2^n n!} x^k D^n (x^2 - 1)^n.$$

Integrating by parts between the end points $x = -1$ and $x = 1$, we get, when $n = 1, 2, \cdots$,

$$2^n n! \int_{-1}^1 x^k P_n(x)\, dx$$

$$= \int_{-1}^1 x^k [D^n (x^2 - 1)^n]\, dx$$

$$= \left[x^k D^{n-1}(x^2 - 1)^n \right]_{-1}^1 - k \int_{-1}^1 x^{k-1}[D^{n-1}(x^2 - 1)^n]\, dx.$$

Since the $(n - 1)$th derivative of $(x^2 - 1)^n$ has $x^2 - 1$ as a factor, the first term of the last member vanishes for $x = 1$ and $x = -1$. Continuing the process of integration by parts, we thus find that

$$\int_{-1}^1 x^k P_n(x)\, dx = 0, \tag{17}$$

for $k < n$. Since $P_k(x)$ is a polynomial of degree k, it follows that

$$\int_{-1}^1 P_k(x) P_n(x)\, dx = 0, \tag{18}$$

for $k < n$. Moreover, since k and n are interchangeable in (18), this relation holds for $k > n$ as well. But, when $k = n$, n successive integrations by parts yield

$$2^n n! \int_{-1}^1 x^n P_n(x)\, dx = (-1)^n n! \int_{-1}^1 (x^2 - 1)^n\, dx = n! \int_{-1}^1 (1 - x^2)^n\, dx.$$

Setting $x = \sin\theta$, $dx = \cos\theta\, d\theta$, this leads to

$$2^n \int_{-1}^1 x^n P_n(x)\, dx = \int_{-\pi/2}^{\pi/2} \cos^{2n+1}\theta\, d\theta$$

$$= 2 \int_0^{\pi/2} \cos^{2n+1}\theta\, d\theta$$

$$= 2\, \frac{2n(2n - 2)\cdots 4 \cdot 2}{(2n + 1)(2n - 1)\cdots 3 \cdot 1}$$

by Wallis's formula (Art. 55). Dividing by 2^n and completing factorials, this becomes

$$\int_{-1}^{1} x^n P_n(x)\, dx = \frac{2^{n+1}(n!)^2}{(2n+1)!}. \tag{19}$$

Hence, from (10) and (18), we have

$$\int_{-1}^{1} [P_n(x)]^2\, dx = \frac{(2n)!}{2^n(n!)^2} \cdot \frac{2^{n+1}(n!)^2}{(2n+1)!} = \frac{2}{2n+1}. \tag{20}$$

These results suggest the following procedure. Let $f(x)$ be a function defined from $x = -1$ to $x = 1$, and assume that an expansion of the form

$$f(x) = \sum_{n=0}^{\infty} B_n P_n(x) \tag{21}$$

is obtainable. To compute the coefficients B_n, multiply both members of (21) by $P_n(x)$ and integrate over the interval of definition of $f(x)$; relations (18) and (20) then yield

$$\int_{-1}^{1} f(x) P_n(x)\, dx = B_n \int_{-1}^{1} [P_n(x)]^2\, dx = \frac{2}{2n+1} B_n,$$

or

$$B_n = \frac{2n+1}{2} \int_{-1}^{1} f(x) P_n(x)\, dx. \tag{22}$$

Example. Find the Legendre-polynomial series representing the function $f(x) = -1,\ -1 < x < 0,\ f(x) = 1,\ 0 < x < 1$.

Formula (22), together with (10), gives

$$B_0 = \tfrac{1}{2}\int_{-1}^{0} (-1)(1)\, dx + \tfrac{1}{2}\int_{0}^{1} (1)(1)\, dx = -\tfrac{1}{2} + \tfrac{1}{2} = 0,$$

$$B_1 = \tfrac{3}{2}\int_{-1}^{0} (-1)(x)\, dx + \tfrac{3}{2}\int_{0}^{1} (1)(x)\, dx = \tfrac{3}{4} + \tfrac{3}{4} = \tfrac{3}{2},$$

$$B_2 = \tfrac{5}{2}\int_{-1}^{0} (-1)\tfrac{1}{2}(3x^2 - 1)\, dx + \tfrac{5}{2}\int_{0}^{1} (1)\tfrac{1}{2}(3x^2 - 1)\, dx = 0,$$

$$B_3 = -\tfrac{7}{2}\int_{-1}^{0} \tfrac{1}{2}(5x^3 - 3x)\, dx + \tfrac{7}{2}\int_{0}^{1} \tfrac{1}{2}(5x^3 - 3x)\, dx = -\tfrac{7}{8},$$

$$B_4 = -\tfrac{9}{2}\int_{-1}^{0} \tfrac{1}{8}(35x^4 - 30x^2 + 3)\, dx + \tfrac{9}{2}\int_{0}^{1} \tfrac{1}{8}(35x^4 - 30x^2 + 3)\, dx = 0,$$

$$B_5 = -\tfrac{11}{2}\int_{-1}^{0} \tfrac{1}{8}(63x^5 - 70x^3 + 15x)\, dx$$

$$+ \tfrac{11}{2}\int_{0}^{1} \tfrac{1}{8}(63x^5 - 70x^3 + 15x)\, dx = \tfrac{11}{16},$$

and so on. Therefore

$$f(x) = \tfrac{3}{2}P_1(x) - \tfrac{7}{8}P_3(x) + \tfrac{11}{16}P_5(x) - \cdots.$$

The function of this example is odd, and consequently its expansion contains only odd Legendre polynomials. Similarly, the series for an even function involves only $P_0(x)$, $P_2(x)$, $P_4(x)$, $\cdots$.

PROBLEMS

1. If $n = 0$ or $n = -1$, solve Legendre's equation to get $y = a_0 + a_1 \tanh^{-1} x$ as general solution. Show that each of these special values of n also yields that solution from series (6) and (7).

2. Verify the statement of Art. 65 that series (6) and (7) converge absolutely for $|x| < 1$.

3. Using relation (13), show that, when n is a positive integer, $P_n(1) = 1$, $P_n(-1) = (-1)^n$, $P_{2n-1}(0) = 0$, $P_{2n}(0) = (-1)^n(2n)!/2^{2n}(n!)^2$.

4. Show that $P_{2n}'(0) = 0$, $P_{2n+1}'(0) = (-1)^n(2n + 1)!/2^{2n}(n!)^2$.

5. Show that $x^2 = \tfrac{2}{3}P_2(x) + \tfrac{1}{3}P_0(x)$, $x^3 = \tfrac{2}{5}P_3(x) + \tfrac{3}{5}P_1(x)$, $x^4 = \tfrac{8}{35}P_4(x) + \tfrac{4}{7}P_2(x) + \tfrac{1}{5}P_0(x)$. Also express x^5 as a linear function of $P_5(x)$, $P_3(x)$, and $P_1(x)$.

6. By differentiation of relation (13), with respect to y, show that

$$(x - y) \sum_{n=0}^{\infty} P_n(x)y^n = (1 - 2xy + y^2) \sum_{n=1}^{\infty} nP_n(x)y^{n-1}.$$

Equating coefficients of y^n, derive the recurrence relation

$$(n + 1)P_{n+1}(x) - (2n + 1)xP_n(x) + nP_{n-1}(x) = 0$$

connecting the Legendre polynomials of degrees $n - 1$, n, and $n + 1$.

7. Differentiate relation (13) partially, with respect to x and y in turn, equate the expressions for $(1 - 2xy + y^2)^{-3/2}$ thus obtained, and hence show that $nP_n(x) = xP_n'(x) - P_{n-1}'(x)$.

8. Using the results of Problems 6 and 7, show that $(2n + 1)P_n(x) = P_{n+1}'(x) - P_{n-1}'(x)$.

9. Show that $\displaystyle\int_{-1}^{1} xP_n(x)P_{n-1}(x)\, dx = 2n/(4n^2 - 1)$.

10. Using the result of Problem 8, show that $P_n'(x) = (2n - 1)P_{n-1}(x) + (2n - 5)P_{n-3}(x) + (2n - 9)P_{n-5}(x) + \cdots$.

11. Using the results of Problems 6 and 10, show that $xP_n'(x) = nP_n(x) + (2n - 3)P_{n-2}(x) + (2n - 7)P_{n-4}(x) + \cdots$.

12. Using the fact that $P_n(x)$ satisfies Legendre's equation, together with the result of Problem 8, show that $(2n + 1)(1 - x^2)P_n'(x) = n(n + 1)[P_{n-1}(x) - P_{n+1}(x)]$.

13. Show that $\displaystyle\int_{-1}^{1} (1 - x^2)[P_n'(x)]^2\, dx = 2n(n + 1)/(2n + 1)$.

14. Using the results of Problems 7 and 8, show that

$$(m + n + 1)\int_0^1 x^m P_n(x)\, dx = m \int_0^1 x^{m-1} P_{n-1}(x)\, dx = (m - n + 2)\int_0^1 x^m P_{n-2}(x)\, dx.$$

15. If $f(x) = 0$, $-1 < x \leqq 0$, and $f(x) = x$, $0 < x < 1$, show that $f(x) = \tfrac{1}{4}P_0(x) + \tfrac{1}{2}P_1(x) + \tfrac{5}{16}P_2(x) - \tfrac{3}{32}P_4(x) + \cdots$.

16. If $f(\theta)$ is defined for $0 < \theta < \pi$, show that

$$f(\theta) = \tfrac{1}{2} \sum_{n=0}^{\infty} (2n + 1)P_n(\cos \theta) \cdot \int_0^{\pi} f(\theta)P_n(\cos \theta) \sin \theta \, d\theta.$$

17. Let $f(\theta) = 1$, $0 < \theta < \pi/2$, $f(\theta) = 0$, $\pi/2 < \theta < \pi$. Using the results of Problems 3, 8, and 16, show that

$$f(\theta) = \frac{1}{2} + \frac{1}{2} \sum_{n=1}^{\infty} \frac{(-1)^{n-1}(2n-2)!(4n-1)}{2^{2n-1}n!(n-1)!} P_{2n-1}(\cos \theta)$$

$$= \tfrac{1}{2} + \tfrac{3}{4} \cos \theta - \tfrac{7}{32}(5 \cos^3 \theta - 3 \cos \theta) + \cdots.$$

18. Changing the independent variable from x to θ by means of the substitution $x = \cos \theta$, show that Legendre's equation can be written as

$$\frac{d^2y}{d\theta^2} + \cot \theta \, \frac{dy}{d\theta} + n(n+1)y = 0.$$

19. Substitute $y = (1 - x^2)^{m/2}z$ in the *associated Legendre equation*

$$(1 - x^2)\mathrm{D}^2y - 2x\mathrm{D}y + \left[n(n+1) - \frac{m^2}{1 - x^2} \right] y = 0,$$

and show that the resulting equation for z has the solution $z = \mathrm{D}^m v(x)$, where $v(x)$ is any solution of Legendre's equation and $\mathrm{D} = d/dx$. The functions defined as

$$P_n^m(x) = (1 - x^2)^{m/2}\mathrm{D}^m P_n(x)$$

are called *associated Legendre functions of the first kind*. If $x = \cos \theta$, show that $P_0^0 = 1$, $P_1^0 = \cos \theta$, $P_1^1 = \sin \theta$, $P_2^0 = \tfrac{1}{2}(3 \cos^2 \theta - 1)$, $P_2^1 = 3 \sin \theta \cos \theta$, $P_2^2 = 3 \sin^2 \theta$.

CHAPTER VII

Partial Derivatives and Partial
Differential Equations

66. Partial derivatives. When dealing with functional relations, the concept of rate of change is of first importance. Thus, if we have a function y of a single variable x, say $y = f(x)$, we speak of the rate of change of y with respect to x. Analytically, this rate of change is expressed by what we call the derivative of y with respect to x, and is denoted by

$$\frac{dy}{dx} = f'(x) = \lim_{\Delta x \to 0} \frac{f(x + \Delta x) - f(x)}{\Delta x} = \lim_{\Delta x \to 0} \frac{\Delta y}{\Delta x},^* \tag{1}$$

where Δy is the change, or increment, of y corresponding to the increment Δx of the variable x. By the definition of limit, (1) implies that the difference between the difference quotient $\Delta y/\Delta x$ and the limit $f'(x)$ will become and remain as small as we please if we keep Δx sufficiently small. Consequently we may write

$$\frac{\Delta y}{\Delta x} - f'(x) = \epsilon, \tag{2}$$

where ϵ is a quantity approaching zero as Δx approaches zero.

Now suppose we have a function z of two variables x and y, $z = g(x, y)$. Here we may speak of two distinct rates of change, one with respect to x, holding y constant, and the other with respect to y, x being held constant. Thus we have two first partial derivatives, defined as

$$\frac{\partial z}{\partial x} = \lim_{\Delta x \to 0} \frac{g(x + \Delta x, y) - g(x, y)}{\Delta x} \tag{3}$$

and

$$\frac{\partial z}{\partial y} = \lim_{\Delta y \to 0} \frac{g(x, y + \Delta y) - g(x, y)}{\Delta y}. \tag{4}$$

Note that, in (3), y is any value of the second argument in the function $g(x, y)$, remaining constant throughout this limit-taking process; sim-

* We assume, throughout this discussion, that the various limits exist

ilarly, in (4), x is any value of the first argument, constant while Δy approaches zero. Just as the relation (2) follows from definition (1), so we have corresponding to (3) and (4),

$$\frac{g(x + \Delta x, y) - g(x, y)}{\Delta x} - \frac{\partial g(x, y)}{\partial x} = \epsilon_1, \tag{5}$$

$$\frac{g(x, y + \Delta y) - g(x, y)}{\Delta y} - \frac{\partial g(x, y)}{\partial y} = \epsilon_2, \tag{6}$$

where $\epsilon_1 \to 0$ as $\Delta x \to 0$, and $\epsilon_2 \to 0$ as $\Delta y \to 0$.

Since the derivatives $\partial g/\partial x$ and $\partial g/\partial y$ are, in general, themselves functions of x and y, they may likewise be differentiated partially, leading to the second partial derivatives

$$\frac{\partial^2 g}{\partial x^2}, \frac{\partial^2 g}{\partial x\,\partial y}, \frac{\partial^2 g}{\partial y\,\partial x}, \frac{\partial^2 g}{\partial y^2}.$$

Here $\partial^2 g/\partial x\,\partial y$ denotes the derivative of $\partial g/\partial y$ with respect to x, while $\partial^2 g/\partial y\,\partial x$ is the derivative of $\partial g/\partial x$ with respect to y. When these two derivatives are continuous functions of x and y, they are equal,

$$\frac{\partial^2 g}{\partial x\,\partial y} = \frac{\partial^2 g}{\partial y\,\partial x};$$

that is, the order of differentiation is immaterial. Similarly, further partial differentiation leads to derivatives of third and higher orders, the values of these derivatives depending only upon the total number of differentiations with respect to each variable and not upon the order in which these differentiations are performed, whenever suitable conditions of continuity prevail.

For example, let $z = \sin (x^2 + 3y)$, for which partial derivatives of all orders exist and are continuous; then we have

$$\frac{\partial z}{\partial x} = 2x \cos (x^2 + 3y), \qquad \frac{\partial z}{\partial y} = 3 \cos (x^2 + 3y),$$

$$\frac{\partial^2 z}{\partial x^2} = -4x^2 \sin (x^2 + 3y) + 2 \cos (x^2 + 3y),$$

$$\frac{\partial^2 z}{\partial x\,\partial y} = -6x \sin (x^2 + 3y) = \frac{\partial^2 z}{\partial y\,\partial x},$$

$$\frac{\partial^2 z}{\partial y^2} = -9 \sin (x^2 + 3y),$$

$$\frac{\partial^3 z}{\partial x^3} = -8x^3 \cos (x^2 + 3y) - 12x \sin (x^2 + 3y),$$

$$\frac{\partial^3 z}{\partial x^2 \, \partial y} = -12x^2 \cos (x^2 + 3y) - 6 \sin (x^2 + 3y) = \frac{\partial^3 z}{\partial y \, \partial x^2},$$

$$\frac{\partial^3 z}{\partial x \, \partial y^2} = -18x \cos (x^2 + 3y) = \frac{\partial^3 z}{\partial y^2 \, \partial x},$$

$$\frac{\partial^3 z}{\partial y^3} = -27 \cos (x^2 + 3y),$$

and so on.

If x and y both take on increments Δx and Δy, respectively, z assumes an increment Δz, so that $z + \Delta z = g(x + \Delta x, y + \Delta y)$, whence

$$\Delta z = g(x + \Delta x, y + \Delta y) - g(x, y). \tag{7}$$

In order to make use of relations (5) and (6), in each of which one argument changes value while the other remains constant, we subtract and add the expression $g(x, y + \Delta y)$ in the right-hand member of (7), giving us

$$\Delta z = g(x + \Delta x, y + \Delta y) - g(x, y + \Delta y) + g(x, y + \Delta y) - g(x, y). \tag{8}$$

But by (5), with y replaced by $y + \Delta y$, we have

$$g(x + \Delta x, y + \Delta y) - g(x, y + \Delta y) = \frac{\partial g(x, y + \Delta y)}{\partial x} \Delta x + \epsilon_1 \, \Delta x. \tag{9}$$

Moreover, since $\lim\limits_{\Delta y \to 0} \dfrac{\partial g(x, y + \Delta y)}{\partial x} = \dfrac{\partial g(x, y)}{\partial x}$, we have

$$\frac{\partial g(x, y + \Delta y)}{\partial x} = \frac{\partial g(x, y)}{\partial x} + \epsilon',$$

where $\epsilon' \to 0$ as $\Delta y \to 0$. Hence we get from (9),

$$g(x + \Delta x, y + \Delta y) - g(x, y + \Delta y) = \frac{\partial g(x, y)}{\partial x} \Delta x + (\epsilon_1 + \epsilon') \, \Delta x, \tag{10}$$

where ϵ_1 and ϵ' approach zero with Δx and Δy. Similarly, we find from (6),

$$g(x, y + \Delta y) - g(x, y) = \frac{\partial g(x, y)}{\partial y} \Delta y + \epsilon_2 \, \Delta y. \tag{11}$$

Replacing the two differences in (8) by their values as given in (10) and (11), we have

$$\Delta z = \frac{\partial g(x, y)}{\partial x} \Delta x + \frac{\partial g(x, y)}{\partial y} \Delta y + (\epsilon_1 + \epsilon') \Delta x + \epsilon_2 \Delta y. \quad (12)$$

Now suppose that x and y are both functions of a single independent variable t. Then, in the preceding discussion, x will have taken on the increment Δx, and y the increment Δy, as a consequence of having given t an increment Δt. Dividing (12) by Δt, there is found

$$\frac{\Delta z}{\Delta t} = \frac{\partial g(x, y)}{\partial x} \frac{\Delta x}{\Delta t} + \frac{\partial g(x, y)}{\partial y} \frac{\Delta y}{\Delta t} + (\epsilon_1 + \epsilon') \frac{\Delta x}{\Delta t} + \epsilon_2 \frac{\Delta y}{\Delta t}.$$

If Δt is made to approach zero so that Δx and Δy also approach zero, then since x and y are functions of t, we shall have $\Delta x / \Delta t$ and $\Delta y / \Delta t$ approaching dx/dt and dy/dt, respectively, while since $z = g(x, y) = G(t)$, say, $\Delta z / \Delta t$ will have dz/dt as limit. It follows that in the limit

$$\frac{dz}{dt} = \frac{\partial g(x, y)}{\partial x} \frac{dx}{dt} + \frac{\partial g(x, y)}{\partial y} \frac{dy}{dt}. \quad (13)$$

In like fashion, if x and y are functions of two independent variables, say r and s, then by dividing (12) by Δr and by Δs in turn, and taking limits as these two increments approach zero in the respective relations, we get

$$\frac{\partial z}{\partial r} = \frac{\partial g(x, y)}{\partial x} \frac{\partial x}{\partial r} + \frac{\partial g(x, y)}{\partial y} \frac{\partial y}{\partial r},$$

$$\frac{\partial z}{\partial s} = \frac{\partial g(x, y)}{\partial x} \frac{\partial x}{\partial s} + \frac{\partial g(x, y)}{\partial y} \frac{\partial y}{\partial s}. \quad (14)$$

As generalizations of equations (13) and (14), we have the following result.

THEOREM. *If z is a function of m variables $x_1, x_2, \cdots, x_m$, $z = f(x_1, x_2, \cdots, x_m)$, with each x a function of a single variable t, then*

$$\frac{dz}{dt} = \frac{\partial f}{\partial x_1} \frac{dx_1}{dt} + \frac{\partial f}{\partial x_2} \frac{dx_2}{dt} + \cdots + \frac{\partial f}{\partial x_m} \frac{dx_m}{dt}. \quad (15)$$

If $z = f(x_1, x_2, \cdots, x_m)$, and each x is a function of p independent variables $t_1, t_2, \cdots, t_p$, then

$$\frac{\partial z}{\partial t_1} = \frac{\partial f}{\partial x_1} \frac{\partial x_1}{\partial t_1} + \frac{\partial f}{\partial x_2} \frac{\partial x_2}{\partial t_1} + \cdots + \frac{\partial f}{\partial x_m} \frac{\partial x_m}{\partial t_1},$$

$$\frac{\partial z}{\partial t_2} = \frac{\partial f}{\partial x_1}\frac{\partial x_1}{\partial t_2} + \frac{\partial f}{\partial x_2}\frac{\partial x_2}{\partial t_2} + \cdots + \frac{\partial f}{\partial x_m}\frac{\partial x_m}{\partial t_2},\qquad(16)$$

$$\cdots\cdots\cdots\cdots\cdots\cdots\cdots\cdots,$$

$$\frac{\partial z}{\partial t_p} = \frac{\partial f}{\partial x_1}\frac{\partial x_1}{\partial t_p} + \frac{\partial f}{\partial x_2}\frac{\partial x_2}{\partial t_p} + \cdots + \frac{\partial f}{\partial x_m}\frac{\partial x_m}{\partial t_p}.$$

Example. Let $z = (2x^2 + 3xy)^3$, $x = t^2 - t$, $y = 2t + 1$. Then

$$\frac{\partial z}{\partial x} = 3(2x^2 + 3xy)^2(4x + 3y),\qquad \frac{\partial z}{\partial y} = 3(2x^2 + 3xy)^2 \cdot 3x,$$

$$\frac{dx}{dt} = 2t - 1,\qquad\qquad\qquad \frac{dy}{dt} = 2,$$

and by equation (13),

$$\frac{dz}{dt} = 3(2x^2 + 3xy)^2(4x + 3y) \cdot (2t - 1) + 9x(2x^2 + 3xy)^2 \cdot 2$$

$$= 3(2x^2 + 3xy)^2(8tx + 6ty + 2x - 3y).$$

The derivative of z with respect to t here involves the three variables t, x, y. If desired, dz/dt may be expressed in terms of t alone by replacing x and y by their expressions in terms of t. The result of doing this,

$$\frac{dz}{dt} = 3t^2(2t^3 + 2t^2 - t - 3)^2(8t^3 + 6t^2 - 2t - 3),$$

may be checked by making the replacements for x and y in terms of t in z directly and differentiating this with respect to t in the usual way.

For a function of a single variable, $y = f(x)$, the derivative dy/dx may be regarded as a quotient by introducing the concept of a differential. It will be recalled that we define the differential of the function $y = f(x)$ as $dy = f'(x)\,\Delta x$, and define the differential of the independent variable x as $dx = \Delta x$, so that $dy = f'(x)\,dx$. Now in equation (13), where each of $x, y,$ and z is a function of the independent variable t, we should naturally like to carry over the definitions of differentials so as to have dx/dt, dy/dt, and dz/dt as quotients of differentials, which would enable us to write

$$dz = \frac{\partial g}{\partial x}\,dx + \frac{\partial g}{\partial y}\,dy.\qquad(17)$$

It is usual, in fact, to define the total differential of $z = g(x, y)$ by (17) when x and y are independent variables; it may then be shown that (17) holds also when x and y depend in turn on one or more other variables.[*]

* See W. F. Osgood, "Advanced Calculus," p. 117.

If x and y are connected by an implicit relation $g(x, y) = 0$, we get from (17), setting $z = g(x, y) = 0$,

$$dz = \frac{\partial g}{\partial x}\, dx + \frac{\partial g}{\partial y}\, dy = 0,$$

or

$$\frac{dy}{dx} = -\frac{\dfrac{\partial g}{\partial x}}{\dfrac{\partial g}{\partial y}}. \tag{18}$$

For example, if $e^x \sin y + xy^2 = 0$, we have

$$\frac{dy}{dx} = -\frac{e^x \sin y + y^2}{e^x \cos y + 2xy}.$$

We shall make use of formula (18) in Chapter X.

67. Differentiation under the integral sign. We are frequently concerned with an integral in which the function to be integrated contains not only the variable of integration but also one or more other quantities which we consider as parameters. Thus, in the complete elliptic integral of the first kind,

$$K(k) = \int_0^{\pi/2} \frac{d\phi}{\sqrt{1 - k^2 \sin^2 \phi}},$$

the integrand involves in addition to the variable of integration the modulus k. As we have seen, the value of K then depends upon the value of k, that is, the integral is a function of the parameter k.

We consider, then, a function of a parameter α defined by the equation

$$F(\alpha) = \int_a^b f(x, \alpha)\, dx, \tag{1}$$

where f is some known function of the variable of integration x and of the parameter α, and where a and b are constants, independent of x and of α. Since F is a function of α, there will exist in general a derivative of F with respect to α,

$$\frac{dF}{d\alpha} = \frac{d}{d\alpha} \int_a^b f(x, \alpha)\, dx. \tag{2}$$

Now in the right-hand member of (2) it is implied that the integration of $f(x, \alpha)$ is first to be performed, and the resulting function of α then differentiated. The question that naturally arises is whether the order in which these two operations are performed can be interchanged; that is, may we first differentiate $f(x, \alpha)$ partially with respect to α and then integrate the function so obtained with respect to x? This question is of more than academic interest, for it may sometimes happen that the function $f(x, \alpha)$ is difficult or even impossible to integrate in terms of a finite number of known functions, whereas $\partial f/\partial \alpha$ may be more readily integrated.

It turns out that if the partial derivative $\partial f/\partial \alpha$ exists and is continuous, which is usually the case in the problems with which we are concerned, the question is answered in the affirmative,* so that we do have

$$\frac{dF}{d\alpha} = \int_a^b \frac{\partial f(x, \alpha)}{\partial \alpha}\, dx. \tag{3}$$

As an example of the use of formula (3), let us find an expression for the function

$$F(\alpha) = \int_{-\infty}^0 \frac{e^{\alpha x} - e^x}{x}\, dx,$$

where $\alpha \geqq 1$. Then we have

$$\frac{dF}{d\alpha} = \int_{-\infty}^0 e^{\alpha x}\, dx$$

$$= \left[\frac{e^{\alpha x}}{\alpha}\right]_{-\infty}^0 = \frac{1}{\alpha},$$

and

$$dF = \frac{d\alpha}{\alpha}.$$

Integration therefore gives us

$$F(\alpha) = \ln \alpha + c,$$

where c is some constant. Now $F(1) = \int_{-\infty}^0 0 \cdot dx = 0$, so that $0 = \ln 1 + c$, $c = 0$, and

$$F(\alpha) = \ln \alpha.$$

Here the integral of $f(x, \alpha) = (e^{\alpha x} - e^x)/x$ could not be readily found, but $\partial f/\partial \alpha = e^{\alpha x}$ could be easily integrated, from which the determination of $F(\alpha)$ followed. Note that $\partial f/\partial \alpha$ is continuous for $x \leqq 0$ and $\alpha \geqq 1$, so that the conditions stated above are met.

A generalization of the problem occurs when one or both of the

---

* See Goursat-Hedrick, "Mathematical Analysis," Vol. I.

limits of integration, a and b, also depend upon α. Consider then the function

$$F(\alpha) = \int_{a(\alpha)}^{b(\alpha)} f(x, \alpha) \, dx, \tag{4}$$

where the notation $a(\alpha)$, $b(\alpha)$ indicates that a and b are functions of the parameter. To emphasize the fact that α enters into the function $F(\alpha)$ through three distinct channels, namely, through $f(x, \alpha)$, $a(\alpha)$, and $b(\alpha)$, let us denote the integral (4) by $\phi(\alpha, a, b)$:

$$F(\alpha) = \phi(\alpha, a, b), \tag{5}$$

where the first argument of ϕ is due to the presence of α in $f(x, \alpha)$. Applying formula (15) of Art. 66, we then have

$$\frac{dF}{d\alpha} = \frac{\partial\phi}{\partial\alpha} \cdot 1 + \frac{\partial\phi}{\partial a}\frac{da}{d\alpha} + \frac{\partial\phi}{\partial b}\frac{db}{d\alpha}. \tag{6}$$

Since $\partial\phi/\partial\alpha$ is found holding a and b constant, we get from (3),

$$\frac{\partial\phi}{\partial\alpha} = \int_{a(\alpha)}^{b(\alpha)} \frac{\partial f(x, \alpha)}{\partial\alpha} \, dx.$$

Now let $g(x, \alpha)$ denote an indefinite integral of $f(x, \alpha)$, assuming the latter function integrated with respect to x, so that

$$\frac{\partial g(x, \alpha)}{\partial x} \equiv f(x, \alpha).$$

Then

$$\phi(\alpha, a, b) = \int_{a(\alpha)}^{b(\alpha)} f(x, \alpha) \, dx = \Big[g(x, \alpha) \Big]_{a(\alpha)}^{b(\alpha)}$$

$$= g(b, \alpha) - g(a, \alpha).$$

We therefore get

$$\frac{\partial\phi}{\partial a} = - \frac{\partial g(a, \alpha)}{\partial a} = -f(a, \alpha),$$

and

$$\frac{\partial\phi}{\partial b} = \frac{\partial g(b, \alpha)}{\partial b} = f(b, \alpha).$$

Consequently, substitution in (6) gives us

$$\frac{dF}{d\alpha} = \int_{a(\alpha)}^{b(\alpha)} \frac{\partial f(x, \alpha)}{\partial\alpha} \, dx - f(a, \alpha) \frac{da}{d\alpha} + f(b, \alpha) \frac{db}{d\alpha}, \tag{7}$$

which is the desired formula. Evidently (7) reduces to (3) when a and b are independent of α, as it should, since here $da/d\alpha = db/d\alpha = 0$.

In order to make the derivation of (7) valid, we impose the same restrictions on $f(x, \alpha)$ as before (in order to obtain the first term of the formula), and also assume that the functions $a(\alpha)$ and $b(\alpha)$ possess derivatives with respect to α.

To illustrate the manner in which (7) is used, let

$$F(\alpha) = \int_{\pi/6\alpha}^{\pi/2\alpha} \frac{\sin \alpha x}{x}\, dx,$$

where $\alpha \neq 0$. Then

$$\frac{dF}{d\alpha} = \int_{\pi/6\alpha}^{\pi/2\alpha} \cos \alpha x \, dx - \frac{\sin (\pi/6)}{\pi/6\alpha}\cdot\left(-\frac{\pi}{6\alpha^2}\right) + \frac{\sin (\pi/2)}{\pi/2\alpha}\cdot\left(-\frac{\pi}{2\alpha^2}\right)$$

$$= \left[\frac{1}{\alpha}\sin \alpha x\right]_{\pi/6\alpha}^{\pi/2\alpha} - \frac{3\alpha}{\pi}\left(-\frac{\pi}{6\alpha^2}\right) + \frac{2\alpha}{\pi}\left(-\frac{\pi}{2\alpha^2}\right)$$

$$= \frac{1}{\alpha} - \frac{1}{2\alpha} + \frac{1}{2\alpha} - \frac{1}{\alpha} = 0.$$

This result indicates that F must here have a value independent of α. That this is so may be seen by making the substitution $y = \alpha x$, whence we get

$$F(\alpha) = \int_{\pi/6}^{\pi/2} \frac{\sin y}{y}\, dy,$$

which obviously does not depend upon α. With the stipulation $\alpha \neq 0$, our example satisfies the conditions under which formula (7) is valid.

PROBLEMS

1. Evaluate $F(1)$ if

$$F(\alpha) = \int_0^1 \frac{x^\alpha - 1}{\ln x}\, dx, \qquad \alpha > -1.$$

2. Evaluate $F(\tfrac{1}{2})$ if

$$F(\alpha) = \int_0^\pi \frac{\ln (1 + \alpha \cos x)}{\cos x}\, dx, \qquad 0 \leq \alpha < 1.$$

3. Evaluate $F(1)$ if

$$F(\alpha) = \int_0^\infty \frac{e^{-\alpha x}\sin x}{x}\, dx, \qquad \alpha > 0.$$

4. Evaluate $F(2)$ if

$$F(\alpha) = \int_0^\infty \frac{e^{-x} - e^{-\alpha x}}{x \sec x}\, dx, \qquad \alpha > 0.$$

5. Evaluate $F(\frac{1}{2})$ if

$$F(\alpha) = \int_{-\pi/2}^{\pi/2} \ln(1 + \alpha \sin x)\, dx, \qquad 0 \leq \alpha < 1.$$

6. Given $\int_0^\infty e^{-\alpha^2 x^2}\, dx = \dfrac{\sqrt{\pi}}{2\alpha}$, where $\alpha > 0$ (cf. Problem 15, Art. 56), show that, for n any positive integer,

$$\int_0^\infty x^{2n} e^{-\alpha^2 x^2}\, dx = \frac{\sqrt{\pi}}{2} \cdot \frac{1 \cdot 3 \cdot 5 \cdots (2n-1)}{2^n \alpha^{2n+1}}.$$

7. Evaluate $\int_0^\infty \dfrac{dx}{x^2 + \alpha^2}$, $\alpha > 0$, and hence show that

$$\int_0^\infty \frac{dx}{(x^2 + \alpha^2)^{n+1}} = \frac{\pi}{2} \cdot \frac{1 \cdot 3 \cdot 5 \cdots (2n-1)}{2 \cdot 4 \cdot 6 \cdots 2n \cdot \alpha^{2n+1}}.$$

8. Evaluate

$$\int_0^\pi \frac{dx}{(4 - \cos x)^2}$$

by first showing that

$$\int_0^\pi \frac{dx}{\alpha - \cos x} = \frac{\pi}{\sqrt{\alpha^2 - 1}}, \qquad \alpha > 1,$$

and then differentiating this relation and substituting $\alpha = 4$ in the result. (Cf. Problem 10, Art. 40.)

9. The Bessel function of zero or integral order n may be defined as

$$J_n(x) = \frac{1}{\pi} \int_0^\pi \cos(nt - x \sin t)\, dt.$$

Using this relation, show that

$$\frac{d}{dx} J_n(x) = \tfrac{1}{2}[J_{n-1}(x) - J_{n+1}(x)].$$

10. (a) If

$$F(p) = \int_{1/p}^{2/p} \frac{\sin px}{x^2}\, dx, \qquad p \neq 0,$$

find the second derivative of $F(p)$ and hence show that $F(p)$ is a linear function of p: $F(p) = Ap + B$. (b) Using the substitution $y = px$ to get another expression for $F(p)$, show that $B = 0$ and find A as a definite integral.

11. By differentiating $F(\alpha) = \int_0^\infty e^{-x^2} \cos \alpha x\, dx$ with respect to α, find the value of

$$\int_0^\infty e^{-x^2} \cos x\, dx.$$

12. The mean-square error μ, arising in the theory of probability (cf. equations (12), Art. 88, and (8'), Art. 89), is defined by the relation

$$\mu^2 = \frac{h}{\sqrt{\pi}} \int_{-\infty}^{\infty} x^2 e^{-h^2 x^2} \, dx.$$

By differentiation of the relation

$$\int_{-\infty}^{\infty} e^{-h^2 x^2} \, dx = \sqrt{\pi}/h,$$

derive a formula for μ in terms of h.

13. If k is a constant, show that

$$y = F(x) = \frac{1}{k} \int_0^x f(t) \sin k(x - t) \, dt$$

is a solution of the differential equation $d^2 y/dx^2 + k^2 y = f(x)$.

14. Given the function

$$\int_0^n x^n \, dx = n^{n+1}/(n + 1),$$

make use of differentiation under the integral sign to determine the area bounded by the curve $y = x \ln x$ and the x-axis.

15. Show that the function of x defined as

$$\frac{2}{\pi} \int_0^1 \frac{\cos xt}{\sqrt{1 - t^2}} \, dt$$

satisfies Bessel's equation of order zero.

16. By differentiating under the integral sign and then using an infinite series, find the area of the minimum strip 1 unit wide extending from the curve $y = e^x/x$ to the positive x-axis.

17. A particle moves from rest at a distance a (ft.) towards a center of attraction, the force varying inversely as the distance. (a) If x (ft.) is the distance from the center and T (sec.) is the time required for the particle to move from $x = a/n$ to $x = a/n^2$, find the value of n for which T is a maximum. (b) By use of series, compute the maximum value of T, if the particle starts from rest at a distance 10 ft. from the center with an acceleration numerically equal to 10 ft./sec.^{2}

18. If K and E are the complete elliptic integrals of the first and second kind, respectively, each with modulus k, show that $k \, dE/dk = E - K$.

19. Derive the differential equation (1), Art. 64, as follows. Take moments about P (Fig. 46), denoting by (x_1, y_1) any point between P and A, and thus get

$$EIy'' = \int_x^L w(y_1 - y) \, dx_1.$$

Now differentiate with respect to x.

68. Linear partial differential equations.

In the preceding chapters, all our problems which led to differential equations involved a single independent variable, and the equations were accordingly ordinary differential equations. When investigating functional dependencies into which two or more independent variables enter, say time and one or more point coordinates (distances), we are naturally led to deal with partial derivatives and partial differential equations.

As may be expected, a wide variety of physical problems can be formulated mathematically as partial differential equations. Applications arise, for example, in connection with vibrations in strings and membranes, which yield equations respectively involving two and three independent variables; heat or fluid flow in one, two, or three dimensions, for which the equations contain two, three, or four independent variables, respectively; electrical transmission, entailing two independent variables; electrostatic and electromagnetic field problems, where the number of independent variables may be two, three, or four; problems involving the drying of porous solids through diffusion and evaporation, entailing the use of as many as four independent variables; gravitational, electrostatic, or electromagnetic potential, with two, three, or four independent variables entering into each type of equation; and elasticity, for which four independent variables are needed, in general. In this and the following chapters, each of the aforementioned applications will be considered. More comprehensive treatments of these topics, and of additional applications as well, may be found in the books and periodicals referred to in the subsequent discussion.

We shall not attempt, in this book, any systematic classification of the various types of partial differential equations together with their formal solutions, similar to that given for ordinary equations in Chapter I. Even were we to limit ourselves to those types of partial equations which arise in physics and engineering, the subject would be too vast and involved for a book such as the present one.* Our aim, therefore, will be to set up merely a few typical and fundamental partial differential equations from their physical origins, and obtain solutions, satisfying the physical requirements, by means of a special process which we shall explain.

Just as linear ordinary equations form an important class, frequently arising in engineering applications, so are linear partial equations often obtained in the formulation of many physical problems into which two or more independent variables enter. By a *linear partial differential equation* we mean an equation linear, i.e., of the first degree, in the dependent variable and its various partial derivatives. Thus, the

---

* The reader wishing to pursue this phase of the subject further will find excellent and extensive material in Riemann-Weber, "Partielle Differentialgleichungen und deren Anwendung auf physikalische Fragen"; Courant-Hilbert, "Methoden der mathematischen Physik"; H. Bateman, "Partial Differential Equations of Mathematical Physics"; Frank and von Mises, "Differential und Integralgleichungen der Mechanik und Physik," 2 vols.

typical linear equation of second order involving the two independent variables x and t and the single dependent variable z is of the form

$$A_1 \frac{\partial^2 z}{\partial x^2} + A_2 \frac{\partial^2 z}{\partial x \partial t} + A_3 \frac{\partial^2 z}{\partial t^2} + B_1 \frac{\partial z}{\partial x} + B_2 \frac{\partial z}{\partial t} + Cz = F, \qquad (1)$$

where the coefficients $A_1, \cdots, F$ are functions of x and t only. If each term contains either the dependent variable or one of its derivatives, we shall say that the equation is *homogeneous*;* for example, if $F = 0$ in (1), that equation will be homogeneous.

Certain properties possessed by the solutions of linear ordinary equations, which made such equations particularly tractable (see Chapter I, Art. 8), carry over into the realm of linear partial equations. Because of its frequent use throughout the remainder of this chapter, we state one of these properties in the form of a theorem, the proof of which is easily made.

THEOREM. *If $z_1, z_2, \cdots, z_n$ are n solutions of a linear homogeneous partial differential equation, then $c_1 z_1 + c_2 z_2 + \cdots + c_n z_n$, where the c's are any constants, is also a solution of the given homogeneous equation.*

As a simple illustration, consider the linear homogeneous equation

$$\frac{\partial^2 z}{\partial x^2} - 2 \frac{\partial z}{\partial x} + \frac{\partial z}{\partial t} = 0. \qquad (2)$$

By a method to be explained in Art. 69, it is possible to obtain as solutions of this equation the functions

$$z_1 = e^{-(x+3t)}, \qquad z_2 = e^{x+2t} \sin x.$$

Now let $z = c_1 e^{-(x+3t)} + c_2 e^{x+2t} \sin x$, where c_1 and c_2 are arbitrary constants. Substituting in the left-hand member of (2), we get

$$\frac{\partial^2 z}{\partial x^2} - 2 \frac{\partial z}{\partial x} + \frac{\partial z}{\partial t} = c_1 e^{-(x+3t)} - c_2 e^{x+2t} \sin x + 2 c_2 e^{x+2t} \cos x$$
$$+ c_2 e^{x+2t} \sin x + 2 c_1 e^{-(x+3t)} - 2 c_2 e^{x+2t} \cos x$$
$$- 2 c_2 e^{x+2t} \sin x - 3 c_1 e^{-(x+3t)} + 2 c_2 e^{x+2t} \sin x,$$

which is identically zero in x, t, c_1, and c_2.

69. Particular solutions. In a problem involving an ordinary differential equation of order n, accompanied by n boundary or initial conditions, we may be able to find the general solution of the equation,

---

* Some writers call the equation in which the dependent variable itself is absent and all the derivatives are of the same order a homogeneous equation. We do not use this connotation in this book.

and then determine proper values of the n arbitrary constants appearing in the general solution so as to yield a particular solution satisfying the given conditions.

However, when a problem gives rise to a linear homogeneous partial differential equation, together with sufficient conditions to fix the desired solution uniquely, it is not usually practicable to find the most general solution, and even when such a solution is obtainable, it is frequently extremely awkward to particularize to a solution meeting the necessary conditions.

On the other hand, it fortunately happens that a number of physical problems leading to linear homogeneous partial equations may be solved by a simple process which yields particular solutions of the equation directly, and then combines these solutions in such a manner as to satisfy the auxiliary conditions.

The first part of this process, by which we get particular solutions, may best be explained by means of an example. Consider the equation

$$\frac{\partial^2 z}{\partial x^2} - 2\frac{\partial z}{\partial x} + \frac{\partial z}{\partial t} = 0, \tag{1}$$

which served as an illustration in Art. 68. We begin by seeking a solution in the form of a product of a function of x alone and a function of t alone,

$$z = X(x)\cdot T(t). \tag{2}$$

Whether (1) possesses any solution of type (2), or whether every solution of (1) involves the variables x and t in such a way that it cannot be factored into the product of two functions each of which involves only one of the variables, we cannot tell initially; thus our method is a tentative one in which we assume the existence of a solution of the form (2) and then endeavor to fulfil our assumption.

Using primes to denote differentiation, so that

$$\frac{dX}{dx} = X'(x) = X', \qquad \frac{dT}{dt} = T'(t) = T',$$

and so on, we get by substituting (2) in (1),

$$X''T - 2X'T + XT' = 0. \tag{3}$$

Now it is possible to separate the variables in (3) and write

$$\frac{X'' - 2X'}{X} = -\frac{T'}{T}. \tag{4}$$

Again, we had no assurance at the beginning that it would be possible to separate the variables as we have done. If separation were not possible, our method would not apply, but when it has been found to be performable, we may be certain that there will exist solutions of the given differential equation of the postulated form (2).

Now let t vary while x remains fixed. Then the left member of (4) is constant, and therefore the right member must be a constant also. Consequently the common value of the two members of (4) must be a constant.

Hence we have

$$\frac{X'' - 2X'}{X} = -\frac{T'}{T} = k,$$

where k is a constant, whence we get the two ordinary differential equations

$$X'' - 2X' - kX = 0, \tag{5}$$

$$T' + kT = 0. \tag{6}$$

Thus the problem of solving the partial equation (1) has been replaced by the problem of solving the two ordinary equations (5) and (6). The constant k may have any value, but its value must be the same for both (5) and (6) in order that (4) hold.

Equations (5) and (6) both being linear with constant coefficients, their solutions are readily found. The auxiliary equation for (5) is

$$m^2 - 2m - k = 0,$$

which has the roots

$$m = 1 \pm \sqrt{1 + k}.$$

Taking $k = 3$, for example, we get as two distinct solutions of (5),

$$X = e^{3x}, \qquad X = e^{-x}.$$

Similarly, corresponding to $k = -2$, particular solutions are

$$X = e^x \sin x, \qquad X = e^x \cos x.$$

Equation (6) has the particular solution

$$T = e^{-kt},$$

which, for the above choices of k, gives us

$$T = e^{-3t}, \qquad T = e^{2t}.$$

Substituting in equation (2), we therefore get as particular solutions of (1),

$$e^{3(x-t)} \qquad e^{-(x+3t)} \qquad (k = 3),$$

$$e^{x+2t} \sin x \qquad e^{x+2t} \cos x \qquad (k = -2).$$

We have chosen the second and third of these as z_1 and z_2 in Art. 68.

70. The vibrating string. As our first physical application, we consider a string of length L (ft.) tightly stretched between two fixed points, one of which we take at the origin O and the other A on the positive x-axis as shown in Fig. 48. Let the string be set vibrating in a plane, and let F (lb.) be the tension in the string, assumed constant, and so large compared with the weight of the string that the gravitational force may be neglected. Let w (lb./ft.) denote the weight of the unstretched string per unit of length, and let y (ft.) be the displacement at any point $P(x, y)$ of the string from the equilibrium position.

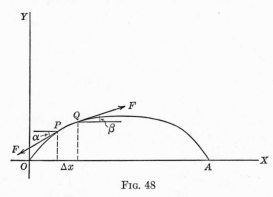

Fig. 48

We wish to investigate the transverse vibrations of the string under the assumption that they are very small compared to the length L. In accordance with this supposition, we may consider the length of the string when it is in an extreme position farthest from the x-axis as sensibly equal to L, and suppose that each point P traverses a straight line perpendicular to the x-axis.

The displacement y is a function of two variables, the distance x along the string and the time t. Thus we may expect our problem to lead to a partial differential equation.

Since the weight of a small segment PQ, originally of length Δx, is $w\,\Delta x$, and the acceleration is $\partial^2 y/\partial t^2$, we have for the force (lb.) acting on this segment

$$\frac{w}{g}\,\Delta x\,\frac{\partial^2 y}{\partial t^2},$$

where $g = 32.17$ ft./sec.^{2} This force must be the resultant of the y-components of the tensions at the two ends; if α and β represent the angles made by the tangential forces F with the horizontal, we have as a second expression for the resultant force

$$F(\sin \beta - \sin \alpha).$$

Now the slopes of the tangents at P and Q are, respectively,

$$\left.\frac{\partial y}{\partial x}\right]_x = \tan \alpha, \qquad \left.\frac{\partial y}{\partial x}\right]_{x+\Delta x} = \tan \beta,$$

so that

$$\sin \alpha = \frac{\tan \alpha}{\sqrt{1 + \tan^2 \alpha}} = \frac{\left.\dfrac{\partial y}{\partial x}\right]_x}{\sqrt{1 + \left(\dfrac{\partial y}{\partial x}\right)_x^2}},$$

$$\sin \beta = \frac{\tan \beta}{\sqrt{1 + \tan^2 \beta}} = \frac{\left.\dfrac{\partial y}{\partial x}\right]_{x+\Delta x}}{\sqrt{1 + \left(\dfrac{\partial y}{\partial x}\right)_{x+\Delta x}^2}}.$$

But for small vibrations, such as we are considering, $\partial y/\partial x$ will be small and its square may be neglected in comparison with unity; consequently we have approximately

$$\sin \alpha = \left.\frac{\partial y}{\partial x}\right]_x, \qquad \sin \beta = \left.\frac{\partial y}{\partial x}\right]_{x+\Delta x}.$$

Substituting these values and equating the two expressions for the vertical force, we get

$$\frac{w}{g} \Delta x \frac{\partial^2 y}{\partial t^2} = F \left(\left.\frac{\partial y}{\partial x}\right]_{x+\Delta x} - \left.\frac{\partial y}{\partial x}\right]_x \right),$$

and

$$\frac{w}{g} \frac{\partial^2 y}{\partial t^2} = F \frac{\left.\dfrac{\partial y}{\partial x}\right]_{x+\Delta x} - \left.\dfrac{\partial y}{\partial x}\right]_x}{\Delta x}.$$

Allowing Δx to approach zero, we therefore get in the limit

$$\frac{\partial^2 y}{\partial t^2} = a^2 \frac{\partial^2 y}{\partial x^2}, \tag{1}$$

where $a^2 = Fg/w$; evidently a has the dimensions of velocity, feet per second. This is the partial differential equation of the vibrating string, the solutions of which represent the displacement y at any distance x from one end and at any time t, for the various possible modes of vibration.

We have not as yet used the facts that the string is of length L and that its ends are situated as stated. Denoting a solution of (1) by $y(x, t)$, we may write the given boundary conditions as

$$y(0, t) = 0, \qquad y(L, t) = 0, \tag{2}$$

these relations to hold identically in t. If, in addition, we specify the manner in which the vibration is brought about, we have a definite physical problem. Suppose that the string is displaced in a sinusoidal arch of height y_0 and then released from rest. Then we have also the initial conditions

$$y(x, 0) = y_0 \sin \frac{\pi x}{L},$$

$$\left. \frac{\partial y}{\partial t} \right]_{t=0} = 0, \tag{3}$$

where these are to hold for every x between 0 and L. Consequently the complete formulation of our problem is comprised of the differential equation (1), the boundary values (2), and the initial conditions (3).

Let us seek a solution of this problem by the method of Art. 69. If we assume

$$y(x, t) = X(x) \cdot T(t),$$

we get by substitution in (1),

$$XT'' = a^2 X'' T,$$

or

$$\frac{X''}{X} = \frac{T''}{a^2 T}.$$

Here we have placed the constant a^2 in the right-hand member, although of course it might equally well appear at the left. By precisely the same reasoning as was employed in the example of Art. 69, we may write

$$\frac{X''}{X} = \frac{T''}{a^2 T} = k,$$

or

$$X'' - kX = 0, \qquad T'' - a^2 k T = 0,$$

where k is a constant. Now we get three types of solutions of these ordinary differential equations, and hence of (1), according as k is positive, negative, or zero. Thus we have

$$y = (c_1 e^{\sqrt{k}x} + c_2 e^{-\sqrt{k}x})(c_3 e^{a\sqrt{k}t} + c_4 e^{-a\sqrt{k}t}) \qquad (k > 0),$$

$$y = (c_5 \sin \sqrt{-k}\, x + c_6 \cos \sqrt{-k}\, x)(c_7 \sin a\sqrt{-k}\, t$$

$$+ \; c_8 \cos a\sqrt{-k}\, t) \qquad\qquad (k < 0),$$

$$y = (c_9 x + c_{10})(c_{11} t + c_{12}) \qquad\qquad\qquad (k = 0),$$

where the c's are any arbitrary constants. We must choose the proper one of these types, in agreement with the physical requirements. Since we are dealing with a periodic motion, every position of the string being reproduced over and over as time goes on, it is evident that we need a solution in which the functions of t are periodic. Consequently k must be negative, and

$$y = (c_5 \sin \sqrt{-k}\, x + c_6 \cos \sqrt{-k}\, x)(c_7 \sin a\sqrt{-k}\, t + c_8 \cos a\sqrt{-k}\, t).$$

The first of boundary conditions (2) gives us from this equation,

$$0 = c_6(c_7 \sin a\sqrt{-k}\, t + c_8 \cos a\sqrt{-k}\, t),$$

for every t, which is most easily met by taking $c_6 = 0$. The second boundary condition then requires that

$$0 = c_5 \sin \sqrt{-k}\, L(c_7 \sin a\sqrt{-k}\, t + c_8 \cos a\sqrt{-k}\, t).$$

We cannot here take $c_5 = 0$, or our solution would be the trivial one $y = 0$, which would be correct only if the string remains at rest in its equilibrium position, contrary to supposition. Likewise, we cannot have $c_7 = c_8 = 0$ for the same reason. But in addition to the c's, the constant k is at our disposal, provided merely that it be negative. Hence if we have

$$\sqrt{-k}\, L = n\pi,$$

where n is an integer, $\sin \sqrt{-k}\, L = 0$ and the above equation is satisfied. Therefore we get as a solution satisfying (1) and (2),

$$y = c_5 \sin \frac{n\pi x}{L}\left(c_7 \sin \frac{na\pi t}{L} + c_8 \cos \frac{na\pi t}{L}\right), \qquad (4)$$

with n any integer.

We next impose the initial conditions (3). Taking the second of these first, as it is the simpler, we see that we must have

$$0 = c_5 \sin \frac{n\pi x}{L} \cdot \frac{c_7 na\pi}{L}.$$

Since c_5 cannot be zero, we set $c_7 = 0$. Then a solution that satisfies (1), (2), and the second of equations (3) is

$$y = c_5 c_8 \sin \frac{n\pi x}{L} \cos \frac{na\pi t}{L}. \tag{5}$$

Finally, the first of equations (3) imposes the condition

$$y_0 \sin \frac{\pi x}{L} = c_5 c_8 \sin \frac{n\pi x}{L},$$

which will be satisfied by taking $c_5 c_8 = y_0$, $n = 1$. Therefore the desired solution is

$$y(x, t) = y_0 \sin \frac{\pi x}{L} \cos \frac{a\pi t}{L}. \tag{6}$$

If the initial displacement of the string, $y(x, 0)$, were other than an arch of a sine curve, the solution of the problem would entail a more extensive analysis. To illustrate, let the first of the initial conditions (3) be replaced by

$$y(x, 0) = k(Lx - x^2), \qquad 0 \leqq x \leqq L, \tag{7}$$

other conditions remaining the same; that is, we suppose the string displaced into a parabolic arc passing through the fixed end points $x = 0$ and $x = L$, where k (ft.$^{-1}$) is a small positive constant, and released from rest.

Now, if we attempt to meet condition (7) with the solution (5), we apparently have to choose numbers $c_5 c_8$ and n such that

$$k(Lx - x^2) = c_5 c_8 \sin \frac{n\pi x}{L}$$

identically for $0 \leqq x \leqq L$. But this is impossible since a sine curve cannot be made to coincide with a parabolic arc over the entire x-range. Faced with this difficulty, we might first think of using the property of a linear homogeneous partial differential equation expressed in the theorem of Art. 68; thus let us try the effect of taking, instead of (5), the sum of a linear combination of terms of that form with $n = 1, 2, \cdots, m$ in turn:

$$y = b_1 \sin \frac{\pi x}{L} \cos \frac{a\pi t}{L} + b_2 \sin \frac{2\pi x}{L} \cos \frac{2a\pi t}{L} + \cdots$$
$$+ b_m \sin \frac{m\pi x}{L} \cos \frac{ma\pi t}{L}. \tag{8}$$

By our theorem, the sum (8) will satisfy the differential equation (1) for any choice of the b's and for any positive integer m. Moreover, since each term of (8) reduces to zero for $x = 0$ and for $x = L$, the sum will satisfy both boundary conditions (2); and since $\partial y/\partial t$, as given by (8), vanishes for $t = 0$, the second of the initial conditions (3) will be met.

Unfortunately the sum (8) is still inadequate as regards the satisfaction of (7). However, the form (8), together with the knowledge we have acquired about the wide applicability of Fourier series, suggests that we generalize to an infinite series, and write

$$ y = b_1 \sin \frac{\pi x}{L} \cos \frac{a\pi t}{L} + \cdots + b_n \sin \frac{n\pi x}{L} \cos \frac{na\pi t}{L} + \cdots . \qquad (9) $$

Formally, the series (9) will satisfy all the conditions satisfied by the finite sum (8); can (7) now be met by a suitable choice of the b's, and will the resulting series converge to the required function $y(x, t)$?

We readily see that the first part of this question will be satisfactorily answered. For, (7) now imposes the condition

$$ k(Lx - x^2) = b_1 \sin \frac{\pi x}{L} + b_2 \sin \frac{2\pi x}{L} + \cdots + b_n \sin \frac{n\pi x}{L} + \cdots , $$

for $0 \leq x \leq L$. Consequently we have to find the half-range sine series representing $k(Lx - x^2)$ over the given interval. Using the method of combination of series (Art. 49), we get (Peirce, 809 and 811, with $c = L$)

$$ kL \cdot \frac{2L}{\pi} \left[\sin \frac{\pi x}{L} - \frac{1}{2} \sin \frac{2\pi x}{L} + \frac{1}{3} \sin \frac{3\pi x}{L} - \cdots \right] $$

$$ - k \cdot \frac{2L^2}{\pi^3} \left[\left(\frac{\pi^2}{1} - \frac{4}{1} \right) \sin \frac{\pi x}{L} - \frac{\pi^2}{2} \sin \frac{2\pi x}{L} + \left(\frac{\pi^2}{3} - \frac{4}{3^3} \right) \sin \frac{3\pi x}{L} - \cdots \right] $$

$$ = \frac{8kL^2}{\pi^3} \left(\sin \frac{\pi x}{L} + \frac{1}{3^3} \sin \frac{3\pi x}{L} + \frac{1}{5^3} \sin \frac{5\pi x}{L} + \cdots \right) . $$

Thus, $b_1 = 8kL^2/\pi^3$, $b_2 = 0$, $b_3 = 8kL^2/3^3\pi^3$, $b_4 = 0$, $b_5 = 8kL^2/5^3\pi^3$, etc. Hence the desired relation takes the form

$$ y(x, t) = \frac{8kL^2}{\pi^3} \left(\sin \frac{\pi x}{L} \cos \frac{a\pi t}{L} + \frac{1}{3^3} \sin \frac{3\pi x}{L} \cos \frac{3a\pi t}{L} + \cdots \right) . \qquad (10) $$

To establish the uniform convergence of (10), we first note that $|\sin (n\pi x/L)| \leq 1$ and $|\cos (na\pi t/L)| \leq 1$ for every x and t and for every n. Hence the terms of the series within the parentheses are in absolute value not greater than the corresponding terms of the series

$$1 + \frac{1}{3^3} + \frac{1}{5^3} + \cdots + \frac{1}{(2n-1)^3} + \cdots.$$

But this series converges since $1/(2n-1)^3 \leqq 1/n^3$, the nth term of the p-series (Art. 37) with $p = 3$. Thus (10) is a valid solution of our problem.

PROBLEMS

1. A tightly stretched string with fixed end points $x = 0$ and $x = L$ is initially in a position given by $y(x, 0) = y_0 \sin^3 (\pi x/L)$. If it is released from rest from this position, find the displacement $y(x, t)$ at any distance x from one end and at any time t.

2. (a) A tightly stretched string with fixed end points $x = 0$ and $x = L$ is initially in its equilibrium position. It is set vibrating by giving to each of its points a velocity

$$\frac{\partial y}{\partial t}\Big]_{t=0} = v_0 \sin^3 \frac{\pi x}{L}.$$

Find the displacement $y(x, t)$. (b) If the string is 3 ft. long, weighs 0.06 lb., and is subjected to a constant tension of 5 lb., and if $v_0 = 1$ ft./sec., find the displacement of the midpoint of the string when $t = 0.01$ sec.

3. (a) A tightly stretched string with fixed end points $x = 0$ and $x = L$ is initially at rest in its equilibrium position. If it is set vibrating by giving to each of its points a velocity

$$\frac{\partial y}{\partial t}\Big]_{t=0} = 3(Lx - x^2),$$

find $y(x, t)$. (b) If the string is 2 ft. long, weighs 0.1 lb., and is subjected to a constant tension of 6 lb., find the displacement of the midpoint when $t = 0.01$ sec.

4. A tightly stretched string with fixed end points $x = 0$ and $x = L$ is initially in a position given by $y(x, 0) = (L^2x - x^3)/100$. If it is released from rest from this position, find $y(x, t)$.

5. A tightly stretched string with fixed end points is 4 ft. long, weighs 2 oz., and is subjected to a constant tension of 10 lb. It is set vibrating by giving to each of its points an initial velocity v ft./sec., where $v = x$, $0 < x \leqq 2$, and $v = 4 - x$, $2 < x < 4$. Find the displacement of the midpoint of the string 0.1 sec. later.

6. A tightly stretched string with fixed end points $x = 0$ and $x = 3$ is initially at rest in its equilibrium position. It is set vibrating by giving to each of its points an initial velocity v, where $v = mx$ for $0 < x \leqq 1$, $v = m$ for $1 < x \leqq 2$, and $v = m(3 - x)$ for $2 < x < 3$. Find $y(x, t)$.

7. A vibrating string is subjected to a damping force which is proportional to the velocity at each point and at each instant. Show that the differential equation has the form

$$\frac{\partial^2 y}{\partial t^2} = a^2 \frac{\partial^2 y}{\partial x^2} - 2b \frac{\partial y}{\partial t},$$

where $a = \sqrt{Fg/w}$ (ft./sec.) and b (sec.$^{-1}$) are constants.

8. If the string of Problem 7 has its ends fixed at $x = 0$ and $x = L$ (ft.), and if it starts from rest with an initial displacement $y(x, 0) = f(x)$ for $0 < x < L$, show that the displacement function $y(x, t)$ is given by

$$y(x, t) = e^{-bt} \sum_{n=1}^{\infty} A_n \left(\cos K_n t + \frac{b}{K_n} \sin K_n t \right) \sin \frac{n\pi x}{L},$$

where $K_n = \sqrt{n^2 \pi^2 a^2 - b^2 L^2}/L$ and

$$A_n = \frac{2}{L} \int_0^L f(x) \sin \frac{n\pi x}{L} dx.$$

9. A horizontal bar of length L (ft.) is initially undeformed and at rest. The end $x = 0$ is fixed, and the other ($x = L$) is suddenly subjected to a constant horizontal stress S (lb./ft.²). Show that the longitudinal displacement $y(x, t)$ satisfies the conditions

$$\frac{\partial^2 y}{\partial t^2} = a^2 \frac{\partial^2 y}{\partial x^2}, \quad \frac{\partial y}{\partial x} \bigg]_{x=L} = \frac{S}{E}, \quad y(0, t) = 0, \quad y(x, 0) = 0, \quad \frac{\partial y}{\partial t} \bigg]_{t=0} = 0,$$

where $a = \sqrt{Eg/\rho}$ (ft./sec.), E (lb./ft.²) is Young's modulus, ρ (lb./ft.³) is density, and $g = 32.17$ ft./sec.²

10. Substitute $y(x, t) = y_1(x) + y_2(x, t)$ in the differential equation of Problem 9, where $y_2(x, t)$ is to be a function satisfying the same differential equation but having two zero boundary values: $\partial y_2/\partial x = 0$ for $x = L$ and $y_2(0, t) = 0$. Hence show that $y_1(x) = Sx/E$, and determine $y_2(x, t)$.

11. An elastic rod is clamped along its length L (ft.) and fixed at its upper end ($x = 0$). If the clamp is suddenly removed, allowing gravity to act, the rod undergoes longitudinal vibrations. Show that the longitudinal displacement $y(x, t)$ satisfies the conditions

$$\frac{\partial^2 y}{\partial t^2} = a^2 \frac{\partial^2 y}{\partial x^2} + g, \quad \frac{\partial y}{\partial x} \bigg]_{x=L} = 0, \quad y(0, t) = 0, \quad y(x, 0) = 0 \quad \frac{\partial y}{\partial t} \bigg]_{t=0} = 0,$$

where $a = \sqrt{Eg/\rho}$ (ft./sec.).

12. Substitute $y(x, t) = y_1(x) + y_2(x, t)$ in the differential equation of Problem 11, where $y_2(x, t)$ is to be a function satisfying the homogeneous equation $\partial^2 y/\partial t^2 = a^2(\partial^2 y/\partial x^2)$ and the same boundary conditions as $y(x, t)$ itself. Hence show that $y_1(x) = gx(2L - x)/2a^2$, and determine $y_2(x, t)$.

71. One-dimensional heat flow.

We turn now to a discussion of flow of heat in a conducting body, from which we can gain knowledge of temperature distribution under various conditions. We base our analysis on the empirical laws stated in Art. 7(d).

Consider (Fig. 49) a homogeneous bar of constant cross-sectional area A (cm.²), and suppose that the sides are insulated so that the streamlines of heat flow are all parallel, and perpen-

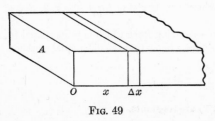

Fig. 49

dicular to the area A. Take the positive x-axis along the direction of flow, the origin O being at one end of the bar. By law I, the quantity of heat in a slab of thickness Δx is $c\rho A \, \Delta x \, (u + 273)$ calories, where ρ is the density (gr./cm.^{3}), u is the temperature (°C.) of the slab, and the constant of proportionality c is called the specific heat (cal./gr. deg.). Then

$$c\rho A \, \Delta x \, \frac{\partial u}{\partial t} = R_1 - R_2,$$

where R_1 and R_2 are the rates (cal./sec.) of inflow and outflow, respectively. Now by law III,

$$R_1 = -KA \left.\frac{\partial u}{\partial x}\right]_x, \qquad R_2 = -KA \left.\frac{\partial u}{\partial x}\right]_{x+\Delta x},$$

the negative sign appearing as a consequence of law II, where K is called the thermal conductivity (cal./cm. deg. sec.). Hence we have

$$c\rho A \, \Delta x \, \frac{\partial u}{\partial t} = KA \left(\left.\frac{\partial u}{\partial x}\right]_{x+\Delta x} - \left.\frac{\partial u}{\partial x}\right]_x \right).$$

Let $\alpha^2 = K/c\rho$, the diffusivity (cm.^{2}/sec.). Dividing by $c\rho A \, \Delta x$ and then passing to the limit as Δx approaches zero, we get the partial differential equation

$$\frac{\partial u}{\partial t} = \alpha^2 \frac{\partial^2 u}{\partial x^2}. \tag{1}$$

Suppose now that we have a bar, 10 cm. long, with its sides impervious to heat so that the heat flow is one-dimensional as assumed above. Let the ends A and B of the bar be kept at 50° C. and 100° C., respectively, until steady-state conditions prevail, that is, until the temperature at any particular point no longer varies with time. The temperature at A is then suddenly raised to 90° and at the same instant that at B is lowered to 60°; these end temperatures are thereafter maintained. We wish to find an expression for the temperature at a distance x from end A and at any time t subsequent to the changes in end temperatures.

We first mathematically formulate our boundary and initial conditions. For the boundary conditions we evidently have

$$u(0, t) = 90, \qquad u(10, t) = 60, \qquad t > 0. \tag{2}$$

To obtain an equation expressing the initial condition, we proceed as follows. Previous to the temperature changes at the ends, when $t = 0$, the heat flow was independent of time. But if the temperature u depends only upon x and not upon t, (1) reduces to

$$\frac{d^2u}{dx^2} = 0, \tag{3}$$

the general solution of which is

$$u = ax + b, \tag{4}$$

where a and b are arbitrary constants. Since $u = 50$ for $x = 0$, and $u = 100$ for $x = 10$, we get from (4), $50 = b$ and $100 = 10a + b$, whence $a = 5$ and $b = 50$. Thus the initial condition is expressed by

$$u(x, 0) = 5x + 50, \qquad 0 < x < 10. \tag{5}$$

We therefore have to find a temperature function $u(x, t)$ satisfying the differential equation (1), the boundary conditions (2), and the initial condition (5).

Now if we immediately follow the procedure adopted in Art. 70, we encounter a difficulty that did not arise there. The two boundary values in each vibrating string problem were both zero, and we were able to find a function that not only satisfied the differential equation but also fulfilled the boundary conditions. Here, however, we have non-zero boundary values, and therefore we modify the procedure.

We break up the required function, $u(x, t)$, into two parts,

$$u(x, t) = u_s(x) + u_t(x, t), \tag{6}$$

where $u_s(x)$ is a solution of (1), involving only x and satisfying the boundary conditions (2); $u_t(x, t)$ is then a function defined by (6). Thus, $u_s(x)$ is a *steady-state* solution, of the form (4), and $u_t(x, t)$ may consequently be regarded as a *transient* solution which numerically decreases with increase of t so as to become negligible after a sufficient lapse of time.

Using the form (4) for $u_s(x)$, we get, since $u_s(0) = 90$ and $u_s(10) = 60$,

$$u_s(x) = 90 - 3x. \tag{7}$$

Consequently we have, from (6), (2), and (7),

$$u_t(0, t) = u(0, t) - u_s(0) = 90 - 90 = 0,$$

$$u_t(10, t) = u(10, t) - u_s(10) = 60 - 60 = 0; \tag{8}$$

and from (6), (5), and (7),

$$u_t(x, 0) = u(x, 0) - u_s(x) = 5x + 50 - 90 + 3x = 8x - 40. \tag{9}$$

Equations (8) and (9) express the boundary and initial conditions relative to the transient solution. Since the boundary values given by (8) are both zero, we now apply the method used in Art. 69 to determine $u_t(x, t)$.

We assume $u_t(x, t)$ to be of the form

$$u_t(x, t) = X(x) \cdot T(t), \tag{10}$$

substitute in (1), and separate the variables. This yields

$$XT' = \alpha^2 X''T,$$

$$\frac{T'}{\alpha^2 T} = \frac{X''}{X} = k, \tag{11}$$

where k is a constant. We then find three types of solutions:

$$u_t = e^{\alpha^2 kt}(c_1 e^{\sqrt{k}x} + c_2 e^{-\sqrt{k}x}), \qquad\qquad k > 0; \tag{12}$$

$$u_t = e^{\alpha^2 kt}(c_3 \sin \sqrt{-k}\, x + c_4 \cos \sqrt{-k}\, x), \qquad k < 0; \tag{13}$$

$$u_t = c_5 x + c_6, \qquad\qquad\qquad\qquad\qquad\qquad k = 0. \tag{14}$$

Since u_t is to decrease numerically with increase of t, form (13) must be chosen. From the first of conditions (8) we get the relation $0 = c_4 e^{\alpha^2 kt}$, which can be met only by taking $c_4 = 0$. The second of conditions (8) then yields $0 = c_3 e^{\alpha^2 kt} \sin 10\sqrt{-k}$, and, since c_3 cannot be zero (or u_t would be identically zero), we take $10\sqrt{-k} = n\pi$, where n is an integer. Hence (13) reduces to

$$u_t = c_3 e^{-n^2 \pi^2 \alpha^2 t/100} \sin \frac{n\pi x}{10}. \tag{15}$$

It is apparent that no sum of a finite number of terms of the form (15) will satisfy initial condition (9). Reasoning as in Art. 70, we are thus led to the infinite series

$$u_t = \sum_{n=1}^{\infty} b_n e^{-n^2 \pi^2 \alpha^2 t/100} \sin \frac{n\pi x}{10}. \tag{16}$$

This series will formally satisfy (1) and (8). Relation (9) now leads to

$$8x - 40 = \sum_{n=1}^{\infty} b_n \sin \frac{n\pi x}{10}, \qquad 0 < x < 10. \tag{17}$$

We easily get the needed Fourier half-range sine series for $8x - 40$ by combining Peirce 809 and 808. Setting $c = 10$ in these series, we find

$$8x - 40 = 8 \cdot \frac{20}{\pi} \left(\sin \frac{\pi x}{10} - \frac{1}{2} \sin \frac{2\pi x}{10} + \frac{1}{3} \sin \frac{3\pi x}{10} - \cdots \right)$$

$$- 40 \cdot \frac{4}{\pi} \left(\sin \frac{\pi x}{10} + \frac{1}{3} \sin \frac{3\pi x}{10} + \cdots \right)$$

$$= - \frac{80}{\pi} \left(\sin \frac{\pi x}{5} + \frac{1}{2} \sin \frac{2\pi x}{5} + \frac{1}{3} \sin \frac{3\pi x}{5} + \cdots \right). \quad (18)$$

Therefore $b_1 = 0$, $b_2 = -80/\pi$, $b_3 = 0$, $b_4 = -80/2\pi$, etc. Substitution in (16) yields

$$u_t = - \frac{80}{\pi} \sum_{n=1}^{\infty} \frac{1}{n} e^{-n^2\pi^2\alpha^2 t/25} \sin \frac{n\pi x}{5}. \quad (19)$$

Finally, combining (7) and (19) into (6), we have the required solution,

$$u(x, t) = 90 - 3x - \frac{80}{\pi} \sum_{n=1}^{\infty} \frac{1}{n} e^{-n^2\pi^2\alpha^2 t/25} \sin \frac{n\pi x}{5}. \quad (20)$$

To establish the uniform convergence of the series (19), we first note that, since $| \sin (n\pi x/5) | \leq 1$ for every x and for every positive integer n, the absolute values of the terms of the series do not exceed the corresponding terms of the series

$$- \frac{80}{\pi} \sum_{n=1}^{\infty} \frac{1}{n} e^{-n^2\pi^2\alpha^2 t/25}.$$

Hence, if this series converges for $t > 0$, so will (19). Applying Cauchy's ratio test to the test series, we get

$$\left| \frac{u_{n+1}}{u_n} \right| = \left| \frac{n}{n+1} e^{-(2n+1)\pi^2\alpha^2 t/25} \right|,$$

and the limit, as n becomes infinite, is zero for any positive value of t. Thus (20) is a valid solution of our problem.

PROBLEMS

1. (a) A rod of length L has its ends A and B kept at $0°$ C. and $100°$ C., respectively, until steady-state conditions prevail. If the temperature of B is then reduced suddenly to $0°$ C. and kept so, while that of A is maintained, find the temperature $u(x, t)$ at distance x from A and at time t. (b) If the rod of part (a) is of silver, 20 cm. long, with specific gravity 10.6, thermal conductivity $K = 1.04$ cal./cm. deg.

sec., and specific heat $c = 0.056$ cal./gr. deg., find the temperature at the midpoint, 1 min. after the change.

2. The ends A and B of a rod 40 cm. long have their temperatures kept at $0°$ C. and $80°$ C., respectively, until steady-state conditions prevail. The temperature of end B is then suddenly reduced to $40°$ C., and kept so, while that of end A is kept at $0°$ C. (a) Find the temperature $u(x, t)$ as a function of x (cm.), the distance from end A, and t (sec.), the time elapsed after the sudden change of temperature at end B. (b) If the rod of part (a) is of copper, with specific gravity 8.89, thermal conductivity $K = 0.84$ cal./cm. deg. sec., and specific heat $c = 0.092$ cal./gr. deg., find the temperature at a point 10 cm. from A, 5 min. after the change.

3. (a) Solve problem 1(a) if the change consists of raising the temperature of A to $50°$ C. and that of B to $150°$ C. (b) If the rod of part (a) is of glass, 20 cm. long, with $\rho = 2.40$ gr./cm.^{3}, $K = 0.0015$ cal./cm. deg. sec., and $c = 0.180$ cal./gr. deg., find the temperature at the midpoint, 2 hr. after the change.

4. (a) Solve Problem 1(a) if the change consists of raising the temperature of A to $25°$ C. and reducing that of B to $75°$ C. (b) If the rod of part (a) is of cast iron, 20 cm. long, with $\rho = 7.20$ gr./cm.^{3}, $K = 0.17$ cal./cm. deg. sec., and $c = 0.113$ cal./gr. deg., find the temperature at a point 5 cm. from A, $\frac{1}{2}$ min. after the change.

5. The temperature distribution in a certain rod, 10 cm. long, is initially given by $u(x, 0) = \frac{1}{10}(10x - x^2)^2$. If the ends are both kept at $0°$ C. thereafter, find the temperature function $u(x, t)$.

6. Two cast-iron rods, AB and CD ($\rho = 7.20$ gr./cm.^{3}, $K = 0.17$ cal./cm. deg. sec., $c = 0.113$ cal./gr. deg.), each 10 cm. long and with insulated sides, are respectively at uniform temperatures of $0°$ C. and $50°$ C. At time $t = 0$ they are set in line, end B of one bar against end C of the other, and the temperature of D is reduced to $10°$ C. If the temperatures at A and D are respectively maintained at $0°$ C. and $10°$ C. thereafter, find the temperature of the midpoint of AB, 4 min. after the change.

7. Each of three copper bars ($\rho = 8.89$ gr./cm.^{3}, $K = 0.84$ cal./cm. deg. sec., $c = 0.092$ cal./gr. deg.) is 10 cm. long and has insulated surfaces. Two are at $0°$ C. throughout their lengths, and the third is at $100°$ C. throughout. At time $t = 0$ they are put in line, the hot bar between the two cold ones, and the outer ends ($x = 0$ and $x = 30$) are kept at $0°$ C. Find the temperature of the midpoint of the set, 1 min. after they are alined.

8. Two steel rods, AB and CD ($\rho = 7.70$ gr./cm.^{3}, $K = 0.086$ cal./cm. deg. sec., $c = 0.118$ cal./gr. deg.), each 25 cm. long and with insulated sides, have the following steady-state conditions. Ends A and B have the temperatures $0°$ C. and $50°$ C., respectively, while ends C and D have the respective temperatures $100°$ C. and $150°$ C. At time $t = 0$ they are set in line, end B against end C, and the temperature of D is reduced to $100°$ C. If the temperatures of A and D are, respectively, maintained at $0°$ C. and $100°$ C. thereafter, find the temperature of the midpoint of CD, $\frac{1}{2}$ hr. after the change.

9. The temperature at one end of a bar, 50 cm. long and with insulated surfaces, is kept at $0°$ C. and that at the other end is kept at $100°$ C. until steady-state conditions prevail. The two ends are then suddenly insulated, so that the temperature gradient is zero at each end thereafter. (a) Show that the sum of the temperatures at any two points equidistant from the center is always $100°$ C. (b) If the bar is of copper ($\rho = 8.89$ gr./cm.^{3}, $K = 0.84$ cal./cm. deg. sec., $c = 0.092$ cal./gr. deg.), find the time required for the temperature at a point 10 cm. from the cooler end to reach 90% of its final steady-state value.

10. A bar with insulated sides is initially at temperature 0° C. throughout. The end $x = 0$ is kept at 0° C., and heat is suddenly applied at the end $x = L$ (cm.) at a constant rate, so that $\partial u/\partial x = A$ for $x = L$, where A is a constant. Find the temperature function $u(x, t)$.

11. Heat is flowing in an insulated wire in which heat is being generated at a constant rate. Show that the temperature function $u(x, t)$ satisfies a differential equation of the form $\partial u/\partial t = \alpha^2(\partial^2 u/\partial x^2) + c$, where α^2 is diffusivity and c is a positive constant. Hence show that this equation has the solution $u(x, t) = v(x, t) + ct$, where $v(x, t)$ is a solution of equation (1), Art. 71.

12. If the ends $x = 0$ and $x = L$ (cm.) of the wire of Problem 11 are kept at 0° C., and if $u(x, 0) = f(x)$, show that

$$u(x, t) = \frac{cx(L - x)}{2\alpha^2} + \frac{2}{L}\sum_{n=1}^{\infty} e^{-n^2\pi^2\alpha^2 t/L^2}\sin\frac{n\pi x}{L}\cdot\int_0^L\left[\frac{cx(x - L)}{2\alpha^2} + f(x)\right]\sin\frac{n\pi x}{L}dx.$$

13. A thin wire is conducting heat along its length and is also radiating heat from its surface. Assume that the diameter is so small that, at any distance x from one end of the wire and at any time t, the temperature $u(x, t)$ does not vary over the cross-section. Assume also that the temperature of the surroundings is 0° C. and that the radiation obeys Newton's law, so that the time rate of change of temperature, due to radiation, is proportional to the temperature. Show that $u(x, t)$ satisfies a differential equation of the form $\partial u/\partial t = \alpha^2(\partial^2 u/\partial x^2) - Bu$, where α^2 is diffusivity and B is a positive constant.

14. Show that the equation of Problem 13 has a solution of the form $u(x, t) = e^{-Bt}v(x, t)$, where $v(x, t)$ satisfies equation (1), Art. 71.

15. Suppose that the wire of Problem 13 is initially at temperature 0° C. throughout its length L (cm.), and that the temperature at the end $x = L$ is suddenly raised to u_0 while that at $x = 0$ is maintained at 0° C. Using the method of Art. 71, in which we set $u(x, t) = u_s(x) + u_t(x, t)$, show that $u_s(x) = u_0(\sinh\sqrt{B}\,x/\alpha)/(\sinh\sqrt{B}\,L/\alpha)$, and determine the function $u_t(x, t)$.

16. Show that the differential equation for radial heat flow in a homogeneous solid sphere is

$$\frac{\partial u}{\partial t} = \alpha^2\left(\frac{\partial^2 u}{\partial r^2} + \frac{2}{r}\frac{\partial u}{\partial r}\right),$$

where r (cm.) is the radial distance from the center to any interior point.

17. Show that the equation of Problem 16 is satisfied by $u(r, t) = v(r, t)/r$, where $v(r, t)$ is a solution of the equation $\partial v/\partial t = \alpha^2(\partial^2 v/\partial r^2)$.

18. The sphere of Problem 17, of radius a (cm.), has the initial temperature distribution $u(r, 0) = c(a - r)$, $0 < r < a$, where c is a constant. If $u(a, t) = 0$, $t > 0$, find $u(r, t)$.

19. The sphere of Problem 17 is initially at temperature 0° C. throughout, and the temperature of the surface is suddenly made and kept at a constant value A. Find the temperature function $u(r, t)$.

72. Two-dimensional heat flow.

As an extension of the heat-flow problem treated in the preceding article, we now suppose the heat streamlines to be curves instead of straight lines, these curves lying in parallel planes, so that the flow is here two-dimensional. Let there be given a sheet of conducting material of uniform thickness τ (cm.), density ρ (gr./cm.^{3}), thermal conductivity K (cal./cm. sec. deg.), and specific heat c (cal./gr. deg.). Let the xy-plane be taken in one face of the sheet, and consider a rectangular region $ABCD$, the coordinates of the corners being those given in Fig. 50. By the second and third

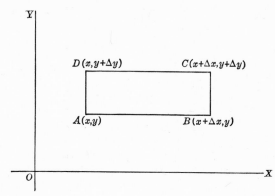

Fig. 50

laws of heat flow, the amount of heat entering the side AB in 1 sec. is approximately equal to *

$$-K\tau\,\Delta x\,\frac{\partial u}{\partial y}\bigg]_y,$$

and the amount leaving CD per second is, nearly,

$$-K\tau\,\Delta x\,\frac{\partial u}{\partial y}\bigg]_{y+\Delta y}.$$

Hence the rate of gain of heat due to these two boundaries is approximately

$$K\tau\,\Delta x\left(\frac{\partial u}{\partial y}\bigg]_{y+\Delta y} - \frac{\partial u}{\partial y}\bigg]_y\right).$$

Similarly, the approximate rate of gain of heat due to the boundaries AD and BC is

$$K\tau\,\Delta y\left(\frac{\partial u}{\partial x}\bigg]_{x+\Delta x} - \frac{\partial u}{\partial x}\bigg]_x\right).$$

---

* Here $\dfrac{\partial u}{\partial y}\bigg]_y$ is the average value of $\dfrac{\partial u}{\partial y}$ along AB. Similarly the other three temperature gradients are average values.

Consequently the approximate total rate of gain of heat in the region $ABCD$ is the sum of these two terms, or

$$K\tau \, \Delta x \, \Delta y \left(\frac{\left.\dfrac{\partial u}{\partial x}\right]_{x+\Delta x} - \left.\dfrac{\partial u}{\partial x}\right]_x}{\Delta x} + \frac{\left.\dfrac{\partial u}{\partial y}\right]_{y+\Delta y} - \left.\dfrac{\partial u}{\partial y}\right]_y}{\Delta y} \right).$$

Moreover, this rate of gain of heat is given approximately by

$$c\rho\tau \, \Delta x \, \Delta y \, \frac{\partial u}{\partial t},$$

by law I. Equating the above two expressions, dividing by $\tau \, \Delta x \, \Delta y$. and then passing to the limit as Δx and Δy both approach zero, we get

$$\alpha^2 \left(\frac{\partial^2 u}{\partial x^2} + \frac{\partial^2 u}{\partial y^2} \right) = \frac{\partial u}{\partial t}, \tag{1}$$

where again $\alpha^2 = K/c\rho$ is the diffusivity. If, in particular, the streamlines are all parallel to the x-axis, the rate of change $\partial u/\partial y$ of temperature in the y-direction will be zero, whence $\partial^2 u/\partial y^2 = 0$ and (1) reduces to the partial differential equation of one-dimensional heat flow found in Art. 71.

When the streamlines are non-planar curves, so that the flow is three-dimensional, precisely similar reasoning leads to the equation

$$\alpha^2 \left(\frac{\partial^2 u}{\partial x^2} + \frac{\partial^2 u}{\partial y^2} + \frac{\partial^2 u}{\partial z^2} \right) = \frac{\partial u}{\partial t}.$$

We shall, however, confine our attention to two-dimensional heat flow.

If the boundaries of our sheet are kept at definite temperatures, the faces being insulated to insure two-dimensional heat flow, there will come a time when the temperature at any particular point remains sensibly constant throughout later time intervals; that is, steady-state conditions will have been attained. Since u will then depend only upon x and y, $\partial u/\partial t$ will be zero at every point, and equation (1) will be replaced by

$$\frac{\partial^2 u}{\partial x^2} + \frac{\partial^2 u}{\partial y^2} = 0. \tag{2}$$

This partial differential equation, which here enters into the investigation of temperature distribution for two-dimensional heat flow, arises also in many other problems of mathematical physics, and is therefore of considerable importance in engineering mathematics. It is called

Laplace's equation, and we shall meet it again in later chapters in connection with other types of problems.

In the study of steady-state temperature distribution in a rectangular sheet, say, it is natural and usually most convenient to deal with rectangular coordinates, as we have done above. Sometimes, however, polar coordinates (r, θ) are more useful than rectangular, so that we should like to have Laplace's equation with the independent variables r and θ instead of the variables x and y. Since the relations between the two coordinate systems, when the polar axis is taken along the positive x-axis with the pole coinciding with the origin, are

$$x = r \cos \theta, \qquad y = r \sin \theta,$$

we have by an application of formulas (16) of Art. 66,

$$\frac{\partial u}{\partial r} = \frac{\partial u}{\partial x} \cos \theta + \frac{\partial u}{\partial y} \sin \theta, \tag{3}$$

$$\frac{\partial u}{\partial \theta} = -\frac{\partial u}{\partial x} r \sin \theta + \frac{\partial u}{\partial y} r \cos \theta, \tag{4}$$

$$\frac{\partial^2 u}{\partial r^2} = \frac{\partial^2 u}{\partial x^2} \cos^2 \theta + 2 \frac{\partial^2 u}{\partial x \, \partial y} \sin \theta \cos \theta + \frac{\partial^2 u}{\partial y^2} \sin^2 \theta, \tag{5}$$

$$\frac{\partial^2 u}{\partial \theta^2} = -\frac{\partial u}{\partial x} r \cos \theta + \frac{\partial^2 u}{\partial x^2} r^2 \sin^2 \theta - 2 \frac{\partial^2 u}{\partial x \, \partial y} r^2 \sin \theta \cos \theta$$

$$-\frac{\partial u}{\partial y} r \sin \theta + \frac{\partial^2 u}{\partial y^2} r^2 \cos^2 \theta. \tag{6}$$

Multiplying (6) by $1/r^2$ and adding to (5), we get, using the identity $\sin^2 \theta + \cos^2 \theta = 1$,

$$\frac{\partial^2 u}{\partial r^2} + \frac{1}{r^2} \frac{\partial^2 u}{\partial \theta^2} = \frac{\partial^2 u}{\partial x^2} + \frac{\partial^2 u}{\partial y^2} - \frac{\partial u}{\partial x} \frac{\cos \theta}{r} - \frac{\partial u}{\partial y} \frac{\sin \theta}{r}. \tag{7}$$

Multiplying (3) by $1/r$ and adding to (7), there is found

$$\frac{\partial^2 u}{\partial r^2} + \frac{1}{r} \frac{\partial u}{\partial r} + \frac{1}{r^2} \frac{\partial^2 u}{\partial \theta^2} = \frac{\partial^2 u}{\partial x^2} + \frac{\partial^2 u}{\partial y^2}. \tag{8}$$

Hence Laplace's equation (2) becomes, in polar coordinates,

$$r^2 \frac{\partial^2 u}{\partial r^2} + r \frac{\partial u}{\partial r} + \frac{\partial^2 u}{\partial \theta^2} = 0. \tag{9}$$

As an illustration of the use of equation (9), consider a semicircular plate of radius a (cm.), and let the bounding diameter be kept at $0°$ C. and the circumference at any fixed temperature $u_0 \neq 0$ until steady-state conditions prevail. In order to find the temperature distribution in the plate, we have therefore to find a solution $u(r, \theta)$ of (9) valid for values of θ between 0 and π * and for values of r (cm.) between 0 and a, subject to the boundary conditions

$$u(r, 0) = 0, \tag{10}$$

$$u(r, \pi) = 0, \tag{11}$$

$$u(a, \theta) = u_0, \tag{12}$$

where (10) and (11) are to hold for any r and (12) for any θ in the given ranges.

We assume that (9) has a solution of the form

$$u(r, \theta) = R(r) \cdot T(\theta),$$

which gives us, upon substitution in (9),

$$r^2 R''T + rR'T + RT'' = 0,$$

or

$$\frac{r^2 R''}{R} + \frac{rR'}{R} = -\frac{T''}{T}.$$

Setting each of these two expressions equal to a constant k, we get the ordinary differential equations

$$r^2 \frac{d^2R}{dr^2} + r \frac{dR}{dr} - kR = 0, \tag{13}$$

$$\frac{d^2T}{d\theta^2} + kT = 0. \tag{14}$$

Let us examine equation (14) for $T(\theta)$ first. We readily find

$$T = c_1 \sin \sqrt{k}\, \theta + c_2 \cos \sqrt{k}\, \theta \qquad (k > 0),$$

$$T = c_3 e^{\sqrt{-k}\theta} + c_4 e^{-\sqrt{-k}\theta} \qquad (k < 0),$$

$$T = c_5 \theta + c_6 \qquad (k = 0).$$

Since u, and therefore T, must be a periodic rather than an increasing or decreasing function of θ, it is evident that k should be chosen as positive.

---

* Or, equally well, for θ between 2π and 3π, etc.

Turning now to equation (13), we see that it is an Euler differential equation (Chapter I, Art. 12); consequently we set $r = e^z$, so that (13) is transformed into

$$\frac{d^2 R}{dz^2} - kR = 0.$$

As k is to be positive, a suitable solution of this equation will be

$$R = c_7 e^{\sqrt{k} z} + c_8 e^{-\sqrt{k} z} = c_7 r^{\sqrt{k}} + c_8 r^{-\sqrt{k}}.$$

Before applying our boundary conditions, we note that since u, and hence R, is to remain finite as r approaches zero, we must have $c_8 = 0$. Then we have

$$u = c_7 r^{\sqrt{k}} (c_1 \sin \sqrt{k}\, \theta + c_2 \cos \sqrt{k}\, \theta).$$

Now from (10),

$$0 = c_7 r^{\sqrt{k}} \cdot c_2,$$

and since c_7 cannot be zero without making u identically zero, we must take $c_2 = 0$. From (11),

$$0 = c_7 r^{\sqrt{k}} \cdot c_1 \sin \sqrt{k}\, \pi,$$

and since neither c_1 nor c_7 is to vanish, we take

$$\sqrt{k} = n,$$

an integer. Finally, since (12) cannot be satisfied by a single term of the form $b r^n \sin n\theta$, nor by the sum of a finite number of such terms, we take

$$u = \sum_{n=1}^{\infty} b_n r^n \sin n\theta.$$

Then (12) gives us

$$u_0 = \sum_{n=1}^{\infty} b_n a^n \sin n\theta, \qquad 0 < \theta < \pi,$$

whence

$$b_n a^n = \frac{2}{\pi} \int_0^{\pi} u_0 \sin n\theta \, d\theta = \left[-\frac{2u_0}{n\pi} \cos n\theta \right]_0^{\pi},$$

$$b_n = \frac{2u_0}{n\pi a^n} (1 - \cos n\pi),$$

and

$$u(r, \theta) = \frac{4u_0}{\pi} \sum_{n=1}^{\infty} \frac{1}{2n-1} \left(\frac{r}{a} \right)^{2n-1} \sin (2n-1)\theta. \tag{15}$$

This is the desired solution.

To prove the validity of (15) for $0 < r < a$ and $0 < \theta < \pi$, we proceed as in the example of Art. 71. Each term of (15) is in absolute value less than or at most equal to the corresponding term of the series

$$\frac{4u_0}{\pi} \sum_{n=1}^{\infty} \frac{1}{2n-1} \left(\frac{r}{a}\right)^{2n-1},$$

and the Cauchy ratio test for this series gives us

$$\lim_{n \to \infty} \left| \frac{u_{n+1}}{u_n} \right| = \lim_{n \to \infty} \left| \frac{2n-1}{2n+1} \left(\frac{r}{a}\right)^2 \right| = \left(\frac{r}{a}\right)^2,$$

which is less than unity for $0 < r < a$. Hence (15) is uniformly convergent. Likewise, all the series derived from (15) by partial differentiation also converge uniformly, and therefore (15) is a legitimate solution of the problem.

PROBLEMS

1. If the radius of the plate in the example of Art. 72 is $a = 10$ cm., find the temperature for $r = 3$ cm. and $\theta = 45°$.

2. The bounding diameter of a semicircular plate, of radius 10 cm., is kept at $0°$ C., and the temperature along the semicircular boundary is given by $u(10, \theta) = 50\theta$, $0 < \theta \leq \pi/2$, $u(10, \theta) = 50(\pi - \theta)$, $\pi/2 < \theta < \pi$. Find the steady-state temperature function $u(r, \theta)$.

3. A plate with insulated surfaces has the shape of a quadrant of a circle of radius 10 cm. The bounding radii, $\theta = 0$ and $\theta = \pi/2$, are kept at $0°$ C., and the temperature along the circular quadrant is kept at $100(\pi\theta - 2\theta^2)$ degrees C., $0 < \theta < \pi/2$. Find the steady-state temperature for $r = 5$, $\theta = \pi/4$.

4. A rectangular plate with insulated surfaces is 8 cm. wide and so long compared to its width that it may be considered infinite in length without introducing an appreciable error. If the temperature along one short edge, $y = 0$, is given by $u(x, 0) = 100 \sin(\pi x/8)$, $0 < x < 8$, while the two long edges, $x = 0$ and $x = 8$, as well as the other short edge, are kept at $0°$ C., find the steady-state temperature function $u(x, y)$.

5. (a) A rectangular plate with insulated surfaces is 10 cm. wide and so long compared to its width that it may be considered infinite in length without introducing an appreciable error. If one short edge, $y = 0$, is kept at $10°$ C., while the two long edges, $x = 0$ and $x = 10$, as well as the other short edge, are kept at $0°$ C., find the steady-state temperature at any point (x, y) of the plate. (b) Draw a curve showing the variation of temperature with distance y along the midsection $x = 5$, and determine graphically the distances y at which the temperatures are $1°$ C. and $5°$ C. Check by showing that $u(5, y) = (40/\pi) \tan^{-1} e^{-\pi y/10}$, and evaluating the required distances y from this formula.

6. Obtain a finite expression for the function $u(x, y)$ of Problem 5 by the following procedure. Let $z = re^{i\theta}$ in the relation

$$\ln \frac{1+z}{1-z} = 2\left(z + \frac{z^3}{3} + \frac{z^5}{5} + \cdots\right),$$

separate real and imaginary parts, and hence get

$$r \sin \theta + \frac{r^3}{3} \sin 3\theta + \cdots = \frac{1}{2} \tan^{-1}\left(\frac{2r \sin \theta}{1 - r^2}\right).$$

Now identify r with $e^{-\pi y/10}$ and θ with $\pi x/10$ in the result of Problem 5, and thus obtain

$$u(x, y) = \frac{20}{\pi} \tan^{-1}\left[\frac{\sin(\pi x/10)}{\sinh(\pi y/10)}\right].$$

7. Solve Problem 4 if the function $u(x, 0)$ given there is replaced by $u(x, 0) = 8x - x^2$.

8. If, in Problem 5(a), the temperature along the edge $y = 0$ is given by $u(x, 0) = 100x - x^3$ for $0 < x < 10$, other boundary conditions remaining the same, find $u(x, y)$.

9. If, in Problem 5(a), the temperature along the edge $y = 0$ is given by $u(x, 0) = 20x$, $0 < x \leqq 5$, $u(x, 0) = 20(10 - x)$, $5 < x < 10$, other conditions remaining the same, find $u(x, y)$.

10. A square plate is bounded by the lines $x = 0$, $y = 0$, $x = a$, $y = a$. Its surfaces are insulated, and the temperature along the upper horizontal edge is $100°$ C. while the other three edges are kept at $0°$ C. Find the steady-state temperatures at the points $(a/2, a/2)$ and $(a/4, a/4)$.

11. If, in Problem 10, the temperature along the edge $y = a$ is given by $u(x, a) = x$, $0 < x \leqq a/2$, $u(x, a) = a - x$, $a/2 < x < a$, other conditions remaining the same, find $u(x, y)$.

12. A rectangular plate is bounded by the lines $x = 0$, $y = 0$, $x = 20$, $y = 10$. Its surfaces are insulated, and the temperature along the upper horizontal edge is given by $u(x, 10) = 20x - x^2$, while the other three edges are kept at $0°$ C. Find the steady-state temperature function $u(x, y)$.

13. A rectangular plate has its edges along the lines $x = 0$, $y = 0$, $x = 20$, $y = 10$. The temperature along the right-hand vertical edge is given by $u(20, y) = y^2$, $0 < y \leqq 5$, $u(20, y) = (10 - y)^2$, $5 < y < 10$, while the other three edges are kept at $0°$ C. If the surfaces of the plate are insulated, find the steady-state temperature function $u(x, y)$.

14. Consider a rectangular plate, a by b cm. Let the temperature distributions along the four edges be given by $u(0, y) = f_1(y)$, $u(a, y) = f_2(y)$, $u(x, 0) = f_3(x)$, $u(x, b) = f_4(x)$. Show that, if u_1, u_2, u_3, and u_4 are four solutions of Laplace's equation, respectively satisfying the boundary conditions

$u_1(0, y) = f_1(y)$,	$u_1(a, y) = 0$,	$u_1(x, 0) = 0$,	$u_1(x, b) = 0$;
$u_2(0, y) = 0$,	$u_2(a, y) = f_2(y)$,	$u_2(x, 0) = 0$,	$u_2(x, b) = 0$;
$u_3(0, y) = 0$,	$u_3(a, y) = 0$,	$u_3(x, 0) = f_3(x)$,	$u_3(x, b) = 0$;
$u_4(0, y) = 0$,	$u_4(a, y) = 0$,	$u_4(x, 0) = 0$,	$u_4(x, b) = f_4(y)$;

then the steady-state temperature function $u(x, y)$ can be taken as

$$u(x, y) = u_1(x, y) + u_2(x, y) + u_3(x, y) + u_4(x, y).$$

Thus, for any given boundary conditions, $u(x, y)$ can be determined by solving at most four problems each of which involves three zero boundary values.

73. Fluid flow. Hydrodynamics, which deals with the motion of fluids, forms another topic into which partial differential equations enter. We shall discuss here only fluid flow in which the fluids are supposed perfect, so that they are homogeneous and continuous in structure and such that viscosity may be neglected. Thus we may consider small elements of a fluid body as having the same physical properties as the entire mass, and may also take all thrusts exerted by the fluid on an immersed surface as being normal to the surface, whether the surface in question is at rest or in motion in the fluid. Although these assumptions are not all realized in practice, they permit a mathematical analysis to be made more readily, and the results thus obtained provide valuable information about fluid flow in general.

Consider three-dimensional fluid flow relative to a set of rectangular axes. Let u, v, w (ft./sec.) be the components of the velocity parallel, respectively, to the x-, y-, and z-axes at a point $P(x, y, z)$ at time t (sec.), so that u, v, w are functions of the four variables x, y, z, t. In a time interval Δt the fluid particle originally at P will have moved to another point $Q(x + \Delta x, y + \Delta y, z + \Delta z)$, and if we consider this one moving particle rather than the successive particles passing through P we shall have the coordinates (x, y, z) of that particle as functions of t. Consequently the components of the acceleration of our particle are, by equation (15), Art. 66,

$$
\begin{aligned}
\frac{du}{dt} &= \frac{\partial u}{\partial x}\frac{dx}{dt} + \frac{\partial u}{\partial y}\frac{dy}{dt} + \frac{\partial u}{\partial z}\frac{dz}{dt} + \frac{\partial u}{\partial t} \\[2mm]
&= u\frac{\partial u}{\partial x} + v\frac{\partial u}{\partial y} + w\frac{\partial u}{\partial z} + \frac{\partial u}{\partial t}, \\[2mm]
\frac{dv}{dt} &= u\frac{\partial v}{\partial x} + v\frac{\partial v}{\partial y} + w\frac{\partial v}{\partial z} + \frac{\partial v}{\partial t}, \\[2mm]
\frac{dw}{dt} &= u\frac{\partial w}{\partial x} + v\frac{\partial w}{\partial y} + w\frac{\partial w}{\partial z} + \frac{\partial w}{\partial t}.
\end{aligned}
\tag{1}
$$

Now let $P(x, y, z)$ be one vertex of a small rectangular parallelepiped of dimensions Δx, Δy, Δz, as shown in Fig. 51, and let $\rho(x, y, z, t)$ (lb./ft.^{3}) be the density at P at any time t. Suppose the fluid to be in motion owing to the action of a force $F(x, y, z, t)$ per unit mass, whose components in the x-, y-, z-directions are F_1, F_2, F_3 (ft./sec.^{2}), respectively, and let $p(x, y, z, t)$ (lb./ft.^{2}) be the pressure at P at time t. Equating the algebraic sum of the forces acting in the x-direction to

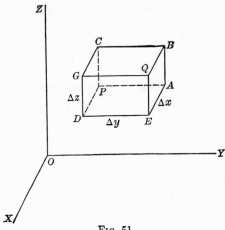

FIG. 51

the product of mass and the x-component of acceleration, we get the approximate relation

$$\frac{\rho}{g} \Delta x \, \Delta y \, \Delta z \, \frac{du}{dt} = F_1 \frac{\rho}{g} \Delta x \, \Delta y \, \Delta z + \left(p \Big]_x - p \Big]_{x+\Delta x} \right) \Delta y \, \Delta z,$$

where $g = 32.17$ ft./sec.^{2} Dividing by $\rho \, \Delta x \, \Delta y \, \Delta z / g$, passing to the limit as Δx, Δy, and Δz all approach zero, and making use of the first of equations (1), we get the equation

$$u \frac{\partial u}{\partial x} + v \frac{\partial u}{\partial y} + w \frac{\partial u}{\partial z} + \frac{\partial u}{\partial t} = F_1 - \frac{g}{\rho} \frac{\partial p}{\partial x}. \tag{2}$$

Similarly, for the y- and z-directions, we find

$$u \frac{\partial v}{\partial x} + v \frac{\partial v}{\partial y} + w \frac{\partial v}{\partial z} + \frac{\partial v}{\partial t} = F_2 - \frac{g}{\rho} \frac{\partial p}{\partial y}, \tag{3}$$

$$u \frac{\partial w}{\partial x} + v \frac{\partial w}{\partial y} + w \frac{\partial w}{\partial z} + \frac{\partial w}{\partial t} = F_3 - \frac{g}{\rho} \frac{\partial p}{\partial z}. \tag{4}$$

Equations (2)–(4) are the partial differential equations of motion of the fluid, for three-dimensional flow. If the flow is two-dimensional, say in planes parallel to the xy-plane, the equations of motion become

$$u \frac{\partial u}{\partial x} + v \frac{\partial u}{\partial y} + \frac{\partial u}{\partial t} = F_1 - \frac{g}{\rho} \frac{\partial p}{\partial x}, \tag{5}$$

$$u \frac{\partial v}{\partial x} + v \frac{\partial v}{\partial y} + \frac{\partial v}{\partial t} = F_2 - \frac{g}{\rho} \frac{\partial p}{\partial y}. \tag{6}$$

In addition to the equations of motion, there exists another relation among our variables, the so-called *equation of continuity*. The rate at which fluid enters the face $PABC$ is $\rho \cdot u \big]_x \Delta y\, \Delta z$, and the rate at which it leaves the opposite face $DEQG$ is $\rho \cdot u \big]_{x+\Delta x} \Delta y\, \Delta z$, so that the rate at which the amount of fluid in the element is changing owing to these two faces is

$$\left(\rho u \big]_x - \rho u \big]_{x+\Delta x} \right) \Delta y\, \Delta z = -\Delta x\, \Delta y\, \Delta z\, \frac{\rho u \big]_{x+\Delta x} - \rho u \big]_x}{\Delta x}.$$

Likewise, the rates of change due to the other two pairs of faces are

$$-\Delta x\, \Delta y\, \Delta z\, \frac{\rho v \big]_{y+\Delta y} - \rho v \big]_y}{\Delta y} \quad \text{and} \quad -\Delta x\, \Delta y\, \Delta z\, \frac{\rho w \big]_{z+\Delta z} - \rho w \big]_z}{\Delta z}.$$

But the weight of the element is $\rho\, \Delta x\, \Delta y\, \Delta z$, and its time rate of change is $(\partial \rho / \partial t)\, \Delta x\, \Delta y\, \Delta z$. Equating this to the sum of the preceding three expressions, dividing by $\Delta x\, \Delta y\, \Delta z$, and passing to the limit, we get

$$\frac{\partial \rho}{\partial t} + \frac{\partial(\rho u)}{\partial x} + \frac{\partial(\rho v)}{\partial y} + \frac{\partial(\rho w)}{\partial z} = 0. \tag{7}$$

If the fluid in question is incompressible, so that ρ is constant, the equation of continuity is

$$\frac{\partial u}{\partial x} + \frac{\partial v}{\partial y} + \frac{\partial w}{\partial z} = 0. \tag{8}$$

For two-dimensional flow, we have instead of (7),

$$\frac{\partial \rho}{\partial t} + \frac{\partial(\rho u)}{\partial x} + \frac{\partial(\rho v)}{\partial y} = 0, \tag{9}$$

and if in addition ρ is constant,

$$\frac{\partial u}{\partial x} + \frac{\partial v}{\partial y} = 0. \tag{10}$$

The quantity whose components are

$$\frac{1}{2}\left(\frac{\partial w}{\partial y} - \frac{\partial v}{\partial z} \right), \quad \frac{1}{2}\left(\frac{\partial u}{\partial z} - \frac{\partial w}{\partial x} \right), \quad \frac{1}{2}\left(\frac{\partial v}{\partial x} - \frac{\partial u}{\partial y} \right), \tag{11}$$

is called the *rotation* of the fluid; a small sphere of the fluid has an instantaneous angular velocity with these expressions as components.

If all three of the expressions (11) are identically zero, the motion is said to be *irrotational*. Now the necessary and sufficient condition that $u\,dx + v\,dy + w\,dz$ be the exact differential of some function of x, y, z is that the quantities (11) vanish identically.* Hence, if fluid motion is irrotational, there will exist a function, which we denote by $-\phi(x, y, z)$, such that

$$-d\phi = u\,dx + v\,dy + w\,dz. \tag{12}$$

The function $\phi(x, y, z)$ so determined is called the *velocity potential*. Since $d\phi = (\partial\phi/\partial x)\,dx + (\partial\phi/\partial y)\,dy + (\partial\phi/\partial z)\,dz$, we have

$$u = -\frac{\partial\phi}{\partial x}, \qquad v = -\frac{\partial\phi}{\partial y}, \qquad w = -\frac{\partial\phi}{\partial z}. \tag{13}$$

When the fluid is incompressible and the motion irrotational, the equation of continuity (8) becomes, in virtue of the relations (13),

$$\frac{\partial^2\phi}{\partial x^2} + \frac{\partial^2\phi}{\partial y^2} + \frac{\partial^2\phi}{\partial z^2} = 0. \tag{14}$$

Thus the velocity potential satisfies Laplace's equation in three dimensions.

The *streamlines* of fluid motion at any instant are defined as curves such that the tangent at any point of each gives the direction in which the fluid at that point is moving at that time. Consequently the values of the velocity components u, v, w at that point are proportional to the direction cosines of the tangent to the streamline. Now at any point of each surface of the family $\phi(x, y, z) =$ const. the partial derivatives $\partial\phi/\partial x$, $\partial\phi/\partial y$, and $\partial\phi/\partial z$ are proportional to the direction cosines of the normal to the surface. It therefore follows from the relations (13) that the streamlines cut each of the velocity equipotential surfaces $\phi =$ const. at right angles.

Suppose now that the motion of an incompressible homogeneous fluid is irrotational, and that no external forces are acting. Since the motion is irrotational, we have

$$\frac{\partial w}{\partial y} = \frac{\partial v}{\partial z}, \qquad \frac{\partial u}{\partial z} = \frac{\partial w}{\partial x}, \qquad \frac{\partial v}{\partial x} = \frac{\partial u}{\partial y},$$

$$u = -\frac{\partial\phi}{\partial x}, \qquad v = -\frac{\partial\phi}{\partial y}, \qquad w = -\frac{\partial\phi}{\partial z}. \tag{15}$$

* This is proved in Chapter VIII, Art. 86.

Making use of these relations, and setting $F_1 = F_2 = F_3 = 0$, the equations of motion (2)–(4) become

$$u \frac{\partial u}{\partial x} + v \frac{\partial v}{\partial x} + w \frac{\partial w}{\partial x} - \frac{\partial}{\partial x} \frac{\partial \phi}{\partial t} = - \frac{g}{\rho} \frac{\partial p}{\partial x},$$

$$u \frac{\partial u}{\partial y} + v \frac{\partial v}{\partial y} + w \frac{\partial w}{\partial y} - \frac{\partial}{\partial y} \frac{\partial \phi}{\partial t} = - \frac{g}{\rho} \frac{\partial p}{\partial y},$$

$$u \frac{\partial u}{\partial z} + v \frac{\partial v}{\partial z} + w \frac{\partial w}{\partial z} - \frac{\partial}{\partial z} \frac{\partial \phi}{\partial t} = - \frac{g}{\rho} \frac{\partial p}{\partial z}.$$

If q denotes the resultant velocity, so that $q^2 = u^2 + v^2 + w^2$, these equations may be written as

$$\frac{\partial}{\partial x} \left(\frac{q^2}{2} \right) - \frac{\partial}{\partial x} \frac{\partial \phi}{\partial t} = - \frac{g}{\rho} \frac{\partial p}{\partial x},$$

$$\frac{\partial}{\partial y} \left(\frac{q^2}{2} \right) - \frac{\partial}{\partial y} \frac{\partial \phi}{\partial t} = - \frac{g}{\rho} \frac{\partial p}{\partial y},$$

$$\frac{\partial}{\partial z} \left(\frac{q^2}{2} \right) - \frac{\partial}{\partial z} \frac{\partial \phi}{\partial t} = - \frac{g}{\rho} \frac{\partial p}{\partial z}.$$

Multiplying respectively by dx, dy, dz and adding, we get for any fixed value of t,

$$d \left(\frac{q^2}{2} \right) - d \frac{\partial \phi}{\partial t} = - \frac{g}{\rho} dp.$$

Integrating, we therefore find

$$\frac{q^2}{2} - \frac{\partial \phi}{\partial t} = - \frac{gp}{\rho} + f(t), \tag{16}$$

the arbitrary element of integration being in general a function of t. If the motion is steady, so that p, q, and ϕ are independent of the time, $f(t)$ may be replaced by a constant, whence

$$p = c - \frac{\rho}{2g} q^2. \tag{17}$$

As an application of the foregoing theory, consider two-dimensional steady irrotational motion of an incompressible fluid near two bounding walls at right angles to each other. We take the positive x- and y-axes in the walls and suppose the lines of flow at a great distance from the origin to be sensibly parallel to the x-axis. Then the streamlines are rectangular hyperbolas,*

$$xy = \text{const.} \qquad (18)$$

Since the velocity equipotentials are the orthogonal trajectories of the streamlines, we find (Chapter I, Art. 7(a)) for the former curves,

$$x^2 - y^2 = \text{const.}, \qquad (19)$$

a second family of equilateral hyperbolas.

Now because the velocity potential ϕ is constant along each of the curves (19), ϕ must be some function of the combination $x^2 - y^2$, say $\phi = f(x^2 - y^2)$. The form of this f-function may be determined from the fact that ϕ satisfies Laplace's equation in two dimensions,

$$\frac{\partial^2\phi}{\partial x^2} + \frac{\partial^2\phi}{\partial y^2} = 0, \qquad (20)$$

to which (14) reduces when flow is two-dimensional. Denoting by f' the derivative of f with respect to its single argument $x^2 - y^2$, we get

$$\frac{\partial\phi}{\partial x} = 2xf', \qquad \frac{\partial^2\phi}{\partial x^2} = 4x^2f'' + 2f',$$

$$\frac{\partial\phi}{\partial y} = -2yf', \qquad \frac{\partial^2\phi}{\partial y^2} = 4y^2f'' - 2f'.$$

Substitution in (20) yields $4(x^2 + y^2)f'' = 0$, whence

$$f'' = 0, \qquad f' = c_1, \qquad f = c_1(x^2 - y^2) + c_2,$$

where c_1 and c_2 are constants of integration. Therefore the potential must be of the form

$$\phi = c_1(x^2 - y^2) + c_2; \qquad (21)$$

the values of c_1 and c_2 will depend upon the system of units employed and the choice of reference position from which potential is measured.

If we arbitrarily take zero potential on the line $y = x$, so that $c_2 = 0$, the velocity components will be, by (13),

$$u = -\frac{\partial\phi}{\partial x} = -2c_1x, \qquad v = -\frac{\partial\phi}{\partial y} = 2c_1y. \qquad (22)$$

Consequently the pressure at any point $P(x, y)$ is, from (17),

$$p = p_0 - \frac{2c_1^2\rho}{g}(x^2 + y^2), \qquad (23)$$

where p_0 is the pressure at the corner $(0, 0)$.

* Cf. Chapter X, Art. 98.

74. Flow of electricity in a cable. In Chapter II, Art. 26, we discussed a cable carrying an electric current under steady-state conditions. We wish now to investigate that problem from a somewhat more general viewpoint, in which we consider not only the resistance and leakance of the line, but also its inductance and capacitance.*
We shall then take into account, in addition to the variation of potential and current with distance along the line, the change in these quantities with time. It is evident that such an analysis will lead to partial differential equations, from which transient effects as well as

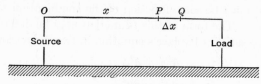

Fig. 52

steady-state conditions may be studied. We measure the distance $x = OP$ (miles) along the cable from the source of e.m.f. taken as origin (Fig. 52), and let

$e = e(x, t) =$ potential (volts) at P at time t (sec.),
$i = i(x, t) =$ current (amp.) at P at time t (sec.),
$r =$ resistance of cable (ohms/mile),
$g =$ leakance to ground (mhos/mile),
$L =$ inductance (henries/mile),
$C =$ capacitance to ground (farads/mile).

Then the drop in potential along a segment $\Delta x = PQ$ will be, approximately,

$$\Delta e = -r\,\Delta x \cdot i - L\,\Delta x\,\frac{\partial i}{\partial t},$$

so that, dividing by Δx and allowing it to approach zero, we get in the limit

$$\frac{\partial e}{\partial x} = -ri - L\frac{\partial i}{\partial t}. \tag{1}$$

Likewise, the drop in current along Δx is, approximately,

$$\Delta i = -g\,\Delta x \cdot e - C\,\Delta x \cdot \frac{\partial e}{\partial t},$$

from which we get

$$\frac{\partial i}{\partial x} = -ge - C\frac{\partial e}{\partial t}. \tag{2}$$

* We suppose these four quantities constant per unit length.

Equations (1) and (2) constitute a system of simultaneous partial differential equations in the independent variables x and t and the dependent variables i and e. We may eliminate i and e in turn, obtaining a single partial equation with one dependent variable, as follows. Differentiate (1) partially with respect to x, obtaining

$$\frac{\partial^2 e}{\partial x^2} = -r\frac{\partial i}{\partial x} - L\frac{\partial^2 i}{\partial x\,\partial t}, \tag{3}$$

and differentiate (2) with respect to t, whence

$$\frac{\partial^2 i}{\partial t\,\partial x} = -g\frac{\partial e}{\partial t} - C\frac{\partial^2 e}{\partial t^2}. \tag{4}$$

Substituting from (2) and (4) in (3), we get

$$\frac{\partial^2 e}{\partial x^2} = rge + rC\frac{\partial e}{\partial t} + Lg\frac{\partial e}{\partial t} + LC\frac{\partial^2 e}{\partial t^2},$$

or

$$\frac{\partial^2 e}{\partial x^2} = LC\frac{\partial^2 e}{\partial t^2} + (rC + Lg)\frac{\partial e}{\partial t} + rge. \tag{5}$$

This is a linear homogeneous equation of second order for the potential e. Likewise, we get by elimination of e from (1) and (2),

$$\frac{\partial^2 i}{\partial x^2} = LC\frac{\partial^2 i}{\partial t^2} + (rC + Lg)\frac{\partial i}{\partial t} + rgi, \tag{6}$$

which is similar to (5); i merely replaces e. Evidently (5) and (6) reduce to the equations for e and i found in Art. 26, Chapter II, if $L = C = 0$. The present equations (5) and (6) are called the *telephone equations*, being used in telephonic theory.

Frequently, as in telegraph transmission, the leakance and inductance produce little effect as compared to the effects of resistance and capacitance. Setting $g = L = 0$ in (1), (2), (5), and (6), we get

$$\frac{\partial e}{\partial x} = -ri, \tag{7}$$

$$\frac{\partial i}{\partial x} = -C\frac{\partial e}{\partial t}, \tag{8}$$

$$\frac{\partial^2 e}{\partial x^2} = rC\frac{\partial e}{\partial t}, \tag{9}$$

$$\frac{\partial^2 i}{\partial x^2} = rC\frac{\partial i}{\partial t}, \tag{10}$$

which are known as the *telegraph equations*. We note that equations (9) and (10) are of the same form as the equation for one-dimensional heat flow (Art. 71). Thus our methods of handling a problem in the flow of heat should be applicable to the study of current flow.

As an example involving the telephone equations, consider a transmission line, 100 mi. long, for which $r = 2$ ohms/mi., $L = 0.02$ henry/mi., $C = 5 \cdot 10^{-7}$ farad/mi., and $g = 5 \cdot 10^{-5}$ mho/mi. Initially the potential at each point is independent of time, with the ends $x = 0$ and $x = 100$ at potentials $100\epsilon = 272$ volts and 100 volts, respectively.* If both ends of the line are suddenly grounded, reducing each end potential to zero, we wish to find the resulting potential function $e(x, t)$.

Substituting the given values of r, L, C, and g in equation (5), we have

$$\frac{\partial^2 e}{\partial x^2} = 10^{-4}e + 2 \cdot 10^{-6}\frac{\partial e}{\partial t} + 10^{-8}\frac{\partial^2 e}{\partial t^2}. \tag{11}$$

Assuming a solution of the form $e(x, t) = X(x) \cdot T(t)$, we get, by the usual procedure,

$$10^8 \frac{X''}{X} = \frac{10{,}000T + 200T' + T''}{T} = k, \tag{12}$$

a constant. This leads to three types of solutions,

$$e = (c_1\epsilon^{10^{-4}\sqrt{k}x} + c_2\epsilon^{-10^{-4}\sqrt{k}x})\epsilon^{-100t}(c_3\epsilon^{\sqrt{k}t} + c_4\epsilon^{-\sqrt{k}t}),$$
$$k > 0; \tag{13}$$

$$e = (c_5 \sin 10^{-4}\sqrt{-k}\, x + c_6 \cos 10^{-4}\sqrt{-k}\, x)\epsilon^{-100t}(c_7 \sin \sqrt{-k}\, t$$
$$+ c_8 \cos \sqrt{-k}\, t), \qquad k < 0; \tag{14}$$

$$e = (c_9x + c_{10})\epsilon^{-100t}(c_{11}t + c_{12}), \qquad k = 0. \tag{15}$$

Now the boundary conditions are

$$e(0, t) = 0, \qquad e(100, t) = 0, \tag{16}$$

for $t > 0$. It is easy to see that these relations can be satisfied only by a solution of type (14). From the first boundary condition we get $c_6 = 0$; from the second, $\sin 10^{-2}\sqrt{-k} = 0$, whence $\sqrt{-k} = 100n\pi$, n being an integer. We therefore have

$$e = c_5 \sin \frac{n\pi x}{100} \cdot \epsilon^{-100t}(c_7 \sin 100n\pi t + c_8 \cos 100n\pi t), \tag{17}$$

---

* The data have been chosen so as to make the computations relatively simple. Also, the symbol ϵ is now used to denote the Napierian base, $2.718\cdots$, to avoid confusion with potential e.

which satisfies the differential equation (5) and boundary conditions (16).

We next consider the initial conditions, of which there are two. First, since the potential at any point of the line before the change is independent of time, and because of the inertial effect of inductance, the initial time rate of change of the potential will be zero:

$$\frac{\partial e}{\partial t}\bigg]_{t=0} = 0, \qquad 0 < x < 100. \tag{18}$$

From (17) we get

$$\frac{\partial e}{\partial t} = c_5 \sin \frac{n\pi x}{100} \cdot \epsilon^{-100t}(100n\pi c_7 \cos 100n\pi t - 100n\pi c_8 \sin 100n\pi t$$
$$-100c_7 \sin 100n\pi t - 100c_8 \cos 100n\pi t), \quad (19)$$

and (18) therefore yields $100n\pi c_7 - 100c_8 = 0$, or $c_8 = n\pi c_7$. Consequently (17) becomes

$$e = c_5 c_7 \sin \frac{n\pi x}{100} \cdot \epsilon^{-100t}(\sin 100n\pi t + n\pi \cos 100n\pi t). \tag{20}$$

To deal with the remaining initial condition, we need a solution of (11) that is independent of t. When e depends only upon x, $e = e_s(x)$, (11) reduces to

$$\frac{d^2 e_s}{dx^2} = 10^{-4} e_{s,} \tag{21}$$

which has the solution

$$e_s(x) = a\epsilon^{x/100} + b\epsilon^{-x/100}. \tag{22}$$

Since $e_s(0) = 100\epsilon$ and $e_s(100) = 100$, we get, from (22), $100\epsilon = a + b$, $100 = a\epsilon + b\epsilon^{-1}$, whence $a = 0$, $b = 100\epsilon = 272$. Consequently our other initial condition is

$$e(x, 0) = 272\epsilon^{-x/100}, \qquad 0 < x < 100. \tag{23}$$

It is apparent that (23) can be fulfilled only by taking an infinite series of terms of type (20):

$$e = \sum_{n=1}^{\infty} b_n \sin \frac{n\pi x}{100} \cdot \epsilon^{-100t}(\sin 100n\pi t + n\pi \cos 100n\pi t). \tag{24}$$

Applying (23), we find

$$272\epsilon^{-x/100} = \sum_{n=1}^{\infty}(n\pi b_n) \sin \frac{n\pi x}{100}. \tag{25}$$

Accordingly, we must have

$$n\pi b_n = \frac{2}{100} \int_0^{100} 272\epsilon^{-x/100} \sin \frac{n\pi x}{100} \, dx,$$

which yields

$$b_n = \frac{544(1 - \epsilon^{-1} \cos n\pi)}{1 + n^2\pi^2}. \tag{26}$$

Inserting these values in (24), we therefore get

$$e = 544 \sum_{n=1}^{\infty} \frac{1 - \epsilon^{-1} \cos n\pi}{1 + n^2\pi^2} \sin \frac{n\pi x}{100} \cdot \epsilon^{-100t}(\sin 100n\pi t$$

$$+ n\pi \cos 100n\pi t). \tag{27}$$

This is the desired potential function.

PROBLEMS

1. Consider two-dimensional steady flow of an incompressible fluid, in which no external forces act, but in which the rotation $\omega = \frac{1}{2}(\partial v/\partial x - \partial u/\partial y) \neq 0$. Making use of the relations $\partial u/\partial t = \partial v/\partial t = 0$, $F_1 = F_2 = 0$, together with the continuity equation (10) of Art. 73, eliminate the pressure p between equations (5) and (6), and thus show that

$$u \frac{\partial \omega}{\partial x} + v \frac{\partial \omega}{\partial y} = 0.$$

Since, in the expression $d\omega/dt = u \, \partial\omega/\partial x + v \, \partial\omega/\partial y + \partial\omega/\partial t$, we have $\partial\omega/\partial t = 0$ for steady motion along a streamline, it follows that the rotation in this type of motion is constant.

2. The components of velocity in a certain steady flow of an incompressible fluid acted upon by no external forces are equal to those of a particle moving with constant angular velocity k in a counterclockwise direction along the circle $x^2 + y^2 = r^2$. Show that the rotation of the fluid is equal to the angular velocity of the particle.

3. If, in the example of Art. 73, the walls make an angle of 60° with each other, it may be shown that the streamlines are given by $3x^2y - y^3 = $ const.* Show that a permissible potential function is $\phi = x^3 - 3xy^2$, and find the corresponding pressure p at any point (x, y) if $p(0, 0) = p_0$.

4. The streamlines of steady, irrotational two-dimensional flow of an incompressible fluid about a rotating cylinder are concentric circles $x^2 + y^2 = $ const. Show that a permissible potential function is $\phi = -\tan^{-1}(y/x)$, and find the corresponding pressure p if $p = p_0$ at an infinite distance from the cylinder.

5. A transmission line 1000 mi. long is initially under steady-state conditions, with potential 1200 volts at the source ($x = 0$) and 1100 volts at the load ($x = 1000$). The terminal end of the line is suddenly grounded, reducing its potential to zero,

* See Problem 7, Art. 101.

but the potential at the source is kept at 1200 volts. Find the potential function $e(x, t)$. Assume negligible inductance and leakance.

6. For the line of Problem 5, find the current function $i(x, t)$. When $x = 1000$ and t is small, show that the current at the end of the line may become seriously large.

7. If, in Problems 5 and 6, $r = 20$ ohms/mi. and $C = 10^{-7}$ farad/mi., find the current at each end of the line 0.1 sec. after the change.

8. A submarine cable 3000 miles long has negligible inductance and leakance, a resistance of 4 ohms/mi., and a capacitance of $5 \cdot 10^{-7}$ farad/mi. Initially both ends of the line are grounded, so that the line is uncharged. At time $t = 0$, a constant e.m.f. E is applied to one end, while the other end is left grounded. Find the percentage of the maximum (steady-state) current value attained at the grounded end at the end of 1, 3, and 5 sec.

9. Find the current function $i(x, t)$ corresponding to the potential function (27) of Art. 74. *Hint:* Find $\partial i/\partial x$ from equation (2) and integrate partially with respect to x. Determine the arbitrary function of t thereby introduced by means of equations (1) and (23) combined with the initial condition $\partial i/\partial t = 0$ for $t = 0$.

10. Apply the method of Art. 69 to equation (5) of Art. 74, and show that there will exist, in general, five distinct types of particular solutions, according as

(1) $k < -\dfrac{(rC - Lg)^2}{4LC}$;   (2) $k = -\dfrac{(rC - Lg)^2}{4LC}$;

(3) $-\dfrac{(rC - Lg)^2}{4LC} < k < 0$;   (4) $k = 0$;

(5) $k > 0$.

75. An eddy-current problem.*

Consider a long copper rod of radius a (cm.) wound with a coil of wire containing N turns per cm., and excited by a current whose magnitude at time t is $I \cos 2\pi ft$ (abamp.) where f is the frequency (cycles per second). We suppose that the length of the solenoid is very large compared to its radius, so that end effects may be neglected and therefore the magnetic field inside the solenoid with an air core may be considered uniform over a cross-section. We wish to find the resultant magnetic field strength arising from the exciting current in the solenoid and the induced eddy currents set up in the copper core, and to determine the power loss due to the eddy currents.

Consider (Fig. 53) a section of the copper rod 1 cm. long. In a central cross-section, a ring of radius x and thickness Δx will have an area $2\pi x \, \Delta x$ approximately, so that if $H(x, t)$ is the resultant magnetic field strength (dynes per unit pole, or lines per sq. cm.) at any point and at time t, the magnetic flux inside the ring will be, approximately,

* The definitions and physical laws referred to in this article may be found in any comprehensive electrical engineering textbook; see, for example, A. S. Langsdorf, "Principles of D. C. Machines."

$\Delta\phi = 2\pi x H \, \Delta x$, and the total flux threading a circle of radius $r < a$ will be

$$\phi(r, t) = 2\pi \int_0^r x H(x, t) \, dx.$$

Hence the e.m.f. induced in a shell of radius r and thickness Δr will be

$$E = -\frac{\partial\phi}{\partial t} = -2\pi \int_0^r x \frac{\partial H(x, t)}{\partial t} \, dx, \tag{1}$$

where we have differentiated under the integral sign, using formula (3) of Art. 67.

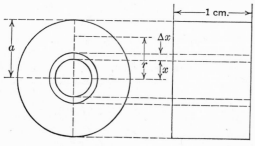

Fig. 53

Now if ρ is the resistivity (abohms/cm.^{3}) of copper, the resistance of the shell of radius r and thickness Δr will be $2\pi\rho r/\Delta r$. Also, if i is the eddy-current density (abamp./cm.^{2}), the eddy current circulating around the shell will be $i \, \Delta r$. Consequently, by Ohm's law, the product of current and resistance must be equal to the potential drop around the shell, which in turn is equal to the induced e.m.f., E, given by equation (1). Hence we have

$$i \, \Delta r \cdot \frac{2\pi\rho r}{\Delta r} = -2\pi \int_0^r x \frac{\partial H(x, t)}{\partial t} \, dx,$$

and

$$i = -\frac{1}{\rho r} \int_0^r x \frac{\partial H(x, t)}{\partial t} \, dx. \tag{2}$$

Next consider the shell of radius r and thickness Δr, but now of length equal to the length L of the entire rod, as a solenoid of one turn. It may be shown that the field intensity at the midsection of a solenoid whose length L is very large compared to its radius is given by $4\pi n I_1/L$, where n is the number of turns and I_1 the current (abamp.) in the solenoid. Since we have here $n = 1$, $I_1 = iL \, \Delta r$, it follows that the approximate change in field intensity $H(r, t)$ due to the eddy current flowing in the shell is $\Delta H = -4\pi i \, \Delta r$. Dividing by Δr and passing to the limit as Δr approaches zero, we get

$$\frac{\partial H(r, t)}{\partial r} = -4\pi i, \tag{3}$$

and from (2) there follows

$$r \frac{\partial H(r, t)}{\partial r} = \frac{4\pi}{\rho} \int_0^r x \frac{\partial H(x, t)}{\partial t} \, dx.$$

Differentiating partially with respect to r, remembering that the integral on the right is a function of its upper limit, we have

$$r \frac{\partial^2 H}{\partial r^2} + \frac{\partial H}{\partial r} = \frac{4\pi r}{\rho} \frac{\partial H}{\partial t}. \tag{4}$$

This is the partial differential equation for the magnetic field intensity $H(r, t)$ as a function of distance r from the axis of the rod and of time t.

In conjunction with equation (4), we have to take into consideration a boundary condition. At the surface of the rod, i.e., for $r = a$, the field strength must be equal to the uniform value of H over the cross-section when an air core replaces the copper rod, whence

$$H(a, t) = 4\pi NI \cos 2\pi ft. \tag{5}$$

Following the usual procedure, suppose that there exists a solution of (4) of the form

$$H(r, t) = R(r) \cdot T(t).$$

Substituting in (4), we get

$$rR''T + R'T = \frac{4\pi r}{\rho} RT',$$

and

$$\frac{R''}{R} + \frac{R'}{rR} = \frac{4\pi}{\rho} \frac{T'}{T}.$$

Now if, as in our previous problems, we set each member of the last equation equal to a constant, and examine the solutions of the resulting ordinary differential equations for positive, negative, and zero values of the constant, we encounter a situation which has not arisen before. For, if the constant were positive, T would be an increasing exponential function of t, and therefore H would build up indefinitely with increase of time; for a negative constant, we should get for T a decreasing exponential function, so that H would damp off indefinitely; and if the constant were zero, T, and therefore H, would be independent of time.

Evidently none of these choices will meet the requirements, since it is apparent on physical grounds that when the exciting current is a periodic function of time, the resultant field must also be periodic, as is indicated by the boundary value (5).

Further consideration of the difficulty, however, shows us that we can get for T a periodic function of the time if we choose as our constant a pure imaginary number, jk, where k is real and j is used to denote $\sqrt{-1}$ to avoid confusion with the symbol i for current. Thus, we get the equation

$$\frac{4\pi}{\rho}\frac{T'}{T} = jk,$$

from which

$$T = c_1 e^{jk\rho t/4\pi} = c_1 \left(\cos\frac{k\rho t}{4\pi} + j\sin\frac{k\rho t}{4\pi} \right),$$

where c_1 is an arbitrary constant. Since the boundary condition (5) requires that the period of T be that of the current flowing in the solenoid, we have $k\rho/4\pi = 2\pi f$, and therefore

$$k = \frac{8\pi^2 f}{\rho}, \tag{6}$$

$$T = c_1 e^{2\pi j f t} = c_1(\cos 2\pi f t + j\sin 2\pi f t). \tag{7}$$

The equation for the determination of the function $R(r)$ is then

$$r\frac{d^2 R}{dr^2} + \frac{dR}{dr} - jkrR = 0, \tag{8}$$

with k given by (6). Equation (8) differs from the differential equation considered in Chapter VI, Art. 63, only in the coefficient of the last term; this suggests the use of the substitution $r = cz$, where z is a new independent variable and c is a constant to be determined. Then we have

$$\frac{dR}{dr} = \frac{1}{c}\frac{dR}{dz}, \qquad \frac{d^2 R}{dr^2} = \frac{1}{c^2}\frac{d^2 R}{dz^2},$$

and (8) becomes

$$z\frac{d^2 R}{dz^2} + \frac{dR}{dz} - jkc^2 zR = 0.$$

This will be the equation discussed in Chapter VI, Art. 63, if c is so chosen that $kc^2 = 1$, or $1/c = \sqrt{k}$. Hence a solution of (8) will be

$$R = J_0(j^{3/2}z) = J_0(j^{3/2}\sqrt{k}\,r).$$

Combining this with (7), we therefore have as a solution of equation (4),

$$H = c_1 J_0(j^{3/2}\sqrt{k}\, r)\epsilon^{2\pi jft}. \tag{9}$$

Now it was shown in Chapter VI, Art. 63, that $J_0(j^{3/2}z)$ is a complex function, with real component ber z and imaginary component bei z,

$$J_0(j^{3/2}z) = \text{ber } z + j\,\text{bei } z.$$

Thus the factor $J_0(j^{3/2}\sqrt{k}\, r)$ in (9), as well as the exponential function $\epsilon^{2\pi jft}$, will be complex quantities, so that for real values of r and t, H as given by (9) will, in general, be a complex number. With the constant c_1 a complex number (which may, of course, be real as a particular case), we then get by separation of real and imaginary components in (9), an expression of the form

$$H = H_1(r, t) + jH_2(r, t),$$

where H_1 and H_2 are real functions of r and t. Substituting in (4), we have the relation

$$r\frac{\partial^2 H_1}{\partial r^2} + \frac{\partial H_1}{\partial r} - \frac{4\pi r}{\rho}\frac{\partial H_1}{\partial t} + j\left(r\frac{\partial^2 H_2}{\partial r^2} + \frac{\partial H_2}{\partial r} - \frac{4\pi r}{\rho}\frac{\partial H_2}{\partial t}\right) = 0,$$

which is satisfied identically in r and t since H is a solution of (4). But if a complex number is equal to zero, its real and imaginary parts must each be zero, whence

$$r\frac{\partial^2 H_1}{\partial r^2} + \frac{\partial H_1}{\partial r} = \frac{4\pi r}{\rho}\frac{\partial H_1}{\partial t},$$

$$r\frac{\partial^2 H_2}{\partial r^2} + \frac{\partial H_2}{\partial r} = \frac{4\pi r}{\rho}\frac{\partial H_2}{\partial t}.$$

That is, the real and imaginary components of H individually satisfy equation (4). We may therefore take as the physically possible solution of our problem the real part H_1 of H as given by (9).

However, it is inconvenient at this stage of our work to break up H into its two components H_1 and H_2 and apply the boundary condition (5) to the function $H_1(r, t)$ so obtained. Instead, we shall for the present continue to deal with the complex function (9), and shall replace (5) by the new boundary condition

$$H(a, t) = 4\pi NI\epsilon^{2\pi jft}. \tag{10}$$

This mode of procedure is certainly permissible, for we then have

$$H(a, t) = H_1(a, t) + jH_2(a, t)$$

$$= 4\pi NI(\cos 2\pi ft + j \sin 2\pi ft),$$

whence

$$H_1(a, t) = 4\pi NI \cos 2\pi ft.$$

Thus the chosen real part of H will take on the proper boundary value. Consequently, applying (10) to (9), we get

$$4\pi NI\epsilon^{2\pi jft} = c_1 J_0(j^{3/2}\sqrt{k}\, a)\, \epsilon^{2\pi jft},$$

$$c_1 = \frac{4\pi NI}{J_0(j^{3/2}\sqrt{k}\, a)},$$

and

$$H = \frac{4\pi NI}{J_0(j^{3/2}\sqrt{k}\, a)} J_0(j^{3/2}\sqrt{k}\, r)\epsilon^{2\pi jft}. \tag{11}$$

We may now find the desired expression for $H_1(r, t)$, as follows. Let the complex function $J_0(j^{3/2}z)$ be expressed in polar form,*

$$J_0(j^{3/2}\sqrt{k}\, r) = M_0(z)\epsilon^{j\theta_0(z)},$$

where $M_0(z)$ is the modulus, and $\theta_0(z)$ the amplitude. In terms of ber z and bei z, we evidently have

$$[M_0(z)]^2 = (\text{ber}\, z)^2 + (\text{bei}\, z)^2,$$

$$\tan \theta_0(z) = \frac{\text{bei}\, z}{\text{ber}\, z}.$$

Then we get from (11),

$$H = \frac{4\pi NI}{M_0(\sqrt{k}\, a)\epsilon^{j\theta_0\sqrt{ka}}} M_0(\sqrt{k}\, r)\epsilon^{j\theta_0(\sqrt{kr})}\epsilon^{2\pi jft}$$

$$= \frac{4\pi NIM_0(\sqrt{k}\, r)}{M_0(\sqrt{k}\, a)} \epsilon^{j[2\pi ft + \theta_0(\sqrt{kr}) - \theta_0(\sqrt{ka})]},$$

and therefore

$$H_1(r, t) = \frac{4\pi NIM_0(\sqrt{k}\, r)}{M_0(\sqrt{k}\, a)} \cos [2\pi ft + \theta_0(\sqrt{k}\, r) - \theta_0(\sqrt{k}\, a)], \tag{12}$$

* The nomenclature used here is discussed in Chapter X, Art. 94.

where the constant k is given by equation (6). This equation gives us the magnetic field intensity at any distance r from the axis of the copper rod and at any time t.*

We next derive an expression for the power lost as heat due to the eddy currents. From equations (3) and (11), we get

$$i = -\frac{1}{4\pi}\frac{\partial H}{\partial r} = -\frac{NI\epsilon^{2\pi jft}}{J_0(j^{3/2}\sqrt{k}\,a)}J_0'(j^{3/2}\sqrt{k}\,r)\cdot j^{3/2}\sqrt{k},$$

where the prime denotes differentiation with respect to the argument $j^{3/2}\sqrt{k}\,r$. But (Chapter VI, Art. 58),

$$\frac{d}{dx}J_0(x) = -J_1(x),$$

and consequently

$$i = \frac{j^{3/2}\sqrt{k}\,NI}{J_0(j^{3/2}\sqrt{k}\,a)}J_1(j^{3/2}\sqrt{k}\,r)\epsilon^{2\pi jft}.$$

It should be remembered that, since we are using the complex function H, the above expression for i will likewise be a complex quantity, $i_1 + ji_2$, the real component of which represents the actual eddy-current density. To get i_1, let

$$J_1(j^{3/2}z) = M_1(z)\epsilon^{j\theta_1(z)},$$

and set $j^{3/2} = (-1)^{3/4} = \epsilon^{3j\pi/4}$. Then

$$i = \frac{\sqrt{k}\,NIM_1(\sqrt{k}\,r)}{M_0(\sqrt{k}\,a)}\epsilon^{j[2\pi ft+\theta_1(\sqrt{k}r)-\theta_1(\sqrt{k}a)+3\pi/4]},$$

and

$$i_1 = \frac{\sqrt{k}\,NIM_1(\sqrt{k}\,r)}{M_0(\sqrt{k}\,a)}\cos\left[2\pi ft + \theta_1(\sqrt{k}\,r) - \theta_1(\sqrt{k}\,a) + \frac{3\pi}{4}\right]. \quad (13)$$

Equation (13) represents the instantaneous eddy-current density at distance r from the axis of the rod. Since the heating effect of a current varies as the square of the current, we require for the power computation the effective (r.m.s.) value of the current. Now it was found (Chapter V, Art. 50) that the mean square value of an alternating current with maximum value I_1, is $I_1^2/2$. Hence

$$\overline{i_1^2} = \frac{kN^2I^2[M_1(\sqrt{k}\,r)]^2}{2[M_0(\sqrt{k}\,a)]^2},$$

* For tables of values of $M_0(z)$ and $\theta_0(z)$, see McLachlan, "Bessel Functions for Engineers," p. 182.

and the power loss in a shell of radius r, thickness Δr, and 1 cm. long will be, approximately,

$$\Delta P_1 = \frac{kN^2I^2[M_1(\sqrt{k}\,r)]^2}{2[M_0(\sqrt{k}\,a)]^2}\Delta r^2 \cdot \frac{2\pi\rho r}{\Delta r}$$

$$= \frac{\pi\rho kN^2I^2}{[M_0(\sqrt{k}\,a)]^2}\,r[M_1(\sqrt{k}\,r)]^2\,\Delta r.$$

Summing for all such shells from $r = 0$ to $r = a$, we get for the total heat loss per centimeter length of rod,

$$P_1 = \frac{\pi\rho kN^2I^2}{[M_0(\sqrt{k}\,a)]^2}\int_0^r r[M_1(\sqrt{k}\,r)]^2\,dr$$

$$= \frac{\pi\rho N^2I^2}{[M_0(\sqrt{k}\,a)]^2}\int_0^{\sqrt{k}a} z[M_1(z)]^2\,dz$$

ergs per second, where $z = \sqrt{k}\,r$.

To carry out the integration, we express $M_1(z)$ in terms of the derivatives of ber z and bei z. We have

$$J_1(j^{3/2}z) = -\frac{dJ_0(j^{3/2}z)}{j^{3/2}\,dz} = j^{1/2}\frac{d}{dz}(\text{ber}\,z + j\,\text{bei}\,z)$$

$$= \epsilon^{j\pi/4}(\text{ber}'\,z + j\,\text{bei}'\,z).$$

Since the modulus of the product of two complex numbers is equal to the product of their moduli, and since the modulus of $\epsilon^{j\pi/4}$ is unity, we get

$$[M_1(z)]^2 = (\text{ber}'\,z)^2 + (\text{bei}'\,z)^2,$$

so that

$$P_1 = \frac{\pi\rho N^2I^2}{[M_0(\sqrt{k}\,a)]^2}\int_0^{\sqrt{k}a}[z(\text{ber}'\,z)^2 + z(\text{bei}'\,z)^2]\,dz.$$

It is now possible to integrate by parts, using the relations of Chapter VI, Art. 63. For the first term, let

$$u = z\,\text{ber}'\,z, \qquad dv = \text{ber}'\,z\,dz,$$

whence

$$du = -z\,\text{bei}\,z\,dz, \qquad v = \text{ber}\,z.$$

In the second term, let

$$u = z\,\text{bei}'\,z, \qquad dv = \text{bei}'\,z\,dz,$$

from which

$$du = z\,\text{ber}\,z\,dz, \qquad v = \text{bei}\,z.$$

Therefore

$$\int_0^{\sqrt{k}a} [z(\text{ber}'\,z)^2 + z(\text{bei}'\,z)^2]\,dz$$

$$= \left[z\,\text{ber}\,z\,\text{ber}'\,z + \int z\,\text{ber}\,z\,\text{bei}\,z\,dz \right.$$

$$\left. + z\,\text{bei}\,z\,\text{bei}'\,z - \int z\,\text{ber}\,z\,\text{bei}\,z\,dz \right]_0^{\sqrt{k}a}$$

$$= \sqrt{k}\,a(\text{ber}\,\sqrt{k}\,a\,\text{ber}'\,\sqrt{k}\,a + \text{bei}\,\sqrt{k}\,a\,\text{bei}'\,\sqrt{k}\,a),$$

and

$$P_1 = \frac{\pi\rho\sqrt{k}\,aN^2I^2}{[M_0(\sqrt{k}\,a)]^2}\,(\text{ber}\,\sqrt{k}\,a\,\text{ber}'\,\sqrt{k}\,a + \text{bei}\,\sqrt{k}\,a\,\text{bei}'\,\sqrt{k}\,a). \quad (14)$$

We thus have an expression for the power loss (ergs/sec.) in 1-cm. length of rod.* The foregoing theory has considerable practical application in connection with induction furnaces.†

76. Diffusion problems.‡ Consider a slab of porous material containing a liquid, being dried by evaporation. Let the thickness of the slab be a (ft.), and suppose the edges coated so as to prevent evaporation from taking place except at the two opposite faces each of area S (ft.^{2}). We shall investigate the "diffusional" stage of drying in which the liquid evaporates from the surfaces as fast as it gets there by diffusion from the interior. The liquid concentration at a surface is constant throughout this stage; we call this concentration the equilibrium liquid concentration. It will be assumed that the initial liquid concentration is uniform throughout the interior, but that at the surface it falls to the equilibrium value immediately at the beginning of the diffusional stage.

The empirical law of diffusion upon which our analysis will be based is similar in form to the third law of heat flow (Art. 71), and may be stated as follows: The rate of diffusion is proportional to the cross-sectional area and to the concentration gradient. Let $c(x, t)$ (lb./ft.^{3}) be the concentration, and take the x-axis in the direction of flow, with origin at the midsection, so that flow takes place from the central

---

* Tables of values of ber z, bei z, ber' z, bei' z also appear in McLachlan, pp. 177–178.

† See Marchbanks, "The Steel-Melting Induction Furnace," *Journal E.E.*, Vol. 73, p. 509, 1933; Dwight and Bagai, "Calculations for Coreless Induction Furnaces," *Electrical Engineering*, March, 1935.

‡ In connection with this problem, see A. B. Newman, "The Drying of Porous Solids: Diffusion Calculations," *Trans. A. I. Chem. E.*, Vol. 27, p. 310, 1931.

plane $x = 0$ to the faces $x = \pm a/2$ (Fig. 54). Let Q (lb.) be the amount of liquid in the slab between $x = 0$ and $x = x$ at time t (hr.). Then by the above law, we have

$$\frac{\partial Q}{\partial t} = KS \frac{\partial c}{\partial x}, \tag{1}$$

where K is the diffusivity constant of proportionality (ft.^{2}/hr.). By

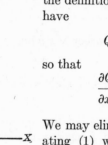

FIG. 54

the definitions of c and Q, we also have

$$Q = \int_0^x cS \, dx,$$

so that

$$\frac{\partial Q}{\partial x} = cS. \tag{2}$$

We may eliminate Q by differentiating (1) with respect to x and (2) with respect to t, and subtracting. Doing this, and dividing the resulting equation by S, we get

$$\frac{\partial c}{\partial t} = K \frac{\partial^2 c}{\partial x^2}. \tag{3}$$

Now let c_0 be the uniform liquid concentration at time $t = 0$, for $-a/2 < x < a/2$, and let c_1 be the equilibrium liquid concentration at $x = \pm a/2$, for all $t > 0$. For simplicity, let $C(x, t)$ denote the concentration in excess of the equilibrium value,

$$C = c - c_1, \tag{4}$$

which we may call the free liquid concentration. Then the initial free liquid concentration will be

$$C_0 = c_0 - c_1. \tag{5}$$

Since $\partial C/\partial t = \partial c/\partial t$ and $\partial^2 C/\partial x^2 = \partial^2 c/\partial x^2$, we may write our differential equation in the form

$$\frac{\partial C}{\partial t} = K \frac{\partial^2 C}{\partial x^2}. \tag{6}$$

We wish to solve (6) subject to the conditions

$$C\left(\pm \frac{a}{2}, t\right) = 0, \tag{7}$$

$$C(x, 0) = C_0. \tag{8}$$

Assuming $C(x, t) = X(x)T(t)$, we get from (6)

$$XT' = KX''T,$$

$$\frac{T'}{KT} = \frac{X''}{X} = k.$$

Since C, and therefore T, must decrease with increase in t, k must be negative; for convenience, let this negative constant be denoted by $-\lambda^2$. Then we have as a particular solution of (6),

$$C = e^{-K\lambda^2 t}(A \cos \lambda x + B \sin \lambda x),$$

where A and B are arbitrary constants. Generalizing to an infinite series of terms of this type, we may write the formal solution of (6) as

$$C = \sum_{n=1}^{\infty} e^{-K\lambda_n^2 t}(A_n \cos \lambda_n x + B_n \sin \lambda_n x),$$

where the λ's, A's, and B's are at our disposal.

Because of symmetry in the plane $x = 0$, $C(x, t) \equiv C(-x, t)$, and therefore we must have $B_n = 0$ for every n. From (7), we get

$$0 = \sum_{n=1}^{\infty} e^{-K\lambda_n^2 t} A_n \cos \frac{\lambda_n a}{2}.$$

This condition will be most easily met by taking all A's with even subscripts equal to zero, and all λ's with odd subscripts equal to odd multiples of π/a:

$$A_{2n} = 0, \qquad \lambda_{2n-1} = \frac{(2n - 1)\pi}{a}.$$

For, $\cos (\lambda_{2n-1}a/2) = \cos [(2n - 1)\pi/2] = 0$, so that each term of the series will vanish, while we have still at our disposal, for use in meeting condition (8), the A's with odd subscripts. Our solution thus becomes

$$C = \sum_{n=1}^{\infty} A_{2n-1} e^{-(2n-1)^2 \pi^2 K t/a^2} \cos \frac{(2n - 1)\pi x}{a}.$$

Now from (8),

$$C_0 = \sum_{n=1}^{\infty} A_{2n-1} \cos \frac{(2n - 1)\pi x}{a}.$$

But it was found (Chapter V, Art. 48) that it was possible to expand unity in a series of precisely this type, valid for $-a/2 < x < a/2$, with $A_{2n-1} = (-1)^{n-1}4/\pi(2n - 1)$. Hence we have

$$C_0 = \frac{4C_0}{\pi} \left(\cos \frac{\pi x}{a} - \frac{1}{3} \cos \frac{3\pi x}{a} + \frac{1}{5} \cos \frac{5\pi x}{a} - \cdots \right),$$

and the solution of (6) which satisfies conditions (7) and (8) is given by

$$C(x, t) = \frac{4C_0}{\pi} \sum_{n=1}^{\infty} \frac{(-1)^{n-1}}{2n - 1} e^{-(2n-1)^2\pi^2Kt/a^2} \cos \frac{(2n - 1)\pi x}{a}. \tag{9}$$

This series, as well as its derivatives, is uniformly convergent for $-a/2 \leq x \leq a/2$ and for $t \geq t_1 > 0$.

It is desirable to have, in addition to (9), an expression for the average concentration $\bar{c}$ at any time t. Thus, if at time t evaporation from the surfaces were stopped, the liquid in the slab would settle down by diffusion to this average concentration.   Let

$$\bar{C} = \bar{c} - c_1 \tag{10}$$

be the average free liquid concentration at time t; evidently $\bar{C} = C_0$ when $t = 0$.   Then the total free liquid content at time t in the slab is

$$\bar{C} \cdot aS = \int_{-a/2}^{a/2} CS \, dx,$$

whence

$$\bar{C} = \frac{2}{a} \int_0^{a/2} C \, dx.$$

Since the series (9) is uniformly convergent, it may be integrated term by term, and therefore

$$\bar{C} = \frac{2}{a} \int_0^{a/2} \frac{4C_0}{\pi} \sum_{n=1}^{\infty} \frac{(-1)^{n-1}}{2n - 1} e^{-(2n-1)^2\pi^2Kt/a^2} \cos \frac{(2n - 1)\pi x}{a} \, dx$$

$$= \left[\frac{8C_0}{\pi^2} \sum_{n=1}^{\infty} \frac{(-1)^{n-1}}{(2n - 1)^2} e^{-(2n-1)^2\pi^2Kt/a^2} \sin \frac{(2n - 1)\pi x}{a} \right]_0^{a/2}$$

$$= \frac{8C_0}{\pi^2} \sum_{n=1}^{\infty} \frac{1}{(2n - 1)^2} e^{-(2n-1)^2\pi^2Kt/a^2}. \tag{11}$$

It is of interest to note that (11) holds for $t = 0$ as well as for $t > 0$; for, using the series

$$\frac{\pi^2}{8} = \sum_{n=1}^{\infty} \frac{1}{(2n - 1)^2} = 1 + \frac{1}{3^2} + \frac{1}{5^2} + \frac{1}{7^2} + \cdots,$$

we get from (11), $\bar{C} = C_0$ when $t = 0$, as we should.

Consider next a porous cylinder with its ends coated, so that the liquid diffuses radially from the axis toward the curved surface, i.e., the liquid flow is now two-dimensional. Let the cylinder be of length L (ft.) and radius a (ft.); then for flow through a cylindrical surface of radius $r < a$, we get from equation (1)

$$\frac{\partial Q}{\partial t} = K 2\pi r L \frac{\partial c}{\partial r}.$$

Moreover,

$$Q = 2\pi L \int_0^r rc \, dr,$$

whence

$$\frac{\partial Q}{\partial r} = 2\pi L rc.$$

Eliminating Q as before, we find

$$r \frac{\partial c}{\partial t} = K \left(r \frac{\partial^2 c}{\partial r^2} + \frac{\partial c}{\partial r} \right),$$

or

$$\frac{\partial c}{\partial t} = K \left(\frac{\partial^2 c}{\partial r^2} + \frac{1}{r} \frac{\partial c}{\partial r} \right). \tag{12}$$

It may be remarked that, by reasoning similar to that employed in Art. 72, we get as the general differential equation for two-dimensional liquid flow,

$$\frac{\partial c}{\partial t} = K \left(\frac{\partial^2 c}{\partial x^2} + \frac{\partial^2 c}{\partial y^2} \right) = K \left(\frac{\partial^2 c}{\partial r^2} + \frac{1}{r} \frac{\partial c}{\partial r} + \frac{1}{r^2} \frac{\partial^2 c}{\partial \theta^2} \right).$$

For the cylinder we are now considering, c will depend only upon r and t, and not upon θ. Hence the last equation reduces in this case to equation (12), which we have derived ab initio.

Since equation (12) applies also to the problem of temperature distribution if we interpret c as temperature and K as thermal diffusivity, the following analysis may be used in the study of the heating or cooling of a cylindrical surface.

Again using C, as given by (4), to denote the free liquid concentration, we may replace (12) by the equation

$$\frac{\partial C}{\partial t} = K \left(\frac{\partial^2 C}{\partial r^2} + \frac{1}{r} \frac{\partial C}{\partial r} \right). \tag{13}$$

Under the same assumptions as before, we have in connection with (13) the conditions

$$C(a, t) = 0,$$ (14)

for $t > 0$, and

$$C(r, 0) = C_0$$ (15)

for $0 < r < a$.

Assuming $C(r, t) = R(r) \cdot T(t)$, (13) leads to

$$RT' = K \left(R''T + \frac{1}{r} R'T \right),$$

$$\frac{T'}{KT} = \frac{R''}{R} + \frac{R'}{rR} = -\lambda^2.$$

From $T' = -K\lambda^2 T$, we get

$$T = Ae^{-K\lambda^2 t},$$ (16)

where A is arbitrary.   Now the equation for $R(r)$ may be written

$$r \frac{d^2R}{dr^2} + \frac{dR}{dr} + \lambda^2 rR = 0,$$ (17)

which closely resembles Bessel's equation of order zero (Art. 57). Letting $r = bs$, where b is a constant to be determined, we have

$$\frac{dR}{dr} = \frac{1}{b} \frac{dR}{ds}, \qquad \frac{d^2R}{dr^2} = \frac{1}{b^2} \frac{d^2R}{ds^2},$$

and (17) becomes

$$s \frac{d^2R}{ds^2} + \frac{dR}{ds} + \lambda^2 b^2 sR = 0.$$

Hence, if we choose $b = 1/\lambda$, we have Bessel's equation, so that a particular solution of (17) is

$$R = J_0(s) = J_0(\lambda r).$$ (18)

Combining (16) and (18), and forming a series of such products, we get as a solution of (13),

$$C = A_1 J_0(\lambda_1 r)e^{-K\lambda_1^2 t} + A_2 J_0(\lambda_2 r)e^{-K\lambda_2^2 t} + \cdots,$$ (19)

where the A's and λ's are at our disposal.

From (14), we get

$$0 = A_1 J_0(\lambda_1 a)e^{-K\lambda_1^2 t} + A_2 J_0(\lambda_2 a)e^{-K\lambda_2^2 t} + \cdots.$$

Now the Bessel function $J_0(x)$ has infinitely many positive zeros (Chapter VI, Art. 59): $R_1 = 2.405$, $R_2 = 5.520$, $R_3 = 8.654$, $\cdots$. Hence condition (14) may be met by choosing $\lambda_n = R_n/a$, so that

$$C = A_1 J_0 \left(R_1 \frac{r}{a} \right) e^{-KR_1^2 t/a^2} + A_2 J_0 \left(R_2 \frac{r}{a} \right) e^{-KR_2^2 t/a^2} + \cdots.$$

From (15), we have

$$C_0 = A_1 J_0 \left(R_1 \frac{r}{a} \right) + A_2 J_0 \left(R_2 \frac{r}{a} \right) + \cdots.$$

Thus we have to expand the constant C_0 in a series of Bessel functions. It was shown in Chapter VI, Art. 61, that the expansion of unity in such a series is

$$1 = \frac{2}{R_1 J_1(R_1)} J_0(R_1 x) + \frac{2}{R_2 J_1(R_2)} J_0(R_2 x) + \cdots,$$

valid for $0 < x < 1$. Letting $x = r/a$, we therefore have

$$C_0 = \frac{2C_0}{R_1 J_1(R_1)} J_0 \left(R_1 \frac{r}{a} \right) + \frac{2C_0}{R_2 J_1(R_2)} J_0 \left(R_2 \frac{r}{a} \right) + \cdots, \qquad (20)$$

which holds for $0 < r < a$.

Therefore the solution of (13) which satisfies conditions (14) and (15) is

$$C(r, t) = 2C_0 \sum_{n=1}^{\infty} \frac{1}{R_n J_1(R_n)} J_0 \left(R_n \frac{r}{a} \right) e^{-KR_n^2 t/a^2}. \qquad (21)$$

It is beyond the scope of this book to examine series (21) for convergence. We shall assume that (21) may be integrated term by term, so as to obtain an expression for the average free liquid concentration, which is our principal result, and examine merely the resulting series for $\bar{C}$.

We have for the total free liquid content in the cylinder at time t,

$$\bar{C} \cdot \pi a^2 L = 2\pi L \int_0^a C r \, dr,$$

whence, from (21),

$$\bar{C} = \frac{4C_0}{a^2} \int_0^a \sum_{n=1}^{\infty} \frac{r J_0 \left(R_n \frac{r}{a} \right)}{R_n J_1(R_n)} e^{-KR_n^2 t/a^2} \, dr.$$

Using the relation $xJ_0(x) = \dfrac{d}{dx}[xJ_1(x)]$ (Chapter VI, Art. 58), we have, with $x = R_n r/a$,

$$R_n \frac{r}{a} J_0\left(R_n \frac{r}{a}\right) = \frac{a}{R_n} \frac{d}{dr}\left[R_n \frac{r}{a} J_1\left(R_n \frac{r}{a}\right)\right],$$

from which

$$\int_0^a rJ_0\left(R_n \frac{r}{a}\right) dr = \frac{a}{R_n}\left[rJ_1\left(R_n \frac{r}{a}\right)\right]_0^a = \frac{a^2}{R_n} J_1(R_n).$$

Consequently we have

$$\bar{C} = 4C_0 \sum_{n=1}^{\infty} \frac{1}{R_n^2} e^{-KR_n^2 t/a^2}. \tag{22}$$

Since $e^{-KR_n^2 t/a^2} \leqq 1$ for $t \geqq 0$, and $R_n > n$, the terms in the summation of (22) are less than the corresponding terms of the convergent series $\sum_{n=1}^{\infty} \dfrac{1}{n^2}.$ Hence (22) converges uniformly for $t \geqq 0$.

When $t = 0$, $\bar{C} = C_0$, so that we get from (22) the interesting relation

$$\sum_{n=1}^{\infty} \frac{1}{R_n^2} = \frac{1}{4}.$$

That is, the sum of the squares of the reciprocals of the positive zeros of $J_0(x)$ is equal to $\frac{1}{4}$. (Cf. Chapter V, Art. 45, Example 2.)

PROBLEMS

1. A copper rod 6 cm. in diameter, 100 cm. long, and of resistivity 1720 abohms/cm.[3], is wound over its entire length with 5000 turns of wire. The coil is excited by a 60-cycle alternating current whose effective value is 0.1 abamp. (a) Compute the magnetic field strength when $t = 0.03$ sec., at the axis, 1 cm. from the axis, and at the surface of the rod. (b) Find the heat loss in watts in the entire rod.

2. Find the r.m.s. value of the field intensity over a cycle at the axis and surface of the rod of Problem 1 and at several intermediate distances. Hence plot a curve showing the variation of effective field strength with distance from the axis.

3. For each of the points used in Problem 2, find the phase difference between the field strength and the exciting current, and plot a curve showing the variation of phase difference with distance from the axis.

4. A porous slab 2.5 in. thick, and with its edges coated, is allowed to dry for 40 hr., during which diffusion controls the drying rate. Initially the concentration is 0.1976 lb./ft.[3], and at the surface the concentration is 0.0309 lb./ft.[3] If the diffusivity constant is $K = 0.000164$ ft.[2]/hr., find the average concentration $\bar{c}$ at the end of 10, 20, 30, and 40 hr., and plot a curve showing the time variation of $\bar{c}$.

5. A porous cylinder, 9 in. in diameter and coated at the ends, is allowed to dry for 40 hr. Using the relevant data of Problem 4, find the value of $\bar{c}$ at the end of 10, 20, 30, and 40 hr. and plot a curve showing the time variation of $\bar{c}$.

77. The vibrating membrane.

As an example of a partial differential equation involving three independent variables, we consider the problem of the vibrating membrane.

Suppose a membrane to be tightly stretched and firmly held by a rigid rectangular frame. Place the membrane in the xy-plane so that its edges are the lines $x = 0$, $x = a$, $y = 0$, and $y = b$, where a and b are measured in feet. Under the action of a disturbance of some kind, the displacement z (ft.) of the membrane will be a function of x, y, and time t (sec.): $z = z(x, y, t)$.

The differential equation to be satisfied by z may be derived in a manner analogous to that of the vibrating string (Art. 70). The result is found to be

$$\frac{\partial^2 z}{\partial t^2} = c^2 \left(\frac{\partial^2 z}{\partial x^2} + \frac{\partial^2 z}{\partial y^2} \right), \tag{1}$$

where $c = \sqrt{Tg/s}$ (ft./sec.), T (lb./ft.) is the constant tension per unit length in any direction in the membrane, g (ft./sec.^{2}) is the gravity constant, and s (lb./ft.^{2}) is the surface density of the material of the membrane. In accordance with the position of the fixed edges, as mentioned above, we also have the following boundary conditions:

$$z(0, y, t) = 0, \qquad 0 < y < b, \quad t > 0; \tag{2}$$

$$z(a, y, t) = 0, \qquad 0 < y < b, \quad t > 0; \tag{3}$$

$$z(x, 0, t) = 0, \qquad 0 < x < a, \quad t > 0; \tag{4}$$

$$z(x, b, t) = 0, \qquad 0 < x < a, \quad t > 0. \tag{5}$$

Suppose that vibration is brought about by giving the membrane an initial displacement $z = f(x, y)$, $0 < x < a$, $0 < y < b$, and releasing it from rest. Then the initial conditions are

$$z(x, y, 0) = f(x, y), \qquad 0 < x < a, \quad 0 < y < b; \tag{6}$$

$$\frac{\partial z}{\partial t}\bigg]_{t=0} = 0, \qquad 0 < x < a, \quad 0 < y < b. \tag{7}$$

Assume that there exists a solution of our problem of the form $z = X(x) \cdot Y(y) \cdot T(t)$. Substituting in (1) and separating the variables, we get

$$\frac{T''}{c^2 T} = \frac{X''}{X} + \frac{Y''}{Y}. \tag{8}$$

Each of the three terms in this equation must be a constant, and in order that the function $T(t)$ be a periodic function of time, each member of (8) must be a negative constant. Moreover, to meet the boundary conditions (2)–(5), z must be a periodic function of x and y as well. Therefore we set

$$\frac{X''}{X} = -\alpha^2, \qquad \frac{Y''}{Y} = -\beta^2, \tag{9}$$

whence (8) yields

$$T'' = -c^2(\alpha^2 + \beta^2)T. \tag{10}$$

Following the usual procedure, we find from (2) that X must have the form $c_1 \sin \alpha x$, where c_1 is a constant, and from (3) that $\alpha = m\pi/a$, where m is an integer. Consequently

$$X = c_1 \sin \frac{m\pi x}{a}. \tag{11}$$

Similarly, boundary conditions (4) and (5) require that

$$Y = c_2 \sin \frac{n\pi y}{b}, \tag{12}$$

where n is an integer. Then (10) becomes

$$T'' = -c^2\left(\frac{m^2}{a^2} + \frac{n^2}{b^2}\right)\pi^2 T = -c^2 K_{mn}^2 \pi^2 T, \tag{13}$$

where

$$K_{mn} = \sqrt{\frac{m^2}{a^2} + \frac{n^2}{b^2}}. \tag{14}$$

Hence

$$T = c_3 \sin cK_{mn}\pi t + c_4 \cos cK_{mn}\pi t, \tag{15}$$

where c_3 and c_4 are constants.

Initial condition (7) now imposes the condition $c_3 = 0$, and we thus have

$$z = c' \sin \frac{m\pi x}{a} \sin \frac{n\pi y}{b} \cos cK_{mn}\pi t, \tag{16}$$

where c' is arbitrary, m and n are integers, and K_{mn} is a corresponding number given by (14). Relation (16) satisfies the differential equation (1), all boundary conditions (2)–(5), and initial condition (7); initial condition (6) remains to be met.

Neither (16) alone nor any finite sum of terms of that type will, in general, serve to satisfy relation (6), but certain special forms of the function $f(x, y)$ may lead to a simple solution. For example, if the initial displacement is

$$f(x, y) = z_0 \sin \frac{\pi x}{a} \sin \frac{\pi y}{b}, \tag{17}$$

where z_0 (ft.) is a constant, it is easily seen that the full solution of the problem is

$$z(x, y, t) = z_0 \sin \frac{\pi x}{a} \sin \frac{\pi y}{b} \cos \frac{c\pi\sqrt{a^2 + b^2}}{ab} t, \tag{18}$$

obtained from (14) and (16) with $m = n = 1$, $c' = z_0$.

In less special cases, however, we are led to formulate the double series

$$z = \sum_{m=1}^{\infty} \sum_{n=1}^{\infty} B_{mn} \sin \frac{m\pi x}{a} \sin \frac{n\pi y}{b} \cos \left(\pi c \sqrt{\frac{m^2}{a^2} + \frac{n^2}{b^2}} \, t \right). \tag{19}$$

This relation will formally satisfy all the conditions of the problem provided that $f(x, y)$ can be represented by the double Fourier series

$$f(x, y) = \sum_{m=1}^{\infty} \sum_{n=1}^{\infty} B_{mn} \sin \frac{m\pi x}{a} \sin \frac{n\pi y}{b}$$

$$= \sum_{m=1}^{\infty} \left(\sum_{n=1}^{\infty} B_{mn} \sin \frac{n\pi y}{b} \right) \sin \frac{m\pi x}{a}, \tag{20}$$

for $0 < x < a$, $0 < y < b$. Now, for each fixed value of y between 0 and b, (20) is the Fourier sine series for $f(x, y)$ if

$$\sum_{n=1}^{\infty} B_{mn} \sin \frac{n\pi y}{b} = \frac{2}{a} \int_0^a f(x, y) \sin \frac{m\pi x}{a} \, dx = g_m(y), \tag{21}$$

say. This in turn will be valid if

$$B_{mn} = \frac{2}{b} \int_0^b g_m(y) \sin \frac{n\pi y}{b} \, dy. \tag{22}$$

Thus, (19) will be the desired result when the coefficients B_{mn} are those given by

$$B_{mn} = \frac{4}{ab} \int_0^b \int_0^a f(x, y) \sin \frac{m\pi x}{a} \sin \frac{n\pi y}{b} \, dx \, dy. \tag{23}$$

It should be noted that, although each individual term in (19) is a periodic function of t, the function z represented by the double series is not, in general, periodic in t. For, the numbers K_{mn} given by (14) are not integral multiples of any fixed number as m and n independently assume the values $1, 2, 3, \cdots$. Consequently a vibrating membrane will not necessarily emit a musical note. In special instances, however, a musical note will be emitted; thus, the function (18) is periodic in t, with period $2ab/c\sqrt{a^2 + b^2}$.

PROBLEMS

1. Let the initial displacement of the rectangular vibrating membrane of Art. **77** be given by

$$z(x, y, 0) = f(x, y) = h(ax - x^2)(by - y^2),$$

where h (ft.$^{-3}$) is a constant. Show that the coefficients of the double series (19) are then

$$B_{mn} = \frac{16a^2b^2h}{\pi^6m^3n^3}(1 - \cos m\pi)(1 - \cos n\pi).$$

2. Suppose a membrane to be stretched over a fixed circular frame, of radius a (ft.), in the xy-plane and with its center at the origin. Let the membrane be given an initial displacement $z = f(r, \theta)$ and released from rest, where (r, θ, z) are cylindrical coordinates. Show that the differential equation and the boundary and initial conditions are given by

$$\frac{\partial^2 z}{\partial t^2} = c^2 \left(\frac{\partial^2 z}{\partial r^2} + \frac{1}{r}\frac{\partial z}{\partial r} + \frac{1}{r^2}\frac{\partial^2 z}{\partial \theta^2} \right),$$

$$z(a, \theta, t) = 0, \qquad \frac{\partial z}{\partial t}\bigg]_{t=0} = 0, \qquad z(r, \theta, 0) = f(r, \theta).$$

3. Obtain a solution of Problem 2 in the form of a Fourier-Bessel expansion:

$$z = \sum_{m=0}^{\infty} \sum_{n=1}^{\infty} J_m(\lambda_{mn}r)(A_{mn}\cos m\theta + B_{mn}\sin m\theta)\cos c\lambda_{mn}t,$$

where J_m is a Bessel function of order m, λ_{mn} are roots of the equation $J_m(a\lambda) = 0$, and

$$A_{0n} = \frac{1}{\pi a^2 J_1^2(a\lambda_{0n})} \int_0^a \int_{-\pi}^{\pi} rJ_0(\lambda_{0n}r)f(r, \theta)\, d\theta\, dr,$$

$$A_{mn} = \frac{2}{\pi a^2 J_{m+1}^2(a\lambda_{mn})} \int_0^a \int_{-\pi}^{\pi} rJ_m(\lambda_{mn}r)f(r, \theta)\cos m\theta\, d\theta\, dr,$$

$$B_{mn} = \frac{2}{\pi a^2 J_{m+1}^2(a\lambda_{mn})} \int_0^a \int_{-\pi}^{\pi} rJ_m(\lambda_{mn}r)f(r, \theta)\sin m\theta\, d\theta\, dr.$$

4. Suppose that the initial displacement of the circular membrane of Problem 2 is a function of r only, say $f(r)$. If the membrane is released from rest, show that the displacement z (ft.) is given by

$$z = \frac{2}{a^2} \sum_{n=1}^{\infty} \frac{J_0(\alpha_n r/a)}{J_1^2(\alpha_n)}\cos\frac{c\alpha_n t}{a} \int_0^a rJ_0(\alpha_n r/a)f(r)\, dr,$$

where a (ft.) is the radius and the α's are the positive roots of $J_0(\lambda) = 0$.

5. If $f(r) = h(a^2 - r^2)$ in Problem 4, where h (ft.$^{-1}$) is a constant, find the displacement function $z(r, t)$. *Hint:* Make use of the results of Problem 22, Art. 64.

78. Potential due to charged sphere.   The potential u at a point P, due to a point charge q at a distance r from P, was defined in Art. 65 to be $u = q/r$.   More generally, the potential at a point $P(x, y, z)$, due to a distribution of charge of density $\rho(x_1, y_1, z_1)$ throughout a volume V, may be defined as

$$u(x, y, z) = k \iiint_V \frac{\rho(x_1, y_1, z_1)\, dx_1\, dy_1\, dz_1}{\sqrt{(x - x_1)^2 + (y - y_1)^2 + (z - z_1)^2}}, \quad (1)$$

where (x_1, y_1, z_1) is a point inside V and k is a constant of proportionality depending upon the units of measurement.

By partial differentiation under the integral sign, we get

$$\frac{\partial u}{\partial x} = -k \iiint_V \frac{x - x_1}{r^3}\, \rho(x_1, y_1, z_1)\, dx_1\, dy_1\, dz_1,$$

where $r^2 = (x - x_1)^2 + (y - y_1)^2 + (z - z_1)^2$.   Similar expressions are obtainable for $\partial u / \partial y$ and $\partial u / \partial z$.   Second differentiations with respect to x, y, and z, respectively, yield

$$\frac{\partial^2 u}{\partial x^2} = -k \iiint_V \left[\frac{1}{r^3} - \frac{3(x - x_1)^2}{r^5} \right] \rho\, dx_1\, dy_1\, dz_1,$$

$$\frac{\partial^2 u}{\partial y^2} = -k \iiint_V \left[\frac{1}{r^3} - \frac{3(y - y_1)^2}{r^5} \right] \rho\, dx_1\, dy_1\, dz_1,$$

$$\frac{\partial^2 u}{\partial z^2} = -k \iiint_V \left[\frac{1}{r^3} - \frac{3(z - z_1)^2}{r^5} \right] \rho\, dx_1\, dy_1\, dz_1.$$

Addition then gives

$$\frac{\partial^2 u}{\partial x^2} + \frac{\partial^2 u}{\partial y^2} + \frac{\partial^2 u}{\partial z^2} = 0; \quad (2)$$

that is, the potential function (1) satisfies Laplace's equation.

Now consider a spherical surface of radius a, carrying a given fixed distribution of charge.   We wish to determine the potential u at each point interior or exterior to the sphere.   To deal with this problem analytically, it is convenient to use spherical coordinates instead of rectangular coordinates.   Let (r, θ, ϕ) denote the spherical coordinates of a point P, whose rectangular coordinates are (x, y, z), chosen so that we have the transformation equations

$$x = r \sin \theta \cos \phi, \qquad y = r \sin \theta \sin \phi, \qquad z = r \cos \theta. \quad (3)$$

Here r denotes the length of the radius vector from the origin O to the point P, θ is the angle from the z-axis to r, and ϕ is the angle from the

xz-plane to the plane of r and the z-axis. Then, by a procedure analogous to that of Art. 72, whereby Laplace's equation in two-dimensional rectangular form was transformed into polar form, relations (3) serve to change the three-dimensional rectangular equation (2) into

$$r^2 \frac{\partial^2 u}{\partial r^2} + 2r \frac{\partial u}{\partial r} + \frac{\partial^2 u}{\partial \theta^2} + \cot \theta \frac{\partial u}{\partial \theta} + \csc^2 \theta \frac{\partial^2 u}{\partial \phi^2} = 0. \qquad (4)$$

Suppose that the potential distribution on the sphere, where $r = a$, is independent of ϕ, and thus is expressible as a function of θ alone, say $f(\theta)$. Then, by symmetry, the required potential function will likewise be independent of ϕ, so that the last term of equation (4) drops out. We shall also require that the potential approach zero as the point P recedes indefinitely far from the sphere. Then the problem is to find a solution $u(r, \theta)$ of the reduced Laplace equation

$$r^2 \frac{\partial^2 u}{\partial r^2} + 2r \frac{\partial u}{\partial r} + \frac{\partial^2 u}{\partial \theta^2} + \cot \theta \frac{\partial u}{\partial \theta} = 0, \qquad (5)$$

satisfying the two boundary conditions

$$u(a, \theta) = f(\theta), \qquad (6)$$

$$\lim_{r \to \infty} u(r, \theta) = 0. \qquad (7)$$

We again use the method of separation of variables, setting $u(r, \theta) = R(r)T(\theta)$. Then, from (5),

$$r^2 R''T + 2rR'T + RT'' + \cot \theta \, RT' = 0,$$

whence

$$\frac{r^2 R'' + 2rR'}{R} = -\frac{T'' + \cot \theta \, T'}{T} = k,$$

a constant. The Euler equation thus obtained for $R(r)$,

$$r^2 R'' + 2rR' - kR = 0,$$

yields the solution

$$R(r) = c_1 r^n + \frac{c_2}{r^{n+1}}, \qquad (8)$$

where $n = -\frac{1}{2} + \sqrt{k + \frac{1}{4}}$, so that $k = n(n + 1)$ and $-\frac{1}{2} - \sqrt{k + \frac{1}{4}} = -n - 1$. Therefore the equation for $T(\theta)$ becomes

$$T'' + \cot \theta \, T' + n(n + 1)T = 0.$$

By setting $x = \cos\theta$, this transforms into Legendre's equation (Art. 65, Problem 18),

$$(1 - x^2)\frac{d^2T}{dx^2} - 2x\frac{dT}{dx} + n(n + 1)T = 0.$$

Consequently the Legendre polynomials are obtainable as solutions, provided that n is zero or a positive integer:

$$T = P_n(x) = P_n(\cos\theta). \tag{9}$$

For points inside the sphere, we choose $c_2 = 0$ in (8), so that u does not become infinite as r approaches zero at the center O. We may then take, for $0 \leqq r \leqq a$,

$$u_1(r, \theta) = \sum_{n=0}^{\infty} B_n r^n P_n(\cos\theta)$$

as a solution which formally satisfies Laplace's equation (5). It remains to determine the coefficients B_n so that boundary condition (6) is met; that is, we must have

$$u_1(a, \theta) = f(\theta) = \sum_{n=0}^{\infty} (B_n a^n) P_n(\cos\theta), \qquad 0 < \theta < \pi.$$

But this can be done (Art. 65, Problem 16), for suitable functions $f(\theta)$, by taking

$$B_n = \frac{2n + 1}{2a^n} \int_0^{\pi} f(\theta) P_n(\cos\theta) \sin\theta \, d\theta.$$

Consequently, for points inside the sphere ($0 \leqq r \leqq a$), the potential function is

$$u_1(r, \theta) = \frac{1}{2} \sum_{n=0}^{\infty} (2n + 1)\left(\frac{r}{a}\right)^n P_n(\cos\theta) \times$$

$$\int_0^{\pi} f(\theta) P_n(\cos\theta) \sin\theta \, d\theta. \tag{10}$$

When the point P is outside the sphere, we take $c_1 = 0$ in (8) so that boundary condition (7) can be met. This gives, for $r \geqq a$,

$$u_2(r, \theta) = \sum_{n=0}^{\infty} \frac{C_n}{r^{n+1}} P_n(\cos\theta),$$

and since we are to have, by (6),

$$u_2(a, \theta) = f(\theta) = \sum_{n=0}^{\infty} \frac{C_n}{a^{n+1}} P_n(\cos \theta),$$

this requires that

$$C_n = \frac{(2n + 1)a^{n+1}}{2} \int_0^{\pi} f(\theta) P_n(\cos \theta) \sin \theta \, d\theta.$$

Hence the required solution for $r \geq a$ is

$$u_2(r, \theta) = \frac{1}{2} \sum_{n=0}^{\infty} (2n + 1) \left(\frac{a}{r}\right)^{n+1} P_n(\cos \theta) \times$$
$$\int_0^{\pi} f(\theta) P_n(\cos \theta) \sin \theta \, d\theta. \quad (11)$$

If, in particular, the potential is constant over the spherical surface, so that $f(\theta) = u_0$, equations (10) and (11) yield simple expressions. For, since

$$\int_0^{\pi} u_0 P_0(\cos \theta) \sin \theta \, d\theta = u_0 \int_0^{\pi} \sin \theta \, d\theta = 2u_0,$$

whereas

$$\int_0^{\pi} u_0 P_n(\cos \theta) \sin \theta \, d\theta = u_0 \int_{-1}^{1} P_n(x) \, dx = 0$$

when $n = 1, 2, \cdots$ [equation (17), Art. 65], (10) gives

$$u_1(r, \theta) = u_0, \qquad 0 \leq r \leq a,$$

and (11) gives

$$u_2(r, \theta) = \frac{u_0 a}{r}, \qquad r \geq a.$$

Thus, all interior points have the same potential as the surface, and at exterior points, the potential varies inversely as the distance from the origin O, just as if we had a point charge at O.

PROBLEMS

1. Find the steady-state temperature function $u(r, \theta)$ within a solid sphere of radius a if the temperature on the surface is $u(a, \theta) = 50(1 + \cos \theta)$.

2. Find the steady-state temperature function $u(r, \theta)$ within a solid sphere of radius a if the upper hemispherical surface ($0 < \theta < \pi/2$) is kept at a constant temperature u_0 and the lower ($\pi/2 < \theta < \pi$) at zero temperature.

3. Find the steady-state temperature function $u(r, \theta)$ within a solid hemisphere of radius a if the hemispherical surface temperature is $u(a, \theta) = 100 \sin^2 \theta$ ($0 < \theta$

$< \pi/2$), and if the plane circular base is insulated, so that $\partial u/\partial \theta = 0$ when $\theta = \pi/2$. *Hint:* Use the result of Problem 4, Art. 65.

4. A spherical shell has inner radius a and outer radius b. If the inner surface temperature is $u(a, \theta) = f(\theta)$, while the outer surface is kept at zero temperature, show that the steady-state temperature function $u(r, \theta)$ within the shell is given by

$$u(r, \theta) = \frac{1}{2} \sum_{n=0}^{\infty} (2n + 1) \frac{b^{2n+1} - r^{2n+1}}{b^{2n+1} - a^{2n+1}} \left(\frac{a}{r}\right)^{n+1} P_n(\cos \theta) \cdot \int_0^\pi f(\theta) P_n(\cos \theta) \sin \theta \, d\theta.$$

As a partial check, take $f(\theta) = u_0$, a constant, and compare the result with that obtained in Problem 57, Art. 14.

5. Find the steady-state temperature function $u(r, \theta)$ within a solid hemisphere of radius a if the hemispherical surface temperature is $u(a, \theta) = u_0$, a constant $(0 < \theta < \pi/2)$, and if the base temperature is zero. *Hint:* Define $u(a, \theta)$ to be $-u_0$ for $\pi/2 < \theta < \pi$, thereby creating an odd function and making possible the necessary expansion in odd Legendre polynomials. See also Problem 3, Art. 65.

6. Find the steady-state temperature function $u(r, \theta)$ within a solid that may be considered infinite in extent if the temperature along the z-axis is given by $u_0 e^{-r^2}$.

7. A non-homogeneous bar, with ends at $x = -1$ and $x = 1$, has thermal conductivity proportional to $1 - x^2$, and density ρ and specific heat c such that the product $c\rho$ is constant throughout. If its sides and ends are insulated, its temperature $u(x, t)$ is then given by (cf. Art. 71)

$$\frac{\partial u}{\partial t} = k \frac{\partial}{\partial x}\left[(1 - x^2)\frac{\partial u}{\partial x}\right],$$

where k is a constant and t is time. If $u(x, 0) = f(x)$, show that

$$u(x, t) = \frac{1}{2} \sum_{n=0}^{\infty} (2n + 1) P_n(x) e^{-kn(n+1)t} \cdot \int_{-1}^1 f(x) P_n(x) \, dx.$$

8. Find the temperature function $u(x, t)$ for the bar of Problem 7 if (a) $f(x) = u_0 x^2$; (b) $f(x) = u_0 x^3$.

9. Show that the gravitational potential, due to a thin homogeneous circular wire of radius a and mass m, is

$$u(r, \theta) = \frac{km}{a}\left[1 - \frac{1}{2}\left(\frac{r}{a}\right)^2 P_2(\cos \theta) + \frac{1 \cdot 3}{2 \cdot 4}\left(\frac{r}{a}\right)^4 P_4(\cos \theta) - \cdots\right], \qquad 0 \leqq r < a,$$

$$u(r, \theta) = \frac{km}{r}\left[1 - \frac{1}{2}\left(\frac{a}{r}\right)^2 P_2(\cos \theta) + \frac{1 \cdot 3}{2 \cdot 4}\left(\frac{a}{r}\right)^4 P_4(\cos \theta) - \cdots\right], \qquad r > a,$$

10. Show that the gravitational potential, due to a thin homogeneous circular plate of radius a and mass m, is

$$u(r, \theta) = \frac{2km}{a}\left[1 - \left(\frac{r}{a}\right) P_1(\cos \theta) + \frac{1}{2}\left(\frac{r}{a}\right)^2 P_2(\cos \theta)\right.$$
$$\left. - \frac{1}{2 \cdot 4}\left(\frac{r}{a}\right)^4 P_4(\cos \theta) + \frac{1 \cdot 3}{2 \cdot 4 \cdot 6}\left(\frac{r}{a}\right)^6 P_6(\cos \theta) - \cdots\right], \qquad 0 \leqq r < a,$$

$$u(r, \theta) = \frac{2km}{a}\left[\frac{1}{2}\left(\frac{a}{r}\right) P_0(\cos \theta) - \frac{1}{2 \cdot 4}\left(\frac{a}{r}\right)^3 P_2(\cos \theta)\right.$$
$$\left. + \frac{1 \cdot 3}{2 \cdot 4 \cdot 6}\left(\frac{a}{r}\right)^5 P_4(\cos \theta) - \cdots\right], \qquad r > a,$$

both for $0 \leqq \theta < \pi/2$.

CHAPTER VIII

Vector Analysis

79. Introduction. Vector analysis is a tool frequently employed in the mathematical treatment of physical and engineering problems, and, as such, merits a place in a book of the present sort. Although it is probably true that any problem which can be solved by vector analysis is also susceptible to non-vectorial methods, there are a number of reasons why familiarity with vector notations and concepts is useful to the engineering student.

In the first place, many books on engineering topics make use of vector symbolism; acquaintance with this subject is therefore necessary to the perusal of such books. Secondly, vector analysis provides a convenient shorthand by means of which mathematical relations between physical quantities may be compactly written and exhibited. In addition, to the student who acquires the ability to interpret physically the various vector expressions, such as divergence and curl, vector analysis becomes a mode of visualizing the underlying physical meaning of mathematical relations and theorems—becomes, indeed, a mode of thought.

The physical quantities with which we deal are of two kinds, scalar quantities and vector quantities. A scalar quantity is one which is completely specified when its magnitude, i.e., size or number of units according to some scale, is given; examples of scalars are mass, length, temperature, electric charge, and quantity of heat. A vector quantity is one whose specification involves, in addition to magnitude, a direction; thus, displacement, velocity, acceleration, force, electric current, and temperature gradient are all vectors, since we speak of these things "in such-and-such a direction."

A scalar may be represented algebraically by a symbol or number, geometrically by a line segment whose length indicates the magnitude of the scalar according to a given scale, but whose position in space may be taken arbitrarily. A vector may be represented algebraically by a symbol, differing in some way from the symbol indicating the magnitude of the vector quantity, and it may be represented geometrically by a directed line segment with arbitrary initial point and with an arrow-head on it, the length indicating magnitude, the inclination indicating direction, and the arrow-head indicating sense. In this book a scalar will be denoted by a number or a letter in italic type, as s, and a vector will be denoted by a letter in Clarendon or bold-faced type, as $\mathbf{v}$,* its magnitude being denoted by the same letter in italic type.

80. Vector algebra. Two parallel line segments of the same length and sense are said to be equal vectors, whatever their initial points may be. Two parallel line segments having the same length but oppositely sensed are said to be one the negative of the other; if one vector is denoted by $\mathbf{v}$, the second is denoted by $-\mathbf{v}$. A vector parallel to a second vector $\mathbf{v}$ and similarly sensed, but m times as long, is denoted by $m\mathbf{v}$.

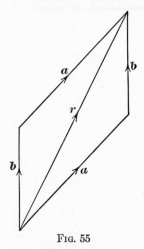

FIG. 55

Let $\mathbf{a}$ and $\mathbf{b}$ be any two vectors. If we place the initial point of $\mathbf{b}$ on the terminal point of $\mathbf{a}$, the vector $\mathbf{r}$ drawn from the initial point of $\mathbf{a}$ to the terminal point of $\mathbf{b}$ is defined as the vector sum of $\mathbf{a}$ and $\mathbf{b}$ (Fig. 55):

$$\mathbf{r} = \mathbf{a} + \mathbf{b}. \tag{1}$$

This is the familiar parallelogram law for the composition of two forces (which are vectors). Evidently the same vector $\mathbf{r}$ will be obtained if we place the initial point of $\mathbf{a}$ on the terminal point of $\mathbf{b}$ and draw the directed line segment from the initial point of $\mathbf{b}$ to the terminal point of $\mathbf{a}$, so that

$$\mathbf{r} = \mathbf{a} + \mathbf{b} = \mathbf{b} + \mathbf{a}. \tag{2}$$

Consequently vector addition is commutative, i.e., the order of the vectors appearing in a sum is immaterial. The extension of our

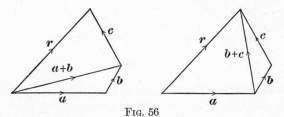

FIG. 56

definition of vector addition to the case of three or more vectors is immediate. It is apparent from Fig. 56 that addition is also associative,

$$\mathbf{r} = (\mathbf{a} + \mathbf{b}) + \mathbf{c} = \mathbf{a} + (\mathbf{b} + \mathbf{c}). \tag{3}$$

Note that $\mathbf{a}$, $\mathbf{b}$, $\mathbf{c}$ need not lie in a single plane.

* In writing vectors, a convenient symbolism is to denote the vector whose magnitude is A by the same letter with a bar over it, as $\bar{A}$.

By the difference $\mathbf{a} - \mathbf{b}$ of two vectors is meant the sum $\mathbf{a} + (-\mathbf{b})$, or, in other words, the vector which added to $\mathbf{b}$ produces $\mathbf{a}$ (Fig. 57):

$$r = a - b, \qquad r + b = a. \tag{4}$$

The two forms (4) being equivalent, it is implied that in such a relation a vector term may be transposed from one side of an equality to

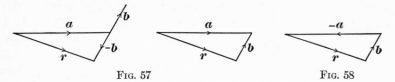

FIG. 57 FIG. 58

the other by changing its sign, just as in scalar algebra. Another form equivalent to the relations (4) is (Fig. 58)

$$r + b - a = 0, \tag{4_1}$$

where the right-hand member 0 signifies a vector of length zero, i.e., a null vector.

To familiarize ourselves with the foregoing definitions, let us apply vector analysis to the proof of the following geometrical theorem: The line which joins one vertex of a parallelogram with the midpoint of an opposite side cuts a diagonal in a point of trisection. Let $\mathbf{a} = AB$ and $\mathbf{b} = AD$ be adjacent sides of the parallelogram as shown in Fig. 59.

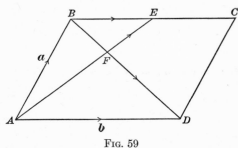

FIG. 59

If E is the midpoint of the side $BC = \mathbf{b}$, we have $BE = \frac{1}{2}\mathbf{b}$, and $AE = \mathbf{a} + \frac{1}{2}\mathbf{b}$. Letting F be the point of intersection of AE and the diagonal BD, the vector AF will be some fraction of AE, or $AF = x\mathbf{a} + (x/2)\mathbf{b}$. Since $BD = \mathbf{b} - \mathbf{a}$, the vector BF will likewise be a fraction of BD, or $BF = y\mathbf{b} - y\mathbf{a}$. Then in the triangle ABF, we have

$$a + yb - ya = xa + \frac{x}{2}b,$$

or

$$(1 - y - x)a + \left(y - \frac{x}{2}\right)b = 0.$$

But since **a** and **b** are differently directed, the above equation can hold only if

$$1 - y - x = 0, \qquad y - \frac{x}{2} = 0.$$

Hence we get $x = \frac{2}{3}$, $y = \frac{1}{3}$, and

$$BF = \tfrac{1}{3}(\mathbf{b} - \mathbf{a}) = \tfrac{1}{3}BD,$$

so that F is a point of trisection of BD. Incidentally, we get also $AF = \frac{2}{3}AE$, so that F is a trisecting point of AE as well.

It is often convenient to refer a vector to a system of coordinate axes, X, Y, Z. This allows for a translation from vector notation to Cartesian notation, and conversely. For definiteness, we shall agree to use a right-handed system of axes,* as shown in Fig. 60. Let **i, j, k**

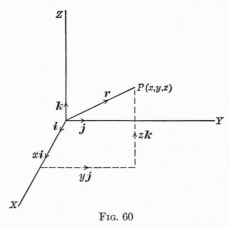

FIG. 60

denote the three unit vectors along the positive directions of the x-, y-, and z-axes respectively. If **r** is the vector from the origin O to any point $P(x, y, z)$, we then have

$$\mathbf{r} = x\mathbf{i} + y\mathbf{j} + z\mathbf{k}. \tag{5}$$

More generally, if **a** is any vector (with arbitrary initial point), whose components along the axes are a_1, a_2, a_3, then

$$\mathbf{a} = a_1\mathbf{i} + a_2\mathbf{j} + a_3\mathbf{k}. \tag{6}$$

If also

$$\mathbf{b} = b_1\mathbf{i} + b_2\mathbf{j} + b_3\mathbf{k},$$

we have

$$\mathbf{a} + \mathbf{b} = (a_1 + b_1)\mathbf{i} + (a_2 + b_2)\mathbf{j} + (a_3 + b_3)\mathbf{k}. \tag{7}$$

* A system is said to be right-handed if a screw with right-handed thread will advance in the positive z-direction when turned through the 90° angle from the positive x-axis to the positive y-axis.

Having discussed vector addition, we turn now to the matter of vector multiplication. Although the symbol **ab** may be given a meaning, this vector operator, which is called a dyad,* will not be considered here. Of principal importance in elementary vector analysis are the two types of multiplication represented by the scalar or dot product of two vectors and the vector or cross product of two vectors.

The scalar or dot product of **a** and **b** is denoted by

$$\mathbf{a} \cdot \mathbf{b} = ab \cos (\mathbf{a}, \mathbf{b}), \qquad (8)$$

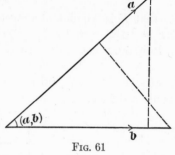

where (**a**, **b**) is the angle between the directions of **a** and **b**. The name dot product is used because of the dot symbolism; the designation scalar product is proper since by definition **a**·**b** is a

FIG. 61

scalar quantity and not a vector. Other notations sometimes used for this product are $S\mathbf{ab}$ and (**ab**). Evidently (Fig. 61) **a**·**b** may be regarded as the number obtained by multiplying the magnitude a of **a** by the projection $b \cos (\mathbf{a}, \mathbf{b})$ of **b** upon **a**, or as the number obtained by multiplying b by the projection $a \cos (\mathbf{a}, \mathbf{b})$ of **a** upon **b**. Since

$$\mathbf{a} \cdot \mathbf{b} = \mathbf{b} \cdot \mathbf{a}, \qquad (9)$$

scalar multiplication is commutative; moreover (Fig. 62), it is distributive, i.e.,

$$\mathbf{a} \cdot (\mathbf{b} + \mathbf{c}) = \mathbf{a} \cdot \mathbf{b} + \mathbf{a} \cdot \mathbf{c}. \qquad (10)$$

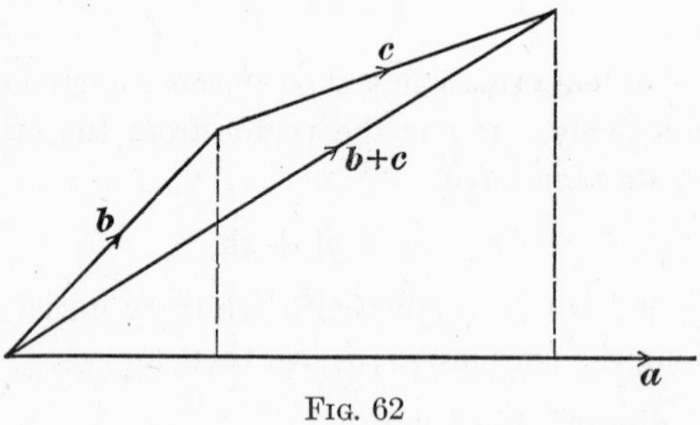

FIG. 62

If **a** and **b** are perpendicular to each other, neither being a null vector, then $\cos (\mathbf{a}, \mathbf{b}) = 0$ and $\mathbf{a} \cdot \mathbf{b} = 0$; if $\mathbf{a} \cdot \mathbf{b} = 0$, and neither **a** nor **b** is a null vector, then **a** is perpendicular to **b**. In particular

$$\mathbf{i} \cdot \mathbf{j} = \mathbf{j} \cdot \mathbf{k} = \mathbf{k} \cdot \mathbf{i} = 0. \qquad (11)$$

* See Gibbs-Wilson, "Vector Analysis," and A. P. Wills, "Vector and Tensor Analysis."

If $\mathbf{b} = \mathbf{a}$, $\mathbf{a} \cdot \mathbf{b} = a^2 = b^2$; in particular,

$$\mathbf{i} \cdot \mathbf{i} = \mathbf{j} \cdot \mathbf{j} = \mathbf{k} \cdot \mathbf{k} = 1. \qquad (12)$$

If $\mathbf{a} = a_1\mathbf{i} + a_2\mathbf{j} + a_3\mathbf{k}$, $\mathbf{b} = b_1\mathbf{i} + b_2\mathbf{j} + b_3\mathbf{k}$, then by relations (8), (11), and (12), we have

$$\mathbf{a} \cdot \mathbf{b} = ab \cos (\mathbf{a}, \mathbf{b}) = (a_1\mathbf{i} + a_2\mathbf{j} + a_3\mathbf{k}) \cdot (b_1\mathbf{i} + b_2\mathbf{j} + b_3\mathbf{k})$$

$$= a_1b_1 + a_2b_2 + a_3b_3. \qquad (13)$$

Consequently

$$\cos (\mathbf{a}, \mathbf{b}) = \frac{a_1}{a}\frac{b_1}{b} + \frac{a_2}{a}\frac{b_2}{b} + \frac{a_3}{a}\frac{b_3}{b},$$

which, since a_1/a, b_1/b, etc., are the direction cosines of the line segments $\mathbf{a}$ and $\mathbf{b}$, is the familiar formula of solid analytic geometry for the angle between two lines.

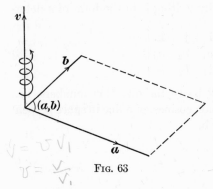

FIG. 63

The vector or cross product of $\mathbf{a}$ and $\mathbf{b}$ is a vector $\mathbf{v}$ (Fig. 63) perpendicular to the plane of $\mathbf{a}$ and $\mathbf{b}$, so sensed that $\mathbf{a}$, $\mathbf{b}$, $\mathbf{v}$ form a right-handed system, and of magnitude $v = ab \sin (\mathbf{a}, \mathbf{b})$. If $\mathbf{v}_1$ is a unit vector in the direction of $\mathbf{v}$, so that $\mathbf{v} = v\mathbf{v}_1$, we have for the vector product of $\mathbf{a}$ and $\mathbf{b}$,

$$\mathbf{v} = \mathbf{a} \times \mathbf{b} = \mathbf{v}_1 ab \sin (\mathbf{a}, \mathbf{b}). \quad (14)$$

Geometrically, the magnitude of $\mathbf{a} \times \mathbf{b}$ is represented by the area of the parallelogram whose adjacent sides are $\mathbf{a}$ and $\mathbf{b}$. Other notations for the cross product are $V\mathbf{ab}$ and $[\mathbf{ab}]$. Vector multiplication is not commutative, for we have

$$\mathbf{b} \times \mathbf{a} = -\mathbf{a} \times \mathbf{b}, \qquad (15)$$

as may be seen by interchanging $\mathbf{a}$ and $\mathbf{b}$ in the figure; hence it is important to preserve the proper order of the vectors in a vector product. It is easily shown geometrically, however, that vector multiplication is distributive, so that

$$\mathbf{a} \times (\mathbf{b} + \mathbf{c}) = \mathbf{a} \times \mathbf{b} + \mathbf{a} \times \mathbf{c}. \qquad (16)$$

If $\mathbf{a}$ is parallel to $\mathbf{b}$, it follows from the definition (14) that $\mathbf{a} \times \mathbf{b} = 0$; if $\mathbf{a} \times \mathbf{b} = 0$, and neither $\mathbf{a}$ nor $\mathbf{b}$ is a null vector, then $\mathbf{a}$ and $\mathbf{b}$ are parallel. The relations

$$i \times i = j \times j = k \times k = 0,$$
$$i \times j = -j \times i = k,$$
$$j \times k = -k \times j = i,$$
$$k \times i = -i \times k = j,$$

(17)

are of particular usefulness. If

$$a = a_1 i + a_2 j + a_3 k, \qquad b = b_1 i + b_2 j + b_3 k,$$

we get from (16) and (17),

$$a \times b = (a_1 i + a_2 j + a_3 k) \times (b_1 i + b_2 j + b_3 k)$$
$$= (a_2 b_3 - a_3 b_2) i + (a_3 b_1 - a_1 b_3) j + (a_1 b_2 - a_2 b_1) k,$$

which may be easily remembered by writing it in the form of a determinant,

$$a \times b = \begin{vmatrix} i & j & k \\ a_1 & a_2 & a_3 \\ b_1 & b_2 & b_3 \end{vmatrix}.$$

(18)

Note that the components of $a \times b$ are the direction numbers, i.e., numbers proportional to the direction cosines, of a line in space perpendicular to the line segments a and b.

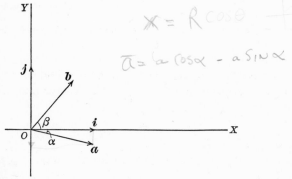

Fig. 64

Let a and b be two unit vectors in the xy-plane, and let α and β be the angles they make with the x-axis as shown in Fig. 64. Then we have

$$a = \cos \alpha\, i - \sin \alpha\, j,$$
$$b = \cos \beta\, i + \sin \beta\, j,$$

$a \times b = ab \, \sin \, \text{angle between}$
$= \sin(\alpha + b)$

and therefore, by (14) and (17),

$$\mathbf{a} \times \mathbf{b} = \sin(\alpha + \beta)\,\mathbf{k} = (\cos\alpha\,\mathbf{i} - \sin\alpha\,\mathbf{j}) \times (\cos\beta\,\mathbf{i} + \sin\beta\,\mathbf{j})$$

$$= (\cos\alpha\,\sin\beta + \sin\alpha\,\cos\beta)\mathbf{k},$$

whence we get

$$\sin(\alpha + \beta) = \sin\alpha\,\cos\beta + \cos\alpha\,\sin\beta,$$

a familiar trigonometric formula.

PROBLEMS

1. Show by vector methods that the diagonals of a parallelogram bisect each other.

2. Show by vector methods that the medians of a triangle meet in a point of trisection of each median.

3. Derive the law of cosines for a triangle. *Hint:* Express one side as the vector sum of the other two, $\mathbf{a} = \mathbf{b} + \mathbf{c}$, and consider the scalar product

$$\mathbf{a}\cdot\mathbf{a} = (\mathbf{b} + \mathbf{c})\cdot(\mathbf{b} + \mathbf{c}).$$

4. Using vector methods, derive the trigonometric formulas

$$\sin(\alpha - \beta) = \sin\alpha\,\cos\beta - \cos\alpha\,\sin\beta,$$

$$\cos(\alpha - \beta) = \cos\alpha\,\cos\beta + \sin\alpha\,\sin\beta.$$

5. Show that

$$\mathbf{a}\cdot(\mathbf{b} \times \mathbf{c}) = \mathbf{b}\cdot(\mathbf{c} \times \mathbf{a}) = \mathbf{c}\cdot(\mathbf{a} \times \mathbf{b}) = \begin{vmatrix} a_1 & a_2 & a_3 \\ b_1 & b_2 & b_3 \\ c_1 & c_2 & c_3 \end{vmatrix},$$

where $\mathbf{a} = a_1\mathbf{i} + a_2\mathbf{j} + a_3\mathbf{k}$, etc. Interpret the scalar triple product $\mathbf{a}\cdot(\mathbf{b} \times \mathbf{c})$ geometrically.

6. Show that

$$\mathbf{a} \times (\mathbf{b} \times \mathbf{c}) = (a_2b_1c_2 - a_2b_2c_1 - a_3b_3c_1 + a_3b_1c_3)\mathbf{i}$$

$$+ (a_3b_2c_3 - a_3b_3c_2 - a_1b_1c_2 + a_1b_2c_1)\mathbf{j}$$

$$+ (a_1b_3c_1 - a_1b_1c_3 - a_2b_2c_3 + a_2b_3c_2)\mathbf{k},$$

where $\mathbf{a} = a_1\mathbf{i} + a_2\mathbf{j} + a_3\mathbf{k}$, etc.

7. Show that

$$\mathbf{a} \times (\mathbf{b} \times \mathbf{c}) = (\mathbf{c} \times \mathbf{b}) \times \mathbf{a}.$$

8. (*a*) Show that the vector triple product $\mathbf{a} \times (\mathbf{b} \times \mathbf{c})$ may be written as

$$\mathbf{a} \times (\mathbf{b} \times \mathbf{c}) = (\mathbf{a}\cdot\mathbf{c})\mathbf{b} - (\mathbf{a}\cdot\mathbf{b})\mathbf{c},$$

whereas

$$(\mathbf{a} \times \mathbf{b}) \times \mathbf{c} = (\mathbf{a}\cdot\mathbf{c})\mathbf{b} - (\mathbf{b}\cdot\mathbf{c})\mathbf{a},$$

so that vector multiplication is in general not associative. (*b*) Show that

$$\mathbf{a} \times (\mathbf{b} \times \mathbf{c}) + \mathbf{b} \times (\mathbf{c} \times \mathbf{a}) + \mathbf{c} \times (\mathbf{a} \times \mathbf{b}) = 0.$$

9. Show that

$$(a \times b) \cdot (c \times d) = \begin{vmatrix} a \cdot c & b \cdot c \\ a \cdot d & b \cdot d \end{vmatrix}.$$

10. Show that

$$(a \times b) \times (c \times d) = [(a \times b) \cdot d]c - [(a \times b) \cdot c]d,$$

and therefore that

$$(a \times b) \times (a \times c) = [(a \times b) \cdot c]a.$$

81. Vector calculus. If, as a scalar variable s varies continuously over some range of values, a vector $\mathbf{v}$ likewise varies continuously in

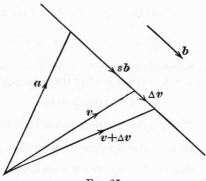

Fig. 65

accordance with a fixed law, the vector $\mathbf{v}$ is said to be a continuous function of the scalar s,

$$\mathbf{v} = \mathbf{v}(s). \tag{1}$$

For example (Fig. 65), the equation of a line passing through the terminal point of a vector $\mathbf{a}$ and parallel to a vector $\mathbf{b}$ may be written in the form

$$\mathbf{v} = \mathbf{a} + s\mathbf{b},$$

where s is a scalar variable and $\mathbf{v}$ is the variable vector drawn from the initial point of $\mathbf{a}$ to any point on the line.

Let the variable s be given an increment Δs, and let $\Delta \mathbf{v}$ be the corresponding vector change in $\mathbf{v}$, so that

$$\Delta \mathbf{v} = \mathbf{v}(s + \Delta s) - \mathbf{v}(s).$$

Then the derivative of the vector $\mathbf{v}$ with respect to the scalar variable s is defined to be, as in scalar calculus,

$$\frac{d\mathbf{v}}{ds} = \lim_{\Delta s \to 0} \frac{\Delta \mathbf{v}}{\Delta s} = \lim_{\Delta s \to 0} \frac{\mathbf{v}(s + \Delta s) - \mathbf{v}(s)}{\Delta s}, \tag{2}$$

provided this limit exists.* Thus, for the vector function $\mathbf{v} = \mathbf{a} + s\mathbf{b}$, we have, since $\mathbf{a}$ and $\mathbf{b}$ are constant vectors,

$$\frac{d\mathbf{v}}{ds} = \lim_{\Delta s \to 0} \frac{\mathbf{a} + (s + \Delta s)\mathbf{b} - \mathbf{a} - s\mathbf{b}}{\Delta s} = \mathbf{b}.$$

From the definition (2), it is easy to show that those formulas of scalar calculus which have meaningful analogs in vector calculus carry over unchanged in form. For example, if $u(s)$ is a scalar function of s, and $\mathbf{v}(s)$ and $\mathbf{w}(s)$ are vector functions of s, then we have

$$\frac{d}{ds}(u\mathbf{v}) = u\frac{d\mathbf{v}}{ds} + \frac{du}{ds}\mathbf{v},$$

$$\frac{d}{ds}(\mathbf{v}\cdot\mathbf{w}) = \mathbf{v}\cdot\frac{d\mathbf{w}}{ds} + \frac{d\mathbf{v}}{ds}\cdot\mathbf{w}, \tag{3}$$

$$\frac{d}{ds}(\mathbf{v}\times\mathbf{w}) = \mathbf{v}\times\frac{d\mathbf{w}}{ds} + \frac{d\mathbf{v}}{ds}\times\mathbf{w}.$$

It is merely necessary, as was noted in Art. 80, to preserve the original order of the vectors in dealing with a vector product.

Just as in scalar calculus, vector integration is regarded as the inverse of vector differentiation, so that if $\mathbf{w}(s)$ is any vector function whose derivative with respect to s is $\mathbf{v}(s)$, the indefinite integral of $\mathbf{v}(s)$ is given by

$$\int \mathbf{v}(s)\,ds = \mathbf{w}(s) + \mathbf{c}, \tag{4}$$

where $\mathbf{c}$ is an arbitrary vector independent of s, and the definite integral of $\mathbf{v}(s)$ from $s = s_1$ to $s = s_2$ is

$$\int_{s_1}^{s_2} \mathbf{v}(s)\,ds = \mathbf{w}(s_2) - \mathbf{w}(s_1). \tag{5}$$

If a vector $\mathbf{v}$ is a function of two or more scalar variables, partial differentiation is defined in the usual way. For example, if

$$\mathbf{r} = x\mathbf{i} + y\mathbf{j} + z\mathbf{k},$$

we have

$$\frac{\partial \mathbf{r}}{\partial x} = \mathbf{i}, \qquad \frac{\partial \mathbf{r}}{\partial y} = \mathbf{j}, \qquad \frac{\partial \mathbf{r}}{\partial z} = \mathbf{k}.$$

* The existence of all the limits encountered in this chapter will be assumed.

Consider now a scalar function of position, $u = u(x, y, z)$. The differential du of u is (Chapter VII, Art. 66),

$$du = \frac{\partial u}{\partial x} dx + \frac{\partial u}{\partial y} dy + \frac{\partial u}{\partial z} dz. \tag{6}$$

Reference to equation (13) of Art. 80 suggests that the above expression for du may be regarded as the scalar product of two vectors whose components are $\partial u/\partial x$, $\partial u/\partial y$, $\partial u/\partial z$, and dx, dy, dz, respectively. Consequently we have

$$du = \left(\frac{\partial u}{\partial x}\mathbf{i} + \frac{\partial u}{\partial y}\mathbf{j} + \frac{\partial u}{\partial z}\mathbf{k}\right) \cdot (dx\,\mathbf{i} + dy\,\mathbf{j} + dz\,\mathbf{k}). \tag{7}$$

If $\mathbf{r} = x\mathbf{i} + y\mathbf{j} + z\mathbf{k}$, the second vector in (7) evidently represents $d\mathbf{r}$. The first vector in (7) is, as we shall see later, of fundamental importance in field problems, and is denoted by ∇u:

$$\nabla u \equiv \frac{\partial u}{\partial x}\mathbf{i} + \frac{\partial u}{\partial y}\mathbf{j} + \frac{\partial u}{\partial z}\mathbf{k}. \tag{8}$$

The symbol ∇, called "del," * therefore represents a vector differential operator, or symbolic vector,

$$\nabla \equiv \mathbf{i}\frac{\partial}{\partial x} + \mathbf{j}\frac{\partial}{\partial y} + \mathbf{k}\frac{\partial}{\partial z}. \tag{9}$$

If $\mathbf{F} = F_1\mathbf{i} + F_2\mathbf{j} + F_3\mathbf{k}$ is a vector function of position, $\mathbf{F} = \mathbf{F}(x, y, z)$, we have

$$\nabla \cdot \mathbf{F} = \left(\mathbf{i}\frac{\partial}{\partial x} + \mathbf{j}\frac{\partial}{\partial y} + \mathbf{k}\frac{\partial}{\partial z}\right) \cdot (F_1\mathbf{i} + F_2\mathbf{j} + F_3\mathbf{k})$$

$$= \frac{\partial F_1}{\partial x} + \frac{\partial F_2}{\partial y} + \frac{\partial F_3}{\partial z}, \tag{10}$$

and

$$\nabla \times \mathbf{F} = \begin{vmatrix} \mathbf{i} & \mathbf{j} & \mathbf{k} \\ \dfrac{\partial}{\partial x} & \dfrac{\partial}{\partial y} & \dfrac{\partial}{\partial z} \\ F_1 & F_2 & F_3 \end{vmatrix}$$

$$= \left(\frac{\partial F_3}{\partial y} - \frac{\partial F_2}{\partial z}\right)\mathbf{i} + \left(\frac{\partial F_1}{\partial z} - \frac{\partial F_3}{\partial x}\right)\mathbf{j} + \left(\frac{\partial F_2}{\partial x} - \frac{\partial F_1}{\partial y}\right)\mathbf{k}. \tag{11}$$

* Sometimes called "nabla" or "atled."

The vector ∇u is called the *gradient* of u, and is then written grad u; the scalar $\nabla \cdot \mathbf{F}$ is called the *divergence* of $\mathbf{F}$, and written div $\mathbf{F}$; the vector $\nabla \times \mathbf{F}$ is called the *curl* of $\mathbf{F}$, and written curl $\mathbf{F}$. The reasons for these names and the utility of these concepts in the applications of

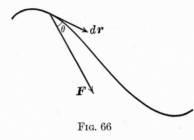

vector analysis to physical problems will be indicated in the following articles.

82. Applications. We are now in a position to consider a few physical problems from the standpoint of vector analysis.

Consider first the motion along a given path of a body acted upon

FIG. 66

by a force. Let the force, which may vary in direction and magnitude, be denoted by the vector $\mathbf{F}$, let $d\mathbf{r}$ be the elementary displacement tangent to the path, and let θ be the variable angle between $\mathbf{F}$ and $d\mathbf{r}$ (Fig. 66). Then the work done by $\mathbf{F}$ in producing the displacement $d\mathbf{r}$ is, approximately,

$$\Delta W = F \, dr \cos \theta.$$

But by definition of the scalar product of two vectors, $F \, dr \cos \theta = \mathbf{F} \cdot d\mathbf{r}$. Hence the work done in moving the body from A to B along the path is given by the line integral

$$W = \int_A^B \mathbf{F} \cdot d\mathbf{r}. \tag{1}$$

As a second illustration of the use of vector notation in mechanics, consider the moment M of a vector force $\mathbf{F}$ about a point O, defined as the product of the magnitude F of the force and the perpendicular distance of the line of action of $\mathbf{F}$ from O. If $\mathbf{r}$ is the vector from O to the point of application of $\mathbf{F}$, and θ is the angle between the directions of $\mathbf{r}$ and $\mathbf{F}$, we have (Fig. 67)

$$M = Fr \sin \theta.$$

This suggests either the vector product $\mathbf{r} \times \mathbf{F}$ or the vector product $\mathbf{F} \times \mathbf{r} = -\mathbf{r} \times \mathbf{F}$ as a vector representation of $\mathbf{M}$. Adopting the convention of making a moment positive when it tends to produce rotation in the counterclockwise sense, we see that when the moment is right-handed about a vector perpendicular to the paper and

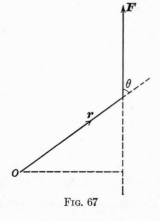

FIG. 67

pointing toward us, as in the figure, a vector pointing in this direction will be a convenient choice. Hence we write

$$\mathbf{M} = \mathbf{r} \times \mathbf{F}. \tag{2}$$

If O is made the origin of the coordinate axes, so that $\mathbf{r} = x\mathbf{i} + y\mathbf{j} + z\mathbf{k}$, then, setting $\mathbf{F} = F_1\mathbf{i} + F_2\mathbf{j} + F_3\mathbf{k}$, we get

$$\mathbf{M} = \mathbf{r} \times \mathbf{F} = \begin{vmatrix} \mathbf{i} & \mathbf{j} & \mathbf{k} \\ x & y & z \\ F_1 & F_2 & F_3 \end{vmatrix}$$

$$= (yF_3 - zF_2)\mathbf{i} + (zF_1 - xF_3)\mathbf{j} + (xF_2 - yF_1)\mathbf{k},$$

whence the components M_x, M_y, M_z of $\mathbf{M}$ are given by

$$M_x = yF_3 - zF_2,$$
$$M_y = zF_1 - xF_3, \tag{3}$$
$$M_z = xF_2 - yF_1,$$

which agree with the usual expressions.

In connection with our next topic, the kinematics of a particle, we require the concept of the curvature of a curve at a point P on it. Let the scalar variable s denote the length of the curve from a reference point R to P, and let $\mathbf{T}$ denote a unit tangent to the curve at P, i.e., a vector of unit length tangent to the curve in the direction of increasing s (Fig. 68). When s is increased by an amount Δs, $\mathbf{T}$ changes, not in

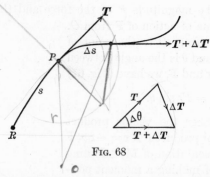

FIG. 68

magnitude but in direction, by an amount $\Delta \mathbf{T}$. For small values of Δs, $\Delta \mathbf{T}$ is approximately equal to the arc of a unit circle with central angle $\Delta \theta$, where $\Delta \theta$ is the angle through which $\mathbf{T}$ turns when s changes by Δs. Hence $\Delta \mathbf{T}/\Delta s$ is approximately equal to $\Delta \theta/\Delta s$ in magnitude, and in the limit as Δs is allowed to approach zero, we have exactly

$$\lim_{\Delta s \to 0} \left| \frac{\Delta \mathbf{T}}{\Delta s} \right| = \left| \frac{d\mathbf{T}}{ds} \right| = \left| \frac{d\theta}{ds} \right|,$$

where the bars indicate the magnitude of the vector or scalar. Since $d\theta/ds$ is by definition the curvature of the curve, we define the vector curvature as

$$\mathbf{K} = \left| \frac{d\mathbf{T}}{ds} \right|. \tag{4}$$

The direction of $\mathbf{K}$ is evidently along the normal at P. Then if $\rho = 1/K$ is the radius of curvature, we have

$$K = \frac{1}{\rho} = \left| \frac{d\mathbf{T}}{ds} \right|. \tag{5}$$

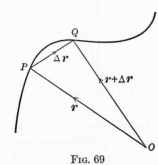

FIG. 69

Now, if at time t, $\mathbf{r}$ is the vector from an origin O to the point P on the path of a particle, we shall have $\mathbf{r}$ a function of time, $\mathbf{r} = \mathbf{r}(t)$. In the time Δt, the particle will have moved from P to Q, say, and its displacement will be roughly equal to $\Delta \mathbf{r}$ (Fig. 69). Consequently the average velocity over the interval Δt is nearly equal to $\Delta \mathbf{r}/\Delta t$, and therefore the instantaneous vector velocity $\mathbf{v}$ at P is

$$\mathbf{v} = v\mathbf{T} = \frac{d\mathbf{r}}{dt}, \tag{6}$$

where v is the speed. The vector acceleration then is

$$\frac{d^2\mathbf{r}}{dt^2} = \frac{d\mathbf{v}}{dt} = \frac{d}{dt}(v\mathbf{T}) = \frac{dv}{dt}\mathbf{T} + v\frac{d\mathbf{T}}{dt}.$$

Now

$$\frac{d\mathbf{T}}{dt} = \frac{d\mathbf{T}}{ds}\frac{ds}{dt} = \mathbf{K}v,$$

so that

$$\frac{d^2\mathbf{r}}{dt^2} = \frac{dv}{dt}\mathbf{T} + v^2\mathbf{K}. \tag{7}$$

Hence we have the familiar result that the vector acceleration of a moving particle is the sum of two vectors, one a tangential component of magnitude dv/dt, the other a radial or normal component of magnitude $v^2K = v^2/\rho$.

We next consider the orbital motion of a particle acted upon by some force of attraction directed toward a fixed center O (Fig. 70). Evidently planetary motion is of this type. If here $\mathbf{r}$ is the vector from the point P of the orbit to the center of attraction, the vector velocity $d\mathbf{r}/dt$ will be directed along the tangent to the orbit, and the vector acceleration $d^2\mathbf{r}/dt^2$ along PO, that is, in the direction of the attractive force. Since the angle between $\mathbf{r}$ and $d^2\mathbf{r}/dt^2$ is zero, we have

$$\frac{d^2\mathbf{r}}{dt^2} \times \mathbf{r} = 0. \tag{8}$$

Now

$$\frac{d}{dt}\left(\frac{d\mathbf{r}}{dt} \times \mathbf{r}\right) = \frac{d\mathbf{r}}{dt} \times \frac{d\mathbf{r}}{dt} + \frac{d^2\mathbf{r}}{dt^2} \times \mathbf{r},$$

and since the vector product of a vector into itself vanishes, (8) may be written

$$\frac{d}{dt}\left(\frac{d\mathbf{r}}{dt} \times \mathbf{r}\right) = 0.$$

Integrating, we get

$$\frac{d\mathbf{r}}{dt} \times \mathbf{r} = \mathbf{c}, \tag{9}$$

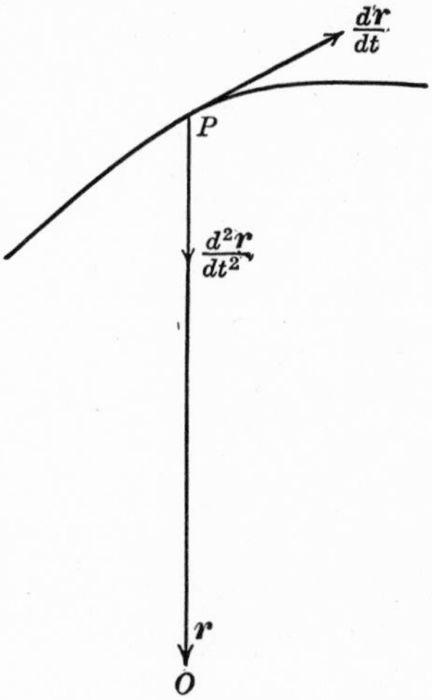

Fig. 70

where $\mathbf{c}$ is a constant vector. Remembering that the magnitude of the cross product of two vectors represents the area of a parallelogram having these two vectors as adjacent sides, we may interpret the left-hand member of (9) as twice the area swept out by the radius vector $\mathbf{r}$ in unit time, so that this quantity, called the areal velocity, is constant for planetary motion.

Consider now the flow of an incompressible liquid in a three-dimensional region. Let $\mathbf{Q}$ denote the quantity (lb.) at a point P of the liquid, flowing in unit time through a unit cross-sectional area perpendicular to the direction of flow, which we take as the direction of $\mathbf{Q}$, and let Q_x, Q_y, Q_z be the components of $\mathbf{Q}$ along the coordinate axes. Consider an elementary volume $\Delta x\, \Delta y\, \Delta z$ of the region, as shown in Fig. 71. Then the quantity flowing into the left-hand face is, approximately,

$$Q_y\, \Delta x\, \Delta z,$$

while that flowing out of the parallel right-hand face is, approximately

$$(Q_y + \Delta Q_y)\, \Delta x\, \Delta z.$$

Hence the approximate net increase of liquid in the parallelepiped due to these two faces is

$$Q_y \, \Delta x \, \Delta z - (Q_y + \Delta Q_y) \, \Delta x \, \Delta z = -\Delta Q_y \, \Delta x \, \Delta z.$$

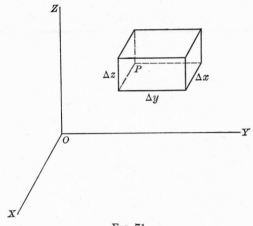

Fig. 71

Similarly, the approximate net increases inside the volume due to the other two sets of parallel faces are

$$-\Delta Q_x \, \Delta y \, \Delta z, \qquad -\Delta Q_z \, \Delta x \, \Delta y,$$

so that the total increase is nearly equal to

$$-\left(\frac{\Delta Q_x}{\Delta x} + \frac{\Delta Q_y}{\Delta y} + \frac{\Delta Q_z}{\Delta z}\right) \Delta x \, \Delta y \, \Delta z.$$

But, for an incompressible liquid, this total increase must be zero, so that, setting the above expression equal to zero, dividing by $-\Delta x \, \Delta y \, \Delta z$, and then passing to the limit as Δx, Δy, and Δz all approach zero, we get

$$\frac{\partial Q_x}{\partial x} + \frac{\partial Q_y}{\partial y} + \frac{\partial Q_z}{\partial z} = 0. \tag{10}$$

This is one form of the so-called equation of continuity. Comparing it with equation (10) of Art. 81, we see that it may be written in the form

$$\operatorname{div} \mathbf{Q} = \nabla \cdot \mathbf{Q} = 0. \tag{11}$$

When the fluid is not incompressible, div $\mathbf{Q}$ will be different from zero, and will indicate the amount by which the inward and outward flow differ. Considerations similar to the above may be made for heat flow and for magnetic or electric flux. For electric flux, a charge within the box will give rise to lines of force which diverge from it; this indicates the reason for the designation divergence for the operation $\nabla\cdot$.

As a final example before proceeding with the development of vector concepts, consider the gradient of a scalar function of position, V,

$$\nabla V \equiv \frac{\partial V}{\partial x}\mathbf{i} + \frac{\partial V}{\partial y}\mathbf{j} + \frac{\partial V}{\partial z}\mathbf{k}.$$

If we operate on both members of this identity with $\nabla\cdot$, i.e., if we take the divergence of the gradient of V, we get

$$\nabla\cdot\nabla V = \left(\mathbf{i}\frac{\partial}{\partial x} + \mathbf{j}\frac{\partial}{\partial y} + \mathbf{k}\frac{\partial}{\partial z}\right)\cdot\left(\frac{\partial V}{\partial x}\mathbf{i} + \frac{\partial V}{\partial y}\mathbf{j} + \frac{\partial V}{\partial z}\mathbf{k}\right)$$

$$= \frac{\partial^2 V}{\partial x^2} + \frac{\partial^2 V}{\partial y^2} + \frac{\partial^2 V}{\partial z^2}. \tag{12}$$

Thus the operator $\nabla\cdot\nabla$, or ∇^2 as it is usually written, is the three-dimensional *Laplacian operator*. The Laplace equation

$$\nabla^2 V = 0 \tag{13}$$

is, as has been noted before, of great importance in mathematical physics, occurring, for example, in the study of three-dimensional steady-state heat flow. We shall have occasion later in this chapter to deal with the scalar operator $\nabla\cdot\nabla = \nabla^2$ in other connections.

PROBLEMS

1. If u is a scalar function of x, y, and z, and $\mathbf{v}$ and $\mathbf{w}$ are vector functions of x, y, z, show that

(a) $\nabla\cdot(u\mathbf{v}) = \nabla u\cdot\mathbf{v} + u\nabla\cdot\mathbf{v}$;

(b) $\nabla\times(u\mathbf{v}) = \nabla u\times\mathbf{v} + u\nabla\times\mathbf{v}$;

(c) $\nabla(\mathbf{v}\cdot\mathbf{w}) = \mathbf{v}\cdot\nabla\mathbf{w} + \mathbf{v}\times(\nabla\times\mathbf{w}) + \mathbf{w}\cdot\nabla\mathbf{v} + \mathbf{w}\times(\nabla\times\mathbf{v})$;

(d) $\nabla\cdot(\mathbf{v}\times\mathbf{w}) = \mathbf{w}\cdot\nabla\times\mathbf{v} - \mathbf{v}\cdot\nabla\times\mathbf{w}$;

(e) $\nabla\times(\mathbf{v}\times\mathbf{w}) = (\nabla\cdot\mathbf{w})\mathbf{v} - (\nabla\cdot\mathbf{v})\mathbf{w} + (\mathbf{w}\cdot\nabla)\mathbf{v} - (\mathbf{v}\cdot\nabla)\mathbf{w}$.

2. If u is a scalar function of position, and $\mathbf{v}$ is a vector function of position, show that

(a) $\nabla\times\nabla u = 0$;

(b) $\nabla\cdot\nabla\times\mathbf{v} = 0$;

(c) $\nabla\times(\nabla\times\mathbf{v}) = \nabla(\nabla\cdot\mathbf{v}) - \nabla^2\mathbf{v}$.

3. If $\mathbf{v} = (x\mathbf{i} + y\mathbf{j} + z\mathbf{k})/\sqrt{x^2 + y^2 + z^2}$, show that

$$\nabla\cdot\mathbf{v} = \frac{2}{\sqrt{x^2 + y^2 + z^2}}, \qquad \nabla\times\mathbf{v} = 0.$$

4. If $r = \sqrt{x^2 + y^2 + z^2}$, and n is a constant, show that

$$\nabla^2 r^n = n(n + 1)r^{n-2},$$

and hence that the function $1/\sqrt{x^2 + y^2 + z^2}$ is a solution of Laplace's equation.

5. If $\mathbf{a}$ is a constant vector, and $r = \sqrt{x^2 + y^2 + z^2}$, show that

$$\mathbf{a} \cdot \nabla \left(\frac{1}{r}\right) = -\frac{1}{r^3} \mathbf{a} \cdot \mathbf{r}.$$

6. If $\mathbf{v}$ is a vector function of x, y, and z, show that

$$\nabla \mathbf{v}^2 = 2(\mathbf{v} \cdot \nabla)\mathbf{v} + 2\mathbf{v} \times (\nabla \times \mathbf{v}).$$

7. Let $\boldsymbol{\omega}$ be the constant angular velocity of rotation of a rigid body about a fixed axis. Taking $\boldsymbol{\omega}$ as a vector along the axis of rotation, its sense being such that rotation in the given direction is right-handed with respect to $\boldsymbol{\omega}$, and letting $\mathbf{r}$ be a vector from a point on the axis to any point P of the body, show that the linear velocity $\mathbf{v}$ of P is given in magnitude and direction by $\mathbf{v} = \boldsymbol{\omega} \times \mathbf{r}$, and that $\boldsymbol{\omega} = \frac{1}{2}\nabla \times \mathbf{v}$. (Cf. expressions (11), Art. 73.)

8. A fluid is flowing across a plane surface with a uniform vector velocity $\mathbf{v}$. If $\mathbf{N}$ is a unit normal to the plane, show that the volume of fluid that passes through a unit area of the plane in unit time is $\mathbf{v} \cdot \mathbf{N}$.

9. Let a ray of light pass from a medium whose index of refraction is n_1 into a medium of index n_2. If $\mathbf{a}$ and $\mathbf{b}$ are unit vectors along the incident and refracted rays respectively, their directions being those of the light rays, and $\mathbf{N}$ is a unit normal to the surface of separation of the two media, show that

$$n_1 \mathbf{N} \times \mathbf{a} = n_2 \mathbf{N} \times \mathbf{b}.$$

10. Consider a particle moving along a plane curve, and let $\mathbf{r}$ be the vector from the origin O of the plane to the position P of the particle at time t, the polar coordinates of P being (r, θ). If $\mathbf{N}$ is a unit vector in the direction of r increasing and $\mathbf{T}$ is a unit vector perpendicular to $\mathbf{r}$ and in the direction of θ increasing, show that

(a) $\dfrac{d\mathbf{r}}{dt} = \dfrac{dr}{dt}\mathbf{N} + r\dfrac{d\theta}{dt}\mathbf{T}$;

(b) $\dfrac{d^2\mathbf{r}}{dt^2} = \left[\dfrac{d^2r}{dt^2} - r\left(\dfrac{d\theta}{dt}\right)^2\right]\mathbf{N} + \left[r\dfrac{d^2\theta}{dt^2} + 2\dfrac{dr}{dt}\dfrac{d\theta}{dt}\right]\mathbf{T}$.

83. Scalar fields; gradient. We have had occasion, in connection with some of the topics already discussed, to deal with a scalar function of position, or scalar point function $u(x, y, z)$. We now wish to examine further this type of function as representing some physical property in a three-dimensional region or field.

When the physical property in question is given by a scalar quantity $u(x, y, z)$, we shall speak of the region throughout which this property is to be investigated as a scalar field. For example, in the study of temperature distribution in a heated body, the region occupied by that body will be a scalar field, since the temperature at any point within it is a scalar point function.

If we set the scalar point function $u(x, y, z)$ (which we assume to be, together with its first partial derivatives, finite, continuous, and single-valued) equal to a constant c, we get the equation of a surface at every point of which u has the same value.   We call the surface

$$u(x, y, z) = c \tag{1}$$

a level surface of the scalar point function u.   Let $\mathbf{r} = x\mathbf{i} + y\mathbf{j} + z\mathbf{k}$ be the vector from the origin O to the point $P(x, y, z)$ on a level surface (1), and let $\mathbf{N}$ be a unit normal to the surface at P in the direction of increasing u (Fig. 72).   If ds denotes the magnitude of the differential vector

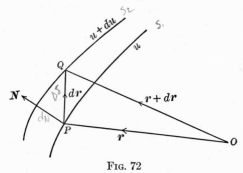

Fig. 72

$d\mathbf{r} = \mathbf{i}\,dx + \mathbf{j}\,dy + \mathbf{k}\,dz$ from P to a point Q on a neighboring level surface, and dN the value of ds when $d\mathbf{r}$ is in particular taken in the direction $\mathbf{N}$, we have

$$dN = \mathbf{N} \cdot d\mathbf{r}, \tag{2}$$

so that the differential du of the function $u(x, y, z)$ will be

$$du = \frac{du}{dN}\,dN = \frac{du}{dN}\,\mathbf{N} \cdot d\mathbf{r}. \tag{3}$$

But we have seen in Art. 81 that du may be written in the form

$$du = \frac{\partial u}{\partial x}\,dx + \frac{\partial u}{\partial y}\,dy + \frac{\partial u}{\partial z}\,dz$$

$$= \left(\mathbf{i}\,\frac{\partial u}{\partial x} + \mathbf{j}\,\frac{\partial u}{\partial y} + \mathbf{k}\,\frac{\partial u}{\partial z}\right) \cdot (\mathbf{i}\,dx + \mathbf{j}\,dy + \mathbf{k}\,dz)$$

$$= \nabla u \cdot d\mathbf{r}.$$

Hence we get

$$\nabla u \cdot d\mathbf{r} = \frac{du}{dN}\,\mathbf{N} \cdot d\mathbf{r}. \tag{4}$$

Since this relation holds for any differential vector $d\mathbf{r}$, it follows that

$$\nabla u = \frac{du}{dN}\,\mathbf{N}. \tag{5}$$

Now the length of path $PQ = ds$ is least along the direction $\mathbf{N}$, i.e., dN is the least value of ds. Consequently the maximum value of du/ds is du/dN. We therefore have the following interpretation of ∇u: *The gradient of u is a vector along a normal to the level surface* $u(x, y, z) = c$ *and in the direction of increasing u, its magnitude being equal to the greatest rate of increase of u.*

The above interpretation of ∇u is of considerable importance in connection with the concept of potential. We shall for definiteness discuss gravitational potential due to matter; similar discussions apply to electric potential due to charges and to magnetic potential due to poles. Let a particle of mass m be situated at the origin O, and let a second particle of unit mass be situated at the point $P(x, y, z)$. If $\mathbf{r} = x\mathbf{i} + y\mathbf{j} + z\mathbf{k}$ is the vector from O to P, the vector force $\mathbf{F}$ which the particle at O exerts on the particle at P is, when the magnitude F of $\mathbf{F}$ is measured in gravitational units,

$$\mathbf{F} = -\frac{m}{r^2}\,\mathbf{r}_1 = -\frac{m}{r^3}\,\mathbf{r}, \tag{6}$$

where $\mathbf{r}_1$ is a unit vector in the direction of $\mathbf{r}$, so that $\mathbf{r} = r\mathbf{r}_1$. We now define the potential at P due to the mass m at O as (cf. Art. 65)

$$u = \frac{m}{r}\,; \tag{7}$$

evidently u is a scalar point function satisfying at every point except the origin O, the conditions imposed at the beginning of this article. Then the gradient of u is

$$\nabla u = m\nabla\left(\frac{1}{r}\right).$$

But $r = (x^2 + y^2 + z^2)^{\frac{1}{2}}$, and consequently

$$\frac{\partial}{\partial x}\left(\frac{1}{r}\right) = -\frac{1}{r^2}\frac{\partial r}{\partial x} = -\frac{x}{r^3},$$

$$\frac{\partial}{\partial y}\left(\frac{1}{r}\right) = -\frac{1}{r^2}\frac{\partial r}{\partial y} = -\frac{y}{r^3},$$

$$\frac{\partial}{\partial z}\left(\frac{1}{r}\right) = -\frac{1}{r^2}\frac{\partial r}{\partial z} = -\frac{z}{r^3},$$

so that

$$\nabla u = -\frac{m}{r^3}(x\mathbf{i} + y\mathbf{j} + z\mathbf{k})$$

$$= -\frac{m}{r^3}\mathbf{r}. \tag{8}$$

Combining (6) and (8), we see that

$$\mathbf{F} = \nabla u = \frac{du}{dN}\mathbf{N}. \tag{9}$$

Thus the force of attraction is directed along the normal to the level (equipotential) surface, and its magnitude is equal to the greatest rate of increase of the potential. From (9) we find also, since $F = du/dN$, that the difference in potentials between two level surfaces is

$$u_2 - u_1 = \int_N F\, dN, \tag{10}$$

where the integration is extended along the path from one level surface to the other, the curve being such as to be normal to all level surfaces intersected. But the right-hand member of (10) also represents the work done * in going from one level surface to the other along the stated path. Moreover, since the potential is constant on a level surface (here a sphere with center O), so that no work is done in moving about on one such surface, it follows that the work done in going from one equipotential to the other by any path is equal to the difference in potential on these surfaces. Since u approaches zero as r becomes infinite, by the definition (7), we infer that the potential at any point P is equal to the work done in bringing the particle from infinity to that point by any path.

We give next an alternative expression, in the form of a surface integral, for the gradient of a scalar point function; we shall make use of this result in our later work. Let P be a point in the scalar field under consideration, let V be a small volume containing the point P and bounded by the closed surface S, and let $\mathbf{N}$ be a unit outward-drawn normal to an element dS of S. We shall now show that

$$\operatorname{grad} u = \lim_{V \to 0} \frac{\iint_S u\mathbf{N}\, dS}{V}, \tag{11}$$

* This work may be done on or by the particle, depending upon the direction of travel; we consider here merely the numerical value of the work done.

where the limit is to be taken as V shrinks down to P. To establish this relation, we shall show that the right-hand member reduces to the expression previously given for ∇u. In the first place, we may write

$$\mathbf{N} = (\mathbf{N}\cdot\mathbf{i})\mathbf{i} + (\mathbf{N}\cdot\mathbf{j})\mathbf{j} + (\mathbf{N}\cdot\mathbf{k})\mathbf{k}, \tag{12}$$

so that the right member of (11), which we denote for brevity by $\mathbf{A}$, becomes

$$\mathbf{A} = \mathbf{i}\lim_{V\to 0}\frac{\iint_S u(\mathbf{N}\cdot\mathbf{i})\,dS}{V} + \mathbf{j}\lim_{V\to 0]}\frac{\iint_S u(\mathbf{N}\cdot\mathbf{j})\,dS}{V}$$

$$+ \mathbf{k}\lim_{V\to 0}\frac{\iint_S u(\mathbf{N}\cdot\mathbf{k})\,dS}{V}. \tag{13}$$

Now let dS_1 and dS_2 denote the elements of area cut from the surface S by an elementary cylinder parallel to the x-axis as shown in Fig. 73, let

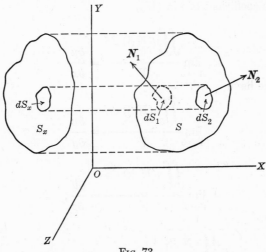

FIG. 73

dS_x be the common projection of dS_1 and dS_2 on the yz-plane, and let S_x be the projection of S on the yz-plane. Then if $\mathbf{N}_1$ and $\mathbf{N}_2$ are the unit normals to dS_1 and dS_2, respectively, we have

$$dS_x = -(\mathbf{N}_1\cdot\mathbf{i})\,dS_1 = (\mathbf{N}_2\cdot\mathbf{i})\,dS_2.$$

Letting u_1 and u_2 denote the values of u on dS_1 and dS_2, respectively, we then get

$$\iint_S u(\mathbf{N} \cdot \mathbf{i}) \, dS = \iint_{S_2} u_2(\mathbf{N}_2 \cdot \mathbf{i}) \, dS_2 + \iint_{S_1} u_1(\mathbf{N}_1 \cdot \mathbf{i}) \, dS_1$$

$$= \iint_{S_x} (u_2 - u_1) \, dS_x.$$

Now let $\Delta u = u_2 - u_1$, and let Δx be the length of the elementary cylinder between dS_1 and dS_2, so that

$$\frac{\iint_S u(\mathbf{N} \cdot \mathbf{i}) \, dS}{V} = \frac{\iint_{S_x} \dfrac{\Delta u}{\Delta x} \Delta x \, dS_x}{V}$$

$$= \left(\frac{\Delta u}{\Delta x}\right)_1,$$

where $(\Delta u/\Delta x)_1$ is the average value of $\Delta u/\Delta x$ over the volume V. If, now, we allow V to shrink down to P, so that Δx approaches zero, $(\Delta u/\Delta x)_1$ will approach the value of $\partial u/\partial x$ at P. Consequently we have for the coefficient of $\mathbf{i}$ in (13),

$$\lim_{V \to 0} \frac{\iint_S u(\mathbf{N} \cdot \mathbf{i}) \, dS}{V} = \frac{\partial u}{\partial x}. \tag{14}$$

Similarly, we have

$$\lim_{V \to 0} \frac{\iint_S u(\mathbf{N} \cdot \mathbf{j}) \, dS}{V} = \frac{\partial u}{\partial y},$$

$$\lim_{V \to 0} \frac{\iint_S u(\mathbf{N} \cdot \mathbf{k}) \, dS}{V} = \frac{\partial u}{\partial z},$$

and therefore

$$\mathbf{A} = \lim_{V \to 0} \frac{\iint_S u\mathbf{N} \, dS}{V} = \mathbf{i}\frac{\partial u}{\partial x} + \mathbf{j}\frac{\partial u}{\partial y} + \mathbf{k}\frac{\partial u}{\partial z} = \nabla u,$$

the desired result.

84. Vector fields; divergence and curl. In the preceding article, we defined a scalar field associated with some physical property which was given by a scalar point function. If, on the other hand, the physical property to be investigated in some region is specified by a vector point function $\mathbf{v}(x, y, z)$, we speak of the region involved as a vector field.

Just as the gradient of a scalar point function plays a large part in scalar field problems, so the divergence and curl of a vector point function enter into various vector field problems. Accordingly, we shall consider the scalar $\nabla \cdot \mathbf{v}$ and the vector $\nabla \times \mathbf{v}$ more in detail in the present article. *

We first establish an alternative expression for the divergence $\nabla \cdot \mathbf{v}$, similar in form to the expression for the gradient ∇u discussed above. The relation to be obtained is

$$\operatorname{div} \mathbf{v} = \lim_{V \to 0} \frac{\iint_S \mathbf{N} \cdot \mathbf{v} \, dS}{V}, \tag{1}$$

where the symbols in the right-hand member have the same meaning as before. If v_1, v_2, v_3 are the components of $\mathbf{v}$, so that $\mathbf{v} = v_1 \mathbf{i} + v_2 \mathbf{j} + v_3 \mathbf{k}$, we have

$$\mathbf{N} \cdot \mathbf{v} = v_1 (\mathbf{N} \cdot \mathbf{i}) + v_2 (\mathbf{N} \cdot \mathbf{j}) + v_3 (\mathbf{N} \cdot \mathbf{k}).$$

Hence the limit on the right side of (1) may be expressed as the sum of three limits, the first of which is

$$\lim_{V \to 0} \frac{\iint_S v_1 (\mathbf{N} \cdot \mathbf{i}) \, dS}{V}.$$

But this is similar to the left-hand member of equation (14), Art. 83, the scalar point function u merely being replaced by the scalar point function v_1. Therefore the first of the three limits whose sum is desired, is $\partial v_1 / \partial x$, and, similarly, the other two are $\partial v_2 / \partial y$ and $\partial v_3 / \partial z$. Consequently we have immediately

$$\lim_{V \to 0} \frac{\iint_S \mathbf{N} \cdot \mathbf{v} \, dS}{V} = \frac{\partial v_1}{\partial x} + \frac{\partial v_2}{\partial y} + \frac{\partial v_3}{\partial z} = \nabla \cdot \mathbf{v},$$

which proves the truth of equation (1).

We may show equally readily that

$$\operatorname{curl} \mathbf{v} = \lim_{V \to 0} \frac{\iint_S \mathbf{N} \times \mathbf{v} \, dS}{V}. \tag{2}$$

---

* The components v_1, v_2, v_3 of v are assumed to satisfy the same conditions imposed on u in Art. 83.

To begin with, we write (cf. equation (12), Art. 83),

$$\mathbf{N} \times \mathbf{v} = \mathbf{i}[\mathbf{i} \cdot (\mathbf{N} \times \mathbf{v})] + \mathbf{j}[\mathbf{j} \cdot (\mathbf{N} \times \mathbf{v})] + \mathbf{k}[\mathbf{k} \cdot (\mathbf{N} \times \mathbf{v})].$$

But for any three vectors $\mathbf{a}$, $\mathbf{b}$, $\mathbf{c}$, we have $\mathbf{a} \cdot (\mathbf{b} \times \mathbf{c}) = \mathbf{b} \cdot (\mathbf{c} \times \mathbf{a})$ (see Problem 5 following Art. 80), so that

$$\mathbf{N} \times \mathbf{v} = \mathbf{i}[\mathbf{N} \cdot (\mathbf{v} \times \mathbf{i})] + \mathbf{j}[\mathbf{N} \cdot (\mathbf{v} \times \mathbf{j})] + \mathbf{k}[\mathbf{N} \cdot (\mathbf{v} \times \mathbf{k})].$$

Consequently the right-hand member of (2) is a vector whose x-component is

$$\lim_{V \to 0} \frac{\iint_S \mathbf{N} \cdot (\mathbf{v} \times \mathbf{i}) \, dS}{V},$$

which, by equation (1), is equal to div $(\mathbf{v} \times \mathbf{i})$. Likewise, we see that the y- and z-components are, respectively, div $(\mathbf{v} \times \mathbf{j})$ and div $(\mathbf{v} \times \mathbf{k})$. But by the definition of divergence, we have

$$\text{div } (\mathbf{v} \times \mathbf{i}) = \nabla \cdot (v_3 \mathbf{j} - v_2 \mathbf{k}) = \frac{\partial v_3}{\partial y} - \frac{\partial v_2}{\partial z},$$

$$\text{div } (\mathbf{v} \times \mathbf{j}) = \nabla \cdot (v_1 \mathbf{k} - v_3 \mathbf{i}) = \frac{\partial v_1}{\partial z} - \frac{\partial v_3}{\partial x},$$

$$\text{div } (\mathbf{v} \times \mathbf{k}) = \nabla \cdot (v_2 \mathbf{i} - v_1 \mathbf{j}) = \frac{\partial v_2}{\partial x} - \frac{\partial v_1}{\partial y},$$

whence

$$\lim_{V \to 0} \frac{\iint_S \mathbf{N} \times \mathbf{v} \, dS}{V} = \mathbf{i} \left(\frac{\partial v_3}{\partial y} - \frac{\partial v_2}{\partial z} \right) + \mathbf{j} \left(\frac{\partial v_1}{\partial z} - \frac{\partial v_3}{\partial x} \right) + \mathbf{k} \left(\frac{\partial v_2}{\partial x} - \frac{\partial v_1}{\partial y} \right)$$

$$= \nabla \times \mathbf{v},$$

and equation (2) follows.

We now proceed to consider a particular relation between a surface integral and a volume integral, known as the divergence theorem, which has a number of uses in further theory and applications. Let $\mathbf{v}$ be a vector point function, and let the associated vector field be a volume V enclosed by a surface S. Then if $\mathbf{N}$ is an outward-drawn unit normal to the element of surface area dS, the **divergence theorem** states that

$$\iiint_V \text{div } \mathbf{v} \, dV = \iint_S \mathbf{N} \cdot \mathbf{v} \, dS. \tag{3}$$

To prove this relation, suppose V to be subdivided, say by planes parallel to the coordinate axes, into small elements or cells. The surface integral in (3) may be replaced by the summation of the surface integrals taken over the aggregate of surfaces of these individual cells, for any surface common to two cells (Fig. 74) will be integrated over twice, the direction of N for one case being opposite to that for the

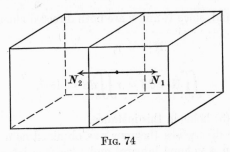

FIG. 74

other, so that $\mathbf{N}_2 \cdot \mathbf{v} = -\mathbf{N}_1 \cdot \mathbf{v}$ and cancellation results from the two integrations. Letting ΔS denote the surface of a typical small cell, we then have

$$\Sigma \iint_{\Delta S} \mathbf{N} \cdot \mathbf{v} \, d(\Delta S) = \iint_S \mathbf{N} \cdot \mathbf{v} \, dS, \tag{4}$$

where the symbol Σ denotes summation over all the cell surfaces. Now if ΔV is the cell volume enclosed by ΔS, the average value of div $\mathbf{v}$ over a cell will be, by equation (1), approximated by the expression

$$\frac{1}{\Delta V} \iint_{\Delta S} \mathbf{N} \cdot \mathbf{v} \, d(\Delta S),$$

and therefore the summation of the divergence over V will be approximately given by

$$\Sigma \, \text{div } \mathbf{v} \, \Delta V \doteq \Sigma \iint_{\Delta S} \mathbf{N} \cdot \mathbf{v} \, d(\Delta S)$$

$$= \iint_S \mathbf{N} \cdot \mathbf{v} \, dS,$$

by equation (4). Allowing the number of cells to become infinite and each ΔV to approach zero, we get in the limit the divergence theorem (3).

As a simple verification of equation (3) for a particular case, let V be a sphere of radius r and with center at the origin O, and let

$$\mathbf{v} = x\mathbf{i} + y\mathbf{j} + z\mathbf{k}.$$

Then

$$\text{div } \mathbf{v} = \left(\mathbf{i}\frac{\partial}{\partial x} + \mathbf{j}\frac{\partial}{\partial y} + \mathbf{k}\frac{\partial}{\partial z}\right) \cdot (x\mathbf{i} + y\mathbf{j} + z\mathbf{k}) = 1 + 1 + 1 = 3,$$

and

$$\iiint_V \text{div } \mathbf{v}\, dV = 3\iiint_V dV = 4\pi r^3.$$

On the other hand, since $\mathbf{N}$ and $\mathbf{v}$ are both directed along the radius of the sphere,

$$\mathbf{N} \cdot \mathbf{v} = r,$$

and

$$\iint_S \mathbf{N} \cdot \mathbf{v}\, dS = r\iint_S dS = 4\pi r^3.$$

Thus equation (3) holds in this instance.

Although the divergence theorem was obtained as a mathematical relation between a volume integral and a surface integral, it has an important physical bearing as well. Regarding $\mathbf{v}$ as a vector representation of a flux, e.g., electric or magnetic flux, heat flow, or fluid velocity, we may state the divergence theorem in words as follows: In a vector field the summation of the normal component of flux over a closed surface S is equal to the summation of the divergence over the volume V enclosed by S, each being a measure of the excess of outward flux over the inward flux.

85. Theorems of Stokes, Gauss, and Green. As a preliminary to the derivation of Stokes's theorem, we first obtain the following lemma. *Let $\mathbf{v}$ be a vector point function, let ΔS be a small element of surface area bounded by a closed curve c, let $\mathbf{T}$ be a unit tangent to c, in an arbitrarily chosen positive direction, and let $\mathbf{N}$ be a unit normal to ΔS in the direction related to the positive direction around c as the thrust and twist of a screw with right-handed thread;* then approximately,

$$(\mathbf{N} \cdot \text{curl } \mathbf{v})\,\Delta S \doteq \int_c \mathbf{v} \cdot \mathbf{T}\, ds, \quad (1)$$

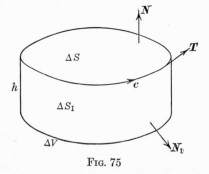

FIG. 75

the approximation being better the smaller and more nearly plane ΔS is taken.

Supposing ΔS to be so small that it is sensibly plane, construct a right cylinder of height h and having ΔS as its upper base (Fig. 75). Let $\Delta V = h\,\Delta S$ denote the volume of this small cylinder, and let $\mathbf{N}_1$ be a unit normal to the lateral surface ΔS_1 of the cylinder. Consider now the surface integral of the scalar function $\mathbf{N} \cdot (\mathbf{N}_1 \times \mathbf{v})$ taken over the total surface of the cylinder. Since the unit normal to the lower base is $-\mathbf{N}$, the upper and lower bases will together contribute nothing to the surface integral, which therefore reduces to

$$\iint_{\Delta S_1} \mathbf{N} \cdot (\mathbf{N}_1 \times \mathbf{v}) \, d(\Delta S_1).$$

Now $\mathbf{N} \cdot (\mathbf{N}_1 \times \mathbf{v}) = \mathbf{v} \cdot (\mathbf{N} \times \mathbf{N}_1)$ (see Problem 5 following Art. 80), and since ΔS_1 is of constant height h, the above integral may be written

$$\int_c \mathbf{v} \cdot (\mathbf{N} \times \mathbf{N}_1) h \, ds.$$

Moreover, $\mathbf{N} \times \mathbf{N}_1 = \mathbf{T}$, and consequently the surface integral over the cylinder becomes

$$\iint_{\Delta S_1} \mathbf{N} \cdot (\mathbf{N}_1 \times \mathbf{v}) \, d(\Delta S_1) = h \int_c \mathbf{v} \cdot \mathbf{T} \, ds. \tag{2}$$

But from equation (2) of Art. 84, we also have the approximation

$$(\mathbf{N} \cdot \operatorname{curl} \mathbf{v}) h \, \Delta S \doteq \iint_{\Delta S_1} \mathbf{N} \cdot (\mathbf{N}_1 \times \mathbf{v}) \, d(\Delta S_1). \tag{3}$$

Combining (2) and (3), we get (1).

Using (1), we may now easily prove **Stokes's theorem,** which may be stated as follows. *Let S be any open surface bounded by a closed curve C with unit tangent* $\mathbf{T}$, *let* $\mathbf{v}$ *be a vector point function, and let* $\mathbf{N}$ *be a positively directed normal to S; then*

$$\iint_S \mathbf{N} \cdot \operatorname{curl} \mathbf{v} \, dS = \int_C \mathbf{v} \cdot \mathbf{T} \, ds. \tag{4}$$

To prove this relation between a surface integral and a contour integral

Fig. 76

suppose S subdivided into small elements of surface ΔS. Then the line integral in (4) may be replaced by the sum of the line integrals around the boundaries of all the subdivisions, an arc common to two elements being traced twice in opposite directions and therefore contributing nothing (Fig. 76). Consequently we have

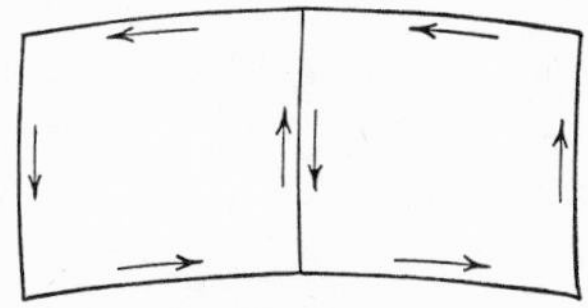

$$\int_C \mathbf{v} \cdot \mathbf{T} \, ds = \Sigma \int_c \mathbf{v} \cdot \mathbf{T} \, ds,$$

where c is the boundary of a typical element and Σ again signifies the summation of all such integrals.   But from equation (1) we get

so that

$$\Sigma(\mathbf{N}\cdot\operatorname{curl}\mathbf{v})\,\Delta S \doteq \Sigma\int_c\mathbf{v}\cdot\mathbf{T}\,ds,$$

$$\Sigma(\mathbf{N}\cdot\operatorname{curl}\mathbf{v})\,\Delta S \doteq \int_C\mathbf{v}\cdot\mathbf{T}\,ds.$$

Passing to the limit as the number of subdivisions becomes infinite and each ΔS approaches zero, we get (4).

Another important theorem is that known as Gauss's, which may be obtained from the divergence theorem of Art. 84,

$$\iiint_V\operatorname{div}\mathbf{v}\,dV = \iint_S\mathbf{N}\cdot\mathbf{v}\,dS,$$

where S is a closed surface enclosing a volume V.   Let $\mathbf{r} = x\mathbf{i} + y\mathbf{j} + z\mathbf{k}$ be the vector from the origin O to any point $P(x, y, z)$, and let $\mathbf{r}_1$ be the unit vector in the direction of $\mathbf{r}$, i.e., from O toward P, so that $\mathbf{r} = r\mathbf{r}_1$. Take as the vector point function $\mathbf{v}$ the vector *

$$\mathbf{v} = -\nabla\frac{1}{r} = \frac{\mathbf{r}_1}{r^2} = \frac{\mathbf{r}}{r^3},$$

so that

$$\iint_S\mathbf{N}\cdot\mathbf{v}\,dS = \iint_S\frac{\mathbf{N}\cdot\mathbf{r}_1}{r^2}\,dS. \tag{5}$$

Also, since

$$\frac{\mathbf{r}}{r^3} = \frac{x\mathbf{i} + y\mathbf{j} + z\mathbf{k}}{r^3},$$

we have

$$\operatorname{div}\frac{\mathbf{r}}{r^3} = \frac{\partial}{\partial x}\left(\frac{x}{r^3}\right) + \frac{\partial}{\partial y}\left(\frac{y}{r^3}\right) + \frac{\partial}{\partial z}\left(\frac{z}{r^3}\right).$$

Now

$$\frac{\partial}{\partial x}\left(\frac{x}{r^3}\right) = \frac{\partial}{\partial x}\left[\frac{x}{(x^2 + y^2 + z^2)^{3/2}}\right] = \frac{y^2 + z^2 - 2x^2}{(x^2 + y^2 + z^2)^{5/2}},$$

$$\frac{\partial}{\partial y}\left(\frac{y}{r^3}\right) = \frac{x^2 + z^2 - 2y^2}{(x^2 + y^2 + z^2)^{5/2}},$$

$$\frac{\partial}{\partial z}\left(\frac{z}{r^3}\right) = \frac{x^2 + y^2 - 2z^2}{(x^2 + y^2 + z^2)^{5/2}},$$

* Cf. Art. 83, where we had $u = m/r$, $\nabla u = -m\mathbf{r}/r^3$.

whence
$$\operatorname{div} \frac{\mathbf{r}}{r^3} = 0, \tag{6}$$

and therefore, from (5) and (6) combined by the divergence theorem,

$$\iint_S \frac{\mathbf{N} \cdot \mathbf{r}_1}{r^2}\, dS = 0. \tag{7}$$

Apparently this is our full result. But let us examine matters a little more critically. We have, in all the foregoing work, confined our attention to formal manipulation, and have given little or no regard to such points as continuity and differentiability in connection with the functions treated. However, although some of our manipulations and limit-taking processes require a more careful study and certain refinements to put them on a firm foundation, fortunately the results obtained are valid and complete for all functions to which they apply in suitable regions of space. Here we see that our result (7) is correct only if the origin O is outside the surface S, so that we do not as yet know the complete story. For, if O is inside S, the function $1/r$, the gradient of which is the negative of our vector point function $\mathbf{v}$, becomes infinite at a point (namely O) of V, and consequently the volume integral of div $\mathbf{v}$ cannot be obtained. Hence we should write our result

$$\iint_S \frac{\mathbf{N} \cdot \mathbf{r}_1}{r^2}\, dS = 0 \ (O \text{ outside } S). \tag{7_1}$$

Now consider the case in which O is within S. We describe about O as center a small sphere S_1 lying entirely inside S and of radius ϵ, and

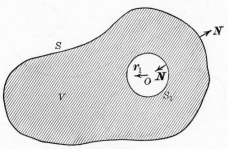

Fig. 77

take as V the volume between S_1 and S (Fig. 77). Then div $\mathbf{v}$ exists in this region, and (7_1) may be applied to the complete boundary, so that we have

$$\iint_S \frac{\mathbf{N} \cdot \mathbf{r}_1}{r^2}\, dS + \iint_{S_1} \frac{\mathbf{N} \cdot \mathbf{r}_1}{r^2}\, dS_1 = 0.$$

Note that since the unit normal $\mathbf{N}$ is to be directed outwardly from V, it must be drawn toward O on the surface S_1. Consequently $\mathbf{N} \cdot \mathbf{r}_1 = -1$ in the second integral, and since $r = \epsilon$ for points on S_1, we get

$$\iint_{S_1} \frac{\mathbf{N} \cdot \mathbf{r}_1}{r^2} dS_1 = -\frac{1}{\epsilon^2} \iint_{S_1} dS_1 = -4\pi,$$

and

$$\iint_{S} \frac{\mathbf{N} \cdot \mathbf{r}_1}{r^2} dS = 4\pi.$$

Allowing ϵ to approach zero, we then have for the volume enclosed by S with merely the point O deleted,

$$\iint_{S} \frac{\mathbf{N} \cdot \mathbf{r}_1}{r^2} dS = 4\pi \ (O \text{ inside } S). \tag{7_2}$$

Relations (7_1) and (7_2) together comprise **Gauss's theorem:**

$$\iint_{S} \frac{\mathbf{N} \cdot \mathbf{r}_1}{r^2} dS = \begin{cases} 0, & O \text{ outside } S, \\ 4\pi, & O \text{ inside } S. \end{cases} \tag{8}$$

Gauss's theorem may be interpreted physically in a simple manner. Consider, for example, the vector field of force surrounding a point O at

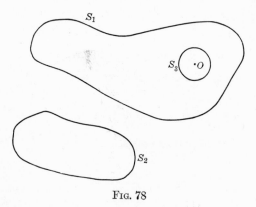

FIG. 78

which is placed an electric charge Q (coulombs). The electric force or field intensity F at any point P will, by Coulomb's law, vary in magnitude inversely as the square of the distance r from O to P. Let S_1 be a closed surface to which O is interior and let S_2 be a second closed surface to which O is exterior (Fig. 78). Describe about O a sphere

S_3 with radius R_1, lying entirely within S_1. Since the flux crossing the sphere S_3 will be equal to that crossing S_1, we have

$$\iint_{S_1} \frac{\mathbf{N} \cdot \mathbf{r}_1}{r^2} \, dS_1 = \iint_{S_3} \frac{\mathbf{r}_1 \cdot \mathbf{r}_1}{R_1^2} \, dS_3 = \frac{1}{R_1^2} \iint_{S_3} dS_3 = 4\pi.$$

On the other hand, any flux entering S_2 will also leave it so that

$$\iint_{S_2} \frac{\mathbf{N} \cdot \mathbf{r}_1}{r^2} \, dS_2 = 0.$$

Since O is inside S_1 but outside S_2, we have here the two cases of Gauss's theorem.

We proceed now to the derivation of **Green's theorem,** which also springs readily from the divergence theorem. Let u and w be two scalar point functions which, together with their first partial derivatives, are continuous and single-valued over a volume V enclosed by a surface S. We first take

$$\mathbf{v} = u \, \nabla w = \mathbf{i} u \frac{\partial w}{\partial x} + \mathbf{j} u \frac{\partial w}{\partial y} + \mathbf{k} u \frac{\partial w}{\partial z},$$

so that

$$\mathbf{N} \cdot \mathbf{v} = u \mathbf{N} \cdot \nabla w,$$

$$\operatorname{div} \mathbf{v} = \frac{\partial}{\partial x}\left(u \frac{\partial w}{\partial x}\right) + \frac{\partial}{\partial y}\left(u \frac{\partial w}{\partial y}\right) + \frac{\partial}{\partial z}\left(u \frac{\partial w}{\partial z}\right)$$

$$= u\left(\frac{\partial^2 w}{\partial x^2} + \frac{\partial^2 w}{\partial y^2} + \frac{\partial^2 w}{\partial z^2}\right) + \frac{\partial u}{\partial x}\frac{\partial w}{\partial x} + \frac{\partial u}{\partial y}\frac{\partial w}{\partial y} + \frac{\partial u}{\partial z}\frac{\partial w}{\partial z}$$

$$= u \, \nabla^2 w + \nabla u \cdot \nabla w.$$

Hence, substituting in the divergence theorem, we get

$$\iiint_V (u \, \nabla^2 w + \nabla u \cdot \nabla w) \, dV = \iint_S u \mathbf{N} \cdot \nabla w \, dS. \tag{9}$$

This is Green's theorem in the first form. Now if we interchange the roles played by u and w in $\mathbf{v}$, we have similarly

$$\iiint_V (w \, \nabla^2 u + \nabla w \cdot \nabla u) \, dV = \iint_S w \mathbf{N} \cdot \nabla u \, dS. \tag{10}$$

Subtracting (10) from (9), we find

$$\iiint_V (u \, \nabla^2 w - w \, \nabla^2 u) \, dV = \iint_S \mathbf{N} \cdot (u \, \nabla w - w \, \nabla u) \, dS, \tag{11}$$

which is Green's theorem in the second form.

86. Further applications. In Art. 82 we considered a few simple examples of the use of vector analysis in physical investigations, these examples being based upon the results obtained in Arts. 80–81. Employing also the material of Arts. 83–85, we may now discuss further applications.

We begin by making use of the divergence theorem in the derivation of the partial differential equation of three-dimensional heat flow.* Since the rate of heat flow across unit area is in the direction of decreasing temperature and is proportional in magnitude to the temperature gradient, we have

$$\frac{\partial \mathbf{Q}}{\partial t} = -K \frac{\partial u}{\partial N} \mathbf{N} = -K \nabla u, \tag{1}$$

by equation (5), Art. 83; here $\partial Q/\partial t$ is measured in calories per second, u is the temperature in degrees centigrade, $\mathbf{N}$ is a unit normal in the direction of flow, and K is the thermal conductivity (cal./cm. deg. sec.). Now if ρ is the specific gravity and c is the specific heat (cal./gr. deg.), the amount of heat which leaves an elementary volume dV in 1 sec. will be, nearly,

$$-c\rho \frac{\partial u}{\partial t} dV,$$

and the total loss of heat per second throughout the volume V is

$$-\iiint_V c\rho \frac{\partial u}{\partial t} dV. \tag{2}$$

Letting S be the surface bounding V, the total amount of heat leaving V in 1 sec. may also be written as

$$\iint_S \mathbf{N} \cdot \frac{\partial \mathbf{Q}}{\partial t} dS = -K \iint_S \mathbf{N} \cdot \nabla u \, dS,$$

by equation (1). Applying the divergence theorem, with $\mathbf{v} = \nabla u$, we therefore have

$$\iint_S \mathbf{N} \cdot \frac{\partial \mathbf{Q}}{\partial t} dS = -K \iiint_V \operatorname{div} \nabla u \, dV. \tag{3}$$

Combining (2) and (3), and remembering that $\operatorname{div} \nabla u = \nabla \cdot \nabla u = \nabla^2 u$, we get

$$\iiint_V \left(c\rho \frac{\partial u}{\partial t} - K \nabla^2 u \right) dV = 0. \tag{4}$$

* Cf. Chapter VII, Arts. 71–72.

But if this relation is to hold for any volume V, the integrand must itself vanish. For, if the integrand were, say, positive throughout any region, however small, V could be chosen as this region, whence the volume integral would also be positive, contrary to (4). Hence we have the equation

$$\frac{\partial u}{\partial t} = \alpha^2 \, \nabla^2 u = \alpha^2 \left(\frac{\partial^2 u}{\partial x^2} + \frac{\partial^2 u}{\partial y^2} + \frac{\partial^2 u}{\partial z^2}\right), \qquad (5)$$

where $\alpha^2 = K/c\rho$. If the flow is one- or two-dimensional, equation (5) reduces to one of the equations obtained in Chapter VII.

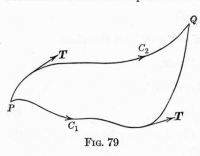

Fig. 79

We next consider the motion of a particle acted upon by a conservative force, which is defined as a force such that the work done in moving a particle from one point to another is independent of the path followed by the particle. Let the vector $\mathbf{F}$ represent a conservative force, let P and Q be any two points in the vector field, and let C_1 and C_2 be any two curves connecting P and Q (Fig. 79). Then the work done in carrying the particle along C_1 and along C_2 will be the same, i.e.,

$$\int_{C_1} \mathbf{F} \cdot \mathbf{T} \, ds = \int_{C_2} \mathbf{F} \cdot \mathbf{T} \, ds,$$

where $\mathbf{T}$ is a unit tangent to either curve. If C denotes the complete circuit from P to Q along C_1 in the positive direction and then back to P along C_2 described in the negative direction, we then have

$$\int_C \mathbf{F} \cdot \mathbf{T} \, ds = 0. \qquad (6)$$

From Stokes's theorem it therefore follows that

$$\iint_S \mathbf{N} \cdot \text{curl } \mathbf{F} \, dS = 0, \qquad (7)$$

where S is any open surface bounded by C. Since C is any curve in the vector field, we conclude that

$$\text{curl } \mathbf{F} = 0$$

everywhere in the field. Conversely, if the curl of any vector force $\mathbf{F}$ is identically zero in a vector field, so that (7) holds, we get by Stokes's theorem the relation (6), and therefore the force is a conservative one.

Hence a force is conservative if and only if its curl vanishes identically. Moreover, when $\mathbf{F}$ is conservative, the work done in moving the particle from the origin O to any other point $P(x, y, z)$ will be dependent only upon the position of P, so that we may write

$$\int_O^P \mathbf{F} \cdot \mathbf{T} \, ds = u(x, y, z), \tag{8}$$

where u is a scalar point function. Consequently, letting $d\mathbf{r} = \mathbf{T} \, ds$, where $\mathbf{r} = x\mathbf{i} + y\mathbf{j} + z\mathbf{k}$, we get from (8),

$$du = \mathbf{F} \cdot d\mathbf{r}.$$

But we have seen in Art. 83 that $du = \nabla u \cdot d\mathbf{r}$, and therefore

$$\mathbf{F} \cdot d\mathbf{r} = \nabla u \cdot d\mathbf{r}.$$

Since this relation holds for any value of $d\mathbf{r}$, we get

$$\mathbf{F} = \nabla u. \tag{9}$$

Thus a vector whose curl is identically zero may be expressed as the gradient of some scalar point function.

This last result may be used to prove a theorem of which we made use in Chapter VII, Art. 73: The necessary and sufficient condition that $u \, dx + v \, dy + w \, dz$, where u, v, w are functions of x, y, and z, be the exact differential of some function is that the curl of the vector $\mathbf{F} = u\mathbf{i} + v\mathbf{j} + w\mathbf{k}$ vanish identically. To show the necessity of this condition, suppose that $u \, dx + v \, dy + w \, dz$ is the exact differential of some function $f(x, y, z)$, so that

$$df = u \, dx + v \, dy + w \, dz.$$

But we have also,

$$df = \frac{\partial f}{\partial x} \, dx + \frac{\partial f}{\partial y} \, dy + \frac{\partial f}{\partial z} \, dz,$$

whence, since dx, dy, and dz are independent, we must have

$$u = \frac{\partial f}{\partial x}, \qquad v = \frac{\partial f}{\partial y}, \qquad w = \frac{\partial f}{\partial z}.$$

Hence

$$\operatorname{curl} \mathbf{F} = \mathbf{i}\left(\frac{\partial w}{\partial y} - \frac{\partial v}{\partial z}\right) + \mathbf{j}\left(\frac{\partial u}{\partial z} - \frac{\partial w}{\partial x}\right) + \mathbf{k}\left(\frac{\partial v}{\partial x} - \frac{\partial u}{\partial y}\right)$$

$$= \mathbf{i}\left(\frac{\partial^2 f}{\partial y \, \partial z} - \frac{\partial^2 f}{\partial z \, \partial y}\right) + \mathbf{j}\left(\frac{\partial^2 f}{\partial z \, \partial x} - \frac{\partial^2 f}{\partial x \, \partial z}\right) + \mathbf{k}\left(\frac{\partial^2 f}{\partial x \, \partial y} - \frac{\partial^2 f}{\partial y \, \partial x}\right)$$

$$= 0.$$

Conversely, if curl $\mathbf{F} = 0$ identically, $\mathbf{F}$ must, by (9), be expressible as the gradient of some function,

$$\mathbf{F} = \nabla f.$$

Therefore

$$u\mathbf{i} + v\mathbf{j} + w\mathbf{k} = \mathbf{F} = \nabla f = \mathbf{i}\frac{\partial f}{\partial x} + \mathbf{j}\frac{\partial f}{\partial y} + \mathbf{k}\frac{\partial f}{\partial z},$$

whence

$$u = \frac{\partial f}{\partial x}, \qquad v = \frac{\partial f}{\partial y}, \qquad w = \frac{\partial f}{\partial z},$$

and

$$u\,dx + v\,dy + w\,dz = \frac{\partial f}{\partial x}\,dx + \frac{\partial f}{\partial y}\,dy + \frac{\partial f}{\partial z}\,dz = df,$$

so that $u\,dx + v\,dy + w\,dz$ is the exact differential of the function $f(x, y, z)$.

Our next problem is concerned with the potential due to a continuous distribution of matter over some region. Let V be any such region

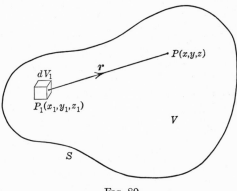

FIG. 80

bounded by a surface S, and let $\rho(x_1, y_1, z_1)$ be the density at any point $P_1(x_1, y_1, z_1)$ of V (Fig. 80). Then the potential at a point $P(x, y, z)$ of V due to the mass of an elementary volume $dV_1 = dx_1\,dy_1\,dz_1$ at P_1 is

$$du = \frac{\rho(x_1, y_1, z_1)\,dV_1}{r},$$

where $r = \sqrt{(x - x_1)^2 + (y - y_1)^2 + (z - z_1)^2}$ is the distance between P_1 and P, and the potential at P due to the entire mass inside S is

$$u = \iiint_V \frac{\rho(x_1, y_1, z_1)}{r}\,dV_1. \tag{10}$$

Since r but not ρ depends upon the coordinates x, y, z, we have, for the gradient of u,

$$\nabla u = \iiint_V \rho(x_1, y_1, z_1) \, \nabla\left(\frac{1}{r}\right) dV_1.$$

Letting $\mathbf{r} = r\mathbf{r}_1$ be the vector from P_1 to P, we have, as in Art. 83,

$$\nabla\left(\frac{1}{r}\right) = -\frac{\mathbf{r}_1}{r^2},$$

so that

$$\nabla u = -\iiint_V \frac{\rho(x_1, y_1, z_1)\mathbf{r}_1}{r^2} \, dV_1. \tag{11}$$

Consider now the surface integral I of the normal component of ∇u over S. For the contribution to I due to the elementary mass $\rho(x_1, y_1, z_1) \, dV_1$ at P_1, we have from (11),

$$dI = -\rho(x_1, y_1, z_1) \, dV_1 \iint_S \frac{\mathbf{N} \cdot \mathbf{r}_1}{r^2} \, dS.$$

Since P_1 and P are inside S, we get by Gauss's theorem,

$$dI = -4\pi\rho(x_1, y_1, z_1) \, dV_1,$$

and hence

$$I = \iint_S \mathbf{N} \cdot \nabla u \, dS = -4\pi \iiint_V \rho(x_1, y_1, z_1) \, dV_1$$

$$= -4\pi \iiint_V \rho(x, y, z) \, dV. \tag{12}$$

But by the divergence theorem,

$$\iint_S \mathbf{N} \cdot \nabla u \, dS = \iiint_V \text{div } \nabla u \, dV = \iiint_V \nabla^2 u \, dV. \tag{13}$$

Combining (12) and (13), we get

$$\iiint_V [\nabla^2 u + 4\pi\rho(x, y, z)] \, dV = 0,$$

and since V is any volume occupied by matter, it follows that

$$\nabla^2 u + 4\pi\rho(x, y, z) = 0,$$

or

$$\frac{\partial^2 u}{\partial x^2} + \frac{\partial^2 u}{\partial y^2} + \frac{\partial^2 u}{\partial z^2} = -4\pi\rho(x, y, z). \tag{14}$$

This is known as Poisson's equation, which is thus satisfied by the potential function u throughout a region occupied by matter. If the region under consideration is devoid of matter, so that $\rho = 0$ at every point, (14) becomes Laplace's equation,

$$\frac{\partial^2 u}{\partial x^2} + \frac{\partial^2 u}{\partial y^2} + \frac{\partial^2 u}{\partial z^2} = 0. \tag{15}$$

Analogous arguments may be formulated for the physical situations in which u is the electric potential due to a region containing charges, the magnetic potential due to poles, or the temperature at each point of a heated body. (Cf. Art. 78.)

Using Green's theorem, we next show that a vector point function $\mathbf{v}$ is uniquely determined, at every point of a volume V bounded by a surface S, when its divergence and curl throughout V and its normal component over S are given. For, suppose that $\mathbf{v}_1$ is a vector point function having the same values as $\mathbf{v}$ for its divergence and curl in V and for its normal component over S, and let $\mathbf{r} = \mathbf{v} - \mathbf{v}_1$; if we show that $\mathbf{r} = 0$ for all points inside and on S, it will follow that $\mathbf{v}_1 = \mathbf{v}$, so that no vector point function but $\mathbf{v}$ can exist with the given properties. Now by supposition,

(I) $\operatorname{div} \mathbf{r} = \operatorname{div} \mathbf{v} - \operatorname{div} \mathbf{v}_1 = 0$, throughout V,

(II) $\operatorname{curl} \mathbf{r} = \operatorname{curl} \mathbf{v} - \operatorname{curl} \mathbf{v}_1 = 0$, throughout V,

(III) $\mathbf{N} \cdot \mathbf{r} = \mathbf{N} \cdot \mathbf{v} - \mathbf{N} \cdot \mathbf{v}_1 = 0$, over S.

From (II), together with the statement following equation (9), we get $\mathbf{r} = \nabla u$, where u is some scalar point function. From (I) and (III) we then have

$$\operatorname{div} \nabla u = \nabla^2 u = 0,$$
$$\mathbf{N} \cdot \nabla u = 0. \tag{16}$$

Consequently, taking $w = u$ in Green's theorem in the first form (equation (9), Art. 85), and using the relations (16), we find

$$\iiint_V \nabla u \cdot \nabla u \, dV = \iiint_V (\nabla u)^2 \, dV = 0.$$

But since $(\nabla u)^2$ cannot be negative, we must have $\nabla u = 0$, whence $\mathbf{r} = 0$ and $\mathbf{v}_1 = \mathbf{v}$.

As a final application, we indicate briefly the manner in which Maxwell's electromagnetic field equations are obtained. We begin with an empirical law, based on the experiments of Faraday and Henry, which states that the work done by an electric force $\mathbf{E}$ (electrostatic c.g.s. units) in moving a unit positive charge around any closed path C is proportional to the time rate of decrease of the flux of magnetic force $\mathbf{H}$ (electromagnetic c.g.s. units) through any open surface S bounded by C. In symbols, this may be written as

$$\int_C \mathbf{E} \cdot \mathbf{T}\, ds = -\frac{\mu}{c}\frac{\partial}{\partial t}\iint_S \mathbf{N} \cdot \mathbf{H}\, dS, \tag{17}$$

where $\mathbf{T}$ is a unit tangent to C in the positive direction, $\mathbf{N}$ is a unit normal on the positive side of S, μ is the permeability of the medium in which the magnetic field acts, and c * is equal to the ratio of a c.g.s. electromagnetic unit to a c.g.s. electrostatic unit of charge. Maxwell, using the results of Ampère's experiments, deduced a corresponding relation in which the roles of $\mathbf{E}$ and $\mathbf{H}$ are interchanged; symbolically, his relation is

$$\int_C \mathbf{H} \cdot \mathbf{T}\, ds = \frac{\epsilon}{c}\frac{\partial}{\partial t}\iint_S \mathbf{N} \cdot \mathbf{E}\, dS, \tag{18}$$

where ϵ is the dielectric constant of the medium in which the electric field acts, and the other notation is the same as in (17). The right-hand member of (18), it should be remarked, is a quantity proportional to a fictitious current called by Maxwell a displacement current. Now by Stokes's theorem we have

$$\int_C \mathbf{E} \cdot \mathbf{T}\, ds = \iint_S \mathbf{N} \cdot \operatorname{curl} \mathbf{E}\, dS,$$

$$\int_C \mathbf{H} \cdot \mathbf{T}\, ds = \iint_S \mathbf{N} \cdot \operatorname{curl} \mathbf{H}\, dS.$$

Using these relations together with (17) and (18), it follows that since S is any surface in the field,

$$\operatorname{curl} \mathbf{E} = -\frac{\mu}{c}\frac{\partial \mathbf{H}}{\partial t},$$

$$\operatorname{curl} \mathbf{H} = \frac{\epsilon}{c}\frac{\partial \mathbf{E}}{\partial t}. \tag{19}$$

* Numerically, $c = 2.998 \times 10^{10}$, the velocity (cm./sec.) of light in vacuo.

These are Maxwell's field equations. If we take the curl of each member of equations (19), we get

$$\nabla \times (\nabla \times \mathbf{E}) = -\frac{\mu}{c}\frac{\partial}{\partial t}\,\mathrm{curl}\,\mathbf{H}$$

$$= -\frac{\epsilon\mu}{c^2}\frac{\partial^2 \mathbf{E}}{\partial t^2},$$

$$\nabla \times (\nabla \times \mathbf{H}) = \frac{\epsilon}{c}\frac{\partial}{\partial t}\,\mathrm{curl}\,\mathbf{E}$$

$$= -\frac{\epsilon\mu}{c^2}\frac{\partial^2 \mathbf{H}}{\partial t^2}.$$

(20)

It is readily shown (Problem 2(c) following Art. 82) that, for any vector $\mathbf{v}$,

$$\nabla \times (\nabla \times \mathbf{v}) = \nabla(\nabla\cdot\mathbf{v}) - \nabla^2\mathbf{v}. \tag{21}$$

Now further experiment shows that $\mathbf{E}$ and $\mathbf{H}$ are such that $\mathrm{div}\,\mathbf{E} = \mathrm{div}\,\mathbf{H} = 0$. Hence, from (20) and (21), we find

$$\nabla^2\mathbf{E} = \frac{\partial^2 \mathbf{E}}{\partial x^2} + \frac{\partial^2 \mathbf{E}}{\partial y^2} + \frac{\partial^2 \mathbf{E}}{\partial z^2} = \frac{\epsilon\mu}{c^2}\frac{\partial^2 \mathbf{E}}{\partial t^2},$$

$$\nabla^2\mathbf{H} = \frac{\partial^2 \mathbf{H}}{\partial x^2} + \frac{\partial^2 \mathbf{H}}{\partial y^2} + \frac{\partial^2 \mathbf{H}}{\partial z^2} = \frac{\epsilon\mu}{c^2}\frac{\partial^2 \mathbf{H}}{\partial t^2}.$$

(22)

These equations represent wave motions, * and indicate that electrostatic and electromagnetic disturbances are propagated through the medium, the common velocity of propagation being $c/\sqrt{\epsilon\mu}$. It is this result which gave rise to Maxwell's celebrated electromagnetic theory of light.

PROBLEMS

1. If u is a scalar point function over a scalar field of volume V enclosed by a surface S, and $\mathbf{N}$ is a unit outward-drawn normal to S, show that

$$\iiint_V \mathrm{grad}\,u\,dV = \iint_S u\mathbf{N}\,dS.$$

2. If $\mathbf{v}$ is a vector point function over a vector field of volume V enclosed by a surface S, and $\mathbf{N}$ is a unit outward-drawn normal to S, show that

$$\iiint_V \mathrm{curl}\,\mathbf{v}\,dV = \iint_S \mathbf{N} \times \mathbf{v}\,dS.$$

* Cf. Chapter VII, Art. 70.

3. If **F** is a vector function normal to the closed surface S at each point, and if V is the volume bounded by S, show that

$$\iiint_V \text{curl } \mathbf{F} \, dV = 0.$$

4. If u is a scalar point function over an open surface S bounded by a curve C, **N** is a positively drawn unit normal to S, and **T** is a positively drawn unit tangent to C, show that

$$\iint_S \mathbf{N} \times \text{grad } u \, dS = \int_C u\mathbf{T} \, ds.$$

5. If α, β, and γ are the direction angles of **N**, and if $\mathbf{v} = v_1\mathbf{i} + v_2\mathbf{j} + v_3\mathbf{k}$, show that the divergence theorem may be written in Cartesian form as

$$\iiint_V \left(\frac{\partial v_1}{\partial x} + \frac{\partial v_2}{\partial y} + \frac{\partial v_3}{\partial z} \right) dV = \iint_S (v_1 \cos \alpha + v_2 \cos \beta + v_3 \cos \gamma) \, dS.$$

6. If α, β, γ are the direction angles of the vector $\mathbf{v} = v_1\mathbf{i} + v_2\mathbf{j} + v_3\mathbf{k}$, show that Stokes's theorem may be written in Cartesian form as

$$\iint_S \left[\left(\frac{\partial v_3}{\partial y} - \frac{\partial v_2}{\partial z} \right) \cos \alpha + \left(\frac{\partial v_1}{\partial z} - \frac{\partial v_3}{\partial x} \right) \cos \beta + \left(\frac{\partial v_2}{\partial x} - \frac{\partial v_1}{\partial y} \right) \cos \gamma \right] dS$$

$$= \int_C (v_1 \, dx + v_2 \, dy + v_3 \, dz).$$

7. Write both forms of Green's theorem in Cartesian coordinates.

8. If v_1, v_2, and v_3 are the components of a vector **v**, u is a scalar point function, and ρ, a and b are constants, express in vector notation the following equations from the theory of elasticity:

$$\rho \frac{\partial^2 v_1}{\partial t^2} = (a + b) \frac{\partial u}{\partial x} + b \left(\frac{\partial^2 v_1}{\partial x^2} + \frac{\partial^2 v_1}{\partial y^2} + \frac{\partial^2 v_1}{\partial z^2} \right),$$

$$\rho \frac{\partial^2 v_2}{\partial t^2} = (a + b) \frac{\partial u}{\partial y} + b \left(\frac{\partial^2 v_2}{\partial x^2} + \frac{\partial^2 v_2}{\partial y^2} + \frac{\partial^2 v_2}{\partial z^2} \right),$$

$$\rho \frac{\partial^2 v_3}{\partial t^2} = (a + b) \frac{\partial u}{\partial z} + b \left(\frac{\partial^2 v_3}{\partial x^2} + \frac{\partial^2 v_3}{\partial y^2} + \frac{\partial^2 v_3}{\partial z^2} \right).$$

9. If u and w are scalar point functions, show that

$$\int_C u \, \nabla w \cdot \mathbf{T} \, ds = - \int_C w \, \nabla u \cdot \mathbf{T} \, ds,$$

where **T** is a unit tangent to the closed curve C.

10. If u is a scalar and **v** a vector point function, show that

$$\iint_S \mathbf{N} \cdot (\nabla u \times \mathbf{v} + u \nabla \times \mathbf{v}) \, dS = \int_C u\mathbf{v} \cdot \mathbf{T} \, dS,$$

where S is an open surface bounded by C, **N** is a positively drawn unit normal to S, and **T** is a positively drawn unit tangent to C.

11. If u is a scalar and $\mathbf{v}$ a vector point function in a volume V bounded by a surface S, show that

$$\iiint_V (u\nabla \cdot \mathbf{v} + \nabla u \cdot \mathbf{v})\, dV = \iint_S u\mathbf{N} \cdot \mathbf{v}\, dS,$$

where $\mathbf{N}$ is an outward-drawn unit normal to S.

12. If u is a non-constant solution of Laplace's equation, show by means of Green's theorem that

$$\iint_S u\mathbf{N} \cdot \nabla u\, dS > 0,$$

where $\mathbf{N}$ is an outward-drawn unit normal to the closed surface S.

13. Let m be the total mass of a sphere of uniform density and radius a. (a) Show that the potential u and gravitational force $\mathbf{F}$ at a distance r from the center of the sphere are given by

$$u = \frac{3m}{2a} - \frac{mr^2}{2a^3}, \qquad \mathbf{F} = -\frac{m\mathbf{r}}{a^3} \qquad (r \leqq a),$$

$$u = \frac{m}{r}, \qquad \mathbf{F} = -\frac{m\mathbf{r}}{r^3} \qquad (r \geqq a).$$

(b) Hence show that u satisfies Poisson's equation at points inside the sphere and that it satisfies Laplace's equation at points outside.

14. If $\mathbf{v}$ is the vector velocity and ρ the variable density of a moving fluid, derive the general form of the equation of continuity,

$$\nabla \cdot \rho\mathbf{v} = -\frac{\partial \rho}{\partial t}.$$

15. Let the region V, bounded by the surface S, be occupied by matter of density $\rho(x, y, z)$, and let $\mathbf{r} = r\mathbf{r}_1$ be the vector from the origin O to any point P of V. (a) Letting $\mathbf{v} = \rho\mathbf{r}_1$ in the divergence theorem, show that the potential at a point inside S is given by

$$u = \frac{1}{2} \iint_S (\mathbf{N} \cdot \mathbf{r}_1)\rho\, dS - \frac{1}{2} \iiint_V \mathbf{r}_1 \cdot \nabla\rho\, dV,$$

where $\mathbf{N}$ is an outward-drawn unit normal to S. (b) If u satisfies Poisson's equation and is such that $\nabla\rho = 0$, show that

$$u = -\frac{1}{8\pi} \iint_S \mathbf{N} \cdot \mathbf{r}_1 \operatorname{div} \mathbf{F}\, dS,$$

where $\mathbf{F}$ is the gravitational force, so that if $\mathbf{F}$ is known at every point of S the potential at all interior points may be found.

CHAPTER IX

Probability and Numerical Methods

87. Introduction. Probability considerations enter into scientific and engineering work in a variety of guises. The theory of probability plays an important role in modern physics and physical chemistry in problems connected with atomic structure, and in quantum theory and wave mechanics. Questions of engineering economics, and quality control in manufacturing, employ the statistical method based on probability.* Frequency curves are used in standardization and sampling operations.† Statistical mechanics is likewise based on the theory of probability, as is the theory of least squares, which is useful in the adjustment of observations and is employed in precise surveying.

In recent years, the entire field of numerical methods has been rapidly growing. Theories basic to such methods and machines capable of handling computations at amazing speed have developed together. In particular, there has been considerable advance in techniques for solving ordinary and partial differential equations numerically.

It is the purpose of this chapter to introduce some of these ideas. For convenient reference, we begin by stating a few of the principles of combinatorial analysis and probability.‡

1. If an event A can happen in m ways, and then an event B can happen in n ways, *both A and B* can happen in this order in mn ways.

2. If two mutually exclusive events A and B can happen in m and n ways, respectively, *either A or B* can happen in $m + n$ ways. (A and B are mutually exclusive if the happening of either precludes the occurrence of the other.)

3. The number of permutations (arrangements) of n things taken r at a time is $P(n, r) = n(n - 1) \cdots (n - r + 1) = n!/(n - r)!$

4. The number of combinations (selections, without regard to ordering) of n things taken r at a time is $C(n, r) = P(n, r)/r! = n!/r!(n - r)!$

5. If the number of ways an event may result can be analyzed into

---

* E. L. Grant, "Principles of Engineering Economy."

† T. C. Fry, "Probability and Its Engineering Uses"; A. Fisher, "The Mathematical Theory of Probabilities," introductory note by M. C. Rorty.

‡ More detailed discussions of permutations, combinations, and the elements of probability may be found in books on college algebra; see, for example, F. H. Miller, "College Algebra and Trigonometry," Chapter XVI.

a successes and *b* failures, each equally likely to occur, the *a priori* (or mathematical) probability of success in a single trial is $p = a/(a + b)$, and the corresponding probability of failure is $q = b/(a + b)$.

6. If *s* successes in *n* trials have been observed, s/n is called the relative frequency of successes. It is assumed that s/n approaches a limit as *n* becomes infinite, and this limit is defined as the *a posteriori* (or statistical, or empirical) probability of success in one trial.

7. If p_1 is the probability that an event E_1 occurs and p_2 is the probability that an event E_2 occurs, then $p_1 p_2$ is the probability that both events occur (in either order or simultaneously if E_1 and E_2 are independent; in the order $E_1 E_2$ if E_2 depends upon E_1, when p_2 is the probability that E_2 happens after E_1 has happened).

8. If p_1 is the probability that an event E_1 occurs and p_2 is the probability that an event E_2 occurs, then, when E_1 and E_2 are mutually exclusive, $p_1 + p_2$ is the probability that either E_1 or E_2 occurs.

9. If *p* is the probability that an event happens, and *q* that it fails to occur, then $C(n, r)p^r q^{n-r}$ is the probability that the event happens exactly *r* times in *n* trials.

88. The probability curve. The observer, taking observations, trying to find the value of some unknown, is analogous to a marksman trying to hit the center of a target. Strange though it may seem, these

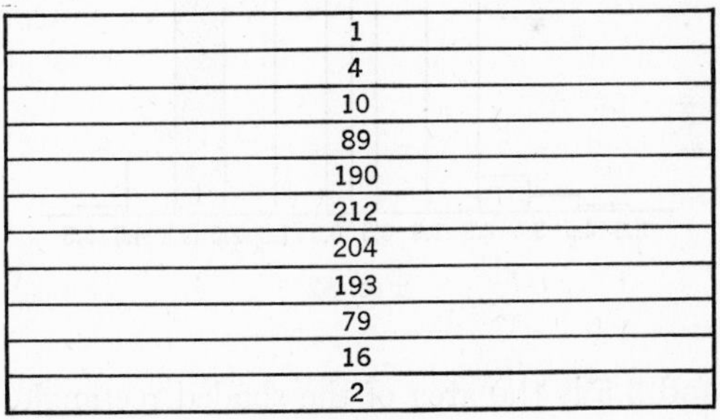

1
4
10
89
190
212
204
193
79
16
2

Fig. 81

errors of observation or deviations of shots follow a mathematical law, or, rather, approximate it more and more closely as the number of observations or shots increases. All constant errors—errors for which a correction can be applied, like the temperature correction for a steel tape, etc.—also mistakes, are supposed to have been eliminated. The mathematical law applies only to unavoidable errors. We shall now find a mathematical expression for this law in the form of an equation —the equation of the curve of error, or the probability curve.

We take an illustration based on a record of 1000 shots fired from a Taylor battery gun at a target 11 ft. high. Fig. 81 shows approximately the number of hits in each division 1 ft. wide, from which, e.g., the (empirical) probability that a shot hits the center rectangle is $\frac{212}{1000}$ or 0.212; i.e., if another shot is fired under the same conditions, the probability is 0.212 that it hits the center rectangle.

If, now, we lay off the 11 intervals each $\Delta x = 1$ unit long on a horizontal x-axis, and draw rectangles whose areas $y \, \Delta x$ (or ordinates y, if $\Delta x = 1$) represent the probability that the shot falls within the rectangle (taking a different convenient unit vertically), we have the diagram shown in Fig. 82. Thus, the probability that the shot falls

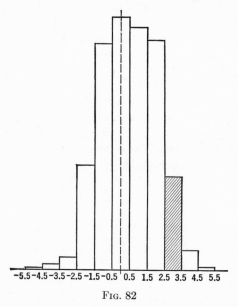

Fig. 82

between 2.5 and 3.5 is the area of the shaded rectangle, $0.079 \times 1 = 0.079$. The sum of all the rectangular areas is 1.

We can imagine the number of shots increased indefinitely while the widths of the intervals get smaller and smaller; then, while the total area of the rectangles always remains 1, the form of the area approaches that of the area under a smooth curve, $y = f(x)$, such that $\int_{-\infty}^{\infty} f(x) \, dx = 1$. We make the limits $-\infty$ and ∞ since no definite finite limits can be assigned which would cover all cases. We now determine the function $f(x)$.

Suppose that we make n observations $s_1, s_2, \cdots, s_n$ on a quantity whose true value is z. Let $x_1, x_2, \cdots, x_n$ be the errors of observation, positive or negative according as the observed values are greater or less than z. Then we have for the errors and their sum:

$$
\begin{aligned}
x_1 &= s_1 - z, \\
x_2 &= s_2 - z, \\
&\cdots\cdots, \\
x_n &= s_n - z,
\end{aligned}
$$
(1)

$$\Sigma x = \Sigma s - nz. \tag{2}$$

Now the true value of a quantity is unknown and can never be determined exactly by observation. If we assume that the arithmetic mean of the observed values is the best value that can be assigned to z, and replace z in (2) by $\Sigma s/n$, we obtain

$$\Sigma x = x_1 + x_2 + \cdots + x_n = 0, \tag{3}$$

an approximation which becomes closer as n increases. This relation (3) is equivalent to the statement that the positive and negative errors are compensating—their algebraic sum is zero—and might have been taken as an assumption from which the relation $z = \Sigma s/n$ would follow.

If Δx is the smallest measured interval for a given set of observations, we say that

$$
\begin{aligned}
f(x_1)\,\Delta x &= \text{probability of error } x_1, \\
f(x_2)\,\Delta x &= \text{probability of error } x_2, \\
&\cdots\cdots\cdots\cdots\cdots\cdots\cdots, \\
f(x_n)\,\Delta x &= \text{probability of error } x_n.
\end{aligned}
$$

Hence

$$P = f(x_1)f(x_2) \cdots f(x_n)\,\overline{\Delta x}^{\,n}$$

is the probability of occurrence of the set of errors x_1, x_2, $\cdots$, x_n. Now, instead of regarding z as a fixed constant, we may think of it as an unknown, capable of being assigned different values depending on the form of the f function. We assume * that when z is assigned the value $\Sigma s/n$, that is, when equation (3) holds, the form of the f function will be such as to give P its maximum value.

In order to make P a maximum we maximize

$$\ln P = \ln f(x_1) + \ln f(x_2) + \cdots + \ln f(x_n) + n \ln \Delta x$$

by equating to zero the derivative of $\ln P$ with respect to z:

$$\frac{f'(x_1)}{f(x_1)}\frac{dx_1}{dz} + \frac{f'(x_2)}{f(x_2)}\frac{dx_2}{dz} + \cdots + \frac{f'(x_n)}{f(x_n)}\frac{dx_n}{dz} = 0. \tag{4}$$

---

* This assumption is open to criticism and has been much discussed, yet it yields the equation of the curve of error according to the method of Gauss.

But, from equations (1),

$$\frac{dx_1}{dz} = \frac{dx_2}{dz} = \cdots = \frac{dx_n}{dz} = -1,$$

and, denoting the function $\frac{f'(x)}{f(x)}$ by $\phi(x)$, equation (4) becomes

$$\phi(x_1) + \phi(x_2) + \cdots + \phi(x_n) = 0. \tag{5}$$

The function ϕ is to be determined from equations (5) and (3); that is, for all positive integral values of n, we must have

$$\phi(x_1) + \phi(x_2) + \cdots + \phi(x_n) = 0,$$
$$x_1 + x_2 + \cdots + x_n = 0. \tag{6}$$

Let us try to satisfy equations (6) by assuming for $\phi(x)$ a power series in x:

$$\phi(x) = a_0 + a_1 x + a_2 x^2 + \cdots. \tag{7}$$

Then the first of equations (6) becomes

$$na_0 + a_1 \Sigma x + a_2 \Sigma x^2 + \cdots = 0. \tag{8}$$

Since $\Sigma x = 0$ by virtue of the second of equations (6), equation (8) is satisfied if a_1 is arbitrary and all the other a's are zero. Hence we have as a solution of equations (6),

$$\phi(x) = \frac{f'(x)}{f(x)} = a_1 x. \tag{9}$$

A more elaborate analysis would show that (9) is the only solution of equations (6).

Integrating (9) with respect to x, we find

$$\ln f(x) = \frac{a_1 x^2}{2} + \ln c.$$

We now demand that our curve of error, $y = f(x)$, be rapidly asymptotic to the x-axis, so that the probability of making an error will decrease very rapidly as the magnitude of the error increases. It follows that a_1 must be negative; we write, for convenience, $a_1/2 = -h^2$, and the equation of the curve of error becomes

$$y = f(x) = ce^{-h^2 x^2}. \tag{10}$$

We now determine c. Since the area under the curve of error is unity, we have

$$\int_{-\infty}^{\infty} ce^{-h^2x^2}\,dx = 2c\int_{0}^{\infty} e^{-h^2x^2}\,dx = 1. \tag{11}$$

Representing the second integral by I, we may evaluate it as follows:

$$I = \int_{0}^{\infty} e^{-h^2x^2}\,dx = \int_{0}^{\infty} e^{-h^2y^2}\,dy,$$

$$I^2 = \int_{0}^{\infty}\int_{0}^{\infty} e^{-h^2(x^2+y^2)}\,dy\,dx.$$

Transforming to polar coordinates, we obtain

$$I^2 = \int_{0}^{\pi/2}\int_{0}^{\infty} e^{-h^2\rho^2}\rho\,d\rho\,d\theta$$

$$= -\frac{1}{2h^2}\int_{0}^{\pi/2} e^{-h^2\rho^2}\Big]_{0}^{\infty}\,d\theta = \frac{\pi}{4h^2}.$$

Therefore

$$I = \int_{0}^{\infty} e^{-h^2x^2}\,dx = \frac{\sqrt{\pi}}{2h}. \tag{12}$$

Substituting in (11), $c = h/\sqrt{\pi}$, whence (10) becomes

$$y = \frac{h}{\sqrt{\pi}} e^{-h^2x^2}, \tag{13}$$

the equation of the *curve of error* or the *probability curve*. Equation (13) is sometimes called the normal law of error, and a set of observations which follows it closely is called a normal distribution.

The constant h is called the *measure of precision* of the set of observations. A large h indicates a high peak and rapid fall in the curve, that is, a large probability of small errors and rapidly decreasing probability of larger errors. The area of the shaded rectangle, $y\,\Delta x$, in Fig. 83 represents the probability of an error x; the total area under the curve is 1.

Denoting by P_x the probability of an error x, and by $P_{a,b}$ the probability that an error is between a and b, we have

$$P_x = \frac{h}{\sqrt{\pi}} e^{-h^2x^2}\,\Delta x, \tag{14}$$

$$P_{a,b} = \frac{h}{\sqrt{\pi}} \int_{a}^{b} e^{-h^2x^2}\,dx. \tag{15}$$

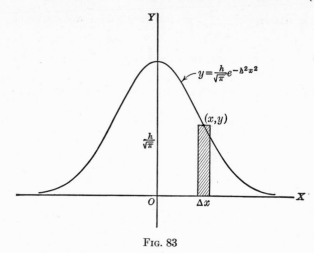

Fig. 83

The probability that an error is between $-X$ and X is then

$$P_{-X,X} = \frac{h}{\sqrt{\pi}} \int_{-X}^{X} e^{-h^2x^2}\, dx = \frac{2h}{\sqrt{\pi}} \int_{0}^{X} e^{-h^2x^2}\, dx.$$

If we let $hx = t$, then $h\,dx = dt$; when $x = 0$, $t = 0$, and when $x = X$, $t = hX$, so that the integral becomes

$$P_{-X,X} = \frac{2}{\sqrt{\pi}} \int_{0}^{hX} e^{-t^2}\, dt.$$

This is the *probability integral,* but in order to get the form given in Peirce's "Tables," where numerical values are tabulated, we replace the upper limit hX by x. The letter used for integration variable is immaterial, since it is replaced by the limits after integration; calling it x instead of t, we have for the probability integral

$$P_{-X,X} = \frac{2}{\sqrt{\pi}} \int_{0}^{x} e^{-x^2}\, dx, \tag{16}$$

where the upper limit $x = hX$. This function $P_{-X,X}$ is sometimes called the error function erf x.

Example.   In a series of observations of an angle taken to tenths of a second, $h = 0.6$. Find (a) the probability of an error $2''$ (i.e., between $1.95''$ and $2.05''$), (b) the probability that the error is not numerically greater than $2''$.

(a) From (14), $P_2 = \dfrac{0.6}{\sqrt{\pi}}\, e^{-0.36\times4}(0.1) = \dfrac{0.06}{\sqrt{\pi}}\, e^{-1.44} = 0.008.$

(b) From (16), $P_{-2,2} = \dfrac{2}{\sqrt{\pi}} \displaystyle\int_0^{1.2} e^{-x^2}\,dx = 0.91$ (from Peirce's "Tables").

89. Probable error; standard deviation.

The number ϵ, such that the probability that an error is between $-\epsilon$ and $+\epsilon$ is $\frac{1}{2}$, is called the *probable error* of a single observation. We have, from (16), Art. 88,

$$P_{-\epsilon,\epsilon} = \frac{2}{\sqrt{\pi}} \int_0^{h\epsilon} e^{-x^2}\,dx = 0.5000.$$

From Peirce's "Tables," the value of the upper limit corresponding to a value 0.5000 for the integral is $h\epsilon = 0.4769$, so that

$$\epsilon = \frac{0.4769}{h}. \tag{1}$$

In Fig. 83, ϵ is the abscissa corresponding to the ordinate which bisects the area under the probability curve to the right of the y-axis.

In Art. 88 we assumed that the true value z could be replaced by the arithmetic mean $\Sigma s/n$, of the n observed values, so that the error x is then the deviation of the observed value from the arithmetic mean of the observed values. When x is so regarded it is usually called a *residual* instead of an error. In terms of the residual ρ, the equation of the probability curve (13), Art. 88, can be written

$$y = \frac{h}{\sqrt{\pi}} e^{-h^2\rho^2}. \tag{2}$$

The *standard deviation, σ,* of a set of observations is defined as the root-mean-square value of the deviation from the arithmetic mean, or the square root of the average squared residual. Thus, if n is the number of observations, we have

$$\sigma = \sqrt{\frac{\Sigma\rho^2}{n}}. \tag{3}$$

We may derive a formula for σ in terms of h as follows. The probability of a residual of size ρ (i.e., between ρ and $\rho + \Delta\rho$) is $(h/\sqrt{\pi})e^{-h^2\rho^2}\,\Delta\rho$. The number of residuals of size ρ, and hence the number of squared residuals of size ρ^2, is $(nh/\sqrt{\pi})e^{-h^2\rho^2}\,\Delta\rho$, where n is the total number of observations and also the total number of residuals. If we multiply the value ρ^2 of a squared residual by the number of such squared residuals, sum for all values of ρ, and divide by the total number of residuals, we obtain the average squared residual.

Thus

$$\sigma^2 = \int_{-\infty}^{\infty} \rho^2 \cdot \frac{h}{\sqrt{\pi}} e^{-h^2\rho^2} \, d\rho$$

$$= -\frac{1}{h\sqrt{\pi}} \int_0^{\infty} \rho \cdot e^{-h^2\rho^2}(-2h^2\rho \, d\rho)$$

$$= -\frac{1}{h\sqrt{\pi}} \left(\left[\rho e^{-h^2\rho^2} \right]_0^{\infty} - \int_0^{\infty} e^{-h^2\rho^2} \, d\rho \right).$$

The first bracket vanishes, and the value of the integral is $\sqrt{\pi}/2h$, by equation (12) of Art. 88, so that

$$\sigma^2 = -\frac{1}{h\sqrt{\pi}} \left(-\frac{\sqrt{\pi}}{2h} \right) = \frac{1}{2h^2} \, ;$$

$$\sigma = \frac{1}{\sqrt{2}\,h}. \tag{4}$$

If we equate the values of σ in (3) and (4) we obtain a formula for computing the measure of precision, h, of a series of observations,

$$h = \sqrt{\frac{n}{2\Sigma\rho^2}}. \tag{5}$$

Replacing h by its value $1/\sqrt{2}\,\sigma$ given by (4), we can write the equation of the probability curve (2) in the form

$$y = \frac{1}{\sqrt{2\pi}\,\sigma} e^{-\rho^2/2\sigma^2}, \tag{6}$$

and from equation (1) we have

$$\epsilon = 0.4769/h = 0.4769\sqrt{2}\,\sigma,$$

or

$$\epsilon = 0.6745\sigma. \tag{7}$$

The value of σ or of ϵ can be used as a measure of dispersion of a set of observations. The form of equation (6) shows that for small σ the curve will have a high peak and fall rapidly, showing a small spread or dispersion in the observations. Let us find the probability that an observed value will deviate not more than σ on either side of the mean.

Using the equation of the probability curve in the form (6), we have for the probability that a deviation is between $-\sigma$ and $+\sigma$,

$$P_{-\sigma,\sigma} = \frac{1}{\sqrt{2\pi}\,\sigma} \int_{-\sigma}^{\sigma} e^{-\rho^2/2\sigma^2}\, d\rho = \frac{\sqrt{2}}{\sqrt{\pi}\,\sigma} \int_0^{\sigma} e^{-\rho^2/2\sigma^2}\, d\rho.$$

Letting $\rho/\sqrt{2}\,\sigma = x$, $d\rho = \sqrt{2}\,\sigma\,dx$, the limits for x will be 0 and $1/\sqrt{2}$, so that

$$P_{-\sigma,\sigma} = \frac{2}{\sqrt{\pi}} \int_0^{0.7071} e^{-x^2}\, dx = 0.683 \text{ (by Peirce's "Tables")}.$$

Thus, in a normal distribution, 68.3% of the observations fall within σ of the arithmetic mean.   Furthermore,

$$P_{-2\sigma,2\sigma} = \frac{2}{\sqrt{\pi}} \int_0^{1.4142} e^{-x^2}\, dx = 0.954,$$

$$P_{-3\sigma,3\sigma} = \frac{2}{\sqrt{\pi}} \int_0^{2.1213} e^{-x^2}\, dx = 0.997,$$

so that 95.4% of the observations fall within a range of 2σ on either side of the arithmetic mean and practically all, 99.7%, are within a distance of 3σ from the mean value.

Collecting the formulas for h, σ, and ϵ, (3), (5), and (7), we now write them in the forms

$$h = \sqrt{\frac{n}{2\Sigma\rho^2}}, \qquad \sigma = \sqrt{\frac{\Sigma\rho^2}{n}}, \qquad \epsilon = 0.6745 \sqrt{\frac{\Sigma\rho^2}{n}}. \qquad (8)$$

As an example suppose we take the data given in Fig. 81 of Art. 88 and represented graphically in Fig. 82. Since the position of no one of the shots is given exactly, their average deviation cannot be found without further assumption. We shall find the average deviation (arithmetic mean of the deviations) of the shots from the middle line of the largest rectangle (the origin of Fig. 82) under the assumption that all the shots in any interval -0.5 to 0.5, 0.5 to 1.5, etc., Fig. 82, are located at the midpoint of that interval, 0, 1, etc., respectively. Following are listed, in the first column, the number of shots; in the second column, their corresponding deviations from 0; in the third column, the products of the corresponding entries in the first two columns. The sum of the third column divided by the sum of the first column will then be the arithmetic mean of the deviations from 0.

2	-5	−10
16	−4	−64
79	−3	-237
193	−2	−386
204	−1	−204
212	0	0
190	1	190
89	2	178
10	3	30
4	4	16
1	5	5
1000		−482

The mean deviation from 0 is therefore -0.482 or, say, -0.5.

We now compute the sum of the squares of the residuals, that is, the sum of the squares of the deviations measured from the arithmetic mean of the deviations, namely, from -0.5. Following are listed, in the first column, the number of shots; in the second column, the corresponding residuals; in the third column, the squares of the residuals; and in the fourth column, the product of the entries in the first and third columns, thus multiplying each value of ρ^2 by the number of times it occurs, so that the sum of the fourth column is $\Sigma\rho^2$.

2	−4.5	20.25	40.5
16	−3.5	12.25	196.
79	−2.5	6.25	493.75
193	−1.5	2.25	434.25
204	−0.5	0.25	51.
212	0.5	0.25	53.
190	1.5	2.25	427.5
89	2.5	6.25	556.25
10	3.5	12.25	122.5
4	4.5	20.25	81.
1	5.5	30.25	30.25
			$2486. = \Sigma\rho^2$

The standard deviation is

$$\sigma = \sqrt{\frac{\Sigma\rho^2}{n}} = \sqrt{2.486} = 1.58,$$

and the probable error of a single shot is

$$\epsilon = 0.6745\sigma = 1.06.$$

If we assume that the shots in each interval, -0.5 to 0.5, 0.5 to 1.5, etc., are uniformly distributed, we find that the number of shots within a range of σ on either side of -0.5, that is between -2.08 and 1.08, is $204 + 212 + 0.58(193 + 190) = 638$, or 64%. The number within a range of $2\sigma = 3.16$ is $79 + 193 + 204 + 212 + 190 + 89 + 0.16(16 + 10) = 971$, or 97%, and the number within a range of $3\sigma = 4.74$ is all but $1 + 0.26(2 + 4) = 3$, or 99.7%. These percentages agree with the theoretical ones for a normal distribution, namely 68.3, 95.4, and 99.7, as well as could be expected, considering the assumptions made and the number of shots yielding the data. Furthermore, the number of deviations within a range of ϵ on either side of -0.5, that is, between -1.56 and 0.56, is $204 + 212 + 0.06(193 + 190) = 439$, or 43.9%, compared with the theoretical value of 50%.

As another example, from the 12 measurements of a base line given in the first column of the following table, find the length of the line L (arithmetic mean of the measurements), the standard deviation σ, the probable error of an observation ϵ, the measure of precision h, and the probable number of deviations within a range of 0.1 on either side of the mean if 88 more observations were taken with the same precision.

506.65	0.10	0.0100
.20	-0.35	0.1225
.45	-0.10	0.0100
.43	-0.12	0.0144
.73	0.18	0.0324
.50	-0.05	0.0025
.80	0.25	0.0625
.50	-0.05	0.0025
.38	-0.17	0.0289
.55	0.00	0.0000
.85	0.30	0.0900
.53	-0.02	0.0004
$12)\ \overline{\ 6.57}$		$\overline{0.3761} = \Sigma\rho^2$

$$L = 506.55$$

In the second column we have the residuals (deviations from the mean $L = 506.55$), and in the third column the squares of the residuals. Hence

$$\sigma = \sqrt{\frac{\Sigma\rho^2}{n}} = \sqrt{\frac{0.3761}{12}} = 0.18^-,$$

$$\epsilon = 0.6745\sigma = 0.12^-,$$

$$h = \sqrt{\frac{n}{2\Sigma\rho^2}} = \sqrt{\frac{6}{0.3761}} = 4.0.$$

The probability of a deviation between -0.1 and 0.1 is

$$\frac{2}{\sqrt{\pi}} \int_0^{(4.0)(0.1)} e^{-x^2}\, dx = \frac{2}{\sqrt{\pi}} \int_0^{0.4} e^{-x^2}\, dx = 0.43,$$

so that if 88 more observations were taken, then, out of the 100 observations, 43 would probably deviate from the mean by not more than 0.1.

We notice that, of the 12 observations, 67% have residuals between $-\sigma$ and σ, and 100% lie within a range of 2σ on either side of the mean, a result agreeing closely enough with the theoretical percentages, considering the small number of observations. Furthermore 50% of the residuals lie between $-\epsilon$ and ϵ.

Note on measures of dispersion. In determining the best value for a quantity by taking the arithmetic mean of a set of observed values, it is desirable to have an accompanying number which will indicate the measure of precision or the measure of dispersion of the observations, but there is no uniformity in the use of such a number. By making certain more or less reasonable assumptions it is possible to obtain a value for h which is $\sqrt{(n-1)/n}$ times the value given in (5); then, according to this theory, a number μ (mean-square error of a single observation) is used, which is $\sqrt{n/(n-1)}$ times the standard deviation, and a number ϵ (probable error of a single observation) is used, which is $\sqrt{n/(n-1)}$ times the value of ϵ used above. Thus *

$$h = \sqrt{\frac{n-1}{2\Sigma\rho^2}}, \qquad \mu = \sqrt{\frac{\Sigma\rho^2}{n-1}}, \qquad \epsilon = 0.6745\sqrt{\frac{\Sigma\rho^2}{n-1}}. \qquad (8')$$

The values of h, μ, ϵ computed from formulas (8') differ slightly from the values of h, σ, ϵ computed from formulas (8), and the difference vanishes with increasing n. Even for $n = 12$ in the previous example on base-line measurements where we found from (8),

$$h = 4.0, \qquad \sigma = 0.18^-, \qquad \epsilon = 0.12^-,$$

we would have from (8')

$$h = 3.8, \qquad \mu = 0.18^+, \qquad \epsilon = 0.12^+.$$

Instead of the numbers σ, ϵ of (8) or μ, ϵ of (8'), any numbers proportional to them could be used as measures of dispersion. We may

---

* See, e.g., D. P. Bartlett, "The Method of Least Squares," and O. M. Leland, "Practical Least Squares."

divide each of these numbers by $\sqrt{n}$ and obtain from (8),

$$\sigma_m = \frac{\sqrt{\Sigma\rho^2}}{n}, \qquad \epsilon_m = 0.6745\,\frac{\sqrt{\Sigma\rho^2}}{n}, \qquad (9)$$

or from (8′)

$$\mu_m = \sqrt{\frac{\Sigma\rho^2}{n(n-1)}}, \qquad \epsilon_m = 0.6745\sqrt{\frac{\Sigma\rho^2}{n(n-1)}}. \qquad (9')$$

The numbers σ_m, μ_m, ϵ_m are called, respectively, the standard deviation of the mean, the mean-square error of the mean, and the probable error of the mean. In writing the value of an arithmetic mean, one of these numbers is sometimes attached to it with a $\pm$ sign, but the usage is not standard in this respect. One must be familiar with the notation of the author in order to know the meaning of the number used. Perhaps the second number of (9′) is the most common; using it we would have for the data given in the previous base-line measurements,

$$\epsilon_m = 0.6745\sqrt{\frac{0.3761}{12\times 11}} = 0.036,$$

and the length of the line would be written

$$L = 506.55 \pm 0.036.$$

In some books the number ϵ_m of (9) is used, which here would be

$$\epsilon_m = 0.6745\,\frac{\sqrt{0.3761}}{12} = 0.034,$$

or ϵ of (8) is used (enclosed in parentheses).* Thus the length of the above base line would be written

$$L = 506.55 \pm 0.034,$$

or

$$L = 506.55\ (\pm 0.12).$$

It is of little importance which of the values of h in (8) or (8′) † or which measure of dispersion is used. We shall avoid the $\pm$ attachment to a mean, and use formulas (8) for determining h, σ, and ϵ.

* For example, C. H. Forsyth, "An Introduction to the Mathematical Analysis of Statistics," Art. 63.
† See R. v. Mises, "Vorlesungen aus dem Gebiete der angewandten Mathematik," Bd. I, Abschnitt III, §12, for a statement of the hypotheses leading to different formulas for measures of dispersion, and a critical discussion thereof.

PROBLEMS

1. Show that the standard deviation is the abscissa of a point of inflection on the probability curve.

2. Locate the points on the probability curve which are nearest the origin.

3. Show that, as h varies, the tangent line to the probability curve at a point of inflection envelops an equilateral hyperbola.

4. In a series of observations of an angle taken to tenths of a second with $h = 0.447$, find (a) the probability of an error between 1.0" and 1.1"; (b) the probability that the error is not numerically greater than 3".

5. A line is measured 400 times, and the probable error of each observation is 0.3 cm. How many positive errors should occur between 0.2 and 0.4 cm.?

6. The weights and volumes of ten samples of a homogeneous substance are measured and the following values of specific gravity are computed. Find the mean value and the standard deviation.

1.736	1.738
1.745	1.751
1.743	1.740
1.739	1.738
1.747	1.752

7. The time required for a body to fall freely in a vacuum through each of ten distances is measured and the following values of the gravity constant are computed. Find the mean value and the standard deviation.

32.12	32.13
32.21	32.20
32.18	32.15
32.16	32.25
32.23	32.19

8. Find the standard deviation and the mean of the following chest measurements of 10,000 men. x = chest measurement in inches, y = number of men.

x	y	x	y
33	5	41	1643
34	38	42	1127
35	127	43	595
36	334	44	220
37	745	45	82
38	1306	46	28
39	1804	47	7
40	1935	48	4

9. From the following observations on the length of an iron bar, find (a) the length of the bar and the standard deviation; (b) the probable error of an observation; (c) the number of residuals numerically between 0.01 and 0.02 theoretically and compare with the actual number; (d) the probability that another measurement taken under the same conditions will deviate from the mean by more than 0.006 numerically.

83.284	83.321
.302	.304
.255	.295
.273	.263
.310	.270

10. From the following twenty angle measurements find the value of the angle, the standard deviation, and the probable error of a single observation.

97° 36′ 39.05″	97° 36′ 40.45″
37.55	34.40
41.45	40.30
38.95	41.45
43.15	42.05
37.75	40.35
40.75	38.25
40.95	37.15
39.00	38.65
36.70	40.70

90. The method of least squares. Let $s_1, s_2, \cdots, s_n$ be n observed values of a quantity, and let S represent the sum of the squares of their deviations from a number q:

$$S = (s_1 - q)^2 + (s_2 - q)^2 + \cdots + (s_n - q)^2. \tag{1}$$

We shall show that S is a minimum when q is equal to the arithmetic mean of the observed values. Differentiating (1) with respect to q, we have

$$\frac{dS}{dq} = -2(s_1 - q) - 2(s_2 - q) - \cdots - 2(s_n - q) = -2(\Sigma s - nq).$$

This derivative vanishes when $q = \Sigma s/n$, and since $d^2S/dq^2 = 2n > 0$, S will have its minimum value.

In Art. 88 we assigned the value $\Sigma s/n$ as the best approximation to the measured quantity z which could be obtained from n observations. We can now also say that we assigned to z a value such that, when the deviations of the observed values are measured from it, the sum of the squares of these deviations is least. This is the principle of least squares as applied to direct measurements of one unknown: Choose as the best approximation to the unknown that value which minimizes the sum of the squares of the deviations from it of the observed values. Here the value chosen for the unknown is simply the arithmetic mean of the observed values.

Suppose, however, that the unknown is to be determined by indirect observations. For example, suppose that we are to determine the area of a circle, not by measuring the area directly, but by taking n measurements of the diameter. Should we compute the n corresponding values of the area and then average them, or should we first average the n measurements of the diameter and then compute the area?

The diameter is the quantity measured, the measured values being, say, $d_1, d_2, \cdots, d_n$. The unknown area A is connected with d by the formula $A = \pi d^2/4$, or $\sqrt{4A/\pi} = d$. The principle of least squares now becomes: Choose as the best approximation to the unknown that value which minimizes the sum of the squares of the deviations of the observed values from the value which the observed quantity would have if computed from the chosen value of the unknown. Applying this principle, we choose that value for A which minimizes the sum of the squares of the differences between the observed values of d and the value of d computed from the formula $d = \sqrt{4A/\pi}$. Hence we minimize

$$ S = \left(d_1 - \sqrt{\frac{4A}{\pi}} \right)^2 + \left(d_2 - \sqrt{\frac{4A}{\pi}} \right)^2 + \cdots + \left(d_n - \sqrt{\frac{4A}{\pi}} \right)^2. $$

Differentiating with respect to A, we have

$$ \frac{dS}{dA} = -\sqrt{\frac{4}{\pi A}} \left(d_1 - \sqrt{\frac{4A}{\pi}} \right) - \sqrt{\frac{4}{\pi A}} \left(d_2 - \sqrt{\frac{4A}{\pi}} \right) - \cdots $$

$$ - \sqrt{\frac{4}{\pi A}} \left(d_n - \sqrt{\frac{4A}{\pi}} \right) = -\frac{2}{\sqrt{\pi A}} \left(\Sigma d - n \sqrt{\frac{4A}{\pi}} \right), $$

which vanishes when $A = \dfrac{\pi}{4} \left(\dfrac{\Sigma d}{n} \right)^2$. The best approximation to A, obtainable from the n observations of the diameter, is therefore found by first averaging the n measurements of the diameter and then computing the area.

Suppose next that x and y are two related variables and that, corresponding to a set of values of x, we have measured a set of values of y. Suppose further that, taking the values of x as abscissas, we have plotted the values of y as ordinates and have found that the points follow approximately a straight line. How shall we find the equation of the straight line which best approximates the linear law connecting y and x, i.e., the equation of the line which best fits the data? If $y = a + bx$ represents the equation of the line, a rough graphical method of determining a and b would be to draw a line by guess, which would seem to best fit the plotted points, then measure a, the y-intercept, and determine b as the negative quotient of the y- and x-intercepts. We shall, however, solve the problem by the method of least squares.

Corresponding to the values x_1, x_2, $\cdots$, x_n of x suppose that we have observed the values y_1, y_2, $\cdots$, y_n of y, and suppose that we know, or have found by plotting, that the points (x_1, y_1), (x_2, y_2), $\cdots$, (x_n, y_n) follow approximately a straight line. We write the so-called observation equations,

$$
\begin{aligned}
y_1 &= a + bx_1, \\
y_2 &= a + bx_2, \\
&\cdots\cdots, \\
y_n &= a + bx_n.
\end{aligned}
\tag{2}
$$

Here there are two unknowns a and b to be determined from n observation equations. It is assumed that $n > 2$; if n were equal to 2 the two equations could be solved exactly for the two unknowns. The principle of least squares now becomes: Choose as the best approximation to the unknowns those values which minimize the sum of the squares of the deviations of the observed values from the corresponding values which the observed quantity would have if computed from the chosen values of the unknowns. Applying this principle, we minimize

$$S = [y_1 - (a + bx_1)]^2 + [y_2 - (a + bx_2)]^2 + \cdots + [y_n - (a + bx_n)]^2.$$

Now S is a function of the two unknowns a and b; hence, in order to minimize S, we equate to zero its two partial derivatives with respect to a and b:

$$
\begin{aligned}
\frac{\partial S}{\partial a} &= -2[y_1 - (a + bx_1)] - 2[y_2 - (a + bx_2)] - \cdots \\
&\qquad\qquad\qquad\qquad - 2[y_n - (a + bx_n)] = 0, \\
\frac{\partial S}{\partial b} &= -2x_1[y_1 - (a + bx_1)] - 2x_2[y_2 - (a + bx_2)] - \cdots \\
&\qquad\qquad\qquad\qquad - 2x_n[y_n - (a + bx_n)] = 0,
\end{aligned}
$$

from which

$$
\begin{aligned}
na + (\Sigma x)b &= \Sigma y, \\
(\Sigma x)a + (\Sigma x^2)b &= \Sigma xy.
\end{aligned}
\tag{3}
$$

Solving equations (3) for a and b, we have

$$a = \frac{N_a}{D}, \qquad b = \frac{N_b}{D}, \tag{4}$$

where

$$D = \begin{vmatrix} n & \Sigma x \\ \Sigma x & \Sigma x^2 \end{vmatrix}, \qquad N_a = \begin{vmatrix} \Sigma y & \Sigma x \\ \Sigma xy & \Sigma x^2 \end{vmatrix}, \qquad N_b = \begin{vmatrix} n & \Sigma y \\ \Sigma x & \Sigma xy \end{vmatrix}.$$

When a and b have been determined from formulas (4), the line $y = a + bx$ will best fit the plotted points; it will not necessarily pass through any of the points, but the sum of the squares of the vertical deviations of the plotted points from this line will be less than for any other straight line that could be drawn.

As an example, let y (gm.) be the weight of potassium chloride which will dissolve in 100 gm. of water at temperature $x°$ C. Suppose that, corresponding to the temperatures x given in the first column, we have the measured values of y given in the second column, whence we compute the corresponding values of x^2 and xy in the third and fourth columns:

x	y	x^2	xy
0	27.6	0	0
10	31.0	100	310
20	34.0	400	680
30	37.0	900	1,110
40	40.0	1,600	1,600
50	42.6	2,500	2,130
60	45.5	3,600	2,730
70	48.3	4,900	3,381
80	51.1	6,400	4,088
90	54.0	8,100	4,860
100	56.7	10,000	5,670
550	467.8	38,500	26,559

Using formulas (4), we have

$$D = \begin{vmatrix} 11 & 550 \\ 550 & 38,500 \end{vmatrix} = 121,000,$$

$$N_a = \begin{vmatrix} 467.8 & 550 \\ 26,559 & 38,500 \end{vmatrix} = 3,402,850,$$

$$N_b = \begin{vmatrix} 11 & 467.8 \\ 550 & 26,559 \end{vmatrix} = 34,859,$$

$$a = \frac{3403}{121} = 28.1, \qquad b = \frac{34.86}{121} = 0.288.$$

Hence the best linear law connecting x and y is

$$y = 28.1 + 0.288x. \tag{5}$$

We may compute the deviations of the measured values of y from the values of y, say y_c, as computed from equation (5). The algebraic sum of these deviations is theoretically zero, as indicated by equation (3) of Art. 88, but will usually differ from zero on account of the decimal approximations in (5). We also compute below the sum of the squares of these deviations; this number is smaller than it would be if any other linear law than (5) were used.

y	y_c	$y - y_c$	$(y - y_c)^2$
27.6	28.1	−0.5	0.25
31.0	31.0	0.0	0.00
34.0	33.9	0.1	0.01
37.0	36.7	0.3	0.09
40.0	39.6	0.4	0.16
42.6	42.5	0.1	0.01
45.5	45.4	0.1	0.01
48.3	48.3	0.0	0.00
51.1	51.1	0.0	0.00
54.0	54.0	0.0	0.00
56.7	56.9	−0.2	0.04
		0.3	0.57

Thus

$$\Sigma(y - y_c) = 0.3, \qquad \Sigma(y - y_c)^2 = 0.57.$$

PROBLEMS

1. Determine the volume of a sphere from the following measurements of the diameter in millimeters: 3.63, 3.59, 3.61, 3.57, 3.60.

2. If p is the pull required to lift a weight w by means of a pulley-block, find a linear law of the form $p = a + bw$ connecting p and w, using the following data.

$$w \text{ (lb.):} \quad 50 \quad 70 \quad 100 \quad 120$$
$$p \text{ (lb.):} \quad 12 \quad 15 \quad 21 \quad 25$$

Compute p when $w = 150$ lb. Also find the sum of the deviations and the sum of the squares of the deviations of the given values of p from the corresponding computed values.

3. In the following table y is the weight of potassium bromide which will dissolve in 100 gm. of water at temperature x.

x (° C.):	0	10	20	30	40	50	60	70	80	90	100
y (gm.):	53.5	59.5	65.2	70.6	75.5	80.2	85.5	90.0	95.0	99.2	104.0

Find a law of the form $y = a + bx$. Also find the sum of the deviations and the sum of the squares of the deviations of the given values of y from the corresponding computed values.

4. A simply supported beam carries a concentrated load P (lb.) at its midpoint. Corresponding to various values of P, the maximum deflection y (in.) is measured.

P:	100	120	140	160	180	200
y:	0.45	0.55	0.60	0.70	0.80	0.85

Find a law of the form $y = a + bP$.

5. If R is the resistance to the motion of a train at speed V, find a law of the form $R = a + bV^2$ connecting R with V.

V (mi./hr.):	10	20	30	40	50
R (lb./ton):	8	10	15	21	30

Note that R is linear in V^2.

6. In the design of elliptic gears for quick-return mechanisms,* the ratio b/a of the ellipse is related to the quick-return ratio r by the equation

$$\frac{b}{a} = \sqrt{\frac{2 \sin [\pi/(r + 1)]}{1 + \sin [\pi/(r + 1)]}}.$$

Taking $r = 1.5, 2.0, 2.5, 3.0, 3.5, 4.0,$ and 4.5, compute the corresponding values of b/a and find a linear relation of the form $b/a = A + Br$.

7. The maximum velocity ratio M for the elliptic gears of Problem 6 is given by

$$M = \tan \frac{\pi r}{2(r + 1)}.$$

Taking the values of r given in Problem 6, find a linear relation of the form $M = A + Br$ and the sum of the squares of the deviations.

8. A tank contains 100 gal. of brine in which 50 lb. of salt are dissolved. Brine containing 1 lb./gal. of salt enters the tank at the rate of 2 gal./min., and the mixture leaves the tank at the same rate. Hence the theoretical salt content Q (lb.) at time t (min.) is given by $Q = 100 - 50e^{-t/50}$ (cf. Art. 7). Measurements yield the following sets of values:

t (min.):	10	20	30	40	50	60
Q (lb.):	59	66	73	78	82	85

Assuming a relation of the form $Q = A + Be^{-t/50}$, compute the values of A and B from the above data and compare with the theoretical result.

9. In the following system of observation equations ($n > 2$), where x and y represent the unknowns,

$$a_1x + b_1y = s_1,$$

$$a_2x + b_2y = s_2,$$

$$\cdots \cdots \cdots,$$

$$a_nx + b_ny = s_n,$$

---

* See "Proportions of Elliptic Gears for Quick Return Mechanisms," F. H. Miller and C. H. Young, *Product Engineering*, July, 1945.

derive the approximate solution:

$$x = \frac{N_x}{D}, \qquad y = \frac{N_y}{D},$$

$$D = \begin{vmatrix} \Sigma a^2 & \Sigma ab \\ \Sigma ab & \Sigma b^2 \end{vmatrix}, \qquad N_x = \begin{vmatrix} \Sigma as & \Sigma ab \\ \Sigma bs & \Sigma b^2 \end{vmatrix}, \qquad N_y = \begin{vmatrix} \Sigma a^2 & \Sigma as \\ \Sigma ab & \Sigma bs \end{vmatrix}.$$

10. The altitudes of A above O, B above A, and B above O are found by measurement to be, respectively, 24.5, 28.0, and 53.0 ft. Apply the result of Problem 9 to find the adjusted value of A above O.

11. Find the best values of x and y to three decimal places from the equations:

$$2x + y + 1 = 0,$$
$$x - 3y + 4 = 0,$$
$$x + 4y - 3 = 0,$$
$$3x - 2y + 6 = 0,$$
$$-x + 2y - 3 = 0,$$
$$x + 3y - 2 = 0.$$

Use the formulas of Problem 9.

12. In an experiment for determining the resistance of a Wheatstone bridge wire, the following observation equations were obtained, where x is the resistance of the bridge wire in ohms, and c that of the connections:

$$0.1x + c = 0.224, \qquad 0.6x + c = 1.208,$$
$$0.2x + c = 0.430, \qquad 0.7x + c = 1.412,$$
$$0.3x + c = 0.615, \qquad 0.8x + c = 1.603,$$
$$0.4x + c = 0.826, \qquad 0.9x + c = 1.798,$$
$$0.5x + c = 1.040, \qquad 1.0x + c = 1.990.$$

Using the formulas of Problem 9, find the resistance of the bridge wire.

13. The weights of three solids were determined by means of an equal-arm balance. Enough standard weights to make all the measurements directly not being available, the following observation equations were obtained by varying the distribution of the solids, x, y, and z representing their weights in grams.

$$x - y = 3.1,$$
$$y - z = 1.5,$$
$$x - z = 4.9,$$
$$x - y + z = 5.5.$$

Obtain values for x, y, and z.

14. Find a law of the form $e = at + bt^2$ from the data in the following table, where e is the thermoelectric e.m.f. at the junction of copper and lead at a temperature $t°$ C. when the other junction is at $10°$ C.

$t(° C.)$:	-200	-100	100	200
$e(10^{-6} \text{ volt})$:	-490	-280	350	770

15. Four points in the order P_1, P_2, P_3, P_4 lie on a line. From a point O outside the line the following angle measurements are taken:

$$\angle P_1OP_2 = 8° \; 27' \; 42.8'',$$

$$\angle P_1OP_3 = 12° \; 45' \; 16.3'',$$

$$\angle P_1OP_4 = 21° \; 13' \; 28.5'',$$

$$\angle P_2OP_3 = 4° \; 17' \; 34.0'',$$

$$\angle P_2OP_4 = 12° \; 45' \; 45.5''.$$

Letting x, y, z represent the excesses of angles P_1OP_2, P_1OP_3, P_1OP_4 over $8° \; 27' \; 42.8''$, $12° \; 45' \; 16.3''$, and $21° \; 13' \; 28.5''$, respectively, the observation equations can be written in the simple form:

$$x = 0,$$

$$y = 0,$$

$$z = 0,$$

$$y - x = 0.5,$$

$$z - x = -0.2.$$

Find the adjusted value of the angle P_1OP_4.

91. Numerical solution of ordinary differential equations. Methods of solving differential equations treated in Chapter I were restricted to certain special types of equations whose integrals are expressible as finite functional relations. Picard's method and the method of Frobenius (Chapter IV) are less restrictive in scope, but these likewise aim to find analytical expressions, either as finite approximating functions or as infinite series in the independent variable, from which numerical results can be computed.

At this point we shall consider a different kind of approach, one which is arithmetic rather than analytic. There are many types of numerical methods; only the most elementary will be touched upon here.*

Let there be given a first order differential equation,

$$y' = F(x, y), \tag{1}$$

where $y' = dy/dx$, together with the condition that y shall have the value y_0 when $x = x_0$. We seek a solution

$$y = f(x), \tag{2}$$

---

* A comprehensive treatment of modern techniques will be found in W. E. Milne's "Numerical Solution of Differential Equations." For related numerical methods involving difference equations and interpolation processes, see also W. E. Milne's "Numerical Calculus," L. M. Milne-Thompson's "Calculus of Finite Differences," J. B. Scarborough's "Numerical Mathematical Analysis," E. T. Whittaker and G. Robinson's "Calculus of Observations."

such that $y_0 = f(x_0)$. Let x_0, x_1, x_2, $\cdots$ be equally spaced values of x, so that $x_{n+1} - x_n = h$, a constant, for $n = 0, 1, 2, \cdots$. Setting $y_n = f(x_n)$, we have, by definition,

$$y_n' = \lim_{x_{n+1} \to x_n} \frac{y_{n+1} - y_n}{x_{n+1} - x_n} = \lim_{h \to 0} \frac{y_{n+1} - y_n}{h}.$$

In place of the given differential equation (1), we then deal with the corresponding *difference equation*

$$\frac{y_{n+1} - y_n}{h} = F(x_n, y_n),$$

or

$$y_{n+1} = y_n + hF(x_n, y_n) = y_n + y_n'h. \tag{3}$$

One fairly obvious way to proceed would be this. Choose a small value of h and, with $n = 0$, compute $y_1 = y_0 + hF(x_0, y_0)$; with $n = 1$, we then calculate $y_2 = y_1 + hF(x_1, y_1)$; and so on, until we arrive at the approximation y_N for the value of y corresponding to $x = x_N$. However, there is no way, in general, of determining how good such an approximation will be; evidently one arbitrarily chosen value of h may give a sufficiently accurate result for some functions $F(x, y)$ and when the final value $n = N$ is not too large, whereas other functions $F(x, y)$ or still larger final values $n = N$ might require a smaller value of h and a considerable amount of tedious calculation to achieve comparable accuracy.

To get an idea of the reliability of our method, let us examine the Taylor's series for the unknown function $f(x)$ in powers of $x - x_n$ (cf. equation (6), Art. 37):

$$f(x) = f(x_n) + f'(x_n)(x - x_n) + \frac{f''(x_n)}{2!}(x - x_n)^2 + \cdots. \tag{4}$$

Let $x = x_{n+1}$, so that $x - x_n = x_{n+1} - x_n = h$; also, using $y_n = f(x_n)$ for convenience, we then have

$$y_{n+1} = y_n + y_n'h + \frac{y_n''}{2!}h^2 + \frac{y_n'''}{3!}h^3 + \cdots. \tag{5}$$

Comparing (3) with (5), we see that the error introduced by using the difference equation (3) is due to the dropping of terms involving h^2 and higher powers of h. We say then that the error involved is of the order of h^2.

Now, to improve the efficiency of the method, we proceed as follows. Let $x = x_{n-1}$ in (4), so that $x - x_n = x_{n-1} - x_n = -h$; then we get

$$y_{n-1} = y_n - y_n'h + \frac{y_n''}{2!}h^2 - \frac{y_n'''}{3!}h^3 + \cdots,$$

and subtraction from (5) yields

$$y_{n+1} = y_{n-1} + 2y_n'h + \frac{y_n'''}{3}h^3 + \cdots. \qquad (6)$$

Accordingly, we may use, instead of (3), the relation

$$y_{n+1} = y_{n-1} + 2y_n'h; \qquad (7)$$

then the error will be of the order of h^3, which, for h sufficiently small, may be expected to be less than when the second power of h is neglected.

Since y_{n-1} appears in (7), this formula first gives, for $n = 1$, $y_2 = y_0 + 2y_1'h$. Accordingly, we must compute y_1 and y_1' by other means to get started on the iterative process. To be consistent with our wish to neglect only third and higher powers of h, we use the first three terms of (5) in the computation of y_1; that is, we calculate

$$y_1 = y_0 + y_0'h + \tfrac{1}{2}y_0''h^2. \qquad (8)$$

The values x_0 and y_0 being given, we thus have to evaluate $y_0' = F(x_0, y_0)$ from the given differential equation (1), and then y_0'' from the result of differentiating (1),

$$y'' = \frac{\partial F}{\partial x} + \frac{\partial F}{\partial y}y', \qquad (9)$$

wherein we put $x = x_0$, $y = y_0$, $y' = y_0'$. The method therefore involves the following successive steps.

1. Use the given differential equation (1) to get $y_0' = F(x_0, y_0)$, and (9) to compute y_0''.

2. Using y_0, y_0', and y_0'', together with a chosen value of h, find y_1 from (8). With $x_1 = x_0 + h$ and y_1, calculate y_1' from (1).

3. From formula (7), get $y_2 = y_0 + 2y_1'h$. With $x_2 = x_1 + h$, find y_2' from (1).

4. Repeat step 3 for y_3 and y_3', y_4 and y_4', and so on, through as many stages as desired.

Example. Find the maximum value of y if

$$y' = \frac{10^6}{(100 + x)^3} - \frac{y}{50}; \qquad x_0 = 0, y_0 = 0. \qquad (10)$$

This differential equation arises in the solution of Problem 4, Art. 42; here x represents time (min.) and y the quantity (lb.) of salt in tank B. By the conditions of that problem, tank B (which originally contains only water) receives salt from tank A; but since the contents of A are being steadily diluted, the amount of salt in B must reach a maximum and thereafter decrease. Although the use of power series serves to determine y for any value of x less than 100 min., this method fails beyond that time; likewise, Picard's method determines y for a given time x, but the successive integrations become more and more complicated, and higher approximations are needed to determine y for relatively large values of x in order to attain a reasonable accuracy. Moreover, neither of those two methods is well suited to the problem of studying the time-variation of salt content, as is needed here to find the maximum value of y.

The steps in the solution are as follows.

1. From (10) we get $y_0' = 10^6/(100)^3 - 0 = 1$, and also

$$ y'' = -\frac{3 \times 10^6}{(100 + x)^4} - \frac{y'}{50}, $$

whence $y_0'' = -3 \times 10^6/(100)^4 - \frac{1}{50} = -0.05$.

2. Let us arbitrarily choose $h = 1$ min.* Then (8) gives $y_1 = 0 + (1)(1) - \frac{1}{2}(0.05) = 0.975$, and therefore $y_1' = 10^6/(101)^3 - 0.975/50 = 0.9511$, by (10).

3. Formula (7), with $n = 1$, yields $y_2 = 0 + 2(0.9511)(1) = 1.902$, whence (10) gives $y_2' = 10^6/(102)^3 - 1.902/50 = 0.9043$.

4. The following stages are indicated, in part, below.

n	y_{n+1}	y_{n+1}'	n	y_{n+1}	y_{n+1}'
2	2.784	0.8594	..	......	....
3	3.621	0.8166	42	15.872	0.0247
4	4.417	0.7755	43	15.889	0.0171
5	5.172	0.7363	44	15.906	0.0099
6	5.889	0.6985	45	15.909	0.0031
7	6.569	0.6625	46	15.912	-0.0034
8	7.214	0.6279	47	15.902	-0.0096
9	7.824	0.5949	48	15.893	-0.0156
..	.....	......	49	15.872	-0.0211

The slope y_n' gradually decreases, changing sign between $x = 46$ and $x = 47$ min. It appears that the maximum value of y is a little more than 15.9 lb.

A variant of the above method, which provides improvement in accuracy and a partial check of the calculations, may be devised in the following way. Instead of using y_n' in difference equation (3), we take the average of the slopes y_n' and y_{n+1}' to provide the so-called trapezoidal formula

$$ y_{n+1} = y_n + \frac{1}{2}(y_n' + y_{n+1}')h. \tag{11} $$

The iterative process then consists of these steps, at the nth stage.

* This choice, upon which the accuracy of the result depends, is necessarily difficult to make in the absence of further knowledge about the variation of y as x increases. Experience with numerical analysis naturally is a help and, as will be indicated later, there exist refinements and checks for the present method.

1. Compute a trial value of y_{n+1}, which may be denoted by $\bar{y}_{n+1}$, from formula (7),

$$\bar{y}_{n+1} = y_{n-1} + 2y_n'h,$$

and the corresponding value of y_{n+1}' from the differential equation (1),

$$\bar{y}_{n+1}' = F(x_{n+1}, \bar{y}_{n+1}).$$

2. Adjust to a second value of y_n, say $\bar{\bar{y}}_{n+1}$, using trapezoidal formula (11),

$$\bar{\bar{y}}_{n+1} = y_n + \tfrac{1}{2}(y_n' + \bar{y}_{n+1}')h,$$

and get $\bar{\bar{y}}_{n+1}' = F(x_{n+1}, \bar{\bar{y}}_{n+1})$.

3. Repeat steps 1 and 2 until no further changes occur in y_{n+1} and y_{n+1}'.

Applied to the illustrative example, for $n = 2$, this new procedure gives $\bar{y}_3 = 2.784$ and $\bar{y}_3' = 0.8594$ (the tabulated values) as trial figures. Then (11) yields

$$\bar{\bar{y}} = 1.902 + \tfrac{1}{2}(0.9043 + 0.8594) = 2.784 = \bar{y}_3,$$

so that no adjustment is needed. On the other hand, for $n = 44$, say, we have $\bar{y}_{45} = 15.906$ and $\bar{y}_{45}' = 0.0099$ as trial values, whence

$$\bar{\bar{y}}_{45} = 15.889 + \tfrac{1}{2}(0.0171 + 0.0099) = 15.903,$$

$$\bar{\bar{y}}_{45}' = \frac{10^6}{(145)^3} - \frac{15.903}{50} = 0.0100.$$

The small difference between $\bar{y}_{45}'$ and $\bar{\bar{y}}_{45}'$ requires no further adjustment, so we take $y_{45} = 15.903$ in place of 15.906, if that much accuracy is warranted and desired. To derive benefit from this method as a refinement of the first, it should of course be used consistently from the beginning of the computation.

In the problems following Art. 92, extensions of the basic methods to the solution of higher order equations and systems of equations are given.

92. Partial differential equations.

Methods for finding numerical solutions of partial differential equations are not, on the whole, as broad in scope as are those devised for solving ordinary equations. Instead, the well-developed and widely used processes are restricted to linear partial equations, mainly those arising in engineering and physics, such as those considered in Chapter VII. Here only a single method will be considered, in connection with a vibrating string problem.

Suppose a taut string of length L (ft.) to be originally at rest in its equilibrium position, the portion of the x-axis from $x = 0$ to $x = L$.

Assuming the displacement y, at distance x (ft.) along the string and at time t (sec.), to be small compared to L, we have the partial differential equation (Art. 70)

$$\frac{\partial^2 y}{\partial t^2} = a^2 \frac{\partial^2 y}{\partial x^2}, \tag{1}$$

where $a = \sqrt{Fg/w}$ (ft./sec.). Let the end $x = L$ be kept fixed, and set the string vibrating by giving to the end $x = 0$ the simple harmonic motion $y = A \sin (a\pi t/L)$. Then the boundary and initial conditions accompanying equation (1) are

$$y(0,\, t) = A \sin \frac{a\pi t}{L}, \qquad y(L,\, t) = 0; \tag{2}$$

$$y(x,\, 0) = 0, \qquad \frac{\partial y}{\partial t}\bigg]_{t=0} = 0. \tag{3}$$

The method of separation of variables previously used does not serve to attack this problem. However, it should be noted that the solutions obtained for the natural vibrations of the string with both ends fixed were periodic functions of time t, the period being $2L/a$ (cf. relation (4), Art. 70), the same as that of the motion imparted here to the end $x = 0$. Accordingly, we may expect a condition of resonance in the present problem.

As in the preceding article, we shall deal with a difference equation. For time $t = t_n$, let $x_{m+1} - x_m = h$ $(m = 0, 1, 2, \cdots)$. Then we have the difference quotient

$$\frac{y(x_{m+1},\, t_n) - y(x_m,\, t_n)}{h} \tag{4}$$

corresponding to the partial derivative $\partial y/\partial x$. Hence we further have

$$\frac{\dfrac{y(x_{m+1},\, t_n) - y(x_m,\, t_n)}{h} - \dfrac{y(x_m,\, t_n) - y(x_{m-1},\, t_n)}{h}}{h}$$

$$= \frac{y(x_{m+1},\, t_n) - 2y(x_m,\, t_n) + y(x_{m-1},\, t_n)}{h^2} \tag{5}$$

corresponding to $\partial^2 y/\partial x^2$. Similarly, if we let $t_n - t_{n-1} = k$, we have, for $x = x_m$,

$$\frac{y(x_m,\, t_{n+1}) - y(x_m,\, t_n)}{k} \tag{6}$$

and

$$\frac{y(x_m,\, t_{n+1}) - 2y(x_m,\, t_n) + y(x_m,\, t_{n-1})}{k^2} \tag{7}$$

as the difference quotients corresponding to $\partial y/\partial t$ and $\partial^2 y/\partial t^2$, respectively. Consequently the difference equation corresponding to the partial differential equation (1) is

$$\frac{y(x_m, t_{n+1}) - 2y(x_m, t_n) + y(x_m, t_{n-1})}{k^2}$$

$$= a^2 \frac{y(x_{m+1}, t_n) - 2y(x_m, t_n) + y(x_{m-1}, t_n)}{h^2}. \qquad (8)$$

For convenience, we may take $h = ak$; then equation (8) reduces to the simpler form

$$y(x_m, t_{n+1}) = y(x_{m+1}, t_n) + y(x_{m-1}, t_n) - y(x_m, t_{n-1}). \qquad (9)$$

It turns out that solutions of the differential equation (1) are necessarily solutions of this difference equation (9) also.* Accordingly, (9) may be expected to produce accurate numerical results provided that the condition $h = ak$ is fulfilled.

To illustrate the procedure, let $h = L/5$, so that $k = L/5a$. For $m = 0, 1, 2, 3, 4$, and 5, we thus have $x = 0, L/5, 2L/5, 3L/5, 4L/5$, and L, respectively; for $n = 0, 1, 2, 3, \cdots$, we therefore have $t = 0, L/5a, 2L/5a, 3L/5a, \cdots$, whence $a\pi t/L = 0, \pi/5, 2\pi/5, 3\pi/5, \cdots$. In the tabulation below, the first column $(m = 0)$ lists the values of $y(0, t_n)/A = \sin{(n\pi/5)}$,† in accordance with the first of the initial conditions (2). The last column $(m = 5)$, of zeros, satisfies the other initial condition. The first row $(n = 0)$ contains only zeros, to meet the first of boundary conditions (3). Now, to deal with the remaining boundary condition for interior points, $0 < x < L$, of the string (that is, for $m = 1, 2, 3$, and 4), we use the difference quotient (6) corresponding to $\partial y/\partial t$. Putting $n = 0$ for $t = 0$, this yields the relation

$$y(x_m, t_1) = y(x_m, 0) = 0,$$

and therefore the four inner entries of the second row are all zeros. Using difference equation (9), the inner entries of the third and following rows are then readily computed, in turn. For example, when

---

* This follows from the fact that every solution of (1) is of the form $y(x, t) = f(x + at) + g(x - at)$. (See, for example, F. H. Miller, "Partial Differential Equations," Art. 62.) Substitution of this in (9) yields an identity if $h = ak$, as is here stipulated.

† Note that the amplitude coefficient A has been suppressed, for simplicity, and consequently *each* entry $y(x_m, t_n)$ must be multiplied by A to get the actual displacement. To be consistent with the assumptions made (Art. 70) in deriving equation (1), A is supposed to be small compared to L.

$m = 2$ and $n = 9$, we get

$$y(x_2, t_{10}) = y(x_3, t_9) + y(x_1, t_9) - y(x_2, t_8)$$
$$= -1.5389 - 0.9511 - (-0.5878) = -1.9022.$$

n \ m	0	1	2	3	4	5
0	0	0	0	0	0	0
1	0.5878	0	0	0	0	0
2	0.9511	0.5878	0	0	0	0
3	0.9511	0.9511	0.5878	0	0	0
4	0.5878	0.9511	0.9511	0.5878	0	0
5	0	0.5878	0.9511	0.9511	0.5878	0
6	−0.5878	0	0.5878	0.9511	0.9511	0
7	−0.9511	−0.5878	0	0.5878	0.3633	0
8	−0.9511	−0.9511	−0.5878	−0.5878	−0.3633	0
9	−0.5878	−0.9511	−1.5389	−1.5389	−0.9511	0
10	0	−1.1756	−1.9022	−1.9022	−1.1756	0

Only one cycle of oscillation of the end $x = 0$ has been treated in this tabulation, but the simple pattern of operations entailed in using relation (9) makes it easy to extend the table, if desired. The ten curves shown in Fig. 84 indicate successive positions of the string.

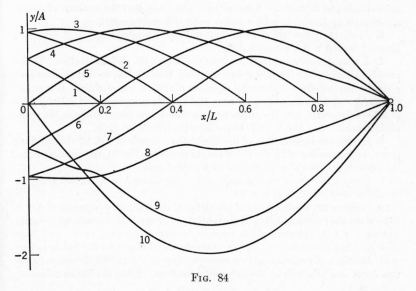

Fig. 84

The effect of resonance is already apparent after the first period, for then the (negative) displacement of the midpoint of the string is numerically twice as great as the amplitude of the motion performed by the end $x = 0$.   Continuation of the given calculations is called for in Problem 8, below; it will be found that departure from the equilibrium position becomes greater as time t increases, cycle by cycle.

With the aid of operational calculus, this problem may also be attacked analytically.   That will be done in Art. 115, using the powerful methods of the Laplace transformation.   We shall there find verification of the results obtained here by numerical methods, and of the inferences resulting from the preceding discussion and the accompanying Problems 8 and 9.

PROBLEMS

1. Taking $h = 2$, rework the illustrative example of Art. 91, and compare results for accuracy.

2. Taking $h = 5$, rework the illustrative example of Art. 91.   Plot the points (x, y) obtained, and from the graph estimate the maximum value of y.

3. Taking $h = 2$, but adjusting with values of $\bar{y}_n$ by means of the trapezoidal formula (11), Art. 91, rework Problem 1.

4. Using the trapezoidal formula for adjustment, rework Problem 2.

5. Show that the numerical methods of Art. 91 are applicable to a system of r first order differential equations involving one independent and r dependent variables.   Show also how a single differential equation of order r may be replaced by a system of r first order equations in the r variables representing the original dependent variable and its first $r - 1$ derivatives, and hence that the methods of Art. 91 are likewise applicable to such a higher order differential equation.

6. Apply the procedure of Problem 5 to Bessel's equation $xy'' + y' + xy = 0$. Hence, taking $h = 0.1$, compute $J_0(1)$.

7. A weight suspended from a spring oscillates with periodic motion.   Resistance is negligible, but the spring does not obey Hooke's law, so that the motion is given by the non-linear differential equation $d^2x/dt^2 = -x - x^3/10$.   If $x = 1$ ft. and $dx/dt = 0$ when time t (sec.) is zero, find the displacement x and velocity dx/dt at 0.1-sec. intervals, plot the points so determined, and hence evaluate the period of the motion.   As a check, find the period using elliptic integrals.

8. Extend the computation of the illustrative example of Art. 92 through three cycles, and determine, with the aid of graphs similar to Fig. 84, the displacement of the midpoint of the string at the end of the third cycle.

9. Rework the illustrative example of Art. 92, taking $h = L/10$, and verify the statement that $y(L/2, 2/a) = -2A$.

10. Suppose the left-hand end of the string of the illustrative example of Art. 92 to be given the motion $y(0, t) = A \sin(\pi at/2)$, other conditions remaining the same. Taking $h = L/5$, calculate $y(x, t)$ through twenty stages (one cycle), and hence show that this motion is periodic.   Draw displacement curves for the first ten stages.

11. Obtain a difference equation corresponding to the partial differential equation $\partial u/\partial t = \alpha^2(\partial^2 u/\partial x^2)$ by the following procedure.   Using the Taylor series

$$u(x_{m+1}, t_n) = u(x_m, t_n) + \frac{\partial u}{\partial x} h + \frac{\partial^2 u}{\partial x^2} \frac{h^2}{2} + \frac{\partial^3 u}{\partial x^3} \frac{h^3}{6} + \frac{\partial^4 u}{\partial x^4} \frac{h^4}{24} + \cdots,$$

where $h = x_{m+1} - x_m$ and the partial derivatives are evaluated at (x_m, t_n), together with that for $u(x_{m-1}, t_n)$, get the second difference quotient (multiplied by α^2)

$$\alpha^2 \frac{u(x_{m+1}, t_n) - 2u(x_m, t_n) + u(x_{m-1}, t_n)}{h^2} = \alpha^2 \frac{\partial^2 u}{\partial x^2} + \alpha^2 \frac{\partial^4 u}{\partial x^4} \frac{h^2}{12} + \cdots.$$

Similarly, with $k = t_{n+1} - t_n$, get the first difference quotient

$$\frac{u(x_m, t_{n+1}) - u(x_m, t_n)}{k} = \frac{\partial u}{\partial t} + \frac{\partial^2 u}{\partial t^2} \frac{k}{2} + \cdots$$

$$= \alpha^2 \frac{\partial^2 u}{\partial x^2} + \alpha^4 \frac{\partial^4 u}{\partial x^4} \frac{k}{2} + \cdots,$$

since $\partial u/\partial t = \alpha^2(\partial^2 u/\partial x^2)$, $\partial^2 u/\partial t^2 = \alpha^4(\partial^4 u/\partial x^4)$, $\cdots$. Now choose $k = h^2/6\alpha^2$ in order to eliminate $\partial^4 u/\partial x^4$ as well as $\partial^2 u/\partial x^2$, and hence derive the relation

$$u(x_m, t_{n+1}) = \tfrac{1}{6}[u(x_{m+1}, t_n) + 4u(x_m, t_n) + u(x_{m-1}, t_n)].$$

This is a difference equation which may be used for the numerical solution of problems in one-dimensional heat flow (Art. 71), electrical transmission in which leakance and inductance are negligible (Art. 74), diffusion (Art. 76), and other phenomena obeying a partial differential equation of the form $\partial u/\partial t = \alpha^2(\partial^2 u/\partial x^2)$. The error involved is of the order of h^4.

12. Use the difference equation of Problem 11 to find the temperature values $u(x, t)$ if the boundary and initial conditions are

$$u(0, t) = 0, \qquad u(10, t) = 0, \qquad u(x, 0) = \tfrac{1}{10}(10x - x^2)^2.$$

Take $h = 1$ and carry the computation through 30 time-stages. Note that, because of symmetry, only the left-hand half of the bar need be considered; that is, calculations need be made only for $m = 1, 2, 3, 4$, and 5. Check your results by using the analytical solution for $u(x, t)$ (see Problem 5, Art. 71) for the midpoint $x = 5$ and times given by $\alpha^2 t = 1, 2, 3, 4$, and 5.

CHAPTER X

Functions of a Complex Variable

93. Introduction. In most of the problems considered up to this point, the constants and variables involved have been real. This has seemed natural, since we should expect an application of a mathematical theory, in which the physical quantities have values represented by real numbers, to be concerned with reals throughout.

Our method of solving the eddy-current problem of Chapter VII, Art. 75, however, led us to consider complex functions from which the physical real expressions for field intensity and heat loss could be obtained. The student who has studied alternating-current-circuit theory will be aware that in this field also complex quantities provide a useful and convenient tool for the engineer.

It therefore seems desirable that we devote some time to the study of functions of a complex variable. Part I of this chapter is concerned with elementary considerations, and is to be regarded as an introduction to the general theory * and its applications. In Part II we discuss briefly, and without going deeply into the underlying theory, the Schwarz-Christoffel transformation and some of its uses in field problems of engineering. Part III deals with further portions of the theory of functions, which we employ in the evaluation of some definite integrals and which underlie the Bromwich treatment of operational methods (Chapter XI, Arts. 112–113).

PART I. ELEMENTARY THEORY OF ANALYTIC FUNCTIONS

94. Analytic functions. We begin by recalling some of the properties of a complex number $a + ib$, where a and b are real and $i = \sqrt{-1}$. Let θ, called the amplitude or argument of $a + ib$, denote the angle between the line drawn from the origin O to the point (a, b) and the

---

* The student will find in the second Carus Mathematical Monograph, "Analytic Functions of a Complex Variable," by D. R. Curtiss, an excellent introduction to the theory.

positive x-axis, and let r, called the modulus or absolute value of $a + ib$, be the length of the line from O to (a, b).   Then we have (Fig. 85)

$$a + ib = r \cos \theta + ir \sin \theta = r(\cos \theta + i \sin \theta),$$

$$r = \sqrt{a^2 + b^2} = |a + ib|,$$

$$\theta = \arctan (b/a) = \text{amp} (a + ib).$$

By Euler's relation, $e^{i\theta} = \cos \theta + i \sin \theta$.*   Hence we may write

$$a + ib = re^{i\theta}.$$

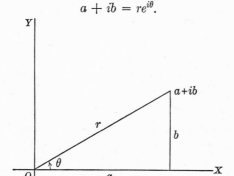

FIG. 85

From this polar representation of a complex number, the rules for the multiplication and division of two complex numbers and De Moivre's theorem follow immediately.   Thus,

$$(a_1 + ib_1) \cdot (a_2 + ib_2) = r_1 e^{i\theta_1} \cdot r_2 e^{i\theta_2} = r_1 r_2 e^{i(\theta_1 + \theta_2)},$$

$$\frac{a_1 + ib_1}{a_2 + ib_2} = \frac{r_1 e^{i\theta_1}}{r_2 e^{i\theta_2}} = \frac{r_1}{r_2} e^{i(\theta_1 - \theta_2)},$$

and

$$(a + ib)^m = (re^{i\theta})^m = r^m e^{im\theta},$$

where m is any real number.

Now let z represent the complex variable $x + iy$, where x and y are real, and let w be a function of z.   In the general sense of function, the latter statement means that, corresponding to each value of z in a given region R, we have one or more values of w.   But when z is given, x and y are known, and hence any complex function of x and y will be a function of z.   Consequently we write

$$w = u(x, y) + iv(x, y) = F(z), \tag{1}$$

where u and v are real functions of x and y.

* This relation is established later in this article.

Suppose now that we wish to find the rate of change of w with respect to z, when $w = F(z)$ is given by (1). For a real function of a single real variable, $y = f(x)$, we had as the rate of change of y with respect to x,

$$\frac{dy}{dx} = \lim_{\Delta x \to 0} \frac{f(x + \Delta x) - f(x)}{\Delta x},$$

by definition. Here no difficulty arose, provided merely that the limit existed, since Δx can approach zero in only one way, the variable x having, geometrically speaking, only one degree of freedom. But if we define the derivative of $w = F(z)$ analogously,

$$\frac{dw}{dz} = \lim_{\Delta z \to 0} \frac{F(z + \Delta z) - F(z)}{\Delta z},$$

as we should like to in order that a function of a real variable be merely a special case of the more general function of a complex variable, with formal differentiation the same for both kinds of function, we see that a complication arises. For any fixed z, to which the point P corresponds, the neighboring point Q, given by $z + \Delta z$, may approach P along any straight or curved path in R joining these points (Fig. 86).

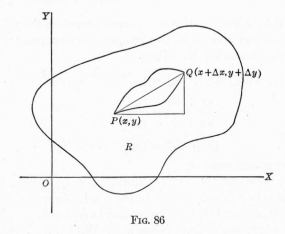

Fig. 86

Thus it appears that dw/dz may depend not only upon x and y (that is, upon z), but also upon the manner in which Δz approaches zero.

To illustrate the situation, consider the simple function obtained by taking $u = 2x + 1$, $v = -y$, so that

$$w = 2x + 1 - iy.$$

Then we get

$$\frac{\Delta w}{\Delta z} = \frac{2(x + \Delta x) + 1 - i(y + \Delta y) - 2x - 1 + iy}{\Delta x + i\,\Delta y}$$

$$= \frac{2\,\Delta x - i\,\Delta y}{\Delta x + i\,\Delta y}.$$

Now (Fig. 87) if Q is chosen on the horizontal line through $P(x, y)$, and

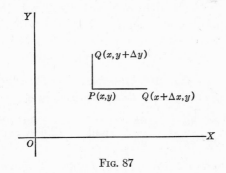

FIG. 87

Q then approaches P along this line, we shall have $\Delta y = 0$, $\Delta z = \Delta x$, and consequently

$$\frac{\Delta w}{\Delta z} = 2, \qquad \frac{dw}{dz} = 2.$$

If, as a second possibility, Q is taken on the vertical line through P, and approaches P along this line, we have $\Delta x = 0$, $\Delta z = i\,\Delta y$, and

$$\frac{\Delta w}{\Delta z} = -1, \qquad \frac{dw}{dz} = -1.$$

For other choices of position of Q and other paths of approach of Q toward P, we can get as many distinct values of dw/dz as we please.

Such functions of $z = x + iy$ as the one we have considered in this example are called non-analytic or non-monogenic functions;* the derivative of such a function at any point has in general many values. From now on we shall not consider such functions but devote our attention to analytic functions of z; the derivative of an analytic function

---

* Also sometimes called polygenic functions. An extensive literature on the theory of polygenic functions has been developed in recent years. See, e.g., E. Kasner: "A New Theory of Polygenic (or Non-Monogenic) Functions," *Science*, Vol. 66, p. 581, 1927; E. R. Hedrick: "Non-Analytic Functions of a Complex Variable," *Bull. Am. Math. Soc.*, Vol. 39, p. 75, 1933.

at any point has only one value, the same for all the ways in which Δz can approach zero. In fact we shall now say that the derivative dw/dz of a function $w = u(x, y) + iv(x, y) = F(z)$ *exists* only when

$$\lim_{\Delta z \to 0} \frac{F(z + \Delta z) - F(z)}{\Delta z}$$

has the same value for all the ways in which Δz can approach zero, and then this limit shall be the definition of dw/dz. Since for an arbitrary choice of u and v, dw/dz does not exist, as shown by the preceding example, it becomes a fundamental problem to determine the necessary and sufficient conditions on u and v in order that dw/dz exist.

This question is settled by the following theorem:

Theorem. *Given* $w = u(x, y) + iv(x, y) = F(z)$. *If* dw/dz *exists for all values of* z *in a region* R, *then everywhere in* R

$$(1°) \quad \frac{\partial u}{\partial x} = \frac{\partial v}{\partial y}, \frac{\partial u}{\partial y} = -\frac{\partial v}{\partial x} \quad \text{and} \quad (2°) \frac{\partial u}{\partial x}, \frac{\partial u}{\partial y}, \frac{\partial v}{\partial x}, \frac{\partial v}{\partial y}$$

are continuous functions of x *and* y; *and conversely, given* $(1°)$ *and* $(2°)$, dw/dz *exists for all values of* z *in* R.

The first part of the theorem states that $(1°)$ and $(2°)$ are necessary conditions for the existence of the derivative dw/dz; the converse states that these conditions are also sufficient.

We first deduce the necessary condition $(1°)$. For any value of z in R, consider the difference quotient

$$\frac{\Delta w}{\Delta z} = \frac{\Delta u + i\,\Delta v}{\Delta z}$$

$$= \frac{u(x + \Delta x, y + \Delta y) + iv(x + \Delta x, y + \Delta y) - u(x, y) - iv(x, y)}{\Delta x + i\,\Delta y}. \quad (2)$$

Since by hypothesis dw/dz exists (i.e., is the same for all ways in which Δz can approach zero) the value of dw/dz must in particular be the same for the two ways of approach used in the above example. For the first way $\Delta z = \Delta x$, $\Delta y = 0$, and (2) becomes

$$\frac{\Delta w}{\Delta z} = \frac{u(x + \Delta x, y) - u(x, y)}{\Delta x} + i\frac{v(x + \Delta x, y) - v(x, y)}{\Delta x},$$

whence

$$\frac{dw}{dz} = \frac{\partial u}{\partial x} + i\frac{\partial v}{\partial x}. \quad (3)$$

For the second way, $\Delta z = i\,\Delta y$, $\Delta x = 0$, and (2) becomes

$$\frac{\Delta w}{\Delta z} = \frac{u(x, y + \Delta y) - u(x, y)}{i\,\Delta y} + \frac{v(x, y + \Delta y) - v(x, y)}{\Delta y},$$

from which, since $1/i = -i$,

$$\frac{dw}{dz} = -i\frac{\partial u}{\partial y} + \frac{\partial v}{\partial y}. \tag{4}$$

Equating the two expressions for dw/dz in (3) and (4), we have

$$\frac{\partial u}{\partial x} + i\frac{\partial v}{\partial x} = \frac{\partial v}{\partial y} - i\frac{\partial u}{\partial y}. \tag{5}$$

Now since u and v are real functions of x and y, their partial derivatives will likewise be real, and hence we may separate the real and imaginary components in (5), thereby getting condition (1°):

$$\frac{\partial u}{\partial x} = \frac{\partial v}{\partial y},$$

$$\frac{\partial u}{\partial y} = -\frac{\partial v}{\partial x}. \tag{6}$$

The second necessary condition (2°) follows from a theorem of Goursat * the proof of which will not be given here.

To prove the converse, condition (2°) enables us to write (equation (12), Chapter VII, Art. 66):

$$\Delta u = \frac{\partial u}{\partial x}\Delta x + \frac{\partial u}{\partial y}\Delta y + \epsilon_1\,\Delta x + \epsilon_2\,\Delta y,$$

$$\Delta v = \frac{\partial v}{\partial x}\Delta x + \frac{\partial v}{\partial y}\Delta y + \epsilon_3\,\Delta x + \epsilon_4\,\Delta y,$$

where ϵ_1, ϵ_2, ϵ_3, ϵ_4 approach zero with Δx and Δy. Now, by virtue of condition (1°), the increments Δu and Δv may be written

$$\Delta u = \frac{\partial u}{\partial x}\Delta x - \frac{\partial v}{\partial x}\Delta y + \epsilon_1\,\Delta x + \epsilon_2\,\Delta y,$$

$$\Delta v = \frac{\partial v}{\partial x}\Delta^r + \frac{\partial u}{\partial x}\Delta y + \epsilon_3\,\Delta x + \epsilon_4\,\Delta y.$$

---

* *Trans. Am. Math. Soc.*, Vol. 1, p. 14, 1900.

Consequently

$$\Delta u + i \, \Delta v = \left(\frac{\partial u}{\partial x} + i \frac{\partial v}{\partial x}\right)(\Delta x + i \, \Delta y) + \eta_1 \, \Delta x + \eta_2 \, \Delta y,$$

where η_1 and η_2 are complex quantities approaching zero as Δx and Δy approach zero. Using this expression for Δw, we get

$$\frac{\Delta w}{\Delta z} = \frac{\partial u}{\partial x} + i \frac{\partial v}{\partial x} + \eta_1 \frac{\Delta x}{\Delta x + i \, \Delta y} + \eta_2 \frac{\Delta y}{\Delta x + i \, \Delta y}.$$

Since $\left| \Delta x/(\Delta x + i \, \Delta y) \right| \leqq 1$ and $\left| \Delta y/(\Delta x + i \, \Delta y) \right| \leqq 1$, and since $\eta_1 \to 0$, $\eta_2 \to 0$, we see that

$$\frac{dw}{dz} = \lim_{\Delta z \to 0} \frac{\Delta w}{\Delta z} = \frac{\partial u}{\partial x} + i \frac{\partial v}{\partial x}. \tag{7}$$

Consequently dw/dz exists, since (7) holds for any manner of approach of $\Delta z = \Delta x + i \, \Delta y$ toward zero.

The relations (6) are called the **Cauchy-Riemann equations,** after the two mathematicians who investigated their bearing on the theory of functions of a complex variable.

In the example considered above, in which $w = 2x + 1 - iy$, we have $\partial u/\partial x = 2$, $\partial u/\partial y = 0$, $\partial v/\partial x = 0$, $\partial v/\partial y = -1$. Hence the second but not the first of the Cauchy-Riemann equations is satisfied, which accounts for the multiplicity of values of dw/dz in this case. But suppose we have $w = x^2 - y^2 + 2ixy$. Then

$$\frac{\partial u}{\partial x} = 2x = \frac{\partial v}{\partial y},$$

$$\frac{\partial u}{\partial y} = -2y = -\frac{\partial v}{\partial x},$$

so that both equations are satisfied, and we get from (7),

$$\frac{dw}{dz} = 2x + 2iy.$$

In the latter case, $w = (x + iy)^2 = z^2$, so that w can actually be expressed in terms of z alone. Whenever w can be so written, the corresponding real functions $u(x, y)$ and $v(x, y)$ will satisfy the Cauchy-Riemann equations. For, let

$$w = u + iv = f(x + iy) = f(z),$$

the functional notation $f(x + iy)$ now indicating that w is expressible in terms of the single argument $x + iy$.   Then

$$\frac{\partial w}{\partial x} = \frac{\partial u}{\partial x} + i\frac{\partial v}{\partial x} = \frac{df}{dz},$$

$$\frac{\partial w}{\partial y} = \frac{\partial u}{\partial y} + i\frac{\partial v}{\partial y} = i\frac{df}{dz},$$

so that

$$\frac{\partial u}{\partial y} + i\frac{\partial v}{\partial y} = i\frac{\partial u}{\partial x} - \frac{\partial v}{\partial x},$$

and

$$\frac{\partial u}{\partial x} = \frac{\partial v}{\partial y}, \qquad \frac{\partial u}{\partial y} = -\frac{\partial v}{\partial x}.$$

A function of z which is single-valued and which possesses a unique derivative with respect to z at every point of some region R is said to be *analytic* in that region.   Unless otherwise stated, the functions discussed in the following are supposed to be analytic except possibly at isolated points of the z-plane.

We shall show in Art. 103 that if $f(z)$ is analytic, derivatives of all orders with respect to z exist.   It follows that all partial derivatives of u and v likewise exist, throughout the region of analyticity of $f(z)$.

Before continuing with the discussion of properties of analytic functions in general, let us examine the particular function $w = e^z$.   We need first of all a definition of the exponential function of a complex variable.   Now it was found in Chapter I, Art. 10, that formal manipulation of the Maclaurin series for the exponential function led to the relation

$$e^{a+ib} = e^a(\cos b + i \sin b).$$

In order, then, that this relation hold, we take, as our definition of e^z,

$$e^z = e^x(\cos y + i \sin y).$$

We now have $u = e^x \cos y$, $v = e^x \sin y$, whence

$$\frac{\partial u}{\partial x} = e^x \cos y = \frac{\partial v}{\partial y},$$

$$\frac{\partial u}{\partial y} = -e^x \sin y = -\frac{\partial v}{\partial x}.$$

Thus the Cauchy-Riemann equations are verified, and the function e^z is analytic.   Moreover, when z assumes the real value x, e^z becomes the familiar real function e^x.   Also, by equation (7),

$$\frac{d}{dz} e^z = \frac{\partial u}{\partial x} + i \frac{\partial v}{\partial x} = e^x \cos y + i e^x \sin y = e^z,$$

so that the derivative of e^z is e^z, just as the derivative of e^x with respect to x is e^x. Finally, we shall see, in Art. 104, that e^z is expressible in a series formally identical with the Maclaurin series for e^x. Our definition is therefore a consistent and desirable one.

We return now to general matters. If we differentiate the first of equations (6) with respect to x, and the second with respect to y, and add, we get

$$\frac{\partial^2 u}{\partial x^2} + \frac{\partial^2 u}{\partial y^2} = 0. \tag{8}$$

Hence the real component of an analytic function is a solution of Laplace's equation, which arose in the discussion of two-dimensional heat flow under steady-state conditions (Chapter VII, Art. 72). Likewise, differentiating the first of equations (6) with respect to y, the second with respect to x, and subtracting, we find that the imaginary component v of an analytic function also satisfies Laplace's equation,

$$\frac{\partial^2 v}{\partial x^2} + \frac{\partial^2 v}{\partial y^2} = 0. \tag{9}$$

Consequently one reason for the importance of analytic functions of a complex variable is that such a function furnishes us with two solutions of Laplace's equation.

A solution of Laplace's equation is called a *harmonic function*, and the two components u and v of an analytic function are called *harmonic conjugates*, or simply *conjugate functions*.

95. Geometrical aspects. Let $w = f(z) = u(x, y) + iv(x, y)$ be an analytic function, and consider the two singly infinite families of curves $u(x, y) = c_1$ and $v(x, y) = c_2$, where c_1 and c_2 are arbitrary constants. By formula (18) of Art. 66, Chapter VII, the slopes of these two families are given by

$$\frac{dy}{dx}\bigg]_u = - \frac{\dfrac{\partial u}{\partial x}}{\dfrac{\partial u}{\partial y}},$$

$$\frac{dy}{dx}\bigg]_v = - \frac{\dfrac{\partial v}{\partial x}}{\dfrac{\partial v}{\partial y}},$$

respectively. Since u and v are conjugate functions, they satisfy the Cauchy-Riemann equations, and consequently the slope of the v-curves may be written as

$$\frac{dy}{dx}\bigg]_v = \frac{\dfrac{\partial u}{\partial y}}{\dfrac{\partial u}{\partial x}}.$$

We then see that we have

$$\frac{dy}{dx}\bigg]_u = -\frac{1}{\dfrac{dy}{dx}\bigg]_v}, \tag{1}$$

so that the two families of curves, $u = c_1$ and $v = c_2$, are orthogonal trajectories of each other. For example, if $w = z^2 = (x + iy)^2 = x^2 - y^2 + 2ixy$, we have as the two families of curves, $x^2 - y^2 = c_1$ and $2xy = c_2$. When $c_1 \neq 0$, the curves $x^2 - y^2 = c_1$ are rectangular hyperbolas with their foci on the x-axis or on the y-axis according as $c_1 > 0$ or $c_1 < 0$, while the straight lines $y = \pm x$, obtained when $c_1 = 0$, also belong to the u-family, and serve as the common asymptotes of the hyperbolas of the family. For $c_2 = 0$, we get the x- and y-axes themselves, which are not perpendicular to the lines $y = \pm x$, but which are normal to the curves $x^2 - y^2 = c_1$, while if $c_2 \neq 0$, the curves $2xy = c_2$ are again rectangular hyperbolas, but now with the coordinate axes as asymptotes, and orthogonal to the u-hyperbolas and to the lines $y = \pm x$ (Fig. 88). The reason that the straight lines of each family do not cut the straight lines of the other family at right angles may be found from an inspection of the two slope expressions,

$$\frac{dy}{dx}\bigg]_u = \frac{x}{y}, \qquad \frac{dy}{dx}\bigg]_v = -\frac{y}{x}.$$

For, the first does not exist when $y = 0$, and the second does not when $x = 0$, so that we cannot say that the relation (1) is satisfied when the lines $x = 0$ and $y = 0$ are involved. However, when $xy \neq 0$, the above slope expressions do have meaning, and since equation (1) then holds, each of the curves $x^2 - y^2 = c_1$, including the lines $y = \pm x$ considered as a single curve (a degenerate hyperbola), cuts each of the hyperbolas $2xy = c_2$, when $c_2 \neq 0$, orthogonally.

We consider next the question of graphing in connection with the function $w = f(z)$. Obviously we cannot plot a single locus showing the variation of w with change in z, as we do in the case of a real function of a real variable, since we should need for complex variables a four-dimensional region with axes along which we could measure the values of the four variables x, y, u, v involved. Instead, we make use of two complex Gauss planes, one for the variable $z = x + iy$ and the other

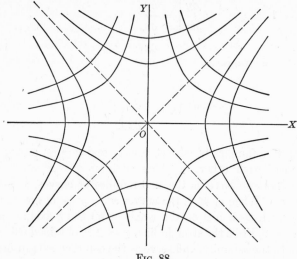

Fig. 88

for the variable $w = u + iv$. If the point z moves about in its plane along some curve, the point w will travel along a corresponding curve in its plane, since to each point (x, y) there corresponds a point (u, v). If we describe a closed curve c_1 in the z-plane, we shall get in general a closed curve c_2 in the w-plane (Fig. 89). We say that a curve, open

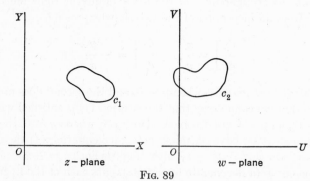

z — plane   w — plane

Fig. 89

or closed, in the z-plane is *mapped* onto the corresponding curve in the w-plane by the function $w = f(z)$, and we call this function a transformation or a mapping function.

As an example, let the mapping function be $w = e^z = e^{x+iy} = e^x(\cos y + i \sin y)$. Then $u = e^x \cos y$, $v = e^x \sin y$, and we have by elimination of x and y in turn,

$$v = u \tan y, \qquad u^2 + v^2 = e^{2x}.$$

The parallel lines $y = $ const. map into the pencil of lines through the origin, and the parallel lines $x = $ const. map into circles concentric with the origin. The rectangular region bounded by the lines $x = 0$, $x = 1$, $y = 0$, $y = \pi/4$, maps onto the sector of a ring as shown in Fig. 90,

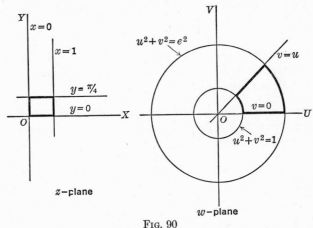

FIG. 90

bounded by the lines $v = 0$, $v = u$, and the circles $u^2 + v^2 = 1$, $u^2 + v^2 = e^2$. Since $e^{z+2n\pi i} = e^x[\cos(y + 2n\pi) + i \sin(y + 2n\pi)] = e^x(\cos y + i \sin y)$ when n is an integer, the map w_0 of the point z_0 corresponds to all points $z_0 + 2n\pi i$. Hence, if we divide the z-plane into horizontal bands by the lines $y = 2n\pi$, and let each strip include its lower but not its upper boundary, then each strip is mapped onto the entire w-plane (with the exception of the point $w = 0$ to which no finite z-point corresponds) by the transformation $w = e^z$.

96. Inverse functions and multiple-valued functions. In connection with the function $w = z^2$, we discussed in Art. 95 the curves $u = x^2 - y^2 = $ const., $v = 2xy = $ const. Viewing this functional relation as a transformation, we may consider the curves $x^2 - y^2 = $ const., $2xy = $ const. as the maps in the z-plane of the horizontal and vertical straight lines $u = $ const., $v = $ const. in the w-plane. But when dealing with the transformation $w = e^z$ we considered the maps in the w-plane of the straight lines $x = $ const., $y = $ const. in the z-plane; i.e., our mapping here proceeded in the direction opposite to that followed in the former problem.

This naturally raises the question whether a given functional relation between the variables z and w will allow us to map straight lines in one plane onto curves in the second and at the same time allow us to map straight lines in the second plane onto curves in the first. The answer to this question is bound up with the concept of inverse functions, since we are really asking whether or not the inverses $x = x(u, v), y = y(u, v)$ of a pair of functions $u = u(x, y), v = v(x, y)$ exist. For, if these inverses do exist, then not only may we map the lines $u = $ const., $v = $ const. onto the z-plane, using the relations $u = u(x, y), v = v(x, y)$, but we may also map the lines $x = $ const., $y = $ const. onto the w-plane, using the relations $x = x(u, v), y = y(u, v)$.

The question of the existence of the functions inverse to given functions is an important one in the theory of functions of real variables, which we cannot discuss fully here; * we shall merely state the theorem as it applies to our discussion.

THEOREM. *If $u = u(x, y)$ and $v = v(x, y)$ are single-valued functions possessing continuous first partial derivatives over some region of the xy-plane, and if the Jacobian determinant*

$$ J \equiv \begin{vmatrix} \dfrac{\partial u}{\partial x} & \dfrac{\partial u}{\partial y} \\ \dfrac{\partial v}{\partial x} & \dfrac{\partial v}{\partial y} \end{vmatrix} $$

is different from zero for x and y in that region, then the inverse functions $x = x(u, v), y = y(u, v)$ exist and are single-valued and continuous over that region.

Let us see what this theorem implies in the case of an analytic function $w = u + iv = f(z)$, for which the hypotheses on u and v, stated in the theorem, are met. In virtue of the Cauchy-Riemann equations, we have

$$ J \equiv \frac{\partial u}{\partial x}\frac{\partial v}{\partial y} - \frac{\partial u}{\partial y}\frac{\partial v}{\partial x} $$
$$ = \left(\frac{\partial u}{\partial x}\right)^2 + \left(\frac{\partial v}{\partial x}\right)^2 $$
$$ = \left|\frac{\partial f}{\partial x}\right|^2 $$
$$ = |f'(z)|^2. $$

* See Goursat-Hedrick, "Mathematical Analysis," Vol. 1, Chap. II.

Hence the inverses $x = x(u, v)$, $y = y(u, v)$ exist and are single-valued and continuous for any region R_1 of the z-plane in which $f'(z) \neq 0$, and consequently the region R_1 of the z-plane and the corresponding region R_2 of the w-plane are mapped one-to-one on each other.

As an example, consider again the function $w = z^2$. Here the region R_1 may be any region not including the point $z = 0$ since $f'(z) = 2z$ vanishes at that point only. The maps of $u = x^2 - y^2 = $ const., $v = 2xy = $ const. have already been examined; the hyperbolas, none

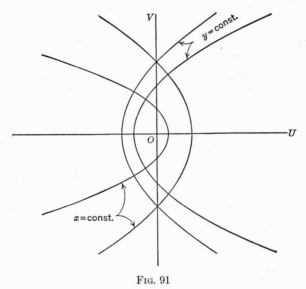

Fig. 91

of which passes through the origin, are proper maps of the straight lines $u = $ const., $v = $ const., while the straight lines $x = 0$, $y = 0$, and $y = \pm x$ give trouble, as we have seen, since they pass through the critical point $z = 0$. Now by elimination of x and y in turn from $u = x^2 - y^2$, $v = 2xy$, we get $v^2 = 4y^2(u + y^2)$, $v^2 = -4x^2(u - x^2)$. These equations evidently represent, for $x = $ const., $y = $ const., confocal and mutually orthogonal parabolas with the u-axis as axis (Fig. 91), provided again that $x \neq 0$, $y \neq 0$; i.e., $z \neq 0$.

Let us now examine more closely the difficulty encountered with the point $z = 0$ for the function $w = z^2$, the inverse of which is $z = w^{\frac{1}{2}}$. When $w = 0$, we get the single value $z = 0$, but for any $w \neq 0$, z is two-valued. For, if we write $w = re^{i\theta}$, $r > 0$, we have

$$z_1 = \sqrt{r}\, e^{i\theta/2}, \qquad z_2 = \sqrt{r}\, e^{i(\theta/2 + \pi)}.$$

We say then that $z = w^{\frac{1}{2}}$ has two *branches*, z_1 and z_2, coalescing at

$w = 0$, and we call $w = 0$ a *branch-point*. By allowing w to describe a circle about the point $w = 0$, and examining the variation of z, we can see how the branches z_1 and z_2 are related. Let the point w start at, say, $w = 1$, and let the function $z = w^{\frac{1}{2}}$ start from the point $z = 1$, so that $r = 1$, $\theta = 0$. Then for a circuit in the positive direction, r remains equal to unity and θ increases from 0 to 2π, so that at the completion of the circuit we have $w = \cos 2\pi + i \sin 2\pi = 1$, while $z = \cos \pi + i \sin \pi = -1$. Thus one branch of z has been changed into the second branch. By a second circuit of the same sort, the second branch will be replaced by the original one.

In the same way, it is easy to show that the inverse of the function $w = w_0 + (z - z_0)^n$, where z_0 and w_0 are complex constants and n is a positive integer greater than one, is n-valued, i.e., has n branches, the branch-point being $w = w_0$.

PROBLEMS

1. The function $w = u + iv = az + b$, where a and b are complex constants, defines an integral linear transformation. (a) Verify the fact that the components $u(x, y)$ and $v(x, y)$ satisfy the Cauchy-Riemann and Laplace equations, and that the lines $u = c_1$, $v = c_2$ are orthogonal to each other. (b) Show that an integral linear transformation is equivalent to a combination of transformations of the forms $w = z_1 + b$, $z_1 = az$, where $w = z_1 + b$ is a translation and $z_1 = az$ is a rotation and stretching transformation. *Hint:* Express a and z in polar form, $a = Ae^{i\alpha}$, $z = re^{i\theta}$.

2. Given the function $w = u + iv = 1/z$, which transforms the whole z-plane with the point $z = 0$ deleted into the w-plane with $w = 0$ deleted. (a) Verify the fact that u and v satisfy the Cauchy-Riemann and Laplace equations in any region not containing the origin, and that $u = c_1$, $v = c_2$ are two families of circles orthogonal to each other when $c_1 c_2 \neq 0$. (b) Show that this transformation is a circular transformation, in which all circles and straight lines in the z-plane are transformed into circles or straight lines in the w-plane. Which circles in the z-plane become straight lines in the w-plane, and which straight lines are transformed into other straight lines?

3. Discuss the general linear transformation $w = (az + b)/(cz + d)$. Show in particular that it may be regarded as a combination of transformations of the types given in Problems 1 and 2 when $ad - bc \neq 0$. What is the map of the entire z-plane when $ad - bc = 0$?

4. Given the function $w = z^3$, where $w = u + iv$. Show that u and v satisfy the Cauchy-Riemann and Laplace equations, and that the families of curves $u = c_1$ and $v = c_2$ are orthogonal to each other.

5. Given the function $w = u + iv = z^4$. Show that u and v satisfy the Cauchy-Riemann and Laplace equations, and that the curves $u = c_1$ and $v = c_2$ are orthogonal to each other.

6. Given the function $w = u + iv = \sin z$ defined for complex values of z by the relation $\sin z = (e^{iz} - e^{-iz})/2i$. (a) Show that u and v satisfy the Cauchy-Riemann and Laplace equations everywhere, and that the maps of the lines

$x = $ const., $y = $ const. form a system of confocal central conics. (b) Find all roots of the equation $\sin z = 2$. Show also that all the zeros of the function $\sin z$ are real.

7. Given the function $w = \cos z$, defined as $\cos z = (e^{iz} + e^{-iz})/2$. Determine the maps in the w-plane of the lines $x = 0$, $y = 0$, $x = 1$, and $y = 1$ in the z-plane. Describe and sketch the trace of the mapping point w as z traces the square bounded by $y = 0$, $x = 1$, $y = 1$, and $x = 0$ in that order.

8. Given the function $w = u + iv = \sinh z = (e^z - e^{-z})/2$. (a) Show that u and v satisfy the Cauchy-Riemann and Laplace equations everywhere, and that the maps of $x = $ const., $y = $ const. form a system of confocal central conics. (b) Find all roots of the equation $\sinh z = 2$.

9. Given the function $w = u + iv = \cosh z = (e^z + e^{-z})/2$. (a) Show that u and v satisfy the Cauchy-Riemann and Laplace equations everywhere, and that the maps of $x = $ const., $y = $ const. are confocal central conics. (b) Solve the equation $\cosh z = i$ and show also that $\cosh z$ has no real zeros.

10. Given the function $w = \ln z$, defined as the inverse of the exponential function, so that w is given by the relation $z = e^w$. (a) Writing z in polar form, show that $\ln z$ is infinitely many-valued. (b) Show that u and v satisfy the Cauchy-Riemann and Laplace equations in any region to which the origin is not interior.

PART II.   THE SCHWARZ-CHRISTOFFEL TRANSFORMATION AND ITS APPLICATIONS

97. The Schwarz-Christoffel transformation.   Our purpose in this part of the present chapter is to consider, from an elementary viewpoint, a few field problems arising in physics and engineering, and to apply the mapping properties of functions of a complex variable to their solution. The fields we deal with are two-dimensional regions of a plane in which some sort of steady flow takes place; the flow may be electric current flow, electrostatic flux (lines of force), heat flow, fluid flow, etc.

We call the curves along which flow takes place the streamlines, and the curves orthogonal to the streamlines we speak of as equipotentials.

Consider first the simple physical situation in which we have electric current flow along straight lines above and parallel to the x-axis, and suppose, for definiteness, that the flow is from right to left. Here the streamlines are the straight lines $y = $ const., and the equipotentials are the straight lines $x = $ const. (Fig. 92). Let the sheet in which the current is flowing be such that the resistance between opposite sides of a unit square is 1 ohm. Then for a current density of k_1 amperes per unit width of path, in the y-direction, we shall have a potential drop of k_1 volts per unit distance in the direction of flow. If we take, for convenience, the line $x = 0$ as our line of zero potential, the potential V at any point (x, y) will then be

$$V = k_1 x.$$

Similarly, we say that the stream-function S is the amount of current we cross in traveling along a line $x =$ const. starting at the edge of the field $y = 0$, so that

$$S = k_1 y.$$

If we combine these two real variables V and S into a complex quantity $F = V + iS$, we have

$$F = V + iS = k_1(x + iy) = k_1 z. \tag{1}$$

We may regard equation (1) as a relation defining a simple transformation mapping the upper half of the z-plane, in which parallel flow

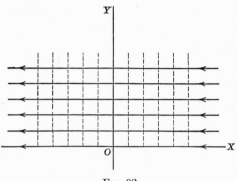

Fig. 92

takes place, onto the upper half of the F-plane, in which we have a similar net of orthogonal lines representing lines of equipotential and lines of constant stream-function. Here, since k_1 is real, our transformation consists of merely a stretching or contracting in the ratio k_1.

It is evident that the preceding discussion, dealing with a flow of current, applies equally well to a parallel flow of heat or of fluid, or to electrostatic flux. In the case of heat flow, the term potential is to be interpreted as temperature, the equipotentials being isotherms, and the stream-function represents quantity of heat instead of the amount of current. For fluid flow, we have the so-called velocity potential replacing potential, and the stream-function representing the amount of fluid. For electrostatic flux, we have again the potential and the lines of force as streamlines.

As a second example, let us examine the flow of heat, in the upper half of the xy-plane, toward a single point on the edge of the sheet, which we take as the origin O. Then the streamlines are radial lines through O and the isotherms are concentric semicircles about O (Fig. 93). Consider half a ring-shaped region of radii r and $r + dr$. The quantity of heat flowing across this half ring per second will be, by the third law of heat flow (Chapter VII, Art. 71), proportional to r and to the temperature gradient dV/dr, where V is the temperature in this region, and since that quantity of heat will be constant for steady flow, we have

$$\frac{dV}{dr} = \frac{k_2}{r},$$

where k_2 is a constant. Hence

$$V = k_2 \ln r + \text{const.},$$

and if we take our temperature scale such that $V = 0$ for $r = 1$, we get

$$V = k_2 \ln r.$$

Now let us choose the physical properties of the sheet, such as thermal conductivity, specific heat, etc., in such a way that the stream-function

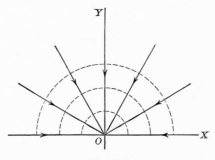

FIG. 93

S, which represents the quantity of heat crossed in traveling along an isotherm from the positive x-axis as starting point, and which is then proportional to the angle θ swept over, will be given by

$$S = k_2\theta,$$

with k_2 the same as in the preceding expression for V; this corresponds to our choice of the resistivity in the current-conducting sheet in the first example. Then we have, writing the complex variable z in polar form, $z = re^{i\theta}$,

$$F = V + iS = k_2(\ln r + i\theta) = k_2 \ln z. \tag{2}$$

Just as equation (1), or the inverse relation $z = F/k_1$, defined a transformation mapping the parallel current flow in the upper half of the z-plane into parallel flow in the upper half of the F-plane, so equation (2), or the inverse relation

$$z = e^{F/k_2}, \tag{2'}$$

defines a transformation mapping the radial heat flow in the upper half of the z-plane into parallel flow in the F-plane. Again, our second problem may be interpreted, with the proper verbal changes, in connection with radial current flow or other similar field problems.

It will be of considerable help in visualizing the effect of a transformation in a specific physical problem to regard it as producing conceptually an actual physical distortion. Let us consider the transformation $(2')$ in connection with the electric field between the plates of a

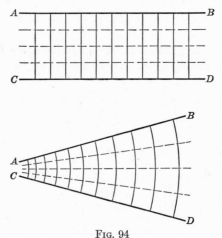

FIG. 94

condenser. Imagine an idealized substance resembling rubber sponge, in which the cells are extremely small and infinitely compressible or expansible, so that the substance will fit into any volume, however small, or will fill any volume, however large. Suppose this ideal substance placed between two long parallel plates AB and CD, and draw in it the streamlines (lines of force) and equipotentials perpendicular and parallel, respectively, to the plates. Now let A and C be brought nearer together, and B and D separated. Then the streamlines and equipotentials will be distorted into circle arcs and radial lines as shown in Fig. 94. We have thus carried through conceptually the idealized physical analog of the mathematical transformation $(2')$. If we could realize a substance of the sort imagined, one way of solving a problem with a complicated pattern of streamlines and equipotentials would be to straighten out the boundaries until they make some simple configuration to which we can fit a system of mutually orthogonal lines or curves, and then fold back the boundaries to the given shape and examine the resulting streamlines and their orthogonal trajectories.

Let us now examine this conceptual process from a mathematical viewpoint. Suppose the streamlines and equipotentials to be, for a given problem, of a more complicated nature than those of our previous examples, owing to the fact that our field is not the upper half-plane with the x-axis as sole boundary, but some other region, open or closed, bounded by straight line segments or rays. When the region is closed, i.e., finite in extent, the boundary then is what is ordinarily called a polygon, and the field will be the interior of the polygon. For an open region, we shall also, for brevity, call the bounding configuration a polygon, and shall speak of the field in question as the interior of the polygon; thus, if the field is the first quadrant of the coordinate plane, the polygon will consist of the positive axes.

Assuming, for the present, that we have a transformation $w = f(z)$ which maps the polygon in the w-plane onto the x-axis, and the interior of the polygon onto the upper half of the z-plane, it follows that the inverse function, $z = g(w)$, will, when obtainable, map the upper half of the z-plane onto the interior of the w-polygon. We then put into the upper half of the z-plane a simple system of streamlines and equipotentials fitting the boundary conditions, say that for parallel flow as given by equation (1). Substituting $z = g(w) = x(u, v) + iy(u, v)$ into (1), we get

$$V + iS = k_1 x(u, v) + ik_1 y(u, v),$$

whence

$$V = k_1 x(u, v), \qquad S = k_1 y(u, v). \tag{3}$$

Our parallel flow in the upper half of the z-plane has now been mathematically transformed into flow inside the w-polygon. Since the potential is constant for $V = \text{const.}$, the curves given by the first of equations (3) will represent equipotentials for the field bounded by the w-polygon; similarly, the curves given by the second of equations (3) will represent streamlines inside the w-polygon.

Our main problem is, therefore, that of finding a transformation which will map a given polygon in one plane onto the axis of reals in a second plane. This mapping problem is solved by the Schwarz-Christoffel transformation,* in which three † complex planes, w, z, F, are employed, where $w = u + iv$, $z = x + iy$, $F = V + iS$. The

---

* Numerous applications of this transformation may be found in Miles Walker's "Conjugate Functions for Engineers." See also Rothe, Ollendorf, and Pohlhausen, "Theory of Functions as Applied to Engineering Problems."

† In some problems it is necessary to employ more than three planes.

given polygon is drawn in the w-plane. The proper Schwarzian transformation, as it is usually called for short, will map this polygon in the w-plane onto the x-axis of the intermediate z-plane, and will at the same time transform the original flux lines and equipotentials. Next the x-axis is mapped onto a polygon in the F-plane in such a way that the field in the z-plane is transformed into a net of orthogonal straight lines in the F-plane.

Consideration of our mapping problem leads us to expect that the required transformation will be given in the form of a differential equation in which the rate of change of w with respect to z appears. For, let

$$dw = \mid dw \mid e^{i\theta_w}, \qquad dz = \mid dz \mid e^{i\theta_z};$$

then

$$\frac{dw}{dz} = \left|\frac{dw}{dz}\right| e^{i(\theta_w - \theta_z)},$$

so that the amplitude of dw/dz represents the angle between the element dw in the w-plane and the element dz in the z-plane. Now, since we wish to straighten out each interior angle of the polygon in the w-plane into an angle π along the x-axis, we should expect each angle of the w-polygon to be related in some way to the change in amp (dw/dz) as we turn through that angle.

To determine the expression to which dw/dz must then be equated, let us examine a few simple transformations. Letting $w = re^{i\theta}$, consider first the transformation $w = z^{1/2}$, or $z = w^2$. Then $z = r^2 e^{2i\theta}$, so that amp $z = 2$ amp w, and the first quadrant in the w-plane is mapped onto the upper half-plane of z; i.e., the 90° angle in the w-plane is straightened out into 180°. Here $dw/dz = \frac{1}{2}z^{-1/2}$. If $w = z^{1/3}$, we have $z = w^3 = r^3 e^{3i\theta}$, and the sector between the u-axis and the 60° line is straightened out into the upper half-plane of z; in this case, $dw/dz = \frac{1}{3}z^{-2/3}$. In general, if $z = w^m = r^m e^{mi\theta}$, where m is any rational number, the angle π/m is opened up into 180°, and $dw/dz = (1/m)z^{1/m-1}$.

Now if $z = cw^m$, where $c = a + ib = Ce^{i\alpha}$, say, then $z = Cr^m e^{i(m\theta + \alpha)}$, so that the w-configuration is stretched or contracted in the ratio $C:1$ and is turned through the angle α by this transformation. Thus the introduction of a complex constant of proportionality serves to change the size and orientation of a figure.

As a final example, let $z - z_0 = c(w - w_0)^m$, where z_0 and w_0 are complex constants. Then the angle π/m having its vertex at w_0 is opened up into a half-plane with "vertex" at z_0 in addition to being rotated; i.e., the figure is translated as well as rotated and fanned out. Here $w - w_0 = c^{-1/m}(z - z_0)^{1/m}$ and $\dfrac{dw}{dz} = \dfrac{c^{-1/m}}{m}(z - z_0)^{1/m-1}$.

Suppose, then, that we wish to straighten out an interior angle $\alpha_k = \pi/m_k$ of a w-polygon and translate the vertex of the angle to a point x_k on the x-axis of the z-plane. Since $1/m_k = \alpha_k/\pi$, it appears that we must have dw/dz proportional to $(z - x_k)^{\alpha_k/\pi-1}$. If the w-polygon has n vertices, dw/dz must then be proportional to each of the n expressions $(z - x_k)^{\alpha_k/\pi-1}$, $(k = 1, 2, \cdots, n)$, and therefore to their product, so that the Schwarzian transformation should be of the form

$$\frac{dw}{dz} = K(z - x_1)^{\alpha_1/\pi-1}(z - x_2)^{\alpha_2/\pi-1} \cdots (z - x_n)^{\alpha_n/\pi-1}. \qquad (4)$$

Here $x_1, x_2, \cdots, x_n$ are real constants, K is in general a complex number, and the interior angles at the n vertices of the w-polygon are $\alpha_1, \alpha_2, \cdots, \alpha_n$.

To clarify further the meaning of equation (4), let us see what happens when the point w moves along the polygon and the mapped point z moves along the x-axis. Let $z - x_k = r_k e^{i\theta_k}$ $(k = 1, 2, \cdots, n)$ and let $K = |K| e^{i\beta}$. Then equation (4) becomes

$$\frac{dw}{dz} = \left|\frac{dw}{dz}\right| e^{i(\theta_w - \theta_z)} = |K| e^{i\beta} r_1^{s_1} e^{is_1\theta_1} r_2^{s_2} e^{is_2\theta_2} \cdots r_n^{s_n} e^{is_n\theta_n},$$

where for brevity s_k is written for $\alpha_k/\pi - 1$. Then the amplitude of dw/dz is given by

$$\text{amp}\,\frac{dw}{dz} = \theta_w - \theta_z = \beta + s_1\,\text{amp}\,(z - x_1) + \cdots + s_n\,\text{amp}\,(z - x_n).$$

Now as w moves along a straight line from, say, w_1 to w_2, z moves along the x-axis from x_1 to x_2. While $x_1 < x < x_2$, amp $(dw/dz) = \theta_w - \theta_z$ remains the same since θ_w and θ_z do not change. When w passes through w_2, so that z passes through x_2, the quantity $z - x_2$ changes sign, and amp$(z - x_2)$ changes by π. But the signs of $z - x_1$, $z - x_3$, $\cdots$, $z - x_n$ remain unchanged when $x_1 < x < x_3$, and consequently amp (dw/dz) changes by $|s_2\pi| = |\alpha_2 - \pi|$ as w passes through w_2. Similarly, amp (dw/dz) changes by $|s_k\pi| = |\alpha_k - \pi|$ as w passes through w_k $(k = 1, 2, \cdots, n)$. Now when $0 < \alpha_k < \pi$, as at w_2 and w_3 in Fig. 95, the change in amp (dw/dz) is an increase, and since $s_k\pi = \alpha_k - \pi$ is negative, the algebraic value of the change is $-s_k\pi = \pi - \alpha_k$, which is evidently the angle through which we turn when passing through w_k. On the other hand, if $\pi < \alpha_k < 2\pi$, as at w_4, the change in amp(dw/dz) is a decrease, and since $s_k\pi = \alpha_k - \pi$ is now positive, the algebraic value of the change is again $-s_k\pi = \pi - \alpha_k$, the angle through which we rotate at w_k. Thus equation (4) is such that the polygon in the w-plane will be mapped onto the x-axis of the z-plane.

The above discussion is meant not as a rigorous derivation of the Schwarzian transformation, but rather as an indication of its geometric

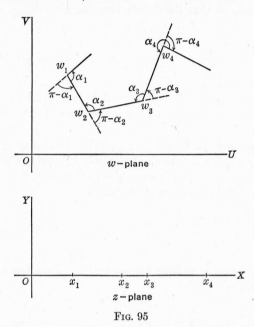

Fig. 95

import. Moreover, even though this transformation will map the w-polygon onto the x-axis, we have not as yet shown that the interior of the w-polygon will thereby map onto the upper half of the z-plane, which is essential to our field problems. Our present mathematical equipment does not allow us to demonstrate this fact; it is, however, shown to be the case in Art. 105.

We proceed now to a consideration of some field problems to which the Schwarzian transformation may be applied. Here, also, since our purpose is merely to give an introduction to the subject, we shall draw freely on geometric and physical concepts.

98. Flow near a right-angled corner. As a simple first example, let us find the equations of the streamlines of current flow and the equations of the equipotentials near the corner of a large square sheet of conducting material. Let the square plate be placed in the first quadrant of the w-plane with the edges along the axes, and let one of the streamlines follow the direction indicated by the arrows (Fig. 96). We map our polygon, here consisting of merely the positive u- and v-axes, onto the x-axis, letting the origin of the w-plane map onto the

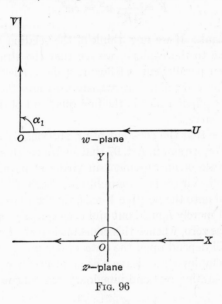

FIG. 96

origin of the z-plane. Then $x_1 = 0$, $\alpha_1 = \pi/2$, and the Schwarzian transformation is

$$\frac{dw}{dz} = Kz^{-\frac{1}{2}},\qquad(1)$$

whence

$$w = 2Kz^{\frac{1}{2}} + K'.$$

Since $z = 0$ when $w = 0$, the constant of integration K' will be zero, and we have

$$w = 2Kz^{\frac{1}{2}},$$

or

$$z = \frac{1}{4K^2}\, w^2.\qquad(2)$$

Since the boundary streamline in the w-plane maps into the x-axis streamline from right to left, we may put into the z-plane a parallel flow of current such that the x-axis is one of the streamlines. Hence the mapping from the z-plane to the final F-plane may be brought about by the simple transformation $F = kz$, where k is a real constant depending upon the system of units, or scale, used; this transformation will certainly change the net of straight lines in the z-plane into a similar net in the F-plane. Then (2) becomes

$$F = \frac{k}{4K^2}\, w^2 = cw^2, \tag{3}$$

where c is constant. If we now think of the relation (3) as mapping from the F-plane to the w-plane, we see that the straight horizontal streamlines of our parallel current flow and the vertical equipotentials orthogonal to the streamlines are transformed into the corresponding streamlines and equipotentials in the first quadrant of the w-plane, i.e., into the desired curves.

It is easy to see that the constant of proportionality c in (3) may be taken as real. For, we saw in Art. 97 that such a constant serves merely to change the scale of measurement in virtue of its modulus, and to rotate the figure in virtue of its amplitude. Since the positive u-axis has been mapped onto the positive V-axis, the figure as a whole has not been rotated but merely fanned out and consequently the amplitude of c may be taken as zero, whence this constant is real. Since the scale of measurement will depend upon the data of our problem and upon the system of units employed, we leave c as an arbitrary real constant.

Therefore, separating real and imaginary components in (3), we get

$$V = c(u^2 - v^2),$$
$$S = 2cuv. \tag{4}$$

It follows that the maps of $V =$ const. are rectangular hyperbolas asymptotic to the line $v = u$, and the maps of $S =$ const. are also rectangular hyperbolas asymptotic to the u- and v-axes. Thus the full curves in Fig. 97 represent streamlines and the dotted curves equipotentials in the neighborhood of a corner of the sheet.

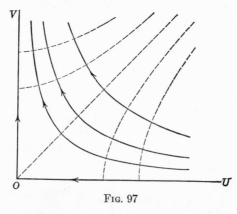

Fig. 97

In the preceding discussion, we have considered the distribution of lines of current flow and of constant potential. It is apparent that we may interpret our result in connection with the analogous problem of heat flow, for which equations (4) give the flux lines and isotherms near a corner, or in connection with fluid flow, for which equations (4) represent flux lines and the lines of velocity equipotential.

99. Flow near two 90° corners. Having considered in our first problem a conducting sheet indefinitely large in two dimensions, we next deal with a rectangular strip of width a and so long compared to a that its length may be supposed infinite. We again place our sheet in the first quadrant of the w-plane as shown in Fig. 98, and suppose that

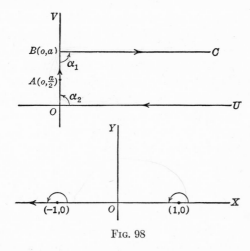

Fig. 98

one streamline is along $UOBC$ as indicated by the arrows. We map this polygon with interior angles $\alpha_1 = \pi/2$, $\alpha_2 = \pi/2$, symmetrically onto the x-axis, the midpoint $A(0, a/2)$ of the edge OB mapping onto the origin of the z-plane, and the corners O and B mapping onto the points $x = 1$, $x = -1$, respectively. The streamline boundary $UOBC$ is thus mapped onto the x-axis, this latter streamline proceeding from right to left.

We then have for the Schwarzian transformation,

$$\frac{dw}{dz} = K(z + 1)^{-\frac{1}{2}}(z - 1)^{-\frac{1}{2}}$$

$$= \frac{K}{(z^2 - 1)^{\frac{1}{2}}}, \tag{1}$$

whence

$$w = K(\cosh^{-1} z + K')$$

or

$$z = \cosh\left(\frac{w}{K} - K'\right),$$

where K' is a constant of integration. Since $z = 1$ when $w = 0$, we get $K' = 0$; since $z = -1$ when $w = ia$, we then have

$$-1 = \cosh\frac{ia}{K} = \cos\frac{a}{K},$$

$$\frac{a}{K} = \pi, \qquad K = \frac{a}{\pi},$$

and

$$z = \cosh\frac{\pi w}{a}. \tag{2}$$

Since we may again put a parallel flow in the z-plane, we may employ the transformation $F = kz$, giving us

$$F = k\cosh\frac{\pi w}{a}, \tag{3}$$

where k is a constant which may, as before, be taken as real. We then get

$$V + iS = k\cosh\frac{\pi}{a}(u + iv)$$

$$= k\left(\cosh\frac{\pi u}{a}\cosh\frac{i\pi v}{a} + \sinh\frac{\pi u}{a}\sinh\frac{i\pi v}{a}\right)$$

$$= k\left(\cosh\frac{\pi u}{a}\cos\frac{\pi v}{a} + i\sinh\frac{\pi u}{a}\sin\frac{\pi v}{a}\right),$$

and therefore

$$V = k\cosh\frac{\pi u}{a}\cos\frac{\pi v}{a}, \qquad S = k\sinh\frac{\pi u}{a}\sin\frac{\pi v}{a}. \tag{4}$$

The maps of $V = $ const. will be the equipotentials (or isotherms), and the maps of $S = $ const. will be the streamlines.

100. Edge effect in a condenser; flow out of a channel. Let the edges of a parallel-plate condenser, or of a channel conveying a liquid, lie along the lines $v = \pm a$ to the left of the points $(-b, \pm a)$ in the second and third quadrants. We suppose these edges so long compared to the distance $2a$ between them that they may be considered infinite in length.

If the plates $v = \pm a$ of a condenser are at different potentials, there will be lines of force between them. Sufficiently far to the left of $u = -b$, these lines will be sensibly straight and vertical, but as we approach the boundaries at $u = -b$ they will evidently be considerably curved. We wish to study this edge effect for the parallel-plate condenser.

Another physical interpretation of the present problem is in connection with fluid flow. Again, far to the left of $u = -b$, the streamlines will be nearly horizontal straight lines, but will curve as we proceed to the right, and diverge as the liquid issues from the channel.

Because of the evident symmetry in the u-axis for both physical problems, we need consider only the upper half of the figure in the w-plane (Fig. 99). We shall then think of our open polygon as running

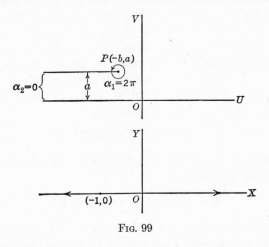

Fig. 99

from A ($u = -\infty$) to $P(-b, a)$, then back along PA and joining on to B at $u = -\infty$, and then to the right along the u-axis. Thus the angles involved are $\alpha_1 = 2\pi$ at P and $\alpha_2 = 0$ at B.

To open out this polygon, we first unfold the line AP by rotating it through 180° about P; this gives us flow in a uniform strip and thus straightens out the equipotentials of the electric field (or the streamlines in the case of liquid flow) into horizontal straight lines. We then fan out the strip between $v = 0$ and $v = a$ by bringing together the edges at $u = -\infty$ and separating those at $u = +\infty$, as in the conceptual process described in Art. 97, until we have a single straight line; this fans out the lines of force (or the velocity equipotentials) into semi-circles, and the electric equipotentials (or fluid streamlines) emanate radially from a point.

For convenience, we map the point $(-b, a)$ onto the point $(-1, 0)$ of the z-plane, and the point $u = -\infty$ (the junction of A and B) onto the origin. Thus the upper edge AP, when unfolded, maps onto the x-axis to the left of $(-1, 0)$, the upper edge PA as it appears in the w-plane maps onto the segment from $(-1, 0)$ to $(0, 0)$, and the lower edge $v = 0$ maps onto the positive x-axis. Hence the Schwarzian transformation will be

$$\frac{dw}{dz} = K(z + 1)z^{-1} = K\left(1 + \frac{1}{z}\right), \tag{1}$$

and therefore

$$w = K(z + \ln z) + K'. \tag{2}$$

Now the fluid streamlines along the boundary of the w-polygon run from left to right along AP and the u-axis, and their maps run away from the origin along the x-axis. Here, therefore, we may put into the z-plane a radial flow emanating from $z = 0$. To transform this radial flow into parallel flow, we take (see Art. 97) the mapping function $z = e^{kF}$. Since the real constant k serves merely to change the scale of our map, giving us kV and kS instead of simply V and S, we set $k = 1$ for simplicity. Then we have

$$w = K(e^F + F) + K'. \tag{3}$$

To determine the constants K and K', write z in polar form, $z = re^{i\theta}$, so that equation (2) becomes

$$w = K(re^{i\theta} + \ln r + i\theta) + K'. \tag{4}$$

As we pass from $v = 0$ to $v = a$ in the w-plane, w changes by ia, and we may think of z as passing from a point on the positive x-axis, where $\theta = 2n\pi$ and n is an integer or zero,* to a point on the negative x-axis, where $\theta = (2n + 1)\pi$, and then allow these points to approach the origin. For these changes we therefore have

$$w\bigg]_0^{ia} = \lim_{r \to 0} \left[K(re^{i\theta} + \ln r + i\theta) + K' \right]_{\theta = 2n\pi}^{\theta = (2n+1)\pi}$$

$$ia = \lim_{r \to 0} [K(-2r + i\pi)] = i\pi K,$$

whence

$$K = \frac{a}{\pi}. \tag{5}$$

* This designation of θ is necessary since $\ln z$ is multiple-valued; see Problem 10 following Art. 96.

Moreover, $z = -1$ when $w = -b + ia$, so that, since $\ln(-1) = \ln 1 + (2n + 1)i\pi = (2n + 1)i\pi$, we get from (4) and (5),

$$-b + ia = \frac{a}{\pi}[-1 + (2n + 1)i\pi] + K',$$

$$K' = \frac{a}{\pi} - b - 2nia.$$

Consequently our transformation takes the form

$$w = \frac{a}{\pi}(e^F + F) + \frac{a}{\pi} - b - 2nia,$$

so that

$$u = \frac{a}{\pi}(e^V \cos S + V + 1) - b,$$

$$v = \frac{a}{\pi}(e^V \sin S + S) - 2na.$$

Now the line $v = 0$ maps onto the line $y = 0$, and since, from $z = e^F$, we have $y = e^V \sin S$, it follows that $v = 0$ corresponds to $S = 0$. Hence, in the above expression for v, we must take $n = 0$, and therefore we get as our final result,

$$u = \frac{a}{\pi}(e^V \cos S + V + 1) - b,$$

$$v = \frac{a}{\pi}(e^V \sin S + S). \tag{6}$$

Letting $V = \text{const.}$ in (6), we obtain equations for u and v in terms of the parameter S, from which we may plot various lines of force of the electrostatic field near the edges of the condenser. By putting $S = \text{const.}$ in (6), we get equations for u and v in terms of the parameter V, which enable us to plot lines of flow of liquid from the channel.

101. Point source and point sink. As our next problem, we investigate the distribution of streamlines and equipotentials in a sheet of conducting material into which current is fed at a point A and out of which it flows at a point B. The points A and B are called, respectively, the source and the sink.

Since here we do not have a polygon in the conducting sheet, it will be more convenient to put the known pattern of streamlines and equipotentials for parallel current flow in the w-plane and transform this into the desired pattern in the z-plane (Fig. 100). Let the source and sink be, respectively, located at $A(a, 0)$ and $B(-a, 0)$ of the z-plane, and let A_1B_1 and A_2B_2 be boundaries of the strip in the w-plane along which parallel flow takes place. Split the upper edge A_2B_2 at its center C–C', rotate the right-hand half about A_2 in the clockwise and the left-hand half about B_2 in the counterclockwise direction, and bring A_2 toward A_1 and B_2 toward B_1. Let $(a, 0)$ in the z-plane correspond

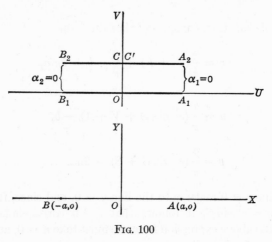

Fig. 100

to the junction of A_1 and A_2, and let $(-a, 0)$ correspond to the junction of B_1 and B_2. Map the origin in the w-plane onto the origin in the z-plane, and let C go into $x = -\infty$ and C' into $x = +\infty$.

The internal angles, α_1 at A_1–A_2 and α_2 at B_1–B_2, being both zero, the Schwarzian transformation will be

$$\frac{dw}{dz} = K(z - a)^{-1}(z + a)^{-1}$$

$$= \frac{K}{z^2 - a^2}.$$

Hence

$$w = \frac{K}{2a} \ln \frac{z - a}{z + a} + K'. \tag{1}$$

Using the relation $w = 0$ when $z = 0$, together with $\ln(-1) = (2n + 1)i\pi$, n an integer or zero, we get $K' = -(2n + 1)i\pi K/2a$, and

$$w = \frac{K}{2a}\left[\ln \frac{z - a}{z + a} - (2n + 1)i\pi\right], \tag{2}$$

The constant K will depend upon the nature of the current-carrying strip in the w-plane and the units employed, and need not be evaluated here.

Since we now have parallel flow in the w-plane instead of in the z-plane, we put $F = kw$, whence, letting $C = kK/2a$, we get

$$F = C\left[\ln\frac{z - a}{z + a} - (2n + 1)i\pi\right]. \tag{3}$$

To separate equation (2) into real and imaginary parts, let $z - a = r_1 e^{i\theta_1}$, $z + a = r_2 e^{i\theta_2}$. Then

$$F = C\left[\ln\frac{r_1}{r_2} + i(\theta_1 - \theta_2 - (2n + 1)\pi)\right]. \tag{4}$$

Evidently $z - a$ and $z + a$ are the vectors drawn from $(a, 0)$ and $(-a, 0)$ respectively to any point z, the lengths of these vectors being r_1 and r_2, and the angle between them being $\theta_1 - \theta_2$ (Fig. 101).

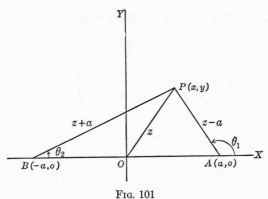

FIG. 101

In transforming the w-configuration into the x-axis, we did not rotate the figure, and therefore C may be taken as real. Consequently we get

$$V = C\ln\frac{r_1}{r_2},$$
$$S = C[\theta_1 - \theta_2 - (2n + 1)\pi]. \tag{5}$$

Now any point of the segment A_1B_1 in the w-plane, for which $v = 0$, maps onto a corresponding point of the segment AB in the z-plane, for which $\theta_1 = \pi$, $\theta_2 = 0$. Hence the second of equations (5) gives us $n = 0$, whence we have

$$V = C\ln\frac{r_1}{r_2},$$
$$S = C(\theta_1 - \theta_2 - \pi). \tag{6}$$

From the first of equations (6), we see that V will be constant if and only if the ratio r_1/r_2 is constant. Thus the maps of the equipotentials $V = $ const. in the w-plane will be given by

$$\frac{r_1}{r_2} = \frac{\sqrt{(x-a)^2 + y^2}}{\sqrt{(x+a)^2 + y^2}} = C_1,$$

or

$$(1 - C_1^2)(x^2 + y^2) - 2a(1 + C_1^2)x + a^2(1 - C_1^2) = 0, \qquad (7)$$

where C_1 is a constant, which must be taken as positive since r_1/r_2 is positive. For $C_1 \neq 1$, (7) represents circles with their centers on the x-axis; when $C_1 = 1$, we get, as could be anticipated from $r_1/r_2 = 1$, the straight line $x = 0$. These, then, are the equipotentials of our problem.

Corresponding to the streamlines $S = $ const., we get

$$\tan\left(\frac{S}{C} + \pi\right) = \tan(\theta_1 - \theta_2)$$

$$= \frac{\dfrac{y}{x-a} - \dfrac{y}{x+a}}{1 + \dfrac{y^2}{x^2 - a^2}}$$

$$= \frac{2ay}{x^2 + y^2 - a^2} = C_2,$$

a constant, or

$$C_2(x^2 + y^2) - 2ay - C_2 a^2 = 0. \qquad (8)$$

When $C_2 \neq 0$, equation (8) also represents circles, which pass through the source and sink, as we should expect; when $C_2 = 0$, we get the straight line $y = 0$, which also passes through A and B. These are the streamlines sought.

PROBLEMS

1. Using equations (4) of Art. 99, plot the equipotentials corresponding to $V = 0, \pm 1, \pm 2, \pm 5, \pm 10$, and the streamlines corresponding to $S = 0, \frac{1}{2}, 1, 5, 10$, in a rectangular strip of width π.

2. Taking $a = \pi, b = 1$ for simplicity in equations (6) of Art. 100, plot the lines of force near the edges of a parallel-plate condenser, corresponding to $V = 0, \pm\frac{1}{2}$, $+1$, and the streamlines of liquid flow from a channel, corresponding to $S = 0$, $\pi/4, \pi/2, 2\pi/3, 3\pi/4, \pi$.

3. Find the orthogonal trajectories of the streamlines (8) of Art. 101, and show that these trajectories are the equipotentials (7).

4. Show from equation (7) of Art. 101 that each equipotential circle encloses either the source or the sink, but not both.

5. (a) Let a tangent be drawn from the source (or sink) of Art. 101 to an equipotential circle. Show that the foot of the perpendicular dropped from the point of tangency to the x-axis is the sink (or source). (b) Let R_1 and R_2 be the radii of any two equipotential circles on opposite sides of the y-axis, and let D be the distance between their centers. Find, in terms of R_1, R_2, and D, the distances from source and sink to the centers of these circles, and the distance between source and sink.

6. Investigate the nature of the streamlines and equipotentials for a point source in a conducting sheet whose boundaries, assumed infinitely distant from the source, constitute the sink. *Hint:* Map a parallel flow of current in the w-plane onto the z-plane, in which the given sheet lies, and show that the Schwarzian transformation may be taken as

$$\frac{dw}{dz} = \frac{K}{z}.$$

7. Using a Schwarzian transformation, map the region in the w-plane bounded by the positive u-axis and the portion of the line $v = \sqrt{3}\, u$ passing through the first quadrant onto the upper half of the z-plane. Taking the potential $V = kx$ and the stream-function $S = ky$, where k is a real constant, find V and S as functions of u and v, so that the curves $V = $ const. are equipotentials and the curves $S = $ const. are streamlines of flow near a 60° corner. Show that the functions V and S satisfy the Cauchy-Riemann and Laplace equations, and that the equipotentials cut the streamlines orthogonally.

8. Using a Schwarzian transformation, map the region in the w-plane bounded by the positive u-axis and the portion of the line $v = u$ passing through the first quadrant onto the upper half of the z-plane. Taking the potential $V = kx$ and the stream-function $S = ky$, where k is a real constant, find V and S as functions of u and v, so that the curves $V = $ const. are equipotentials and the curves $S = $ const. are streamlines of flow near a 45° corner. Show that the functions V and S satisfy the Cauchy-Riemann and Laplace equations, and that the equipotentials cut the streamlines orthogonally.

9. Generalize Problems 7 and 8 to the consideration of flow inside an angle π/n, and show that the mapping function is $F = cw^n$, where c is a real constant. Setting $w = re^{i\theta} = r(\cos\theta + i\sin\theta)$, show that $V = cr^n \cos n\theta$, $S = cr^n \sin n\theta$, and hence that the streamlines are symmetric with respect to the angle-bisecting line $\theta = \pi/2n$.

10. Consider planar flow around the edge of a semi-infinite thin wall, represented by the positive u-axis in the w-plane. Map this flow onto the z-plane, take $F = V + iS = kz$, and find u and v as functions of V and S. Determine the nature of the streamlines $S = $ const. and of the equipotentials $V = $ const.

PART III. FURTHER THEORY OF ANALYTIC FUNCTIONS

102. Line integrals. We shall devote the remainder of this chapter to some topics in the theory of analytic functions of a complex variable. We shall make use of this theory in the evaluation of certain definite integrals, and, in Chapter XI, shall apply it to the solution of problems in which the operational calculus may be employed.

For the definite integral

$$\int_a^b f(x)\,dx, \tag{1}$$

where x is a real variable and $f(x)$ is a real function of x, we may speak of the field of integration as the segment of the x-axis from $x = a$ to $x = b$. Now let $g(x, y)$ be a real function of two real variables, and consider a segment C of a continuous curve, with initial point A and terminal point B, and such that it is cut by a line parallel to either coordinate axis in only one point (Fig. 102). We divide C into n arcs

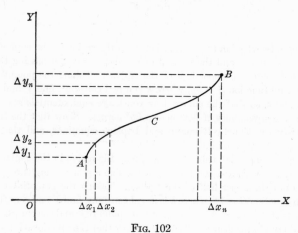

FIG. 102

$\Delta s_1, \Delta s_2, \cdots, \Delta s_n$, whose projections on the x-axis are $\Delta x_1, \Delta x_2, \cdots, \Delta x_n$, and whose projections on the y-axis are $\Delta y_1, \Delta y_2, \cdots, \Delta y_n$, respectively, as shown. Letting (x_k, y_k) denote a point on Δs_k, we form the sums

$$\sum_{k=1}^n g(x_k, y_k)\,\Delta s_k, \qquad \sum_{k=1}^n g(x_k, y_k)\,\Delta x_k, \qquad \sum_{k=1}^n g(x_k, y_k)\,\Delta y_k.$$

When the limits, as n becomes infinite and as each subsegment approaches zero, of these sums exist, we call these limits line or contour integrals, and denote them by

$$\int_C g(x, y)\,ds, \qquad \int_C g(x, y)\,dx, \qquad \int_C g(x, y)\,dy, \tag{2}$$

respectively. We say then that C is the field of integration.

If we have several curve segments C_k ($k = 1, 2, \cdots, n$), each cut by a line parallel to a coordinate axis in only one point, and forming a continuous curve C, we say that a line integral over C is equal to the corresponding sum of the line integrals over $C_1, C_2, \cdots, C_n$ in turn. Also, for later convenience, we say that the integral over C from B to A is the negative of that from A to B. If the equation of C_k is $y = f(x)$, the integral $\int_{C_k} g(x, y)\, dx$ may be evaluated by replacing y in $g(x, y)$ by $f(x)$ and integrating between the values of x representing the abscissas of the endpoints of C_k. Similarly, if C_k is given by $x = F(y)$, the integral $\int_{C_k} g(x, y)\, dy$ may be found by reducing it to an ordinary integral.

A frequently occurring line integral is one made up of the sum of integrals of the second and third types,

$$\int_C [P(x, y)\, dx + Q(x, y)\, dy]. \tag{3}$$

If A and B have the coordinates (a, b) and (c, d), respectively, (3) is sometimes written as

$$\int_{(a,b)}^{(c,d)} [P(x, y)\, dx + Q(x, y)\, dy]. \tag{4}$$

However, when the notation (4) is used, the curve C must also be specified, since the value of the integral is in general dependent upon the path from A to B.

As an example, consider the integral

$$I = \int_C [(x^2 + 2y)\, dx + (x - 5y^2)\, dy], \tag{5}$$

where C is first the path from $(0, 0)$ to $(1, 0)$ and thence to $(1, 3)$ along the straight lines shown in Fig. 103. Along the x-axis, we have $y = 0$, $dy = 0$, and along the second part of our path, $x = 1$, $dx = 0$. Hence we get

$$I_1 = \int_0^1 x^2\, dx + \int_0^3 (1 - 5y^2)\, dy = -\frac{125}{3}.$$

Secondly, let C be the straight line $y = 3x$ joining $(0, 0)$ and $(1, 3)$. Then in the first term we substitute $y = 3x$, and in the second, $x = y/3$, whence we find

$$I_2 = \int_0^1 (x^2 + 6x)\, dx + \int_0^3 \left(\frac{y}{3} - 5y^2\right) dy = -\frac{241}{6}.$$

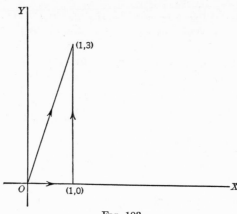

FIG. 103

Consider next the double integral of a real function $g(x, y)$ taken over a region R bounded by a closed curve C such that a line parallel to a coordinate axis cuts it in at most two points,

$$\iint_R g(x, y) \, dR.$$

Express the function $g(x, y)$ by the notation $\partial Q(x, y)/\partial x$, and consider the equivalent iterated integral

$$\iint_R \frac{\partial Q(x, y)}{\partial x} \, dx \, dy. \tag{6}$$

Let R be circumscribed by a rectangle with sides $x = a$, $x = b$, $y = c$,

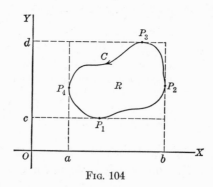

FIG. 104

$y = d$, as shown in Fig. 104, tangent to C at the points P_1, P_2, P_3, P_4, and let the positive direction along C be that indicated by the arrow.

If the equations of the segments $P_3P_4P_1$ and $P_1P_2P_3$ are respectively $x = F_1(y)$ and $x = F_2(y)$, we get for the integral (6),

$$\iint_R \frac{\partial Q(x,y)}{\partial x}\, dx\, dy = \int_c^d \int_{F_1(y)}^{F_2(y)} \frac{\partial Q(x,y)}{\partial x}\, dx\, dy$$

$$= \int_c^d [Q(F_2, y) - Q(F_1, y)]\, dy$$

$$= \int_c^d Q(F_2, y)\, dy - \int_c^d Q(F_1, y)\, dy.$$

We see that the first of the above integrals is the line integral of $Q(x, y)$ along $P_1P_2P_3$, while the second is the line integral of Q along $P_1P_4P_3$. Since the latter is the negative of the line integral along $P_3P_4P_1$, we have

$$\iint_R \frac{\partial Q}{\partial x}\, dx\, dy = \int_{P_1P_2P_3} Q\, dy + \int_{P_3P_4P_1} Q\, dy = \int_C Q\, dy. \qquad (7)$$

Similarly, for a function $f(x, y) = \partial P(x, y)/\partial y$, we would have

$$\iint_R \frac{\partial P}{\partial y}\, dy\, dx = \int_{P_4P_3P_2} P\, dx + \int_{P_2P_1P_4} P\, dx = -\int_C P\, dx. \qquad (8)$$

Combining (7) and (8), we get

$$\int_C (P\, dx + Q\, dy) = \iint_R \left(\frac{\partial Q}{\partial x} - \frac{\partial P}{\partial y} \right) dR. \qquad (9)$$

This relation between a line integral and the double integral taken over the region enclosed by the contour, is known as **Green's lemma,** having been given by Green in a paper on mathematical physics. It holds also when C is cut by a parallel to a coordinate axis in more than two points, and when the region R has subregions cut out of it, if we take as C the totality of bounding curves, along which the positive sense is in each case that leaving the region R to the left. Thus, if R is a ring-shaped region, the positive senses along the boundary circles will be the counterclockwise direction on the outer circle and the clockwise direction on the inner circle.

Examination of equation (9) shows immediately that if $\partial Q/\partial x = \partial P/\partial y$ at every point of R,[*] the line integral on the left will vanish. It follows that if C_1 and C_2 are any two curves connecting the distinct

[*] Note that this condition implies the existence of $\partial P/\partial y$ and $\partial Q/\partial x$ in R.

points A and B (Fig. 105), and lying wholly inside the region R in which $\partial Q/\partial x = \partial P/\partial y$, then

$$\int_{C_1} (P\,dx + Q\,dy) = \int_{C_2} (P\,dx + Q\,dy).$$

For, if C is composed of C_1 taken in the positive sense, and C_2 taken in the negative sense, we have $\int_{C_1} - \int_{C_2} = \int_{C_1} + \int_{-C_2} = 0$, whence $\int_{C_1} = \int_{C_2}$. Referring to the example given by (5), we see that $P = x^2 + 2y$, $Q = x - 5y^2$, so that $\partial P/\partial y = 2$, $\partial Q/\partial x = 1$, and $\partial P/\partial y \neq \partial Q/\partial x$. Consequently it is not surprising that I_1 and I_2 were different.

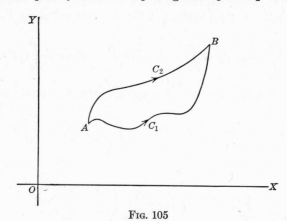

Fig. 105

If we had taken, instead, $P = x^2 + y$, we should have had $\partial Q/\partial x = \partial P/\partial y = 1$, and both paths would have yielded the same value, as would all others connecting $(0, 0)$ and $(1, 3)$.

We may usefully apply the above results to analytic functions of a complex variable. Let $f(z)$ be analytic over a simply connected region R, by which we shall mean a region bounded by a single closed curve; let C be any curve connecting two points A and B of R and lying wholly in R. Consider now the integral of $f(z)$ along C, defined by

$$\int_C f(z)\,dz = \lim_{n \to \infty} \sum_{k=1}^{n} f(z_k)\,\Delta z_k, \qquad (10)$$

where the points z_k lie on C and $\Delta z_k = z_k - z_{k-1}$. Setting $f(z) = u(x, y) + iv(x, y)$, we have

$$\int_C f(z)\, dz = \int_C (u + iv)(dx + i\, dy)$$

$$= \int_C (u\, dx - v\, dy) + i \int_C (v\, dx + u\, dy), \qquad (11)$$

which is the sum of two line integrals. Now since $f(z)$ is analytic, the Cauchy-Riemann equations,

$$\frac{\partial u}{\partial x} = \frac{\partial v}{\partial y}, \qquad \frac{\partial u}{\partial y} = -\frac{\partial v}{\partial x},$$

are satisfied. But these are precisely the conditions that the two line integrals in (11) be independent of the path C joining A and B. Consequently $\int_C f(z)\, dz$ will depend only upon the values of z at the points A and B. In particular, if C is a closed curve which does not cut itself, and which lies inside the simply connected region R, $\int_C f(z)\, dz = 0$.

When R is not simply connected, the integral over a single closed curve C lying in R, of a function analytic in R, may be different from

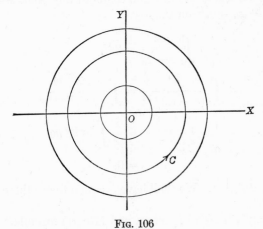

Fig. 106

zero. To illustrate this possibility, let R be a ring-shaped region bounded by the circles with centers at the origin and of radii a and b, let C be a circle of radius r, where $a < r < b$ (Fig. 106), and let $f(z) = 1/z$. Then $f(z)$ is analytic in R, and we get

$$\int_C \frac{dz}{z} = \int_C \frac{rie^{i\theta}\, d\theta}{re^{i\theta}} = \int_C i\, d\theta = 2\pi i,$$

since θ changes by 2π in traversing the circle C. It might have been expected that this result would come out zero, since we are dealing with an integral around a closed curve. It should be noted, however, that Green's lemma does not apply. While the function $f(z) = 1/z$ is analytic at every point of R, it is not analytic at every point in the region enclosed by C. For the derivative $f'(z) = -1/z^2$ exists everywhere except at the point $z = 0$, which is interior to C. Consequently the Cauchy-Riemann equations are not satisfied for $x = 0$, $y = 0$; we have, in fact,

$$\frac{\partial u}{\partial x} = \frac{y^2 - x^2}{(x^2 + y^2)^2} = \frac{\partial v}{\partial y},$$

$$\frac{\partial u}{\partial y} = \frac{-2xy}{(x^2 + y^2)^2} = -\frac{\partial v}{\partial x},$$

so that the four partial derivatives do not exist at this point. Thus the condition $\partial Q/\partial x = \partial P/\partial y$ at every point inside C, which was applied to the line integrals (11), will not be met for $x = 0$, $y = 0$, and therefore we cannot conclude that the line integral $\int_C f(z)\,dz$ will be zero.

When C is a circle of radius r and center at any point $z = z_0$, we get by setting $z - z_0 = re^{i\theta}$ on C,

$$\int_C \frac{dz}{z - z_0} = 2\pi i,$$

$$\int_C \frac{dz}{(z - z_0)^{n+1}} = \int_C \frac{rie^{i\theta}\,d\theta}{r^{n+1}e^{i(n+1)\theta}} \tag{12}$$

$$= \frac{i}{r^n} \int_C e^{-in\theta}\,d\theta$$

$$= 0,$$

for $n = \pm 1, \pm 2, \cdots$. We shall have occasion to use these relations in our later work.

103. Cauchy's integral theorem and integral formula. Let $f(z)$ be analytic over the region R and continuous * on the boundary C of R (Fig. 107). Then the integral of $f(z)$, extended in the positive sense over the entire boundary C, which may consist of one or more closed curves, will vanish,

$$\int_C f(z)\,dz = 0. \tag{1}$$

---

* $f(z) = u(x, y) + iv(x, y)$ is continuous if u and v are continuous.

This result, known as **Cauchy's integral theorem,** follows from the discussion of Art. 102, being based upon the Cauchy-Riemann equations and Green's lemma.   An equivalent statement is that the integral

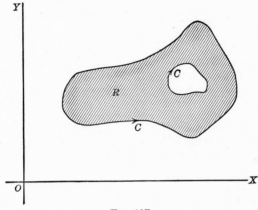

FIG. 107

taken in the positive (counterclockwise) sense over the outer boundary is equal to the sum of the integrals along the inner boundaries in the negative (clockwise) sense with respect to R, which will be the positive sense with respect to the regions enclosed by these curves.

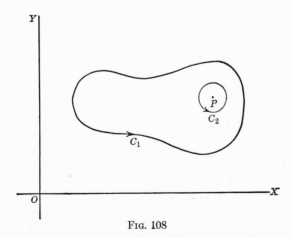

FIG. 108

An important consequence of Cauchy's integral theorem is as follows: Let C_1 be any single closed curve enclosing or lying inside a region over which $f(z)$ is analytic, let P be any point inside the region bounded by

C_1, and let C_2 be a circle with center at P and having all its points in the region enclosed by C_1 (Fig. 108).   Then

$$\int_{C_1} f(z)\, dz = \int_{C_2} f(z)\, dz, \tag{2}$$

where each integral is taken in the positive (counterclockwise) direction. Thus an integral over any single closed curve C_1 may be replaced by an integral over a circle C_2, and conversely, provided C_1 and C_2 are such that $f(z)$ is analytic over the suitable regions.   In particular, it follows that the relations (12) of Art. 102 hold when C is any single closed curve enclosing the point z_0.

Now suppose $f(z)$ is analytic over a region R, simply or multiply connected, whose complete boundary is C, and let z_0 be any point inside R (Fig. 109).   Let C' be a circle with center z_0 and small enough

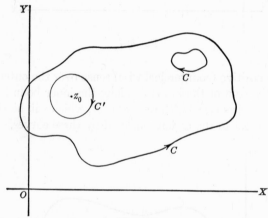

Fig. 109

so that every point on C' lies in R, and denote by R' the region obtained by removing the points interior to C' from R.   Then the function $f(z)/(z - z_0)$ satisfies the conditions of Cauchy's integral theorem in R', so that

$$\int_C \frac{f(z)}{z - z_0}\, dz + \int_{C'} \frac{f(z)}{z - z_0}\, dz = 0, \tag{3}$$

where the integral along C' is taken in the clockwise sense.   Setting $z - z_0 = re^{i\theta}$ for z a point on C', the second integral above may be written

$$\int_{C'} \frac{f(z)}{z - z_0}\, dz = \int_{C'} if(z_0 + re^{i\theta})\, d\theta.$$

If we let r approach zero, the last integral will approach

$$i \int_{C'} f(z_0) \, d\theta = -2\pi i f(z_0),$$

$f(z_0)$ being constant as regards θ, and the minus sign appearing because of our integration in the clockwise direction. Consequently we get from (3),

$$\int_C \frac{f(z)}{z - z_0} \, dz - 2\pi i f(z_0) = 0.$$

or

$$f(z_0) = \frac{1}{2\pi i} \int_C \frac{f(z)}{z - z_0} \, dz.$$

Since z_0 is any point in R, and since the notation for the variable of integration is immaterial, we may write the above equation in the form

$$f(z) = \frac{1}{2\pi i} \int_C \frac{f(t)}{t - z} \, dt. \tag{4}$$

This relation is called **Cauchy's integral formula.**

The integrand in (4) being a function of the variable of integration t and of the parameter z, we have here an integral of the kind discussed in Chapter VII, Art. 67. We may, in fact, differentiate under the integral sign, obtaining the formulas

$$f'(z) = \frac{1}{2\pi i} \int_C \frac{f(t)}{(t - z)^2} \, dt,$$

$$f''(z) = \frac{2}{2\pi i} \int_C \frac{f(t)}{(t - z)^3} \, dt,$$

and, in general,

$$f^{(n)}(z) = \frac{n!}{2\pi i} \int_C \frac{f(t)}{(t - z)^{n+1}} \, dt, \tag{5}$$

for n any positive integer. Thus derivatives of all orders of an analytic function exist, and are given by (5).

We next give an inequality which we shall need in Art. 104. Let C be any curve, open or closed, and let M be the maximum value of $|f(z)|$ on C. Then if L is the length of C,

$$\left| \int_C f(z) \, dz \right| \leqq ML. \tag{6}$$

To obtain this relation, we note first (Fig. 110) that if α and β are any complex numbers, $\left|\,\alpha + \beta\,\right| \leqq \left|\,\alpha\,\right| + \left|\,\beta\,\right|$, and, in general, if $\alpha = \alpha_1 + \alpha_2 + \cdots + \alpha_n$, $\left|\,\alpha\,\right| \leqq \left|\,\alpha_1\,\right| + \left|\,\alpha_2\,\right| + \cdots + \left|\,\alpha_n\,\right|$.   Hence

$$\left| \sum_{k=1}^{n} f(z_k)\, \Delta z_k \right| \leqq \sum_{k=1}^{n} \left|\,f(z_k)\,\right| \cdot \left|\,\Delta z_k\,\right|.$$

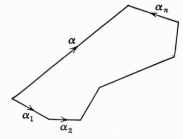

Fig. 110

Now let $\left|\,\Delta z_k\,\right| = L_k$; then

$$\sum_{k=1}^{n} \left|\,f(z_k)\,\right| \cdot \left|\,\Delta z_k\,\right| \leqq M(L_1 + L_2 + \cdots + L_n),$$

and since $L_1 + L_2 + \cdots + L_n$ approaches the length L of C as n becomes infinite, we have

$$\lim_{n \to \infty} \left| \sum_{k=1}^{n} f(z_k)\, \Delta z_k \right| \leqq ML,$$

whence, by (10), Art. 102, we get (6).   Applying (6) to (5), where we take as C a circle of radius r and center z, we find also

$$\left|\,f^{(n)}(z)\,\right| \leqq \frac{n!}{2\pi} \cdot \frac{M}{r^{n+1}} \cdot 2\pi r = \frac{Mn!}{r^n}, \tag{7}$$

where M is the maximum value of $f(t)$ on C.

104. Series expansions and singular points.   Consider a function $f(z)$ analytic in a region R.   Let a be any point of R, and let C be any circle in R and with center a. Then $f(z)$ admits of an expansion in a Taylor's series,

$$f(z) = f(a) + f'(a)(z-a) + \cdots + \frac{f^{(n)}(a)}{n!}(z-a)^n + \cdots, \qquad (1)$$

valid at least for z inside C.

To derive series (1), we begin with Cauchy's integral formula, and write

$$f(z) = \frac{1}{2\pi i} \int_C \frac{f(t)\,dt}{t-z} = \frac{1}{2\pi i} \int_C \frac{f(t)\,dt}{(t-a)-(z-a)}.$$

We now make use of the algebraic identity

$$\frac{1}{A-B} = \frac{1}{A} + \frac{B}{A^2} + \cdots + \frac{B^n}{A^{n+1}} + \frac{B^{n+1}}{A^{n+1}(A-B)},$$

setting $A = t - a$, $B = z - a$. Then we have

$$f(z) = \frac{1}{2\pi i} \int_C \frac{f(t)\,dt}{t-a} + \frac{z-a}{2\pi i} \int_C \frac{f(t)\,dt}{(t-a)^2} + \cdots$$

$$+ \frac{(z-a)^n}{2\pi i} \int_C \frac{f(t)\,dt}{(t-a)^{n+1}} + \frac{(z-a)^{n+1}}{2\pi i} \int_C \frac{f(t)\,dt}{(t-a)^{n+1}(t-z)}.$$

Hence, by Cauchy's integral formula (4) and formula (5) of Art. 103, we get

$$f(z) = f(a) + f'(a)(z-a) + \cdots$$

$$+ \frac{f^{(n)}(a)}{n!}(z-a)^n + \frac{(z-a)^{n+1}}{2\pi i} \int_C \frac{f(t)\,dt}{(t-a)^{n+1}(t-z)}. \qquad (2)$$

Equation (2) expresses Taylor's theorem with remainder R_{n+1}, where

$$R_{n+1} = \frac{(z-a)^{n+1}}{2\pi i} \int_C \frac{f(t)\,dt}{(t-a)^{n+1}(t-z)}. \qquad (3)$$

If we can show that R_{n+1} approaches zero as n becomes infinite, we shall have series (1), convergent for z inside C. To do this, let r be the radius of C, and let $|f(z)| \leq M$ on C (Fig. 111). Then since $|t-a| = r$ for t on C, and $|t-z| \geq r - |z-a|$, we get from the inequality (6) of Art. 103,

$$|R_{n+1}| \leq \frac{|z-a|^{n+1}}{2\pi} \cdot \frac{M}{r^{n+1}(r-|z-a|)} \cdot 2\pi r$$

$$= \frac{Mr}{r-|z-a|} \left(\frac{|z-a|}{r} \right)^{n+1} \qquad (4)$$

But $|z - a| < r$, and therefore $|R_{n+1}|$ may be made as small as we please by taking n sufficiently large. Thus Taylor's series (1) is established.

Since series (1) for an analytic function of a complex variable is identical in form with the Taylor's series for a function of a real variable, it is possible to define the various elementary functions of a complex

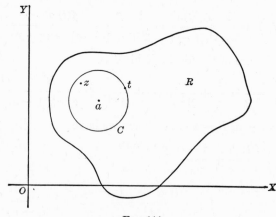

FIG. 111

variable by means of series which are also correct when the variable takes on real values only. For example, we have

$$e^z = 1 + z + \frac{z^2}{2!} + \frac{z^3}{3!} + \cdots,$$

$$\sin z = z - \frac{z^3}{3!} + \frac{z^5}{5!} - \frac{z^7}{7!} + \cdots,$$

$$\cosh z = 1 + \frac{z^2}{2!} + \frac{z^4}{4!} + \frac{z^6}{6!} + \cdots.$$

Consider next the series

$$c_1 u + c_2 u^2 + \cdots + c_n u^n + \cdots,$$

where u is a function of z. If this series converges for $|u| < r$, then evidently the series obtained by setting $u = 1/(z - a)$,

$$\frac{c_1}{z - a} + \frac{c_2}{(z - a)^2} + \cdots + \frac{c_n}{(z - a)^n} + \cdots, \qquad (5)$$

will converge for z outside the circle with center a and radius $1/r$.

Now suppose we have a ring-shaped region R bounded by two circles with centers at $z = a$ and of radii r_1 and r_2. Let the series $f_1(z) = c_0 + c_1(z - a) + \cdots + c_n(z - a)^n + \cdots$ converge inside the larger circle, and let the series $f_2(z) = c_{-1}(z - a)^{-1} + c_{-2}(z - a)^{-2} + \cdots + c_{-n}(z - a)^{-n} + \cdots$ converge outside the smaller circle. Then **Laurent's theorem** states that the function

$$f(z) = f_1(z) + f_2(z) = c_0 + c_1(z - a) + c_2(z - a)^2 + \cdots$$
$$+ c_{-1}(z - a)^{-1} + c_{-2}(z - a)^{-2} + \cdots$$
$$= \sum_{n=-\infty}^{\infty} c_n(z - a)^n \qquad (6)$$

is analytic inside R.

Laurent's series (6) may be obtained in the general case by an argument similar to that employed in deriving Taylor's series (1); it is found that if C is a circle of radius r, where $r_1 < r < r_2$, then the coefficients c_n of (6) are given by

$$c_n = \frac{1}{2\pi i} \int_C \frac{f(z)\, dz}{(z - a)^{n+1}} \qquad (n = 0, \pm 1, \pm 2, \cdots). \qquad (7)$$

This formula, for $n \geq 0$, also gives the coefficients of the Taylor's series (1).

Let R be a region bounded by a circle C with center at $z = a$ with the point a removed. If the Laurent expansion for $f(z)$ in this region contains no negative powers of $(z - a)$ and if $f(a) = c_0$, i.e., if $f(z)$ is then given by a Taylor's series, the function $f(z)$ will be analytic inside C, including the point $z = a$. If, however, the Laurent series does have negative powers of $(z - a)$, $f(z)$ will not be analytic at $z = a$; we say in such a case that $z = a$ is an *isolated singular point* of $f(z)$. If the number of negative powers of $(z - a)$ is finite, and if $(z - a)^{-m}$ is the lowest power, the singularity is called a *pole* of order m; if the number of negative powers is infinite, $f(z)$ is said to have an *essential singularity* at $z = a$.

To illustrate, consider first the function $f(z) = \cos z / z^2$. Since the derivative $f'(z) = -(z \sin z + 2 \cos z)/z^3$ exists for every point except $z = 0$, this function will be analytic everywhere except at the origin. Then for C any circle with center at $z = 0$, we have for the Laurent expansion

$$\frac{\cos z}{z^2} = \frac{1}{z^2} - \frac{1}{2!} + \frac{z^2}{4!} - \frac{z^4}{6!} + \cdots,$$

so that this function possesses a pole of order 2 at the origin but is elsewhere analytic. As a second example, let $f(z) = e^{1/z}$, for which we have the series

$$e^{1/z} = 1 + \frac{1}{z} + \frac{1}{z^2 2!} + \frac{1}{z^3 3!} + \cdots.$$

In this case our function evidently has an essential singularity at $z = 0$.

105. Residues. Let $f(z)$ have an isolated singularity at $z = a$, and let its Laurent expansion be

$$f(z) = c_0 + c_1(z - a) + c_2(z - a)^2 + \cdots$$
$$+ c_{-1}(z - a)^{-1} + c_{-2}(z - a)^{-2} + \cdots.$$

By the *residue* of $f(z)$ at $z = a$ is meant the coefficient c_{-1} of $(z - a)^{-1}$. Let C be a circle about the point $z = a$, and such that no singularities of $f(z)$ other than $z = a$ are inside C. By formula (7) of Art. 104, the residue is

$$c_{-1} = \frac{1}{2\pi i} \int_C f(z) \, dz. \tag{1}$$

As an example, consider the function $f(z) = e^z/z^3$, which has the Laurent expansion

$$\frac{e^z}{z^3} = \frac{1}{z^3} + \frac{1}{z^2} + \frac{1}{2!z} + \frac{1}{3!} + \frac{z}{4!} + \cdots.$$

Then by definition, the residue at the pole $z = 0$ is $\frac{1}{2}$. Otherwise regarded, for C a circle about the origin, the right-hand member of (1) becomes

$$\frac{1}{2\pi i} \int_C f(z) \, dz = \frac{1}{2\pi i} \int_C \frac{dz}{z^3} + \frac{1}{2\pi i} \int_C \frac{dz}{z^2} + \frac{1}{2\pi i} \int_C \frac{dz}{2z} + \frac{1}{2\pi i} \int_C f_1(z) \, dz,$$

where $f_1(z) = \frac{1}{3!} + \frac{z}{4!} + \frac{z^2}{5!} + \cdots$ is analytic inside C. Now by relations (12) of Art. 102, the first two of the above integrals vanish, while

$$\frac{1}{2\pi i} \int_C \frac{dz}{2z} = \frac{1}{2};$$

moreover, $\int_C f_1(z) \, dz = 0$ by Cauchy's integral theorem. Thus we again get for the residue, at $z = 0$, the value $\frac{1}{2}$.

If $z = a$ is a simple pole of $f(z)$, i.e., a pole of order 1, the residue of $f(z)$ at $z = a$ is given by

$$\lim_{z \to a} (z - a)f(z).$$

This important result, which materially simplifies the computation of a residue in a large number of cases, is easily proved. By hypothesis, $f(z)$ may be expanded in a Laurent series of the form

$$f(z) = \frac{c_{-1}}{z - a} + c_0 + c_1(z - a) + c_2(z - a)^2 + \cdots.$$

Then

$$(z - a)f(z) = c_{-1} + c_0(z - a) + c_1(z - a)^2 + \cdots,$$

and

$$\lim_{z \to a} (z - a)f(z) = c_{-1},$$

which is by definition the residue of $f(z)$ at $z = a$.

Let R be a simply connected region within which $f(z)$ is analytic except at isolated singularities $z = a_1, a_2, \cdots, a_n$, and let C be the boundary of R. Then the sum of the residues of $f(z)$ inside C is given by

$$S = \frac{1}{2\pi i} \int_C f(z) \, dz. \tag{2}$$

For, let small circles $C_1, C_2 \cdots, C_n$ be drawn, each circle lying inside R and enclosing one singularity. Then, by Cauchy's integral theorem, applied to the function $f(z)$, which is analytic inside the region obtained from R by deleting the points interior to $C_1, C_2, \cdots, C_n$, we get

$$\int_C f(z) \, dz - \int_{C_1} f(z) \, dz - \cdots - \int_{C_n} f(z) \, dz = 0,$$

where each integral is extended in the counterclockwise sense. Dividing this equation throughout by $2\pi i$, and noting that $\dfrac{1}{2\pi i} \displaystyle\int_{C_k} f(z) \, dz$ represents the residue of $f(z)$ at $z = a_k$, we get our result (2).

Now suppose $f(z)$ to be analytic inside the simply connected region R bounded by a curve C, and let $f(z)$ have a zero of order p_k at the point $z = a_k$ within R $(k = 1, 2, \cdots, n)$, i.e.,

$$f(z) = c_1(z - a_k)^{p_k} + c_2(z - a_k)^{p_k+1} + \cdots, \qquad c_1 \neq 0.$$

Then

$$f'(z) = c_1 p_k(z - a_k)^{p_k-1} + c_2(p_k + 1)(z - a_k)^{p_k} + \cdots,$$

and consequently

$$\frac{f'(z)}{f(z)} = \frac{p_k}{z - a_k} + F(z),$$

where $F(z)$ is a Taylor's series. Hence the residue of the function $f'(z)/f(z)$ at $z = a_k$ is p_k, whence we get from equation (2),

$$\frac{1}{2\pi i} \int_C \frac{f'(z)}{f(z)} \, dz = p_1 + p_2 + \cdots + p_n = N, \tag{3}$$

where N is the total number of zeros of $f(z)$ inside C, counting a zero, at $z = a_k$, p_k times in the usual way.

Relation (3) may be used to prove that the Schwarzian transformation of Art. 97 maps the interior of a closed w-polygon of n sides onto the upper half of the z-plane. In the first place, consider the linear transformation

$$\zeta = \frac{i - z}{i + z}, \quad \text{or} \quad z = \frac{i(1 - \zeta)}{1 + \zeta}, \tag{4}$$

where $\zeta = \xi + i\eta$. Then

$$|\zeta| = \left|\frac{i - z}{i + z}\right| = \sqrt{\frac{x^2 + y^2 + 1 - 2y}{x^2 + y^2 + 1 + 2y}}.$$

Hence the map of the x-axis, $y = 0$, is the unit circle in the ζ-plane, and, since $|\zeta| < 1$ for $y > 0$, the upper half of the z-plane is mapped onto the interior of the circle $|\zeta| = 1$ in the ζ-plane. Now let the points $x_1, x_2, \cdots, x_n$ of the x-axis correspond to the points $\zeta_1, \zeta_2, \cdots, \zeta_n$ on the circle $|\zeta| = 1$. Then we have

$$z - x_k = i\left(\frac{1 - \zeta}{1 + \zeta} - \frac{1 - \zeta_k}{1 + \zeta_k}\right)$$

$$= \frac{-2i}{1 + \zeta_k}\frac{\zeta - \zeta_k}{1 + \zeta},$$

$$dz = \frac{-2i\, d\zeta}{(1 + \zeta)^2}.$$

Substituting these expressions in equation (4) of Art. 97, we get, since

$$\left(\frac{\alpha_1}{\pi} - 1\right) + \left(\frac{\alpha_2}{\pi} - 1\right) + \cdots + \left(\frac{\alpha_n}{\pi} - 1\right) = \frac{\alpha_1 + \alpha_2 + \cdots + \alpha_n}{\pi} - n$$

$$= \frac{(n - 2)\pi}{\pi} - n = -2,$$

$$dw = \frac{K(-2i)^{-2}(\zeta - \zeta_1)^{\alpha_1/\pi - 1} \cdots (\zeta - \zeta_n)^{\alpha_n/\pi - 1}(-2i\, d\zeta)}{(1 + \zeta_1)^{\alpha_1/\pi - 1} \cdots (1 + \zeta_n)^{\alpha_n/\pi - 1}(1 + \zeta)^{-2}(1 + \zeta)^2}$$

$$= K'(\zeta - \zeta_1)^{\alpha_1/\pi - 1} \cdots (\zeta - \zeta_n)^{\alpha_n/\pi - 1}\, d\zeta, \tag{5}$$

where

$$K' = \frac{iK}{2(1 + \zeta_1)^{\alpha_1/\pi - 1} \cdots (1 + \zeta_n)^{\alpha_n/\pi - 1}}.$$

Since the Schwarzian transformation maps the w-polygon onto the x-axis, while (4) maps the x-axis on the circle $|\zeta| = 1$, it follows that the resultant transformation (5) maps the w-polygon onto the circle $|\zeta| = 1$ directly. Now suppose that $w = w_0$ is any point inside the w-polygon. Then we have

$$\frac{1}{2\pi i} \int_P \frac{dw}{w - w_0} = 1,$$

where the integration is taken around the w-polygon. But from (5) we get w as some function of ζ; let $w - w_0 = f(\zeta)$, so that

$$\frac{1}{2\pi i} \int_C \frac{f'(\zeta)}{f(\zeta)} \, d\zeta = 1,$$

where the integration extends over the circle $|\zeta| = 1$. For ζ inside the circle C, $dw/d\zeta$ as given by (5), and therefore $f(\zeta)$, will be analytic. Hence it follows from equation (3) that $f(\zeta)$ vanishes at just one point,

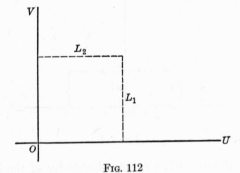

FIG. 112

$\zeta = \zeta_0$, inside the circle C, and consequently $w = w_0$ for $\zeta = \zeta_0$. Therefore the point $w = w_0$ inside the w-polygon maps onto one and only one point $\zeta = \zeta_0$ inside the circle $|\zeta| = 1$, and since any such point $\zeta = \zeta_0$ maps, by (4), onto a point in the upper half of the z-plane, it follows that the Schwarzian transformation maps the interior of the closed w-polygon upon the upper half of the z-plane, and conversely. Now if the w-polygon is an open configuration, as in the examples of Arts. 98–101, we may introduce additional straight lines so as to produce a closed polygon, apply the preceding argument, and then allow the auxiliary lines introduced to recede to infinity in such a way that the given configuration results. Thus, in the example of Art. 98, lines L_1 and L_2, parallel respectively to the coordinate axes as shown in Fig. 112, will complete a square to which our argument applies; if we then suppose L_1 and L_2 to move indefinitely far to the right and upward respectively, the square field becomes the given field covering the first quadrant.

One of the principal uses of the theory of residues is in the evaluation of certain definite real integrals.* As a first example, let it be required to evaluate the integral

$$\int_{-\infty}^{\infty} \frac{e^{x/3}\,dx}{1 + e^x}, \tag{6}$$

where x is real. We may do this by evaluating in two ways the contour integral

$$\int_C \frac{e^{z/3}\,dz}{1 + e^z}, \tag{7}$$

where C is the contour shown in Fig. 113, consisting of the x-axis and the lines $x = \pm A$, $y = 2\pi$. Our first method is to apply equation (2), as follows. Inside C, the only value of z making $1 + e^z$ vanish is

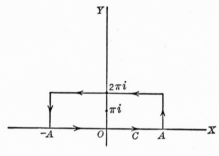

Fig. 113

$z = \pi i$; hence this point is the only singularity of the integrand $f(z) = e^{z/3}/(1 + e^z)$ within the contour. Developing $e^{z/3}$ and $(1 + e^z)$ in Taylor's series about the point $z = \pi i$, we find

$$e^{z/3} = e^{\pi i/3} + \tfrac{1}{3}e^{\pi i/3}(z - \pi i) + \cdots,$$

$$1 + e^z = 0 - (z - \pi i) - \tfrac{1}{2}(z - \pi i)^2 - \cdots.$$

Consequently we get by division,

$$f(z) = \frac{e^{z/3}}{1 + e^z} = -\frac{e^{\pi i/3}}{z - \pi i} + \frac{1}{6}e^{\pi i/3} + \cdots,$$

whence we see that $f(z)$ has a simple pole at $z = \pi i$ with a residue $-e^{\pi i/3}$ there. Therefore we have, by (2),

$$\frac{1}{2\pi i}\int_C \frac{e^{z/3}\,dz}{1 + e^z} = -e^{\pi i/3}. \tag{8}$$

* Numerous examples will be found in T. M. MacRobert, "Functions of a Complex Variable."

The second method, which is direct line integration, gives us

$$\int_C \frac{e^{z/3}\,dz}{1+e^z} = \int_{-A}^A \frac{e^{x/3}\,dx}{1+e^x} + i\int_0^{2\pi} \frac{e^{\frac{1}{3}(A+iy)}\,dy}{1+e^{A+iy}}$$

$$+ \int_A^{-A} \frac{e^{\frac{1}{3}(x+2\pi i)}\,dx}{1+e^x} + i\int_{2\pi}^0 \frac{e^{\frac{1}{3}(-A+iy)}\,dy}{1+e^{-A+iy}}. \quad (9)$$

Now (Fig. 114), for α and β, any two complex numbers, with $|\alpha| \geqq |\beta|$,

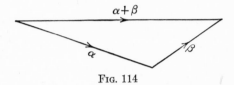

$$\alpha+\beta$$

FIG. 114

we have $|\alpha + \beta| \geqq |\alpha| - |\beta|$, so that $|e^{A+iy} + 1| \geqq e^A - 1$. Also,

$$|e^{\frac{1}{3}(A+iy)}| = e^{A/3},$$

and therefore we get for the integrand in the second integral above,

$$\left| \frac{e^{\frac{1}{3}(A+iy)}}{1+e^{A+iy}} \right| \leqq \frac{e^{A/3}}{e^A - 1}. \quad (10)$$

Similarly, we have for the integrand in the fourth integral,

$$\left| \frac{e^{\frac{1}{3}(-A+iy)}}{1+e^{-A+iy}} \right| \leqq \frac{e^{-A/3}}{1 - e^{-A}}. \quad (11)$$

Hence, if we allow A to become infinite in (9), we get, since the right-hand members of (10) and (11) approach zero,

$$\int_C \frac{e^{z/3}\,dz}{1+e^z} = \int_{-\infty}^\infty \frac{e^{x/3}\,dx}{1+e^x} + e^{2\pi i/3}\int_\infty^{-\infty} \frac{e^{x/3}\,dx}{1+e^x},$$

and

$$\frac{1}{2\pi i}\int_C \frac{e^{z/3}\,dz}{1+e^z} = \frac{1 - e^{\frac{2}{3}\pi i}}{2\pi i}\int_{-\infty}^\infty \frac{e^{x/3}\,dx}{1+e^x}. \quad (12)$$

Combining (8) and (12), there is found

$$\int_{-\infty}^\infty \frac{e^{x/3}\,dx}{1+e^x} = -\frac{2\pi i e^{\pi i/3}}{1 - e^{2\pi i/3}} = \frac{\pi}{\sin(\pi/3)} = \frac{2\pi}{\sqrt{3}}. \quad (13)$$

This integral may also be evaluated directly; the student should verify the result.

As a second example, we obtain Peirce's formula 484, with $m = 1$,

$$\int_0^\infty \frac{\sin x}{x}\, dx = \frac{\pi}{2}. \tag{14}$$

To do this, we consider the contour integral

$$\int_C \frac{e^{iz}}{z}\, dz, \tag{15}$$

where C consists of the x-axis from $-A$ to $-a$, the upper small semicircle $|z| = a$, the x-axis from a to A, and the upper large semicircle $|z| = A$ (Fig. 115). Since the function e^{iz}/z has no singularities

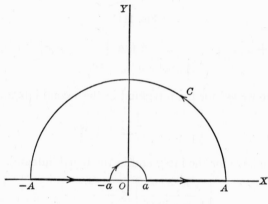

FIG. 115

inside C, its only singular point being a simple pole at $z = 0$, the integral (15) has the value zero. Therefore

$$\int_{-A}^{-a} \frac{e^{ix}}{x}\, dx + \int_\pi^0 i e^{ia\,(\cos\theta + i\sin\theta)}\, d\theta$$

$$+ \int_a^A \frac{e^{ix}}{x}\, dx + \int_0^\pi i e^{iA\,(\cos\theta + i\sin\theta)}\, d\theta = 0. \tag{16}$$

Now

$$\left| e^{iA\,(\cos\theta + i\sin\theta)} \right| = \left| e^{-A\sin\theta + iA\cos\theta} \right| = e^{-A\sin\theta},$$

and hence we have for the fourth integral, I_4, above,

$$|I_4| \leqq \int_0^\pi e^{-A\sin\theta}\, d\theta = 2 \int_0^{\pi/2} e^{-A\sin\theta}\, d\theta.$$

But for $0 \leq \theta \leq \pi/2$, $(\sin \theta)/\theta \geq 2/\pi$, so that

$$|I_4| \leq 2 \int_0^{\pi/2} e^{-2A\theta/\pi}\, d\theta = \frac{\pi}{A}(1 - e^{-A}),$$

and therefore I_4 approaches zero as A becomes infinite. Also, as $a \to 0$, the second integral, I_2, approaches $-i\pi$, and so we get in the limit,

$$\int_{-\infty}^0 \frac{e^{ix}}{x}\, dx + \int_0^\infty \frac{e^{ix}}{x}\, dx = i\pi. \tag{17}$$

If in the first of these integrals we replace x by $-x$, we find

$$-\int_0^\infty \frac{e^{-ix}}{x}\, dx + \int_0^\infty \frac{e^{ix}}{x}\, dx = i\pi, \tag{18}$$

whence

$$\int_0^\infty \frac{2i \sin x}{x}\, dx = i\pi,$$

and (14) follows.

PROBLEMS

1. (a) If R is a region bounded by a single closed curve C, show that the area of R is given by

$$\tfrac{1}{2} \int_C (x\, dy - y\, dx).$$

(b) Using this result, find the area of an ellipse. *Hint:* Take the parametric equations of the ellipse.

2. Derive formula (8) of Art. 102.

3. Assuming that a function $f(z)$, analytic inside a circle C of radius r and center a, may be developed in a series of the form

$$f(z) = c_0 + c_1(z - a) + \cdots + c_n(z - a)^n \cdots,$$

show that

$$c_n = \frac{1}{2\pi i} \int_C \frac{f(z)\, dz}{(z - a)^{n+1}} = \frac{f^{(n)}(a)}{n!}.$$

Using the inequality (7) of Art. 103 show directly that the series converges uniformly for $|z - a| < r$.

4. If $f(z)$ is analytic inside a circle C with center at $z = a$, and if $f(z)$ has a simple zero at $z = a$, so that

$$f(z) = c_1(z - a) + c_2(z - a)^2 + \cdots, \qquad c_1 \neq 0,$$

show that

$$a = \frac{1}{2\pi i} \int_C \frac{z f'(z)}{f(z)}\, dz.$$

5. Find the residue of the function $f(z) = 1/(z^3 + 1)^2$ at each of its singularities.

6. By contour integration, show that for n a positive integer

$$\int_0^{2\pi} \cos^n x \, dx = \begin{cases} 0 \text{ if } n \text{ is odd,} \\ \dfrac{1 \cdot 3 \cdot 5 \cdots (n-1)}{2 \cdot 4 \cdot 6 \cdots n} \, 2\pi \text{ if } n \text{ is even.} \end{cases}$$

Hint: Set $\cos x = \frac{1}{2}(w + 1/w)$, where $w = e^{ix}$, and integrate along the circle of unit radius centered at the origin of the complex w-plane.

7. Show that (Peirce, 490)

$$\int_0^\infty \frac{\cos mx}{1+x^2} \, dx = \frac{\pi e^{-m}}{2}$$

for $m > 0$, by integrating the function $e^{imz}/(1+z^2)$ along the contour consisting of the x-axis from $-A$ to A and the upper semicircle $|z| = A$.

8. Given $\displaystyle\int_0^\infty e^{-x^2} \, dx = \sqrt{\pi}/2$, obtain the Fresnel integrals (Peirce, 487),

$$\int_0^\infty \cos x^2 \, dx = \int_0^\infty \sin x^2 \, dx = \frac{\sqrt{2\pi}}{4},$$

by integrating the function e^{-z^2} along the contour consisting of the x-axis from 0 to A, the arc of the circle $|z| = A$ from $\theta = 0$ to $\theta = \pi/4$, and the line $\theta = \pi/4$ from $|z| = A$ to 0.

9. Given $\displaystyle\int_0^\infty e^{-x^2} \, dx = \sqrt{\pi}/2$, show that

$$\int_0^\infty e^{-x^2} \cos 2bx \, dx = \frac{\sqrt{\pi} \, e^{-b^2}}{2},$$

by integrating the function e^{-z^2} along the rectangle with sides $y = 0$, $y = b$, $x = \pm A$. Cf. Peirce, 508.

10. By integrating $e^{az}/\cosh \pi z$ along the rectangle with sides $y = 0$, $y = 1$ $x = \pm A$, show that

$$\int_{-\infty}^\infty \frac{e^{ax}}{\cosh \pi x} \, dx = \sec \frac{a}{2} \qquad (-\pi < a < \pi).$$

CHAPTER XI

Operational Calculus

106. Introduction. In Chapter I, Art. 9, we introduced the concept of an operator D, denoting differentiation with respect to the independent variable. This operator was found to be a powerful tool for the solution of linear differential equations with constant coefficients, and it was therefore employed in a number of our problems.

We propose in this chapter to study operational methods and their application to engineering work in more detail. The culmination of our work will be what is known as the operational calculus, initiated by the engineer Oliver Heaviside, and used by him in the solution of a variety of physical problems.

Unfortunately, Heaviside's treatment * of operators was somewhat unsystematic and lacking in clarity, so that it is rather difficult to follow his methods and to be sure of their validity. However, Bromwich,† using the theory of functions of a complex variable, and Carson,‡ by means of integral equations, have given rigorous proofs and connected accounts of Heaviside's methods.

In Part I, we examine an integrating operator as a basis for Heaviside's methods, which we then use to solve electrical network problems. In Part II, we consider Bromwich's line integrals § and their connection with and application to the Heaviside techniques. Laplace transforms, which have recently been extensively used in operational work, are briefly treated in Part III.

PART I. ELEMENTARY OPERATIONAL METHODS

107. The operator Q. Consider the linear differential equation of first order,

$$\frac{dy}{dt} = Fy + G, \qquad (1)$$

---

* O. Heaviside, "Electromagnetic Theory," 3 vols.

† T. J. I'A. Bromwich, "Normal Coordinates in Dynamical Systems," *Proc. London Math. Soc.*, 1916.

‡ J. Carson, "Electric Circuit Theory and the Operational Calculus."

§ See H. Jeffreys, "Operational Methods in Mathematical Physics."

where F and G are functions of t only. Suppose F and G bounded in the interval $0 \leq t \leq t_0$, so that $|F| \leq A$, $|G| \leq A_1$ for $0 \leq t \leq t_0$, and assume these functions integrable over this region. We shall seek the solution of equation (1) which is such that $y = y_0$ when $t = 0$. Let Q be an operator which, acting on a function $g(t)$, yields the definite integral of $g(t)$ between the limits 0 and t,

$$Qg(t) \equiv \int_0^t g(t)\, dt. \tag{2}$$

Operating on both members of (1) with Q, we then have

$$y - y_0 = Q(Fy + G),$$

$$(1 - QF)y = y_0 + QG, \tag{3}$$

or

$$y = y_0 + QG + QFy. \tag{4}$$

Here the symbol QFy means that y is to be multiplied by F and the product operated upon by Q. Equation (4) is evidently equivalent to the original differential equation (1) together with the condition $y|_{t=0} = y_0$. If we substitute for y in QFy the entire expression for y as given by (4), we get

$$y = y_0 + QG + QF(y_0 + QG + QFy)$$

$$= (y_0 + QG) + QF(y_0 + QG) + (QF)^2 y, \tag{5}$$

where $(QF)^2 y$ is merely a short way of writing $QFQFy$, and means that QFy is multiplied by F and the resulting product operated upon by Q. Again substituting the expression (4) for y in $(QF)^2 y$, (5) becomes

$$y = (y_0 + QG) + QF(y_0 + QG) + (QF)^2(y_0 + QG) + (QF)^3 y.$$

Continuing this process, we are led to the infinite series

$$y = [1 + QF + (QF)^2 + \cdots + (QF)^n + \cdots](y_0 + QG). \tag{6}$$

Let us examine this series. For the range $0 \leq t \leq t_0$, we have $|F| \leq A$; also, since $|G| \leq A_1$, it follows that $|y_0 + QG| \leq B$. Then

$$|QF(y_0 + QG)| = \left| \int_0^t F(y_0 + QG)\, dt \right|$$

$$\leq ABt,$$

$$\left| (QF)^2(y_0 + QG) \right| = \left| QF[QF(y_0 + QG)] \right|$$

$$\leq \left| \int_0^t FABt \, dt \right|$$

$$\leq \frac{A^2 Bt^2}{2},$$

$$\left| (QF)^3(y_0 + QG) \right| = \left| QF[(QF)^2(y_0 + QG)] \right|$$

$$\leq \left| \int_0^t \frac{FA^2 Bt^2}{2} \, dt \right|$$

$$\leq \frac{A^3 Bt^3}{3!},$$

and, in general,

$$\left| (QF)^n(y_0 + QG) \right| \leq \frac{A^n Bt^n}{n!},$$

as may be easily shown by induction. Consequently the terms of series (6) do not exceed numerically the corresponding terms of the series

$$B\left(1 + At + \frac{A^2 t^2}{2!} + \cdots + \frac{A^n t^n}{n!} + \cdots \right), \qquad (7)$$

which evidently converges for $0 \leq t \leq t_0$, and in fact represents the function Be^{At}. Hence, by this comparison test, the series (6) converges to some function $y(t)$. Substitution of (6) in (4) shows that this function $y(t)$ satisfies the differential equation (1) and also the condition $y = y_0$ when $t = 0$, so that we have in (6) a solution of our problem.

Now the series in brackets in equation (6) is the formal expansion of $(1 - QF)^{-1}$. We may therefore write symbolically, in place of (6),

$$y = \frac{1}{1 - QF} (y_0 + QG). \qquad (8)$$

But this is merely the solution of equation (3) carried out as if $1 - QF$ were an algebraic quantity. Thus the integrating operator Q may in this case be manipulated formally if we agree that the symbolic relation (8) is a shorthand way of writing the series solution (6).

The operator Q may also be profitably made use of in connection with certain differential equations of order higher than the first. As an example, consider the Bessel equation of order zero (equation (1), Art. 60),

$$t \frac{d^2y}{dt^2} + \frac{dy}{dt} + ty = 0, \tag{9}$$

and let the accompanying conditions be that $y = 1$ and $dy/dt = 0$ when $= 0$. Since $\dfrac{d}{dt}\left(t\dfrac{dy}{dt}\right) = t\dfrac{d^2y}{dt^2} + \dfrac{dy}{dt}$, (9) may be written as

$$\frac{d}{dt}\left(t\frac{dy}{dt}\right) = -ty.$$

Applying the operator Q to this equation, we get

$$t\frac{dy}{dt} = -Qty,$$

and

$$\frac{dy}{dt} = -\frac{1}{t}Qty.$$

A second application of Q then gives us

$$y - 1 = -Q\frac{1}{t}Qty. \tag{10}$$

Replacing y in the right-hand member by its value as given by (10), we have successively

$$y = 1 - Q\frac{1}{t}Qt\left(1 - Q\frac{1}{t}Qty\right)$$

$$= 1 - \frac{t^2}{2^2} + \left(Q\frac{1}{t}Qt\right)^2\left(1 - Q\frac{1}{t}Qty\right)$$

$$= 1 - \frac{t^2}{2^2} + \frac{t^4}{2^2 \cdot 4^2} - \left(Q\frac{1}{t}Qt\right)^3\left(1 - Q\frac{1}{t}Qty\right)$$

$$= \cdots \cdots \cdots \cdots \cdots \cdots \cdots \cdots \cdots$$

$$= 1 - \frac{t^2}{2^2} + \frac{t^4}{2^2 \cdot 4^2} - \cdots + (-1)^n \frac{t^{2n}}{2^2 \cdot 4^2 \cdots (2n)^2} + \cdots, \tag{11}$$

which is the familiar expansion of $J_0(t)$.

Before continuing with our investigation of operational methods, let us first take stock, so to speak, and determine what advance we have made by introducing the operator Q. As was pointed out in Chapter I,

the use of the differential operator D enabled us to shorten markedly
the labor of finding the general solution of a linear differential equation
with constant coefficients. Now in our physical applications, we are
usually not interested so much in the general solution of a differential
equation as we are in a particular solution satisfying given initial or
boundary conditions. Hence a method which leads us directly to the
desired particular solution, without having to determine, as a separate
problem, the proper values of the arbitrary elements in the general
solution, is more desirable from the standpoint of the engineer. As far
as the linear equation of first (and sometimes higher) order is concerned,
we have seen that the use of an integrating operator does have this
advantage of directness.

On the other hand, it may seem from the form of the solution (6) that
the Q-method has the disadvantage of always yielding a series representing the required function of t, instead of a solution in finite form which is
usually more convenient to handle in computational work. However,
we shall see that it is possible in many specific problems to obtain finite
expressions for our results; in other cases, the series form may be the
best obtainable by any process.

Having discussed the linear equation of first order and with variable
coefficients, we next consider the linear equation of second order,

$$a_0 \frac{d^2y}{dt^2} + a_1 \frac{dy}{dt} + a_2 y = T(t) \qquad (a_0 \neq 0),\qquad (12)$$

in which the coefficients a_0, a_1, a_2 are constants and $T(t)$ is any bounded
and integrable function of t for $0 \leq t \leq t_0$, accompanied by the initial
conditions

$$y = y_0, \qquad \frac{dy}{dt} = y_1,\qquad (13)$$

for $t = 0$. Operating upon (12) with Q, we get

$$a_0\left(\frac{dy}{dt} - y_1\right) + a_1(y - y_0) + a_2 Qy = QT,$$

or

$$a_0 \frac{dy}{dt} + a_1 y + a_2 Qy = a_0 y_1 + a_1 y_0 + QT.$$

A second application of Q then gives us

$$a_0(y - y_0) + a_1 Qy + a_2 Q^2 y = a_0 Qy_1 + a_1 Qy_0 + Q^2 T,$$
or
$$(a_0 + a_1 Q + a_2 Q^2)y = (a_0 + a_1 Q)y_0 + a_0 Qy_1 + Q^2 T.\qquad (14)$$

For convenience, let $\phi(Q)$, $\phi_0(Q)$, $\phi_1(Q)$ denote the operators acting upon y, y_0, y_1 respectively.   Now, remembering that $a_0 \neq 0$, the function

$$\phi^{-1}(z) = \frac{1}{\phi(z)} = \frac{1}{a_0 + a_1 z + a_2 z^2},$$

where z is a complex variable, may evidently be represented by a Maclaurin series in z.   If we operate on both members of equation (14) with the corresponding operator series $\phi^{-1}(Q)$, we get, since $\phi^{-1}(Q)\phi(Q) = 1$,

$$y = \phi^{-1}(Q)\phi_0(Q)y_0 + \phi^{-1}(Q)\phi_1(Q)y_1 + \phi^{-1}(Q)Q^2 T. \qquad (15)$$

When the indicated operations in (15) are carried out, we thus obtain a series solution of equation (12), satisfying the conditions (13).   The convergence of the resulting series may be established following the procedure employed for series (6), and consequently (15) will be a valid solution of our problem.

Symbolically, (15) may be written

$$y = \frac{\phi_0(Q)}{\phi(Q)} y_0 + \frac{\phi_1(Q)}{\phi(Q)} y_1 + \frac{Q}{\phi(Q)} QT. \qquad (16)$$

Now since, for c a constant and u and v any permissible functions * of t, we have

$$Q(cu) = cQ(u),$$

$$Q(u + v) = Qu + Qv,$$

$$Q^m Q^n u = Q^n Q^m u = Q^{m+n} u,$$

where m and n are positive integers, we see that Q behaves in these manipulations as if it were an algebraic quantity, just as the differential operator D was found so to behave in Chapter I.   This suggests that we may express the solution y by resolving the fractions in (16) into partial fractions.   We shall suppose first, for simplicity, that $a_2 \neq 0$, so that each of the fractions in (16) is a proper fraction, i.e., one in which the degree of the numerator is less than that of the denominator, and that the roots of $\phi(z) = 0$ are distinct.   Then each of the fractions ϕ_0/ϕ, ϕ_1/ϕ may be resolved into a sum of partial fractions of the form

$$\frac{A}{1 - rQ},$$

* Here, as in all the cases in which the operator Q is employed, it is assumed that the functions operated upon have the properties stated at the beginning of this article.

where $1/r$ is a root of $\phi(z) = 0$. We have then to interpret the expression

$$Y_1 = \frac{1}{1 - rQ} Ay_k \qquad (k = 0 \text{ or } 1). \tag{17}$$

This is evidently of the form (8), and therefore yields

$$Y_1 = [1 + (rQ) + (rQ)^2 + \cdots]Ay_k$$

$$= Ay_k\left[1 + (rt) + \frac{(rt)^2}{2!} + \frac{(rt)^3}{3!} + \cdots\right]$$

$$= Ay_k e^{rt}. \tag{18}$$

Thus each of the first two terms of the right member of (16) may be interpreted as a sum of exponential functions of t, the coefficients of which may be found by the method of partial fractions. Similarly, the last term of (16) will yield a sum of terms of the type

$$Y_2 = \frac{A}{1 - rQ} QT. \tag{19}$$

By equation (8), with $y_0 = 0$, Y_2 is the solution, vanishing with t, of the differential equation

$$\frac{dY_2}{dt} - rY_2 = AT.$$

We easily find, by the usual process,

$$Y_2 = Ae^{rt}QTe^{-rt}, \tag{20}$$

and therefore the last term of (16) may be interpreted.

In case a fraction in (16) is not proper, it may, by carrying out the indicated division, be reduced to the sum of a polynomial in Q and a proper fraction. The polynomial in Q will yield a polynomial in t upon interpretation, and the proper fraction may be treated as indicated above. The case in which the equation $\phi(z) = 0$ has multiple roots requires that the above procedure undergo certain modifications, which we shall not stop to discuss.

Linear equations of higher order and with constant coefficients may evidently be similarly treated, and it is not necessary to give a detailed discussion of the general equation. Our purpose here has been merely to indicate the manner in which an integrating operator may be employed, and to lead into the discussion of Heaviside's methods.

For the sake of making the above argument more concrete, and to create facility in the use of operators, we give an example of the process. Let the given equation be

$$\frac{d^2y}{dt^2} - 3\frac{dy}{dt} + 2y = 12e^{-t},$$

and let the associated conditions be

$$y\Big]_{t=0} = y_0 = 4, \qquad \frac{dy}{dt}\Big]_{t=0} = y_1 = 5.$$

Then equation (16) is here

$$y = \frac{1 - 3Q}{1 - 3Q + 2Q^2}\, 4 + \frac{Q}{1 - 3Q + 2Q^2}\, 5 + \frac{Q}{1 - 3Q + 2Q^2}\, Q(12e^{-t}).$$

We readily find

$$\frac{1 - 3Q}{1 - 3Q + 2Q^2} = \frac{2}{1 - Q} - \frac{1}{1 - 2Q},$$

$$\frac{Q}{1 - 3Q + 2Q^2} = -\frac{1}{1 - Q} + \frac{1}{1 - 2Q}.$$

Hence we get

$$\frac{1 - 3Q}{1 - 3Q + 2Q^2}\, 4 = 8e^t - 4e^2$$

$$\frac{Q}{1 - 3Q + 2Q^2}\, 5 = -5e^t + 5e^{2t}$$

$$\frac{Q}{1 - 3Q + 2Q^2}\, Q(12e^{-t}) = -e^t Q(12e^{-t}\cdot e^{-t}) + e^{2t}Q(12e^{-t}\cdot e^{-2t})$$
$$= -6e^t + 6e^{-t} + 4e^{2t} - 4e^{-t},$$

whence the required solution is

$$y = 2e^{-t} - 3e^t + 5e^{2t}.$$

PROBLEMS

Using the methods of Art. 107, find the solution of each of the following differential equations, subject to the given conditions.

1. $\dfrac{dy}{dt} = ty + 6t - 3t^3;\ y = 0$ for $t = 0$.

2. $\dfrac{dy}{dt} = 2y + e^{3t};\ y = 1$ for $t = 0$.

3. $\dfrac{d^2y}{dt^2} - y = t$; $y = -1$ and $\dfrac{dy}{dt} = 4$ for $t = 0$.

4. $\dfrac{d^2y}{dt^2} - y = 6e^{3t}$; $y = 8$ and $\dfrac{dy}{dt} = -5$ for $t = 0$.

5. $\dfrac{d^2y}{dt^2} + \dfrac{dy}{dt} - 2y = 2(1 + t - t^2)$; $y = 0$ and $\dfrac{dy}{dt} = 3$ for $t = 0$.

108. Heaviside's operator p. The procedure outlined in Art. 107 is substantially that employed by Heaviside in connection with a system of differential equations arising in electric circuit theory. Heaviside's notation for our operator Q was p^{-1}; this symbol, which he regarded as the inverse of the differential operator $p = d/dt$, is somewhat more useful in application, since it allows for the joint use of differential and integrating operators in the same problem.

However, when applying both p and Q to a function, care must be taken. For, while p and Q separately satisfy the fundamental laws of algebra, they are not necessarily commutative with each other. Thus,

$$pQg(t) = \frac{d}{dt}\int_0^t g(t)\,dt = g(t),$$

but

$$Qpg(t) = \int_0^t g'(t)\,dt = g(t) - g(0),$$

so that unless $g(0) = 0$, pQg and Qpg have different meanings.

In order to make p the true inverse of Q, it is therefore necessary to stipulate that, whenever p and Q both appear in an operator, the p operations should *follow* the Q operations.

Even with this understanding, the symbol p should not always be interpreted as d/dt directly. For, suppose that we operate upon equation (14) of Art. 107 with p^2; then we have

$$(a_0p^2 + a_1p + a_2)y = (a_0p^2 + a_1p)y_0 + a_0py_1 + T. \tag{1}$$

If, now, we first set $p = d/dt$ in the right-hand member of (1), and then divide by the operator $F(p) = a_0p^2 + a_1p + a_2$, we get, since $p^m y_k = 0$, merely

$$y = \frac{1}{F(p)}\,T,$$

and the effect of the initial conditions has been lost. Instead, we should divide by $F(p)$ first, getting

$$y = \frac{F_0(p)}{F(p)}\,y_0 + \frac{F_1(p)}{F(p)}\,y_1 + \frac{1}{F(p)}\,T, \tag{2}$$

where $F_0(p)$ and $F_1(p)$ are the operators acting on y_0 and y_1 respectively in (1), and then interpret the operators in equation (2) properly.

What should be the proper interpretation of the operators in (2)? The answer to this important question is easily found in the light of our discussion of Art. 107: Expand the fractions F_0/F and F_1/F in series of *negative* powers of p, interpreting p^{-m} as Q^m. This procedure will then be entirely equivalent to the Q-method, with merely a different symbolism.

In a specific problem, for which we desire a solution in finite form, the conversion from the p-method to the Q-method may of course be made directly. For example, equation (2) for the problem of Art. 107 will be

$$y = \frac{p^2 - 3p}{p^2 - 3p + 2}\,4 + \frac{p}{p^2 - 3p + 2}\,5 + \frac{1}{p^2 - 3p + 2}\,12e^{-t}. \quad (3)$$

Dividing numerator and denominator of each fraction by p^2, and replacing p^{-1} by Q, p^{-2} by Q^2, we get

$$y = \frac{1 - 3Q}{1 - 3Q + 2Q^2}\,4 + \frac{Q}{1 - 3Q + 2Q^2}\,5 + \frac{Q}{1 - 3Q + 2Q^2}\,Q(12e^{-t}),$$

which is identical with our previous formulation.

If, on the other hand, we were to expand the fractions in equation (2) in positive powers of p, we would get the wrong result. To illustrate, consider again the above problem. Referring to equation (3), we would have

$$\frac{p^2 - 3p}{p^2 - 3p + 2} = -\frac{3}{2}p - \frac{7}{4}p^2 - \cdots,$$

$$\frac{p}{p^2 - 3p + 2} = \frac{1}{2}p + \frac{3}{4}p^2 + \cdots,$$

$$\frac{1}{p^2 - 3p + 2} = \frac{1}{2} + \frac{3}{4}p + \cdots,$$

$$y = (-\tfrac{3}{2}p - \tfrac{7}{4}p^2 - \cdots)4 + (\tfrac{1}{2}p + \tfrac{3}{4}p^2 + \cdots)5$$
$$+ (\tfrac{1}{2} + \tfrac{3}{4}p + \cdots)12e^{-t}$$
$$= 6e^{-t} - 9e^{-t} + \cdots.$$

But this infinite series is entirely meaningless.

Moreover, while the series in positive powers of Q operating on $T(t)$ always yield convergent series, this is not always true of series in powers of p. Thus, consider the expression

$$\frac{1}{p-1} t^{1/2}.$$

If we write

$$\frac{1}{p-1} = -(1 + p + p^2 + \cdots + p^{n-1} + \cdots),$$

we get

$$\frac{1}{p-1} t^{1/2} = -t^{1/2} - \frac{1}{2} t^{-1/2} + \left[\frac{1}{4} t^{-3/2} - \frac{3}{8} t^{-5/2} + \cdots \right.$$

$$\left. + (-1)^{n-1} \frac{1 \cdot 3 \cdot 5 \cdots (2n-1)}{2^{n+1}} t^{-(2n+1)/2} + \cdots \right].$$

Applying Cauchy's ratio test to this series, we find

$$\lim_{n \to \infty} \left| \frac{u_{n+1}}{u_n} \right| = \lim_{n \to \infty} \left| \frac{2n+1}{2t} \right| = \infty,$$

so that the series diverges for all values of t. On the other hand, we have

$$\frac{1}{p-1} t^{1/2} = \frac{Q}{1-Q} t^{1/2} = (Q + Q^2 + \cdots + Q^n + \cdots) t^{1/2}$$

$$= \frac{2}{3} t^{3/2} + \frac{4}{15} t^{5/2} + \frac{8}{105} t^{7/2} + \cdots + \frac{2^n}{3 \cdot 5 \cdot 7 \cdots (2n+1)} t^{(2n+1)/2} + \cdots,$$

whence

$$\lim_{n \to \infty} \left| \frac{u_{n+1}}{u_n} \right| = \lim_{n \to \infty} \left| \frac{2t}{2n+3} \right| = 0,$$

and therefore this series converges for all values of t.

It is therefore apparent that the operator Q, or p^{-1}, is fundamental when we wish to solve a differential equation subject to given initial conditions.

In view of what has been said about the operators p and Q, it is natural to ask why the operator p should be employed at all. One answer to this question is found in the historical background of the subject of operational calculus. Heaviside, using the operator p boldly, was able to obtain many important physical results in a much easier and shorter manner than had been previously possible, and later workers in the field of operational analysis followed Heaviside's technique in extending the applicability of his operators, or established the validity of Heaviside's results by giving them a firm mathematical foundation. Another reason for not abandoning the operator p is that, as has been already stated, this operator is frequently the simpler to use in our physical applications; this will become more apparent as we continue our study of operational methods.

Let us now interpret some particular operators acting on unity. To begin with, we have, as has been seen,

$$p^{-1} \cdot 1 = Q \cdot 1 = t,$$

$$p^{-2} \cdot 1 = Q^2 \cdot 1 = \frac{t^2}{2!},$$

and in general,

$$p^{-n} \cdot 1 = Q^n \cdot 1 = \frac{t^n}{n!}, \tag{4}$$

where n is any positive integer. Likewise, we get

$$\frac{p}{p-a} \cdot 1 = \frac{1}{1-aQ} \cdot 1 = (1 + aQ + a^2Q^2 + \cdots) \cdot 1$$

$$= 1 + at + \frac{a^2t^2}{2!} + \cdots$$

$$= e^{at}. \tag{5}$$

If we differentiate the relation $(1 - aQ)^{-1} \cdot 1 = e^{at}$ partially with respect to a, we get

$$Q(1 - aQ)^{-2} \cdot 1 = te^{at},$$

$$2Q^2(1 - aQ)^{-3} \cdot 1 = t^2 e^{at},$$

$$3!Q^3(1 - aQ)^{-4} \cdot 1 = t^3 e^{at},$$

and in general,

$$(n - 1)!Q^{n-1}(1 - aQ)^{-n} \cdot 1 = t^{n-1} e^{at},$$

whence

$$\frac{Q^{n-1}}{(1 - aQ)^n} \cdot 1 = \frac{p}{(p-a)^n} \cdot 1 = \frac{t^{n-1} e^{at}}{(n-1)!}. \tag{6}$$

This formula may also be obtained by direct expansion and interpretation.

We next consider the rational function $f(p)/F(p)$, where $f(p)$ and $F(p)$ are polynomials in p, and the degree of $f(p)$ does not exceed that of $F(p)$. Let $a_1, a_2, \cdots, a_n$ denote the roots of $F(z) = 0$, which we suppose to be distinct and different from zero, and let $F'(a_k)$ denote the value of $dF'(z)/dz$ for $z = a_k$. Then **Heaviside's expansion theorem** states that

$$\frac{f(p)}{F(p)} \cdot 1 = \frac{f(0)}{F(0)} + \sum_{k=1}^{n} \frac{f(a_k)}{a_k F'(a_k)} e^{a_k t}. \tag{7}$$

To prove this theorem, consider the resolution of $f(p)/pF(p)$ into partial fractions,*

$$\frac{f(p)}{pF(p)} = \frac{A_0}{p} + \frac{A_1}{p - a_1} + \frac{A_2}{p - a_2} + \cdots + \frac{A_n}{p - a_n}.$$

Then

$$f(p) = A_0 F(p) + A_1 \frac{pF(p)}{p - a_1} + \cdots + A_n \frac{pF(p)}{p - a_n}.$$

Setting $p = 0$, we get $f(0) = A_0 F(0)$, so that

$$A_0 = \frac{f(0)}{F(0)}.$$

Likewise, for $p = a_k$, there is found

$$f(a_k) = A_k a_k \lim_{p \to a_k} \frac{F(p)}{p - a_k} = A_k a_k \lim_{p \to a_k} \frac{\dfrac{d}{dp} F(p)}{\dfrac{d}{dp}(p - a_k)}$$

$$= A_k a_k F'(a_k),$$

whence

$$A_k = \frac{f(a_k)}{a_k F'(a_k)} \qquad (k = 1, 2, \cdots, n).$$

Inserting the values found for $A_0, A_1, \cdots, A_n$, in the partial fractions, and multiplying throughout by p, we have

$$\frac{f(p)}{F(p)} = \frac{f(0)}{F(0)} + \sum_{k=1}^{n} \frac{f(a_k)}{a_k F'(a_k)} \frac{p}{p - a_k}.$$

Finally, interpreting p as d/dt, and operating on unity with $f(p)/F(p)$, we get, using formula (5), the Heaviside expansion theorem (7).

There exist modifications of equation (7) for the cases in which $F(z) = 0$ has zero or multiple roots. However, we shall not have sufficient need for these special formulas to warrant their derivation in

---

* Temporarily, p may be regarded as an algebraic quantity, and interpreted as an operator in the final result.

general terms. If, in a particular case, some of the a's are equal or zero, the resolution of $f(\mathrm{p})/\mathrm{p}F(\mathrm{p})$ into partial fractions will contain terms of the form $A/(\mathrm{p} - a_k)^m$, where m is an integer greater than unity. Then $f(\mathrm{p})/F(\mathrm{p})$ will contain terms of the form A/p^{m-1} or of the form $A\mathrm{p}/(\mathrm{p} - a_k)^m$, which can be interpreted by means of formulas (4) and (6), respectively.

We now apply (7) to the interpretation of a few operational formulas. Consider first the operator $\mathrm{p}/(\mathrm{p}^2 + a^2)$. Here $f(\mathrm{p}) = \mathrm{p}$, $F(\mathrm{p}) = \mathrm{p}^2 + a^2 = (\mathrm{p} - ia)(\mathrm{p} + ia)$, so that we get

$$\frac{\mathrm{p}}{\mathrm{p}^2 + a^2} \cdot 1 = 0 + \frac{ia}{ia \cdot 2ia} e^{iat} + \frac{-ia}{(-ia)(-2ia)} e^{-iat}$$

$$= \frac{1}{a} \frac{e^{iat} - e^{-iat}}{2i} = \frac{1}{a} \sin at. \tag{8}$$

As another example, consider the operator $\mathrm{p}^2/(\mathrm{p}^2 + a^2)$. Here we have

$$\frac{\mathrm{p}^2}{\mathrm{p}^2 + a^2} \cdot 1 = 0 + \frac{-a^2}{ia \cdot 2ia} e^{iat} + \frac{-a^2}{(-ia)(-2ia)} e^{-iat}$$

$$= \frac{e^{iat} + e^{-iat}}{2}$$

$$= \cos at. \tag{9}$$

Note that if we interpret p as d/dt, formula (9) may be obtained directly from (8). This interpretation of p, however, is not always valid, as we have seen.

By changing a into ia in (8) and (9), we get the additional formulas,

$$\frac{\mathrm{p}}{\mathrm{p}^2 - a^2} \cdot 1 = \frac{1}{a} \sinh at, \tag{10}$$

$$\frac{\mathrm{p}^2}{\mathrm{p}^2 - a^2} \cdot 1 = \cosh at. \tag{11}$$

An interesting application of formula (8) is found in the following resonance problem. A simple pendulum, originally hanging in equilibrium, is subjected to a force varying sinusoidally in a period equal to the natural period of the pendulum, assuming the natural period to be constant and independent of the amplitude of swing; find the angular displacement θ at any time t. Here the differential equation of the motion is evidently

$$\frac{d^2\theta}{dt^2} + a^2\theta = A \sin at,$$

where a and A are constants. Now let us use equation (8) backwards, so to speak, that is, let us replace sin at by the equivalent operational expression. Then we have

$$\frac{d^2\theta}{dt^2} + a^2\theta = A \frac{ap}{p^2 + a^2} \cdot 1.$$

Since $\theta = d\theta/dt = 0$ for $t = 0$, we may write the solution of this equation in the form

$$\theta = A \frac{ap}{(p^2 + a^2)^2} \cdot 1.$$

Now the right-hand member may be interpreted as follows. Differentiate equation (8) partially with respect to a, getting

$$\frac{-2ap}{(p^2 + a^2)^2} \cdot 1 = \frac{t}{a} \cos at - \frac{1}{a^2} \sin at.$$

Then

$$\frac{ap}{(p^2 + a^2)^2} \cdot 1 = \frac{1}{2a^2} (\sin at - at \cos at), \tag{12}$$

and

$$\theta = \frac{A}{2a^2} (\sin at - at \cos at).$$

Our problem, incidentally, has furnished us with a new operational formula (12). Despite its novel derivation, it is valid, as the solution of Problem 8 below will show. Other new operational formulas may be similarly obtained and justified.

PROBLEMS

In Exercises 1–5, use the methods of Art. 108 to find the solution of each differential equation, subject to the given conditions.

1. $\dfrac{d^2y}{dt^2} + y = 2$; $y = 1$ and $\dfrac{dy}{dt} = 1$ for $t = 0$.

2. $\dfrac{d^2y}{dt^2} + y = 2 \sin t$; $y = -1$ and $\dfrac{dy}{dt} = 2$ for $t = 0$.

3. $\dfrac{d^3y}{dt^3} - \dfrac{dy}{dt} = 6e^{2t}$; $y = 5$, $\dfrac{dy}{dt} = -2$, and $\dfrac{d^2y}{dt^2} = 6$ for $t = 0$.

4. $\dfrac{d^3y}{dt^3} + \dfrac{dy}{dt} = 2$; $y = 3$, $\dfrac{dy}{dt} = 1$, and $\dfrac{d^2y}{dt^2} = -2$ for $t = 0$.

5. $\dfrac{d^4y}{dt^4} - y = 1$; $y = 1$, $\dfrac{dy}{dt} = 2$, $\dfrac{d^2y}{dt^2} = 0$, and $\dfrac{d^3y}{dt^3} = 0$ for $t = 0$.

6. By expanding $Q^{n-1}/(1 - aQ)^n$ in a series of positive powers of Q, and operating with the series on unity, derive formula (6) of Art. 108.

7. Derive the operational formula

$$\frac{a^2}{(p - a)^2} \cdot 1 = 1 + (at - 1)e^{at}$$

by operating upon both members of equation (6), Art. 108, with p^{-1}. Justify the procedure.

8. Derive formula (12) of Art. 108 by resolving the operator into partial fractions and then using the result of Problem 7.

Derive the following operational formulas.

9. $\dfrac{1}{p - a} \cdot 1 = \dfrac{1}{a} (e^{at} - 1).$

10. $\dfrac{1}{(p - a)(p - b)} \cdot 1 = \dfrac{a - b + be^{at} - ae^{bt}}{ab(a - b)}.$

11. $\dfrac{p^2}{(p - a)^2} \cdot 1 = (1 + at)e^{at}.$

12. $\dfrac{ap}{(p + b)^2 + a^2} \cdot 1 = e^{-bt} \sin at.$

13. $\dfrac{ap}{(p + b)^2 - a^2} \cdot 1 = e^{-bt} \sinh at.$

14. $\dfrac{p^2 + bp}{(p + b)^2 + a^2} \cdot 1 = e^{-bt} \cos at.$

15. $\dfrac{p^2 + bp}{(p + b)^2 - a^2} \cdot 1 = e^{-bt} \cosh at.$

109. Electrical networks.

In Chapter I, Art. 14(d), we considered some simple electrical circuits containing a source of e.m.f. and the constant parameters, resistance R, inductance L, and capacitance C, of the circuits. We now proceed to set up the differential equations of more complicated circuits or combinations of circuits, and to solve these equations by operational methods.

Our formulations and results, although couched in the terminology of electricity and referring principally to electrical circuits, may be interpreted also in connection with analogous mechanical, thermodynamic, or aerodynamic problems.*

By an electrical network is meant a coupled group of circuits made up of branches each of which may contain resistances, inductances,

---

* See, for example, V. Bush, "Gimbal Stabilization," *Jour. Franklin Inst.*, August, 1919; O. G. C. Dahl, "Temperature and Stress Distribution in Hollow Cylinders," *Trans. A.S.M.E.*, Vol. 46, p. 161, 1924; R. T. Jones, "Calculation of the Motion of an Airplane under the Influence of Irregular Disturbances," *Journal of Aeronautical Sciences*, Vol. 3, p. 419, 1936.

capacitances, and sources of e.m.f. in series. Coupling may consist of a physical connection by means of a current-carrying conductor, or it may be electromagnetic in nature, as between the primary and secondary of a transformer.

We shall denote resistance, self-inductance, and capacitance by the letters R, L, C, respectively, and shall use single subscripts to denote the branches to which these parameters belong, as indicated in Fig. 116.

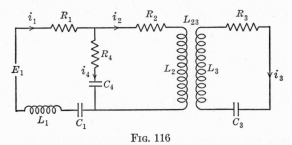

FIG. 116

When two branches are coupled electromagnetically, as are the second and third branches in Fig. 116, we use the letter L with double subscript to denote the parameter of mutual inductance; this inductance may be positive or negative, depending upon the relative mode of winding of the two coils involved. A source of e.m.f. in any branch is denoted by E with the proper single subscript. Currents flowing in the various branches are designated by i with suitable single subscripts, and their directions of flow are arbitrarily assumed and indicated by arrows, as in Fig. 116.

One branch, or two or more branches in series connection, may constitute a mesh or circuit; thus, in Fig. 116, branches 1 and 2 constitute one circuit, branches 1 and 4 a second circuit, branches 2 and 4 a third circuit, and branch 3 alone a fourth circuit.

Kirchhoff's current and e.m.f. laws,* upon which all network analyses rest, may be stated as follows:

I. At any junction point of three or more branches, the algebraic sum of the currents, considered as positive when flowing toward the point and negative when flowing away from the point, is zero.

II. The algebraic sum of all the e.m.f.'s and potential drops around any circuit is zero.

To illustrate the classic procedure for any given network and to lead up to the general operational analysis of circuits, we apply Kirch-

---

* These laws, restated here for convenient reference, were given also in Art. 14 (*d*). It is assumed that the method of applying the second law to simple circuits is familiar to the student.

hoff's laws to the network of Fig. 116. For either of the junction points of branches 1, 2, and 4, law I gives us the relation

$$i_1 = i_2 + i_4. \tag{1}$$

Law II applied to the circuits made up of branches 1 and 4, 2 and 4, and 3, in turn yields the further relations

$$R_1 i_1 + R_4 i_4 + \frac{1}{C_4} \int i_4 \, dt + \frac{1}{C_1} \int i_1 \, dt + L_1 \frac{di_1}{dt} = E_1,$$

$$R_2 i_2 + L_2 \frac{di_2}{dt} + L_{23} \frac{di_3}{dt} - \frac{1}{C_4} \int i_4 \, dt - R_4 i_4 = 0, \tag{2}$$

$$R_3 i_3 + \frac{1}{C_3} \int i_3 \, dt + L_3 \frac{di_3}{dt} + L_{23} \frac{di_2}{dt} = 0.$$

We need not write the equation for the circuit consisting of branches 1 and 2, since this relation may be obtained by adding the first and second of equations (2). If, now, we make use of equation (1) to eliminate i_4, our network e.m.f. relations (2) may be written in the form

$$L_1 \frac{di_1}{dt} + (R_1 + R_4)i_1 + \left(\frac{1}{C_1} + \frac{1}{C_4} \right) \int i_1 \, dt - R_4 i_2 - \frac{1}{C_4} \int i_2 \, dt = E_1,$$

$$-R_4 i_1 - \frac{1}{C_4} \int i_1 \, dt + L_2 \frac{di_2}{dt} + (R_2 + R_4)i_2$$

$$+ \frac{1}{C_4} \int i_2 \, dt + L_{23} \frac{di_3}{dt} = 0,$$

$$L_{23} \frac{di_2}{dt} + L_3 \frac{di_3}{dt} + R_3 i_3 + \frac{1}{C_3} \int i_3 \, dt = 0. \tag{3}$$

Equations (3) yield a system of three simultaneous linear differential equations in the three dependent variables i_1, i_2, i_3. If we solve this system subject to suitable given initial conditions, and then find, from (1), i_4 as $i_1 - i_2$, we shall have expressions for the currents in all four branches of the network.

We next consider the same problem from another viewpoint, which is that usually adopted in circuit analysis. We regard the network as made up of three independent circuits (Fig. 117), the first consisting of branches 1 and 4, the second of branches 2 and 4, and the third of branch 3, and let I_1, I_2, I_3 denote the currents, conventionally assumed to flow in the clockwise sense, in the three *circuits*. If we apply Kirchhoff's second law to these three circuits in turn, we get directly equations like (3) except that I_1, I_2, I_3, respectively, replace i_1, i_2, i_3. The new relations then determine the *circuit* currents I_1, I_2, I_3, from which

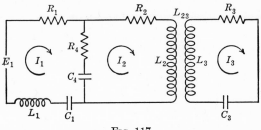

FIG. 117

the resultant *branch* currents i_1, i_2, i_3, i_4 either are directly known, or, for branch 4, may be found by use of Kirchhoff's first law.

The fact that the equations for the circuit currents are exactly like equations (3) for the branch currents is of course due to the equivalence of I_1 and i_1, I_2 and i_2, I_3 and i_3. If the three circuits chosen for analysis in this network had been other than those indicated in Fig. 117, the correspondence in form between such circuit equations and (3) would not have been so complete, although the ultimate determination of branch currents i_1, i_2, i_3, i_4 would necessarily lead to the same result in any event. There are, however, networks in which a circuit current may correspond to no actual branch current. For example, consider

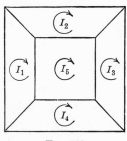

FIG. 118

the network represented schematically in Fig. 118, where there are five independent circuits which may be taken as indicated. Here circuit currents I_1, I_2, I_3, I_4 are actually measurable as flowing in the outside branches of the network, but circuit current I_5 is fictitious in that it cannot be measured by an instrument placed in any branch. Instead, the current flowing in each of the four inner branches is the resultant of I_5 and other of the remaining four circuit currents.

As indicated by our first example, the second method is usually more direct. Moreover, it is more readily applied to the general problem of a network possessing m independent circuits. We proceed now to consider this general problem.

Let R_{kk}, L_{kk}, C_{kk}, respectively, taken as positive, denote the *total* resistance, inductance, and capacitance in series in circuit k, and let

R_{jk}, L_{jk}, C_{jk}, with signs determined in accordance with the clockwise convention for positive current flow, denote the corresponding mutual elements common to or between circuits j and k. Evidently $R_{jk} = R_{kj}$, $L_{jk} = L_{kj}$, $C_{jk} = C_{kj}$.

To illustrate these conventions and notations, let us refer again to the network of Fig. 117. We have here

$$L_{11} = L_1, \qquad R_{11} = R_1 + R_4, \qquad \frac{1}{C_{11}} = \frac{1}{C_1} + \frac{1}{C_4},$$

$$L_{22} = L_2, \qquad R_{22} = R_2 + R_4, \qquad \frac{1}{C_{22}} = \frac{1}{C_4},$$

$$L_{33} = L_3, \qquad R_{33} = R_3, \qquad \frac{1}{C_{33}} = \frac{1}{C_3},$$

$$L_{12} = L_{21} = 0, \qquad R_{12} = R_{21} = -R_4, \qquad \frac{1}{C_{12}} = \frac{1}{C_{21}} = -\frac{1}{C_4},$$

$$L_{23} = L_{32} = L_{23}, \qquad R_{23} = R_{32} = 0, \qquad \frac{1}{C_{23}} = \frac{1}{C_{32}} = 0,$$

$$L_{31} = L_{13} = 0, \qquad R_{31} = R_{13} = 0, \qquad \frac{1}{C_{31}} = \frac{1}{C_{13}} = 0.$$

Consequently the equations of this network may be written as

$$L_{11}\frac{dI_1}{dt} + R_{11}I_1 + \frac{1}{C_{11}}\int I_1\,dt + R_{12}I_2 + \frac{1}{C_{12}}\int I_2\,dt = E_1,$$

$$R_{21}I_1 + \frac{1}{C_{21}}\int I_1\,dt + L_{22}\frac{dI_2}{dt} + R_{22}I_2 + \frac{1}{C_{22}}\int I_2\,dt + L_{23}\frac{dI_3}{dt} = 0,$$

$$L_{32}\frac{dI_2}{dt} + L_{33}\frac{dI_3}{dt} + R_{33}I_3 + \frac{1}{C_{33}}\int I_3\,dt = 0. \tag{3'}$$

In the classical treatment of network equations (3) or (3'), we should begin by differentiating each equation with respect to t, in order to remove the integral terms, which are at present indefinite. However, we wish to treat such equations from the operator viewpoint, taking into account initial conditions. Accordingly, we shall stipulate that, in all our network problems, the charges, which are represented by the time integrals of the various currents, shall be initially zero. Then the integrals may have 0 and t as their lower and upper limits, respectively, and we may write QI_k for $\int I_k\,dt$.

Consider now a general type of network made up of m simple independent circuits. Each circuit may contain an e.m.f., resistances, inductances, and capacitances, and in each a circuit current will flow. From the manner in which equations (3′) were set up, it is now easy to see that we get by an application of Kirchhoff's e.m.f. law to each mesh in turn, equations of the form

$$L_{11}\frac{dI_1}{dt} + R_{11}I_1 + \frac{1}{C_{11}}QI_1 + L_{12}\frac{dI_2}{dt} + R_{12}I_2 + \frac{1}{C_{12}}QI_2 + \cdots$$

$$+ L_{1m}\frac{dI_m}{dt} + R_{1m}I_m + \frac{1}{C_{1m}}QI_m = E_{11}(t),$$

$$L_{21}\frac{dI_1}{dt} + R_{21}I_1 + \frac{1}{C_{21}}QI_1 + L_{22}\frac{dI_2}{dt} + R_{22}I_2 + \frac{1}{C_{22}}QI_2 + \cdots$$

$$+ L_{2m}\frac{dI_m}{dt} + R_{2m}I_m + \frac{1}{C_{2m}}QI_m = E_{22}(t),\quad (4)$$

$$\cdots\cdots\cdots\cdots\cdots\cdots\cdots\cdots\cdots\cdots\cdots\cdots\cdots,$$

$$L_{m1}\frac{dI_1}{dt} + R_{m1}I_1 + \frac{1}{C_{m1}}QI_1 + L_{m2}\frac{dI_2}{dt} + R_{m2}I_2 + \frac{1}{C_{m2}}QI_2 + \cdots$$

$$+ L_{mm}\frac{dI_m}{dt} + R_{mm}I_m + \frac{1}{C_{mm}}QI_m = E_{mm}(t),$$

where $E_{11}(t), \cdots, E_{mm}(t)$ are the e.m.f.'s applied to the m circuits. To save space, we may write equations (4) in the shorthand form *

$$\sum_{k=1}^{m}\left(L_{jk}\frac{dI_k}{dt} + R_{jk}I_k + \frac{1}{C_{jk}}QI_k\right) = E_{jj}(t)\qquad (j = 1, 2, \cdots, m).\quad (5)$$

If we operate upon (5) with Q, we get

$$\sum_{k=1}^{m}\left(L_{jk} + R_{jk}Q + \frac{1}{C_{jk}}Q^2\right)I_k = \sum_{k=1}^{m}L_{jk}I_{k0} + QE_{jj}$$
$$(j = 1, 2, \cdots, m),\quad (6)$$

where I_{k0} is the value of I_k for $t = 0$. These equations correspond to equation (14) of Art. 107. If we now operate upon (6) with p, and write $1/p$ for Q, we find

$$\sum_{k=1}^{m}\left(L_{jk}p + R_{jk} + \frac{1}{C_{jk}p}\right)I_k = \sum_{k=1}^{m}pL_{jk}I_{k0} + E_{jj}$$
$$(j = 1, 2, \cdots, m),\quad (7)$$

* To follow the argument clearly, the student should write out the subsequent equations in full for, say, $m = 2$ or 3.

which correspond to equation (1) of Art. 108. Letting $z_{jk}(\mathrm{p})$ denote the operator acting on I_k in the jth equation,

$$z_{jk}(\mathrm{p}) = L_{jk}\mathrm{p} + R_{jk} + \frac{1}{C_{jk}\mathrm{p}}, \tag{8}$$

equations (7) become, when written out in full,

$$z_{11}(\mathrm{p})I_1 + z_{12}(\mathrm{p})I_2 + \cdots + z_{1m}(\mathrm{p})I_m$$
$$= \mathrm{p}(L_{11}I_{10} + L_{12}I_{20} + \cdots + L_{1m}I_{m0}) + E_{11},$$

$$z_{21}(\mathrm{p})I_1 + z_{22}(\mathrm{p})I_2 + \cdots + z_{2m}(\mathrm{p})I_m$$
$$= \mathrm{p}(L_{21}I_{10} + L_{22}I_{20} + \cdots + L_{2m}I_{m0}) + E_{22},$$

$$\cdots\cdots\cdots\cdots\cdots\cdots\cdots\cdots\cdots\cdots\cdots\cdots\cdots, \tag{9}$$

$$z_{m1}(\mathrm{p})I_1 + z_{m2}(\mathrm{p})I_2 + \cdots + z_{mm}(\mathrm{p})I_m$$
$$= \mathrm{p}(L_{m1}I_{10} + L_{m2}I_{20} + \cdots + L_{mm}I_{m0}) + E_{mm}.$$

Equations (9) may, for any specific problem, be solved for the currents I_k by the methods given in Art. 108. Such a set of values I_k would not only satisfy the network equations (4), but would automatically meet the initial conditions, $I_k = I_{k0}$ for $t = 0$, without the necessity of solving for the proper values of the arbitrary constants in the general solution of system (4).

In most network investigations, however, the problem of principal importance is to find the response of the network when initially in equilibrium, i.e., when no currents are flowing at time $t = 0$. We shall therefore assume in the following that $I_{k0} = 0$ $(k = 1, 2, \cdots, m)$, and shall discuss methods of solving the system

$$z_{11}(\mathrm{p})I_1 + z_{12}(\mathrm{p})I_2 + \cdots + z_{1m}(\mathrm{p})I_m = E_{11},$$

$$z_{21}(\mathrm{p})I_1 + z_{22}(\mathrm{p})I_2 + \cdots + z_{2m}(\mathrm{p})I_m = E_{22}, \tag{10}$$

$$\cdots\cdots\cdots\cdots\cdots\cdots\cdots\cdots\cdots\cdots,$$

$$z_{m1}(\mathrm{p})I_1 + z_{m2}(\mathrm{p})I_2 + \cdots + z_{mm}(\mathrm{p})I_m = E_{mm},$$

thus obtained from (9).

We may make a second simplification in our general problem as follows. Since we are dealing here with the linear equations of circuits containing constant parameters, we may make use of the principle of superposition, which, stated for such circuits, says that when several e.m.f.'s are acting in a network of fixed parameters, each produces its own effect independently of the others, and the response for each may then be calculated separately and the results combined. That this is legitimate may be shown from the theory of linear differential equations; from a physical viewpoint, it is evident that, when a circuit parameter is constant in value, a single e.m.f. will produce the same response no matter what other sources of potential may be acting at the same time.

It follows that we may treat, instead of equations (10), a system of the form

$$z_{11}(\text{p})I_1 + z_{12}(\text{p})I_2 + \cdots + z_{1m}(\text{p})I_m = E(t),$$

$$z_{21}(\text{p})I_1 + z_{22}(\text{p})I_2 + \cdots + z_{2m}(\text{p})I_m = 0, \tag{11}$$

$$\cdots \cdots \cdots \cdots \cdots \cdots \cdots \cdots \cdots,$$

$$z_{m1}(\text{p})I_1 + z_{m2}(\text{p})I_2 + \cdots + z_{mm}(\text{p})I_m = 0,$$

where we have written, for convenience, $E(t)$ for $E_{11}(t)$. Then if more than one source of e.m.f. is present in the network, we may consider each in turn, using equations of type (11), and combine the various results.

With the proper interpretations of operators involving p, we may now solve equations (11) formally, regarding them as linear algebraic equations in the I's, the coefficients $z_{jk}(\text{p})$ being treated as algebraic quantities. Solving by determinants, we therefore get

$$I_k = \frac{M_{1k}(\text{p})}{\Delta(\text{p})} \cdot E(t), \tag{12}$$

where $\Delta(\text{p})$ is the determinant of the system,

$$\Delta(\text{p}) = \begin{vmatrix} z_{11}(\text{p}) & z_{12}(\text{p}) & \cdots & z_{1m}(\text{p}) \\ z_{21}(\text{p}) & z_{22}(\text{p}) & \cdots & z_{2m}(\text{p}) \\ \cdot & \cdot & \cdots & \cdot \\ z_{m1}(\text{p}) & z_{m2}(\text{p}) & \cdots & z_{mm}(\text{p}) \end{vmatrix}, \tag{13}$$

and $M_{1k}(\text{p})$ is the cofactor, i.e., $(-1)^{k-1}$ times the minor, of $z_{1k}(\text{p})$. The operator $M_{1k}(\text{p})/\Delta(\text{p})$ acting on $E(t)$ may evidently be expressed as a rational function of p.

If $E(t)$ is a constant, it is possible to find I_k by the use of Heaviside's expansion theorem or similar operational formulas. But if $E(t)$ varies with t, as does, for example, a sinusoidal e.m.f., some other procedure is indicated. We therefore consider next the superposition theorem, which bridges the gap, so to speak, between a constant e.m.f. and one varying with the time.

110. The superposition theorem. Since I_k is proportional to $E(t)$ when the latter is constant, it will then suffice to determine the response to an e.m.f. of magnitude unity applied at time $t = 0$ to a network in equilibrium.

To bring into evidence the sudden change in the behavior of the network when a unit e.m.f. is applied at $t = 0$, Heaviside introduced into his work the concept of the "unit function." This function is defined to be equal to zero for $t \leqq 0$ and equal to unity for $t > 0$, so that it has a discontinuity at $t = 0$. The unit function was denoted by Heaviside by the symbol $\mathbf{1}$.

Accordingly, the equation

$$I_k = \frac{M_{1k}(\mathrm{p})}{\Delta(\mathrm{p})} \cdot \mathbf{1}$$

represents the current in mesh k at any time t, positive or negative, when an e.m.f. of unit magnitude is applied to mesh 1 at $t = 0$. For, when $t \leqq 0$, $\mathbf{1} = 0$ and $I_k = 0$, but when $t > 0$, $\mathbf{1} = 1$ and I_k is obtainable as some function of t.

However, since in all our work the network is in equilibrium at $t = 0$, it is known that $I_k = 0$ for $t < 0$, and the expression for I_k when $t > 0$ is all that is needed. We shall therefore dispense with the unit function and take as operand the number 1 in all cases where the Heaviside technique would employ $\mathbf{1}$.

When $E(t) = 1$, the current flowing in mesh 1, where the unit e.m.f. acts, is called the *indicial admittance*, and is denoted by $A_{11}(t)$. The current in circuit k $(k \neq 1)$, due to unit e.m.f. in circuit 1, is called the *transfer indicial admittance*, and is denoted by $A_{1k}(t)$.

If $E(t)$ is any varying function of t, the *superposition theorem* then states that the current in circuit k $(k = 1, 2, \cdots, m)$, is given by

$$I_k(t) = E(0)A_{1k}(t) + \int_0^t A_{1k}(t - z)E'(z)\, dz, \tag{1}$$

where $E'(z)$ denotes $dE(z)/dz$. Before deriving this formula, let us illustrate its application to a simple circuit (Fig. 119). Let an inductance L and a resistance R be in series with a sinusoidal e.m.f. $E_0 \sin \omega t$. If the e.m.f. were a unit e.m.f., the indicial admittance would then be given by the equation

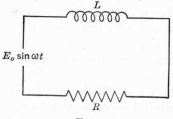

$$L\frac{dA}{dt} + RA = 1.$$

FIG. 119

We easily find, remembering that $A(0) = 0$,

$$A(t) = \frac{1}{R}(1 - e^{-Rt/L}).$$

Consequently the response to the sine e.m.f. will be, from equation (1),

$$I = \frac{1}{R} \int_0^t (1 - e^{-R(t-z)/L}) E_0 \omega \cos \omega z \; dz,$$

from which we get, after some reduction,

$$I = \frac{E_0}{R^2 + L^2\omega^2} (R \sin \omega t - L\omega \cos \omega t + L\omega e^{-Rt/L}).$$

This is precisely what we should have obtained as that solution of the equation

$$L \frac{dI}{dt} + RI = E_0 \sin \omega t$$

which satisfies the condition $I(0) = 0$.

To derive equation (1), we consider the current response as made up of two parts, which may be combined by the principle of superposition. For a time interval $0 \leqq t \leqq t_1$ (Fig. 120), where t_1 is any positive num-

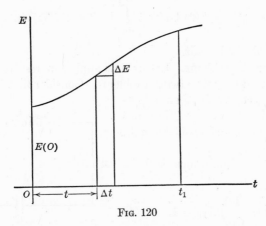

FIG. 120

ber, the first part will correspond to the sudden jump in voltage at time $t = 0$, namely $E(0)$. Since $A_{1k}(t_1)$ is the response at time $t = t_1$ to unit e.m.f., the initial contribution to the total current $I_k(t_1)$ will be the product of the constant e.m.f. $E(0)$ and the indicial admittance,* or $E(0)A_{1k}(t_1)$. The second part, corresponding to the interval $0 < t \leqq t_1$, may be approximated by treating the voltage $E(t)$ as a sum of similar but smaller jumps. Consider any time $t = t$ as the initial time for one

* When $k > 1$, the indicial admittance referred to will of course be a transfer indicial admittance.

of these small jumps ΔE occurring in the time Δt. Then the corresponding indicial admittance will be $A_{1k}(t_1 - t)$, so that the contribution in the subinterval Δt will be $A_{1k}(t_1 - t) \Delta E$. Now when Δt is small, ΔE will be approximated by $dE = E'(t) \Delta t$, so that the small contribution to $I_k(t_1)$ is approximately equal to $A_{1k}(t_1 - t)E'(t) \Delta t$. If we add up all these small pieces, and then take the limit as Δt approaches zero and the number of such subintervals becomes infinite, we get exactly

$$\int_0^{t_1} A_{1k}(t_1 - t)E'(t) \, dt.$$

Hence the total response will be given by

$$I_k(t_1) = E(0)A_{1k}(t_1) + \int_0^{t_1} A_{1k}(t_1 - t)E'(t) \, dt,$$

and since t_1 is any value of the time, we get by changing t_1 into t, and also by changing the variable of integration from t to z,

$$I_k(t) = E(0)A_{1k}(t) + \int_0^{t} A_{1k}(t - z)E'(z) \, dz, \tag{1}$$

which is the desired result.

111. Network problems. Let us now apply our results of the preceding articles to a few network problems. Consider first (Fig. 121) a simple circuit consisting of an inductance L and a capacitance C in series with a source of sinusoidal e.m.f., $E_0 \sin \omega t$.

The indicial admittance will be given by

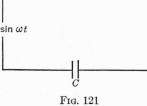

FIG. 121

$$\left(Lp + \frac{1}{Cp}\right) A_{11} = 1, \tag{1}$$

so that

$$A_{11} = \frac{1}{Lp + \dfrac{1}{Cp}} \cdot 1 = \frac{1}{L} \frac{p}{p^2 + a^2} \cdot 1,$$

where $a = 1/\sqrt{LC}$. By formula (8) of Art. 108, we then get

$$A_{11} = \frac{1}{aL} \sin at. \tag{2}$$

Hence, by the superposition theorem of Art. 110, the current response to an e.m.f. $E_0 \sin \omega t$ will be

$$I_1 = E(0)A_{11}(t) + \int_0^t A_{11}(t-z)E'(z)\,dz$$

$$= \frac{E_0\omega}{aL}\int_0^t \sin a(t-z)\cdot\cos\omega z\,dz$$

$$= \frac{E_0\omega}{2aL}\int_0^t \sin(at-az+\omega z)\,dz \qquad (3)$$

$$+ \frac{E_0\omega}{2aL}\int_0^t \sin(at-az-\omega z)\,dz.$$

Now we have to distinguish two cases, according as ω is or is not equal to a. If $\omega = a$, we get

$$I_1 = \frac{E_0}{2L}\left[z\sin at + \frac{\cos(at-2az)}{2a}\right]_0^t$$

$$= \frac{E_0}{2L}t\sin at; \qquad (4)$$

this is the familiar case of resonance. If $\omega \neq a$, there is found

$$I = \frac{E_0\omega}{2aL}\left[-\frac{\cos(at-az+\omega z)}{\omega-a} + \frac{\cos(at-az-\omega z)}{\omega+a}\right]_0^t$$

$$= \frac{E_0\omega}{2aL}\left(-\frac{\cos\omega t}{\omega-a}+\frac{\cos\omega t}{\omega+a}+\frac{\cos at}{\omega-a}-\frac{\cos at}{\omega+a}\right)$$

$$= \frac{E_0\omega}{L(\omega^2-a^2)}(\cos at - \cos\omega t)$$

$$= \frac{2E_0\omega}{L(\omega^2-a^2)}\sin\frac{(\omega+a)t}{2}\sin\frac{(\omega-a)t}{2}. \qquad (5)$$

Consider next the network shown in Fig. 122, in which the impressed e.m.f. E is constant. We have as the network equations,

$$(L_1p+R_1)I_1 - (L_1p+R_1)I_2 = E,$$

$$-(L_1p+R_1)I_1 + [(L_1+L_2)p+R_1+R_2]I_2 = 0. \qquad (6)$$

Then we get

$$\Delta(p) = \begin{vmatrix} L_1 p + R_1 & -(L_1 p + R_1) \\ -(L_1 p + R_1) & (L_1 p + R_1) + (L_2 p + R_2) \end{vmatrix}$$

$$= (L_1 p + R_1)(L_2 p + R_2),$$

$$M_{11}(p) = (L_1 p + R_1) + (L_2 p + R_2),$$

$$M_{12}(p) = L_1 p + R_1,$$

and

$$I_1(t) = A_{11}(t) = \left(\frac{1}{L_1 p + R_1} + \frac{1}{L_2 p + R_2} \right) \cdot E,$$

$$I_2(t) = A_{12}(t) = \frac{1}{L_2 p + R_2} \cdot E. \tag{7}$$

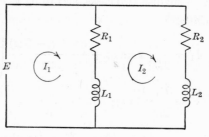

FIG. 122

To evaluate I_1 and I_2, we must therefore interpret expressions of the form

$$\frac{1}{p + a} \cdot 1.$$

By Heaviside's expansion theorem, we have

$$\frac{1}{p + a} \cdot 1 = \frac{1}{a} + \frac{1}{-a \cdot 1} e^{-at}$$

$$= \frac{1}{a} (1 - e^{-at}). \tag{8}$$

Consequently we get

$$I_1(t) = \frac{E}{R_1} (1 - e^{-R_1 t / L_1}) + \frac{E}{R_2} (1 - e^{-R_2 t / L_2}),$$

$$I_2(t) = \frac{E}{R_2} (1 - e^{-R_2 t / L_2}). \tag{9}$$

As a final example, consider the air-core transformer network shown in Fig. 123, with an e.m.f. $E = 10 \cos t$ volts impressed on the primary. The equations for this network are

$$(2p + 1)I_1 - pI_2 = 10 \cos t,$$
$$-pI_1 + (2p + 1)I_2 = 0. \tag{10}$$

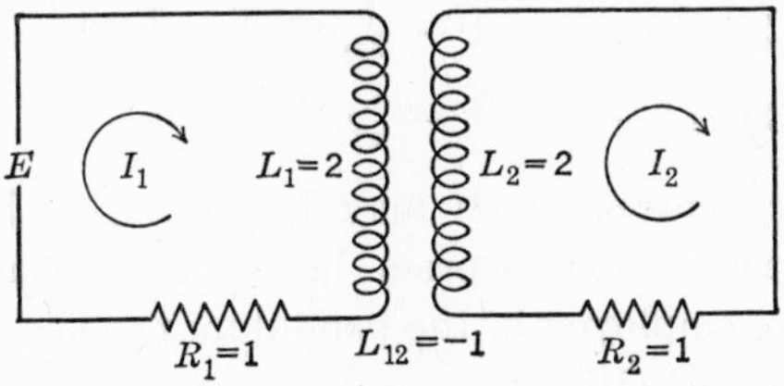

FIG. 123

Hence the indicial admittance $A_{11}(t)$ and the transfer indicial admittance $A_{12}(t)$ are given by

$$A_{11} = \frac{2p + 1}{\begin{vmatrix} 2p + 1 & -p \\ -p & 2p + 1 \end{vmatrix}} \cdot 1 = \frac{2p + 1}{3p^2 + 4p + 1} \cdot 1,$$

$$A_{12} = \frac{p}{3p^2 + 4p + 1} \cdot 1.$$

Using Heaviside's expansion theorem, we get, since $3p^2 + 4p + 1 = (3p + 1)(p + 1)$,

$$A_{11} = 1 + \frac{\frac{1}{3}}{(-\frac{1}{3})(2)} e^{-t/3} + \frac{-1}{(-1)(-2)} e^{-t}$$

$$= 1 - \tfrac{1}{2}e^{-t/3} - \tfrac{1}{2}e^{-t}, \tag{11}$$

$$A_{12} = \frac{-\frac{1}{3}}{(-\frac{1}{3})(2)} e^{-t/3} + \frac{-1}{(-1)(-2)} e^{-t}$$

$$= \tfrac{1}{2}e^{-t/3} - \tfrac{1}{2}e^{-t}.$$

From the superposition theorem, we find for the primary current $I_1(t)$, using formula 414 of Peirce,

$$I_1 = 10 \left(1 - \frac{e^{-t/3}}{2} - \frac{e^{-t}}{2}\right) + \int_0^t \left(1 - \frac{e^{(z-t)/3}}{2} - \frac{e^{-t+z}}{2}\right)(-10 \sin z)\, dz$$

$$= 10 - 5e^{-t/3} - 5e^{-t} - 10 \left[-\cos z - \frac{e^{(z-t)/3}(\frac{1}{3} \sin z - \cos z)}{2(\frac{1}{9} + 1)} \right.$$

$$\left. - \frac{e^{-t+z}(\sin z - \cos z)}{2(1 + 1)} \right]_0^t$$

$$= 10 - 5e^{-t/3} - 5e^{-t} - 10[-\cos t - \tfrac{3}{20} \sin t + \tfrac{9}{20} \cos t$$

$$-\tfrac{1}{4} \sin t + \tfrac{1}{4} \cos t + 1 - \tfrac{9}{20}e^{-t/3} - \tfrac{1}{4}e^{-t}]$$

$$= 4 \sin t + 3 \cos t - \tfrac{1}{2}e^{-t/3} - \tfrac{5}{2}e^{-t}. \tag{12}$$

The secondary current $I_2(t)$ may be similarly obtained. Instead of using the superposition theorem, however, we shall determine $I_2(t)$ by the procedure employed in the pendulum problem of Art. 108. We have, from equations (10),

$$I_2 = \frac{p}{3p^2 + 4p + 1} \cdot 10 \cos t. \tag{13}$$

Now from formula (9) of Art. 108, $\cos t = \dfrac{p^2}{p^2 + 1} \cdot 1$. Consequently we may write

$$I_2 = 10 \frac{p}{3p^2 + 4p + 1} \times \frac{p^2}{p^2 + 1} \cdot 1 = 10 \frac{p^3}{3p^4 + 4p^3 + 4p^2 + 4p + 1} \cdot 1.$$

Using Heaviside's expansion theorem, we therefore get, with $a_1 = -\frac{1}{3}$, $a_2 = -1$, $a_3 = i$, $a_4 = -i$, and $F'(p) = 12p^3 + 12p^2 + 8p + 4$,

$$I_2 = 10 \left[\frac{-\frac{1}{27}}{(-\frac{1}{3})(\frac{20}{9})} e^{-t/3} + \frac{-1}{(-1)(-4)} e^{-t} \right.$$

$$\left. + \frac{-i}{(i)(-4i - 8)} e^{it} + \frac{i}{(-i)(4i - 8)} e^{-it} \right]$$

$$= \frac{1}{2} e^{-t/3} - \frac{5}{2} e^{-t} + \frac{2 - i}{2} e^{it} + \frac{2 + i}{2} e^{-it}$$

$$= \tfrac{1}{2}e^{-t/3} - \tfrac{5}{2}e^{-t} + 2 \cos t + \sin t. \tag{14}$$

Whenever the impressed e.m.f. $E(t)$ can be replaced by an operational expression, as in the above example, the circuit currents may thus be directly determined. This procedure obviates the necessity of first finding the indicial admittances $A_{1k}(t)$ and then using the superposition theorem. However, the latter method has the advantage of complete generality, whatever the function $E(t)$, and may be advantageously employed when the expansion theorem does not apply or entails more awkward computations.

The student will find it instructive to solve the examples of this section by the classical method and to compare his solutions with the ones given. As facility in the use of operational methods is gained, they will often be found to be quicker and more direct. However, the principal value of operational methods lies in their ability to handle the general theory and to attack new problems, rather than in their usefulness in simple numerical problems.

PROBLEMS

1. In the network shown in Fig. 124, the values of the parameters are $R_1 = R_2 = R_3 = 10$ ohms, and $L_1 = L_2 = 10$ henries. The network is in equilibrium at time $t = 0$, when the e.m.f. E_1 is impressed. Find the current flowing in each mesh at time t if (a) $E_1 = 100$ volts; (b) $E_1 = 10 \sin t$ volts.

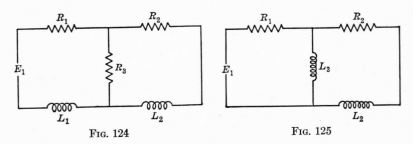

FIG. 124   FIG. 125

2. In the network shown in Fig. 125, which is in equilibrium at time $t = 0$, $R_1 = 10$ ohms, $R_2 = 20$ ohms, $L_2 = 20$ henries, $L_3 = 10$ henries. The e.m.f. E_1 is applied at $t = 0$. Find the branch currents if (a) $E_1 = 100$ volts; (b) $E_1 = 10 \cos 2t$ volts.

3. In the network shown in Fig. 126, $R_1 = 500$ ohms, $R_2 = 1000$ ohms, $L_2 = 20$ henries, $C_3 = 10^{-5}$ farad. The e.m.f. E_1 is impressed at time $t = 0$, when the

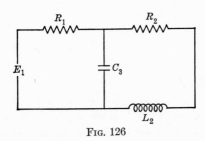

FIG. 126

network is in equilibrium. (a) Find the current in each mesh if $E_1 = 100$ volts. (b) Find the current flowing through R_2 if $E_1 = 160 \cos 120\pi t$ volts.

4. In the network shown in Fig. 127, $R_1 = 2$ ohms, $R_2 = 4$ ohms, $R_3 = 5$ ohms, $L_2 = 2$ henries, $L_3 = 3$ henries, and $L_{23} = -2$ henries. If the network is in

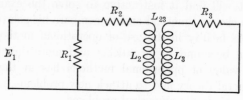

Fig. 127

equilibrium at time $t = 0$, when the e.m.f. $E_1 = 2 \cos 5t$ volts is impressed, find (a) the indicial admittance and transfer indicial admittances; (b) the current through R_3 at time t.

5. In the network shown in Fig. 128, each resistance is 3 ohms and each inductance is 1 henry. If the network is initially in equilibrium, and at time $t = 0$ a unit e.m.f. E is applied, find the current through each resistance when $t = 0.1$ sec.

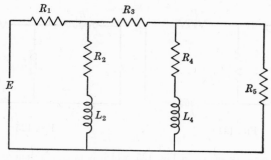

Fig. 128

PART II. OPERATIONAL METHODS BASED ON THE THEORY OF FUNCTIONS

112. Bromwich's line integrals. Problems involving only linear ordinary differential equations, such as the network problems considered above, will give rise to operators which are rational functions of p. In such problems, the interpretations by means of Heaviside's expansion theorem or similar devices can frequently be obtained without much trouble. However, many physical problems * lead, as we have seen in Chapter VII, to partial differential equations, which often give rise to operator expressions which are not rational functions of p, so that the methods outlined in Part I do not apply.

* A few of such problems are considered in Art. 113.

We shall therefore discuss, as a second method of interpreting operational expressions acting on unity or on a function of t, two powerful methods or rules based on contour integration in the complex z-plane.* These rules are as follows. If $\phi(z)$ is a function of z analytic except for possible isolated singularities, then for $t > 0$,

$$\phi(\mathrm{p}) \cdot 1 = \frac{1}{2\pi i} \int_c \frac{e^{tz}}{z} \phi(z) \, dz, \tag{1}$$

where c is a simple closed curve, for example, a circle, enclosing all the singularities of the integrand $e^{tz}\phi(z)/z$; if $\phi(z)$ is analytic as before, or has isolated branch points, then for $t > 0$,

$$\phi(\mathrm{p}) \cdot 1 = \frac{1}{2\pi i} \int_{c'} \frac{e^{tz}}{z} \phi(z) \, dz, \tag{2}$$

where c' is an open curve lying to the right of the imaginary axis, from $-i\infty$ to $+i\infty$, and such that all singularities of the integrand are on the left-hand side of the curve. In those linear network problems for which the only singularities of $\phi(z) = M_{1k}(z)/\Delta(z)$ (see equation (12), Art. 109) are a finite number of isolated poles, formula (1) may conveniently be used; in some other physical problems, for which $\phi(z)$ has branch points, or in which the singularities are infinite in number such that no closed curve can contain all of them, formula (2) is applicable.

To show how formula (1) is applied, let us first use it to obtain anew some of the formulas of Art. 108. If $\phi(\mathrm{p}) = \mathrm{p}^{-n}$, where n is a positive integer, we get from (1),

$$\mathrm{p}^{-n} \cdot 1 = \frac{1}{2\pi i} \int_c \frac{e^{tz}}{z^{n+1}} \, dz$$

$$= \frac{1}{2\pi i} \int_c \frac{1}{z^{n+1}} \left(1 + tz + \frac{t^2 z^2}{2!} + \cdots + \frac{t^n z^n}{n!} + \cdots \right) dz.$$

Evidently the only singularity of the integrand is the pole of order $n + 1$ at $z = 0$, and consequently c may be taken as any circle with center at the origin. Since the residue, namely the coefficient of $1/z$, is $t^n/n!$, we get immediately

$$\mathrm{p}^{-n} \cdot 1 = t^n/n!, \tag{3}$$

which agrees with equation (4) of Art. 108.

---

* These rules are due to Bromwich, *loc. cit.* Their derivation is beyond the scope of this book.

If $\phi(\mathrm{p}) = \mathrm{p}/(\mathrm{p} - a)^n$, formula (1) gives us

$$\frac{\mathrm{p}}{(\mathrm{p} - a)^n} \cdot 1 = \frac{1}{2\pi i} \int_c \frac{e^{tz}}{(z - a)^n}\, dz$$

$$= \frac{e^{at}}{2\pi i} \int_c \frac{e^{t(z-a)}}{(z - a)^n}\, dz,$$

and since the integrand, expanded in powers of $(z - a)$, has the residue $t^{n-1}/(n - 1)!$ at the pole $z = a$, we find

$$\frac{\mathrm{p}}{(\mathrm{p} - a)^n} \cdot 1 = \frac{t^{n-1}e^{at}}{(n - 1)!}, \tag{4}$$

which is the same as formula (6) of Art. 108.

We next derive Heaviside's expansion theorem. If $\phi(\mathrm{p}) = f(\mathrm{p})/F(\mathrm{p})$, where $f(\mathrm{p})$ and $F(\mathrm{p})$ are polynomials with no common factor, the degree of $f(\mathrm{p})$ being no greater than that of $F(\mathrm{p})$, and in particular

$$F(\mathrm{p}) = b(\mathrm{p} - a_1)(\mathrm{p} - a_2)\cdots(\mathrm{p} - a_n),$$

with all the a's distinct and different from zero, we have by (1),

$$\frac{f(\mathrm{p})}{F(\mathrm{p})} \cdot 1 = \frac{1}{2\pi i} \int_c \frac{e^{tz}}{z} \cdot \frac{f(z)\, dz}{b(z - a_1)(z - a_2)\cdots(z - a_n)}. \tag{5}$$

Now the integrand has simple poles at $z = a_k$ ($k = 1, 2, \cdots, n$), and, if $f(0) \neq 0$, also at $z = 0$. Suppose first that $f(0) \neq 0$. Then the residue of the integrand function at $z = 0$ is given (see Chapter X, Art. 105) by

$$\lim_{z \to 0} z\left[\frac{e^{tz}f(z)}{zF(z)}\right] = \lim_{z \to 0} \frac{e^{tz}f(z)}{F(z)} = \frac{f(0)}{F(0)}.$$

Consequently $f(0)/F(0)$ is one term in the expression (5) when $f(0) \neq 0$. If $f(0) = 0$, the integrand is analytic at $z = 0$, so that the contribution to the sum of the residues for this point is zero. But here $f(0)/F(0)$ is also zero, and therefore we may write as the first term in (5), $f(0)/F(0)$, whether $f(0)$ vanishes or not. For the simple pole $z = a_k$, the residue of the integrand is

$$\lim_{z \to a_k} (z - a_k)\frac{e^{tz}f(z)}{zF(z)} = \frac{e^{a_k t}f(a_k)}{a_k} \lim_{z \to a_k} \frac{\dfrac{d}{dz}(z - a_k)}{\dfrac{d}{dz}F(z)}$$

$$= \frac{e^{a_k t}f(a_k)}{a_k F'(a_k)}.$$

Hence, since the line integral (5) represents the sum of all the residues of the integrand function, we get

$$\frac{f(\mathrm{p})}{F(\mathrm{p})} \cdot 1 = \frac{f(0)}{F(0)} + \sum_{k=1}^{n} \frac{e^{a_k t} f(a_k)}{a_k F'(a_k)}, \tag{6}$$

which is formula (7) of Art. 108.

Consider next the operator $\mathrm{p}/(\mathrm{p}^2 + a^2)$, where a is any constant. From (1) we get

$$\frac{\mathrm{p}}{\mathrm{p}^2 + a^2} \cdot 1 = \frac{1}{2\pi i} \int_c \frac{e^{tz}}{z^2 + a^2} \, dz.$$

Now the singularities of the integrand are simple poles at $z = \pm ia$. Hence

$$\frac{\mathrm{p}}{\mathrm{p}^2 + a^2} \cdot 1 = \lim_{z \to ia} (z - ia) \frac{e^{tz}}{z^2 + a^2} + \lim_{z \to -ia} (z + ia) \frac{e^{tz}}{z^2 + a^2}$$

$$= \lim_{z \to ia} \frac{e^{tz}}{z + ia} + \lim_{z \to -ia} \frac{e^{tz}}{z - ia}$$

$$= \frac{e^{iat}}{2ia} + \frac{e^{-iat}}{-2ia}$$

$$= \frac{1}{a} \sin at. \tag{7}$$

Similarly, we get

$$\frac{\mathrm{p}^2}{\mathrm{p}^2 + a^2} \cdot 1 = \lim_{z \to ia} \frac{z e^{tz}}{z + ia} + \lim_{z \to -ia} \frac{z e^{tz}}{z - ia}$$

$$= \frac{e^{iat}}{2} + \frac{e^{-iat}}{2}$$

$$= \cos at. \tag{8}$$

Equations (7) and (8) are, respectively, identical with formulas (8) and (9) of Art. 108.

Let us now get an interpretation of $\mathrm{p}^n \cdot 1$, where n is a positive integer. Although, as we have seen, the operator $\mathrm{p}^{-1} = Q$ is the basic operator, with the proper interpretation of $\phi(\mathrm{p})$ being that obtained when $\phi(\mathrm{p})$ is expanded in powers of p^{-1}, formula (1) gives us

$$\mathrm{p}^n \cdot 1 = \frac{1}{2\pi i} \int_c z^{n-1} e^{tz} \, dz = 0, \tag{9}$$

since the integrand is analytic for all finite values of z. This suggests the interpretation of p as d/dt, at least in certain cases. Now if we differentiate both members of (1) with respect to t, we get

$$\frac{d}{dt}\phi(\mathrm{p})\cdot 1 = \frac{1}{2\pi i}\frac{d}{dt}\int_c \frac{e^{tz}}{z}\phi(z)\,dz$$

$$= \frac{1}{2\pi i}\int_c e^{tz}\phi(z)\,dz.$$

But this line integral is the expression for $\mathrm{p}\phi(\mathrm{p})\cdot 1$. Hence

$$\frac{d}{dt}\phi(\mathrm{p})\cdot 1 = \mathrm{p}\phi(\mathrm{p})\cdot 1, \qquad (10)$$

which shows that p may be regarded as a differential operator when the operation it denotes follows an operation involving $Q = \mathrm{p}^{-1}$. This agrees with our previous interpretation.

Up to the present, our operational expressions have all been rational functions of p, or of p^{-1}, and these two operators have been interpretable as differential and integrating operators, respectively. Moreover, since a rational function is analytic everywhere except for a finite number of poles, Bromwich's line integral (1) has been applicable to each of these expressions. In some physical problems, however, formal manipulation of the operator p leads to the necessity of interpreting the rather curious operational expression $\mathrm{p}^{\frac{1}{2}}$.* Now $\phi(z) = z^{\frac{1}{2}}$ is, as we have seen in Chapter X, Art. 96, a two-valued and therefore non-analytic function of z in the neighborhood of the origin, having a branch point at $z = 0$ as a singularity. Consequently formula (1) cannot be used to interpret $\mathrm{p}^{\frac{1}{2}}\cdot 1$. But by means of the line integral (2), $\mathrm{p}^{\frac{1}{2}}\cdot 1$ may be given a meaning, as follows. Consider the contour c_1 shown in Fig. 129. ABC is a contour beginning on the negative y-axis and ending on the positive y-axis, passing through the fourth and first quadrants; CD and HA are quadrants of a large circle of radius R and

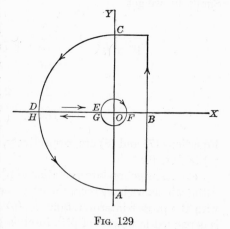

FIG. 129

* We shall make use of this operator in Art. 113.

center O; EFG is a small circle of radius r and center O; DE and GH are segments of the negative x-axis, oppositely sensed as indicated by the arrows, and on which z is taken as $\rho e^{i\pi}$ and $\rho e^{-i\pi}$, respectively. Evidently the function $e^{tz}\phi(z)/z = z^{-\frac{1}{2}}e^{tz}$ is analytic on and within the contour c_1: $ABCDEFGHA$, so that Cauchy's integral theorem gives us

$$\int_{c_1} z^{-\frac{1}{2}}e^{tz}\, dz = 0. \tag{11}$$

Since $z = Re^{i\theta}$ on CD and HA, and $z = re^{i\theta}$ on EFG, we may then write (11) as

$$\int_{ABC} z^{-\frac{1}{2}}e^{tz}\, dz + \int_{\pi/2}^{\pi} R^{-\frac{1}{2}}e^{-i\theta/2}e^{tR(\cos\theta+i\sin\theta)}Rie^{i\theta}\, d\theta$$

$$+ \int_{R}^{r} \rho^{-\frac{1}{2}}e^{-i\pi/2}e^{-t\rho}e^{i\pi}\, d\rho + \int_{\pi}^{-\pi} r^{-\frac{1}{2}}e^{-i\theta/2}e^{tr(\cos\theta+i\sin\theta)}rie^{i\theta}\, d\theta$$

$$+ \int_{r}^{R} \rho^{-\frac{1}{2}}e^{i\pi/2}e^{-t\rho}e^{-i\pi}\, d\rho$$

$$+ \int_{-\pi}^{-\pi/2} R^{-\frac{1}{2}}e^{-i\theta/2}e^{tR(\cos\theta+i\sin\theta)}Rie^{i\theta}\, d\theta = 0. \tag{12}$$

In the second and sixth of these integrals, we have

$$\left| R^{-\frac{1}{2}}e^{-i\theta/2}e^{tR(\cos\theta+i\sin\theta)}Rie^{i\theta} \right| = R^{\frac{1}{2}}e^{tR\cos\theta} = \frac{R^{\frac{1}{2}}}{e^{-tR\cos\theta}}. \tag{13}$$

Remembering that t and R are positive whereas $\cos\theta$ is negative in the second and third quadrants, we see that $R^{\frac{1}{2}}/e^{-tR\cos\theta}$ approaches zero as R becomes infinite, and therefore in the limit the second and sixth integrals vanish. For the fourth integral,

$$\left| r^{-\frac{1}{2}}e^{-i\theta/2}e^{tr(\cos\theta+i\sin\theta)}rie^{i\theta} \right| = r^{\frac{1}{2}}e^{tr\cos\theta}, \tag{14}$$

which approaches zero with r, and consequently this integral contributes nothing in the limit. Now as r approaches zero and R becomes infinite, the path ABC becomes a contour c' of the type designated in connection with equation (2), and hence we have from (12),

$$p^{\frac{1}{2}} \cdot 1 = \frac{1}{2\pi i} \int_{c'} z^{-\frac{1}{2}}e^{tz}\, dz$$

$$= \frac{1}{2\pi i} \int_{0}^{\infty} \rho^{-\frac{1}{2}}e^{-t\rho}(e^{i\pi/2} - e^{-i\pi/2})\, d\rho$$

$$= \frac{1}{\pi} \int_{0}^{\infty} \rho^{-\frac{1}{2}}e^{-t\rho}\, d\rho. \tag{15}$$

Letting $s = t\rho$, so that $ds = t\,d\rho$, (15) becomes

$$p^{\frac{1}{2}} \cdot 1 = \frac{1}{\pi t^{\frac{1}{2}}} \int_0^\infty s^{-\frac{1}{2}} e^{-s}\,ds. \tag{16}$$

But this integral we recognize as the gamma function $\Gamma(\frac{1}{2}) = \sqrt{\pi}$ (equation (6), Art. 54), and therefore

$$p^{\frac{1}{2}} \cdot 1 = \frac{1}{\sqrt{\pi t}}, \tag{17}$$

which is the desired result. It is of interest to note that formula (3), which holds for n a positive integer, will formally yield (17) when n is set equal to $-\frac{1}{2}$, for we get

$$p^{\frac{1}{2}} \cdot 1 = \frac{t^{-\frac{1}{2}}}{(-\frac{1}{2})!} = \frac{1}{\Gamma(\frac{1}{2})\sqrt{t}} = \frac{1}{\sqrt{\pi t}}.$$

This circumstance, however, is in no sense a derivation of (17).

Consider next the operator $p\phi(p - b)/(p - b)$, where $\phi(z - b)$ is some function of $z - b$. By formula (2), we have

$$\frac{p\phi(p - b)}{p - b} \cdot 1 = \frac{1}{2\pi i} \int_{c'} \frac{e^{tz}\phi(z - b)}{z - b}\,dz$$

$$= \frac{e^{bt}}{2\pi i} \int_{c'} \frac{e^{t(z-b)}\phi(z - b)}{z - b}\,d(z - b).$$

If we replace $(z - b)$ in the last integral by z, which amounts to a translation of axes in the z-plane, we get

$$\frac{p\phi(p - b)}{p - b} \cdot 1 = \frac{e^{bt}}{2\pi i} \int_{c'} \frac{e^{tz}\phi(z)}{z}\,dz$$

$$= e^{bt}\phi(p) \cdot 1,$$

whence

$$\phi(p) \cdot 1 = e^{-bt} \frac{p\phi(p - b)}{p - b} \cdot 1. \tag{18}$$

This relation, which we shall refer to as the *shifting formula*, may often be advantageously applied when we suspect the presence of an exponential function e^{-bt} in the expression $\phi(p) \cdot 1$ after interpretation. For example, let us obtain the formula (cf. Problem 12 following Art. 108),

$$\frac{ap}{(p + b)^2 + a^2} \cdot 1 = e^{-bt} \sin at.$$

We get from (18),

$$\frac{ap}{(p+b)^2 + a^2} \cdot 1 = e^{-bt} \frac{pa(p-b)}{(p^2 + a^2)(p-b)} \cdot 1$$

$$= e^{-bt} \frac{ap}{p^2 + a^2} \cdot 1.$$

But by formula (7), $\dfrac{ap}{p^2 + a^2} \cdot 1 = \sin at$, and the desired result follows immediately.

Suppose that $\phi(p) \cdot 1$ is known as some analytic function of t, say $f(t)$. Let us examine the effect of operating on $f(t)$ with e^{hp}, where h is any constant. From formula (1) we get

$$e^{hp} f(t) = e^{hp} \phi(p) \cdot 1 = \frac{1}{2\pi i} \int_c \frac{e^{tz} e^{hz} \phi(z)}{z} \, dz$$

$$= \frac{1}{2\pi i} \int_c \frac{e^{(t+h)z} \phi(z)}{z} \, dz.$$

But this is similar to

$$\phi(p) \cdot 1 = \frac{1}{2\pi i} \int_c \frac{e^{tz} \phi(z)}{z} \, dz,$$

the only difference being that t is replaced by $t + h$. We therefore infer that

$$e^{hp} \cdot f(t) = f(t+h). \tag{19}$$

Formally, we have also

$$e^{hp} \cdot f(t) = \left(1 + hp + \frac{h^2 p^2}{2!} + \frac{h^3 p^3}{3!} + \cdots \right) \cdot f(t)$$

$$= f(t) + h f'(t) + \frac{h^2 f''(t)}{2!} + \frac{h^3 f'''(t)}{3!} + \cdots$$

$$= f(t+h),$$

by Taylor's expansion. We therefore call e^{hp} the *Taylor's operator*, and define it by equation (19).

We next examine the operator $e^{-a\sqrt{p}}$, where a is positive. Since $e^{-a\sqrt{z}}$ has a branch-point at $z = 0$, we use formula (2), from which

$$e^{-a\sqrt{p}} \cdot 1 = \frac{1}{2\pi i} \int_{c'} \frac{e^{tz}}{z} \left(1 - a z^{1/2} + \frac{a^2 z}{2!} - \frac{a^3 z^{3/2}}{3!} + \cdots \right) dz.$$

Now it is not difficult to see that all the positive integral powers of z contribute nothing to the integral. We therefore get by term-by-term interpretation,

$$e^{-a\sqrt{p}} \cdot 1 = \left(1 - ap^{\frac{1}{2}} - \frac{a^3 p^{\frac{3}{2}}}{3!} - \frac{a^5 p^{\frac{5}{2}}}{5!} - \cdots\right) \cdot 1.$$

It may be shown by direct differentiation with respect to t of formula (17), that for n a positive integer,

$$p^{\frac{1}{2}+n} \cdot 1 = \frac{(-1)^n \Gamma(n + \frac{1}{2})}{\pi t^{n+\frac{1}{2}}}.$$

Hence

$$e^{-a\sqrt{p}} \cdot 1$$

$$= 1 - \left[\frac{a\Gamma(\frac{1}{2})}{\pi t^{\frac{1}{2}}} - \frac{a^3 \Gamma(\frac{3}{2})}{\pi t^{\frac{3}{2}}} + \frac{a^5 \Gamma(\frac{5}{2})}{\pi t^{\frac{5}{2}}} - \cdots\right]$$

$$= 1 - \frac{2}{\sqrt{\pi}} \left[\frac{a}{2t^{\frac{1}{2}}} - \frac{1}{2^2 \cdot 3!} \frac{a^3}{t^{\frac{3}{2}}} + \frac{1 \cdot 3}{2^3 \cdot 5!} \frac{a^5}{t^{\frac{5}{2}}} - \frac{1 \cdot 3 \cdot 5}{2^4 \cdot 7!} \frac{a^7}{t^{\frac{7}{2}}} + \cdots\right]$$

$$= 1 - \frac{2}{\sqrt{\pi}} \left[\frac{a}{2t^{\frac{1}{2}}} - \frac{1}{3}\left(\frac{a}{2t^{\frac{1}{2}}}\right)^3 + \frac{1}{5 \cdot 2!}\left(\frac{a}{2t^{\frac{1}{2}}}\right)^5 - \frac{1}{7 \cdot 3!}\left(\frac{a}{2t^{\frac{1}{2}}}\right)^7 + \cdots\right].$$

Now this is the series for the error function (equation (16), Art. 88),

$$\text{erf } s = \frac{2}{\sqrt{\pi}} \int_0^s e^{-s^2} ds$$

$$= \frac{2}{\sqrt{\pi}} \int_0^s \left(1 - s^2 + \frac{s^4}{2!} - \frac{s^6}{3!} + \cdots\right) ds$$

$$= \frac{2}{\sqrt{\pi}} \left[s - \frac{s^3}{3} + \frac{s^5}{5 \cdot 2!} - \frac{s^7}{7 \cdot 3!} + \cdots\right].$$

Consequently we may write

$$e^{-a\sqrt{p}} \cdot 1 = 1 - \text{erf } \frac{a}{2\sqrt{t}}. \qquad (20)$$

Another operational expression which appears in a number of physical problems is $\dfrac{p}{\sqrt{p^2 + a^2}} \cdot 1$. This may be interpreted by the use of formula (2) since the function $z/\sqrt{z^2 + a^2}$ has only branch points, at

$z = \pm ia$. Since the procedure here is very similar to that employed in obtaining the formula $p^{\frac{1}{2}} \cdot 1 = 1/\sqrt{\pi t}$, we shall indicate merely the principal steps and leave it to the student to fill in the details. We take

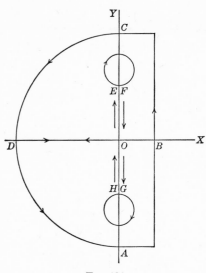

FIG. 130

as our contour (Fig. 130) the path ABC from $-iR$ to $+iR$ as before, the quadrant CD of radius R, the x-axis from D to O, then OE, where E is the point $z = i(a - r)$, and on the left of the y-axis, then the circle of radius r about $z = ia$, the straight line FOG on the right of the y-axis, the circle of radius r about $z = -ia$, the segment HO on the left of the y-axis, OD, and finally the quadrant DA of radius R. On OE and FO, $z = i\rho$, where ρ is real and positive, and on OG and HO, $z = -i\rho$. Along FO and OG, we have the branch $\sqrt{a^2 - \rho^2}$ of $\sqrt{z^2 + a^2}$, while along OE and HO, we have the branch $-\sqrt{a^2 - \rho^2}$. We then get by Cauchy's integral theorem,

$$\int_{ABC} \frac{e^{tz}\, dz}{\sqrt{z^2 + a^2}} + \int_{\pi/2}^{\pi} \frac{e^{tR(\cos\theta + i\sin\theta)} Rie^{i\theta}\, d\theta}{\sqrt{R^2 e^{2i\theta} + a^2}} - \int_{R}^{0} \frac{e^{-t\rho}\, d\rho}{\sqrt{\rho^2 + a^2}}$$

$$+ \int_{0}^{a-r} \frac{e^{it\rho}(i\, d\rho)}{-\sqrt{a^2 - \rho^2}} + \int_{3\pi/2}^{-\pi/2} \frac{e^{iat + tr(\cos\theta + i\sin\theta)} rie^{i\theta}\, d\theta}{\sqrt{r^2 e^{2i\theta} + 2iare^{i\theta}}}$$

$$+ \int_{a-r}^{0} \frac{e^{it\rho}(i\, d\rho)}{\sqrt{a^2 - \rho^2}} + \int_{0}^{a-r} \frac{e^{-it\rho}(-i\, d\rho)}{\sqrt{a^2 - \rho^2}}$$

$$+ \int_{\pi/2}^{-3\pi/2} \frac{e^{-iat + tr(\cos\theta + i\sin\theta)} rie^{i\theta}\, d\theta}{\sqrt{r^2 e^{2i\theta} - 2iare^{i\theta}}} + \int_{a-r}^{0} \frac{e^{-it\rho}(-i\, d\rho)}{-\sqrt{a^2 - \rho^2}}$$

$$- \int_{0}^{R} \frac{e^{-t\rho}\, d\rho}{\sqrt{\rho^2 + a^2}} + \int_{-\pi}^{-\pi/2} \frac{e^{tR(\cos\theta + i\sin\theta)} Rie^{i\theta}\, d\theta}{\sqrt{R^2 e^{2i\theta} + a^2}} = 0.$$

The second and last of these integrals approach zero as R becomes infinite, and the fifth and eighth approach zero with r. Consequently we get in the limit

$$\frac{\mathrm{p}}{\sqrt{\mathrm{p}^2 + a^2}} \cdot 1 = \frac{1}{2\pi i} \int_{c'} \frac{e^{tz}\,dz}{\sqrt{z^2 + a^2}} = \frac{1}{\pi} \int_0^a \frac{e^{it\rho} + e^{-it\rho}}{\sqrt{a^2 - \rho^2}}\,d\rho$$

$$= \frac{2}{\pi} \int_0^a \frac{\cos t\rho\,d\rho}{\sqrt{a^2 - \rho^2}}.$$

This last expression is of course a function of t; call it $F(t)$. This function satisfies the differential equation $tF'' + F' + a^2tF = 0$. For, we get by differentiation under the integral sign (Art. 67),

$$tF'' + F' + a^2tF = \frac{2}{\pi} \int_0^a \frac{d\rho}{\sqrt{a^2 - \rho^2}}\,(-t\rho^2 \cos t\rho - \rho \sin t\rho + a^2 t \cos t\rho)$$

$$= \frac{2}{\pi} \int_0^a \left(t \cos t\rho \cdot \sqrt{a^2 - \rho^2} - \frac{\rho \sin t\rho}{\sqrt{a^2 - \rho^2}} \right) d\rho$$

$$= \frac{2}{\pi} \int_0^a d(\sin t\rho \cdot \sqrt{a^2 - \rho^2})$$

$$= \frac{2}{\pi} \left[\sin t\rho \cdot \sqrt{a^2 - \rho^2} \right]_0^a = 0.$$

Moreover,

$$F(0) = \frac{2}{\pi} \int_0^a \frac{d\rho}{\sqrt{a^2 - \rho^2}} = \frac{2}{\pi} \left[\sin^{-1} \frac{\rho}{a} \right]_0^a = 1.$$

We therefore identify $F(t)$ as the Bessel function of order zero, with argument at, whence

$$\frac{\mathrm{p}}{\sqrt{\mathrm{p}^2 + a^2}} \cdot 1 = J_0(at). \tag{21}$$

113. Applications. We shall discuss in this article a few physical problems which give rise to the operators previously obtained. Our treatment, following Heaviside's technique, will be purely formal, but will serve to indicate the manner in which operational calculus may be employed in connection with partial differential equations.

Consider first the wave equation,

$$\frac{\partial^2 y}{\partial t^2} - a^2 \frac{\partial^2 y}{\partial x^2} = 0, \tag{1}$$

which gives the transverse vibrations of a stretched string (Chapter VII, Art. 70). Suppose that the initial displacement of each point of the string with end points at $x = 0$ and $x = L$ is given by

$$y\Big]_{t=0} = f(x), \qquad 0 \leqq x \leqq L, \tag{2}$$

where f is a known function of the distance x along the string, and suppose the string then released from rest. Let $D = \partial/\partial x$, and let Q again denote the operation of integrating with respect to time from 0 to t. Applying Q twice in turn to (1), we get

$$\frac{\partial y}{\partial t} - a^2 Q D^2 y = 0,$$

$$y - a^2 Q^2 D^2 y = f(x). \tag{3}$$

Now let $p = \partial/\partial t$, and operate upon (3) with p^2. Then

$$(p^2 - a^2 D^2)y = p^2 f(x).$$

Symbolically, then,

$$y = \frac{p^2}{p^2 - a^2 D^2} f(x).$$

Now

$$\frac{p^2}{p^2 - a^2 D^2} = \frac{1}{2}\left(\frac{p}{p - aD} + \frac{p}{p + aD}\right),$$

so that from formula (4) of Art. 112,

$$y = \frac{1}{2}(e^{atD} + e^{-atD}) \cdot f(x).$$

Consequently, by the Taylor's operator (19) of Art. 112, we get

$$y(x, t) = \frac{1}{2}[f(x + at) + f(x - at)]. \tag{4}$$

That y as given here satisfies the differential equation (1) as well as the condition (2) is readily checked. Equation (4) gives the well-known solution which represents two waves traveling in opposite directions with velocity a. It is thus informative, but its usefulness in computation is restricted to those cases in which $f(x)$ is of the proper form and may be suitably specified outside the interval $0 \leqq x \leqq L$.[*]

* See Jeffreys, "Operational Methods," second edition, p. 50.

Consider next the partial differential equation for one-dimensional heat flow (Chapter VII, Art. 71),

$$\frac{\partial u}{\partial t} - \alpha^2 \frac{\partial^2 u}{\partial x^2} = 0. \tag{5}$$

Let a uniform rod with insulated sides and of length L be initially at temperature u_0, and let the end $x = L$ be cooled to temperature zero at time $t = 0$ while the end $x = 0$ is left at temperature u_0. Applying Q to (5), and p to the result, we get

$$pu - \alpha^2 \frac{\partial^2 u}{\partial x^2} = pu_0. \tag{6}$$

Now let an operator q be defined by the relation

$$p = \alpha^2 q^2; \tag{7}$$

if we treat p as if it were an algebraic quantity, we then get an operational solution as a function of q, which must be expressed ultimately in terms of p when the operational solution is interpreted. Equation (6) may now be written as

$$\frac{\partial^2 u}{\partial x^2} - q^2 u = -q^2 u_0. \tag{8}$$

If q were constant, the general solution of (8) would then be

$$u = u_0 + c_1 \sinh qx + c_2 \cosh qx.$$

From the boundary conditions, $u = u_0$ when $x = 0$ and $u = 0$ when $x = L$, we find

$$u_0 = u_0 + c_2,$$

$$0 = u_0 + c_1 \sinh qL + c_2 \cosh qL,$$

whence $c_1 = -u_0/\sinh qL$, $c_2 = 0$, and

$$u = \left(1 - \frac{\sinh qx}{\sinh qL}\right) u_0. \tag{9}$$

We have now to interpret the operational expression

$$\frac{\sinh qx}{\sinh qL} \cdot 1.$$

Since

$$\frac{\sinh qx}{\sinh qL} = \frac{qx + \dfrac{q^3x^3}{3!} + \dfrac{q^5x^5}{5!} + \cdots}{qL + \dfrac{q^3L^3}{3!} + \dfrac{q^5L^5}{5!} + \cdots}$$

$$= \frac{x + \dfrac{q^2x^3}{3!} + \dfrac{q^4x^5}{5!} + \cdots}{L + \dfrac{q^2L^3}{3!} + \dfrac{q^4L^5}{5!} + \cdots}$$

$$= \frac{x + \dfrac{px^3}{\alpha^2 3!} + \dfrac{p^2x^5}{\alpha^4 5!} + \cdots}{L + \dfrac{pL^3}{\alpha^2 3!} + \dfrac{p^2L^5}{\alpha^4 5!} + \cdots},$$

this operator is an analytic function of p. But since $\sinh in\pi = 0$ for n an integer or zero, the function $e^{tz}\sinh\dfrac{x\sqrt{z}}{\alpha} \Big/ z\sinh\dfrac{L\sqrt{z}}{\alpha}$ has infinitely many simple poles at $z = -n^2\pi^2\alpha^2/L^2$. Hence formula (1) of Art. 112 does not apply. Instead, we use Bromwich's second line integral, and write

$$\frac{\sinh qx}{\sinh qL}\cdot 1 = \frac{1}{2\pi i}\int_{c'}\frac{e^{tz}\sinh(x\sqrt{z}/\alpha)}{z\sinh(L\sqrt{z}/\alpha)}\,dz. \tag{10}$$

Using the contour shown in Fig. 131, where ABC is a path from $-iR$ to iR lying to the right of the poles, and CDA is a semicircle of radius R, we then get for the residues at the points inside this contour,

$$\frac{1}{2\pi i}\int_{ABC}\frac{e^{tz}\sinh(x\sqrt{z}/\alpha)}{z\sinh(L\sqrt{z}/\alpha)}\,dz$$

$$+ \frac{1}{2\pi}\int_{\pi/2}^{3\pi/2}\frac{e^{tR(\cos\theta+i\sin\theta)}\sinh(xR^{1/2}e^{i\theta/2}/\alpha)}{\sinh(LR^{1/2}e^{i\theta/2}/\alpha)}\,d\theta. \tag{11}$$

The residue at $z = 0$ is given by

$$\lim_{z\to 0}\frac{e^{tz}\sinh(x\sqrt{z}/\alpha)}{\sinh(L\sqrt{z}/\alpha)} = \lim_{z\to 0}e^{tz}\frac{x + zx^3/\alpha^2 3! + \cdots}{L + zL^3/\alpha^2 3! + \cdots} = \frac{x}{L},$$

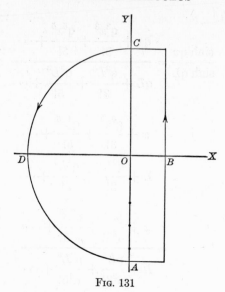

FIG. 131

and that at $z = -n^2\pi^2\alpha^2/L^2$ $(n \neq 0)$, by

$$\lim_{z \to -n^2\pi^2\alpha^2/L^2} \frac{e^{tz} \sinh (x\sqrt{z}/\alpha) \, (z + n^2\pi^2\alpha^2/L^2)}{z \sinh (L\sqrt{z}/\alpha)}$$

$$= \frac{e^{-n^2\pi^2\alpha^2 t/L^2} \sinh (in\pi x/L)}{-n^2\pi^2\alpha^2/L^2} \lim_{z \to -n^2\pi^2\alpha^2/L^2} \frac{z + n^2\pi^2\alpha^2/L^2}{\sinh (L\sqrt{z}/\alpha)}$$

$$= -\frac{iL^2 e^{-n^2\pi^2\alpha^2 t/L^2} \sin (n\pi x/L)}{n^2\pi^2\alpha^2} \lim_{z \to -n^2\pi^2\alpha^2/L^2} \frac{1}{(L/2\alpha\sqrt{z}) \cosh (L\sqrt{z}/\alpha)}$$

$$= -\frac{iL^2 e^{-n^2\pi^2\alpha^2 t/L^2} \sin (n\pi x/L)}{n^2\pi^2\alpha^2} \cdot \frac{2in\pi\alpha^2}{L^2 \cosh in\pi}$$

$$= \frac{2}{\pi} \frac{(-1)^n}{n} \sin \frac{n\pi x}{L} e^{-n^2\pi^2\alpha^2 t/L^2}.$$

If we now allow R to become infinite, the second of integrals (11) will approach zero, and we get

$$\frac{\sinh qx}{\sinh qL} \cdot 1 = \frac{x}{L} + \frac{2}{\pi} \sum_{n=1}^{\infty} \frac{(-1)^n}{n} \sin \frac{n\pi x}{L} e^{-n^2\pi^2\alpha^2 t/L^2}.$$

Consequently we have from equation (9),

$$u = u_0 \left[1 - \frac{x}{L} - \frac{2}{\pi} \sum_{n=1}^{\infty} \frac{(-1)^n}{n} \sin \frac{n\pi x}{L} e^{-n^2\pi^2\alpha^2 t/L^2} \right]. \tag{12}$$

This gives the temperature at any point x and any time t. Equation (12) may, of course, also be obtained by the methods of Chapter VII.

Now when $\pi\alpha\sqrt{t}/L$ is small, the series (12) converges slowly, and is thus not very suitable for computation. In this case, we may express the solution of our problem in a more convenient form. We have

$$1 - \frac{\sinh qx}{\sinh qL} = 1 - \frac{e^{qx} - e^{-qx}}{e^{qL} - e^{-qL}} = 1 - \frac{e^{-q(L-x)} - e^{-q(L+x)}}{1 - e^{-2qL}}$$

$$= 1 - (e^{-q(L-x)} - e^{-q(L+x)})(1 + e^{-2qL} + e^{-4qL} + \cdots)$$

$$= 1 - e^{-q(L-x)} + e^{-q(L+x)} - e^{-q(3L-x)} + e^{-q(3L+x)}$$

$$- e^{-q(5L-x)} + e^{-q(5L+x)} - \cdots.$$

But

$$e^{-aq} \cdot 1 = e^{-a\sqrt{p}/\alpha} \cdot 1 = 1 - \operatorname{erf} \frac{a}{2\alpha\sqrt{t}}$$

by formula (20), Art. 112. Hence we get from (9),

$$u = u_0 \left[\operatorname{erf} \frac{L-x}{2\alpha\sqrt{t}} + \left(1 - \operatorname{erf} \frac{L+x}{2\alpha\sqrt{t}}\right) - \left(1 - \operatorname{erf} \frac{3L-x}{2\alpha\sqrt{t}}\right) + \cdots \right]. (13)$$

This series, the terms of which may be calculated by the tables in Peirce, converges rapidly for t small since $1 - \operatorname{erf} s$ is small for s large.

As our final application, we consider briefly * a transmission line or cable, originally in equilibrium, with resistance r (ohms/mile), inductance L (henries/mile), and capacitance C (farads/mile). The differential equations for such a line are (Chapter VII, Art. 74)

$$\frac{\partial E}{\partial x} = -rI - L\frac{\partial I}{\partial t},$$

$$\frac{\partial I}{\partial x} = -C\frac{\partial E}{\partial t}, \tag{14}$$

where E (volts) and I (amp.) are the potential and current, respectively, at distance x (mi.) from one end and at time t (sec.). Elimination of I and E in turn from equations (14) gives us

$$\frac{\partial^2 E}{\partial x^2} - (LC\mathrm{p}^2 + rC\mathrm{p})E = 0,$$

$$\frac{\partial^2 I}{\partial x^2} - (LC\mathrm{p}^2 + rC\mathrm{p})I = 0, \tag{15}$$

* A more complete discussion may be found in V. Bush, "Operational Circuit Analysis," Chapters XI and XII.

where we have written p for $\partial/\partial t$. Treating these equations as if p were a constant, we readily find as solutions of (15) the operational expressions

$$E(x, t) = e^{-x\alpha}K_1(t) + e^{x\alpha}K_2(t),$$
$$I(x, t) = e^{-x\alpha}K_3(t) + e^{x\alpha}K_4(t),$$

$$(16)$$

where α is an operator given by

$$\alpha^2 = LCp^2 + rCp, \tag{17}$$

and the K's are, instead of constants, to be interpreted as functions of t. Suppose now that we are dealing with a cable so long that it may be considered as infinite in length, and let an e.m.f. be impressed at the end $x = 0$, the voltage and current decreasing as x increases. If p were a constant, we should then necessarily have $K_2 = K_4 = 0$, and

$$E(x, t) = e^{-x\alpha}K_1,$$
$$I(x, t) = e^{-x\alpha}K_3.$$

$$(18)$$

Now let E_0, a constant, be taken as the value of E at $x = 0$, and let $I = I_1(t)$ be the entering current. Then $E_0 = K_1$, $I_1(t) = K_3$, and

$$E(x, t) = e^{-x\alpha}E_0,$$
$$I(x, t) = e^{-x\alpha}I_1(t).$$

$$(19)$$

Substituting these values of E and I in the first of equations (14), we get

$$-\alpha e^{-x\alpha}E_0 = -re^{-x\alpha}I_1(t) - Lpe^{-x\alpha}I_1(t),$$

so that, putting $x = 0$, we find

$$I_1(t) = \frac{\alpha}{r + Lp}E_0 = \sqrt{\frac{Cp}{r + Lp}} \cdot E_0. \tag{20}$$

Letting $a = r/2L$, (20) may be written in the form,

$$I_1(t) = E_0\sqrt{\frac{C}{L}}\frac{1}{\sqrt{1 + 2a/p}} \cdot 1.$$

Using the shifting formula (18) of Art. 112, we have

$$\frac{1}{\sqrt{1 + 2a/p}} \cdot 1 = e^{-at}\frac{p}{p - a}\frac{1}{\sqrt{1 + 2a/(p - a)}} \cdot 1$$

$$= e^{-at}\frac{p}{\sqrt{p^2 - a^2}} \cdot 1.$$

But the last operator is that of formula (21), Art. 112, with a replaced by ia. Hence we get finally

$$I_1(t) = E_0 \sqrt{\frac{C}{L}}\, e^{-rt/2L} J_0\left(\frac{irt}{2L}\right). \tag{21}$$

Since E_0 is constant, I_1/E_0 is an indicial admittance. By use of the superposition theorem of Art. 110, the entering current corresponding to any impressed e.m.f. may be found, the necessary integration being performed by graphical or mechanical means. The values so obtained, when the e.m.f. is sinusoidal, have been found to agree very well with experimental results.* The operational method here employed may be extended so as to yield expressions for the voltage and current at any distance x along the cable and at any time t.

PROBLEMS

Establish the operational formulas in Problems 1–5.

1. (a) $p^m \cdot 1 = \dfrac{(\sin m\pi)\Gamma(m)}{\pi t^m}$　　　$(0 < m < 1)$;

(b) $p^{m+n} \cdot 1 = \dfrac{(-1)^n(\sin m\pi)\Gamma(m + n)}{\pi t^{m+n}}$　$(0 < m < 1,\ n$ a positive integer$)$;

(c) $p^{-\frac12} \cdot 1 = 2\sqrt{t/\pi}$.

2. (a) $\dfrac{p}{\sqrt{p + a}} \cdot 1 = \dfrac{e^{-at}}{\sqrt{\pi t}}$;

(b) $\dfrac{1}{\sqrt{p + a}} \cdot 1 = \dfrac{1}{\sqrt{\pi}} \displaystyle\int_0^t t^{-\frac12} e^{-at}\, dt$;

(c) $\sqrt{p + a} \cdot 1 = \dfrac{e^{-at}}{\sqrt{\pi t}} + \dfrac{a}{\sqrt{\pi}} \displaystyle\int_0^t t^{-\frac12} e^{-at}\, dt$.

3. $\phi(p) \cdot e^{-at} = e^{-at}\phi(p - a) \cdot 1$.

4. $p e^{-a\sqrt{p}} \cdot 1 = \dfrac{a}{2\sqrt{\pi}} t^{-\frac32} e^{-a^2/4t}$.

5. $e^{-a/p} \cdot 1 = J_0(2\sqrt{at})$.

6. A tightly stretched string with fixed end points, $x = 0$ and $x = L$, is initially in a position given by $y(x, 0) = y_0 \sin (\pi x/L)$. If it is released from rest from this position, find the displacement $y(x, t)$ at any distance x from the left-hand end and at any time t, using equation (4) of Art. 113, and show that your result is identical with that obtained in Chapter VII, Art. 70.

7. A glass rod 20 cm. long, for which the specific gravity is 2.40, the thermal conductivity 0.0015 cal./cm. deg. sec., and the specific heat 0.180 cal./gr. deg., is at

* See *E. E. Research Bull.* 50, Massachusetts Institute of Technology.

a uniform temperature of $100°$ C. If one end is suddenly cooled to $0°$ C., find the temperature at a point 5 cm. from the hot end 1 hr. after the change (a) using series (12) of Art. 113; (b) using series (13) of Art. 113.

8. An infinite cable with negligible leakance, resistance 0.1 ohm/mi., inductance 0.2 henry/mi., and capacitance 2×10^{-7} farad/mi., has impressed at the home end a constant e.m.f. of 100 volts at time $t = 0$. Find the value of the entering current for $t = 0, 1, 2$, and 4 sec.

9. An infinite cable with resistance r ohms/mi., capacitance C farads/mi., and negligible inductance and leakance, is subjected to a constant e.m.f. E_0 at the home end at time $t = 0$. Using the operational method of Art. 113, show that the entering current at any subsequent time t is

$$I_1(t) = E_0 \sqrt{\frac{C}{\pi r t}}.$$

10. An infinite cable with resistance r ohms/mi., capacitance C farads/mi., inductance L henries/mi., and leakance g mhos/mi., is subjected to a constant e.m.f. E_0 at the home end at time $t = 0$. Show that the entering current at any subsequent time t is

$$I_1(t) = E_0 \sqrt{\frac{C}{L}} e^{-at} J_0(ibt) + E_0 \frac{g}{\sqrt{LC}} \int_0^t e^{-at} J_0(ibt) \, dt,$$

where

$$a = \frac{r}{2L} + \frac{g}{2C}, \qquad b = \frac{r}{2L} - \frac{g}{2C}.$$

If the line is distortionless, i.e., if $r/L = g/C$, show that the entering current is steady and equal to $E_0\sqrt{C/L}$ for all $t > 0$.

PART III. LAPLACE TRANSFORMS

114. The Laplace transformation. An approach to operational methods which frequently appears in the literature is that based on a certain type of integral-function which we here take in the form

$$g(p) = \int_0^\infty e^{-pt} f(t) \, dt, \tag{1}$$

where p is a *parameter*. It is assumed that the function $f(t)$ is defined for all positive values of the real variable t and such that the improper (infinite) integral (1) exists. We call the function $g(p)$ thus obtained the Laplace transform of $f(t)$, and for brevity and convenience write

$$g(p) = L\{f(t)\}. \tag{2}$$

Unfortunately, there is lack of uniformity in the definition of the Laplace transform by various writers. Some use (1) as their definition, others take that integral multiplied by the factor p. Accordingly, each usage of a Laplace transformation should be examined in order to make sure which of the two forms, our present $g(p)$ or $pg(p)$, is being employed. The p-multiplied form has certain advantages, as pointed out in N. W. McLachlan's "Modern Operational Calculus" (page 2, footnote); in particular, it yields an exact correspondence between many Laplace transforms and Heaviside operational formulas. However, the form (1) has been chosen here because it lends itself more readily to a number of techniques and operations, notably the exponential shift (cf. relation (18), Art. 112, and equation (12), below), derivatives and integrals of transforms, and the solution of linear differential equations with variable coefficients, as will be found.

The Bromwich integral (equation (1), Art. 112) may be used, as we have seen, to find the result of operating on unity with a given operator $\phi(p)$ to produce a function of the variable t. On the other hand, the Laplace transformation serves directly to obtain a function of the parameter p corresponding to a known function of t. Later, we shall see how to apply the Laplace transform to the solution of differential equations; first, however, let us find the transforms of a few familiar functions, and thus build up a short table of transforms for convenient reference.

If $f(t) = t^n$ we get, from (1),

$$L\{t^n\} = \int_0^\infty e^{-pt}t^n \, dt = \frac{1}{p^{n+1}} \int_0^\infty e^{-(pt)}(pt)^n \, d(pt)$$

$$= \frac{\Gamma(n+1)}{p^{n+1}}, \tag{3}$$

by (3), Art. 54. When n is a positive integer, $\Gamma(n+1) = n!$, and consequently relation (3), giving $p^{-(n+1)}$ as the Laplace transform of $t^n/n!$, is analogous to equation (4), Art. 108. When n is any real constant greater than -1, we get a more general result, which includes, for example, the analog of equation (17), Art. 112, for $n = -\frac{1}{2}$.

If $f(t) = e^{at}$, (1) easily yields

$$L\{e^{at}\} = \int_0^\infty e^{-pt} \cdot e^{at} \, dt = \int_0^\infty e^{-(p-a)t} \, dt$$

$$= \left[-\frac{e^{-(p-a)t}}{p-a} \right]_0^\infty = \frac{1}{p-a}, \tag{4}$$

provided only that $p > a$. This constitutes the analog of relation (5),

Art. 108. From (4) we then readily get

$$L\{\sinh at\} = L\left\{\frac{e^{at} - e^{-at}}{2}\right\} = \frac{1}{2}\left(\frac{1}{p-a} - \frac{1}{p+a}\right)$$

$$= \frac{a}{p^2 - a^2}, \tag{5}$$

and

$$L\{\cosh at\} = L\left\{\frac{e^{at} + e^{-at}}{2}\right\} = \frac{1}{2}\left(\frac{1}{p-a} + \frac{1}{p+a}\right)$$

$$= \frac{p}{p^2 - a^2}, \tag{6}$$

which match with equations (10) and (11), Art. 108. By formally replacing a by ia in (5) and (6), we may infer the existence of the transforms

$$L\{\sinh iat\} = L\{i \sin at\} = \frac{ia}{p^2 + a^2},$$

$$L\{\sin at\} = \frac{a}{p^2 + a^2}, \tag{7}$$

and

$$L\{\cosh iat\} = L\{\cos at\} = \frac{p}{p^2 + a^2}, \tag{8}$$

corresponding to relations (8) and (9), Art. 108. To validate this formal procedure, however, we shall derive transforms (7) and (8) by other means.

We next determine Laplace transforms of derivative functions $f'(t)$, $f''(t)$, $\cdots$, $f^{(n)}(t)$. Applying integration by parts, we have

$$L\{f'(t)\} = \int_0^\infty e^{-pt} f'(t)\, dt$$

$$= \left[e^{-pt} f(t)\right]_0^\infty + p \int_0^\infty e^{-pt} f(t)\, dt.$$

Now if $f(t)$ is a function such that $\left| e^{-kt} f(t) \right| < M$, say, for $t > t_1$, k and M being some positive constants, then $f(t)$ is said to be of *exponential order*. When $f(t)$ is of exponential order, as is true of the usual functions arising in practice, $e^{-pt} f(t)$ will approach zero as t becomes infinite; assuming this, we get

$$L\{f'(t)\} = -f(0) + pL\{f(t)\}. \tag{9}$$

One application of (9) may be made as follows. Let $F(t) = \int_0^t f(t)\, dt$, so that $F'(t) = f(t)$ and $F(0) = 0$. Then, from (9),

$$L\{f(t)\} = L\{F'(t)\} = pL\{F(t)\},$$

or

$$L\left\{\int_0^t f(t)\, dt\right\} = \frac{1}{p} L\{f(t)\}. \tag{10}$$

Therefore division of the transform of a function by p corresponds to integration of that function from 0 to t. The parameter p in Laplace transformations thus plays a role precisely analogous to the Heaviside operator p (equation (2), Art. 107, and Art. 108).

Likewise, under similar suitable assumptions on $f'(t)$, we find, from (9),

$$L\{f''(t)\} = -f'(0) + pL\{f'(t)\}$$
$$= -f'(0) - f(0)p + p^2 L\{f(t)\}$$

and, in general,

$$L\{f^{(n)}(t)\}$$
$$= p^n L\{f(t)\} - f(0)p^{n-1} - f'(0)p^{n-2} - \cdots - f^{(n-1)}(0). \tag{11}$$

To illustrate the use of (11), we may now derive relation (7) directly. When $f(t) = \sin at$, $f'(t) = a \cos at$ and $f''(t) = -a^2 \sin at$, whence (11) gives

$$-a^2 L\{\sin at\} = p^2 L\{\sin at\} - 0 \cdot p - a,$$

$$(p^2 + a^2)L\{\sin at\} = a,$$

$$L\{\sin at\} = \frac{a}{p^2 + a^2}.$$

The transform of $\cos at$ may similarly be found to be given by (8), and the transforms of other functions are also obtainable by these means.

Another important property of Laplace transforms, from which further useful results can be derived, is the following. If we replace p by $p - b$ in a transform $g(p)$, where b is some constant, (1) gives

$$g(p - b) = \int_0^\infty e^{-(p-b)t} f(t)\, dt = \int_0^\infty e^{-pt}[e^{bt}f(t)]\, dt$$

$$= L\{e^{bt}f(t)\}. \tag{12}$$

Thus, the replacement of the parameter p by $p - b$ in a transform corresponds to the multiplication of the original function $f(t)$ by e^{bt}. Relation (12), which may be referred to as the exponential shift (cf. equation (18), Art. 112), immediately yields the following new transforms. From (3), we get

$$L\{e^{bt}t^n\} = \frac{\Gamma(n+1)}{(p-b)^{n+1}};$$ (13)

from (7),

$$L\{e^{bt}\sin at\} = \frac{a}{(p-b)^2+a^2};$$ (14)

and from (8),

$$L\{e^{bt}\cos at\} = \frac{p-b}{(p-b)^2+a^2}.$$ (15)

If we differentiate relation (1), with respect to p, under the integral sign (Art. 67),* we get

$$g'(p) = \int_0^\infty e^{-pt}[-tf(t)]\,dt = L\{-tf(t)\}.$$

Similarly, $g''(p) = L\{t^2f(t)\}$, and, in general,

$$g^{(n)}(p) = L\{(-t)^nf(t)\}.$$ (16)

Applying (16) to (7), for example, we find

$$-\frac{2ap}{(p^2+a^2)^2} = L\{-t\sin at\},$$

or

$$L\{t\sin at\} = \frac{2ap}{(p^2+a^2)^2}.$$ (17)

Likewise, (8) and (16) give

$$L\{t\cos at\} = \frac{p^2-a^2}{(p^2+a^2)^2}.$$ (18)

Integration of a Laplace transform also produces useful relations and properties. If c is sufficiently large, we have

$$\int_p^c g(p)\,dp = \int_p^c \left[\int_0^\infty e^{-pt}f(t)\,dt\right]dp$$

$$= \int_0^\infty f(t)\left[\int_p^c e^{-pt}\,dp\right]dt$$

$$= \int_0^\infty f(t)\left[-\frac{e^{-pt}}{t}\right]_p^c dt$$

$$= \int_0^\infty \frac{f(t)}{t}(e^{-pt}-e^{-ct})\,dt.$$

---

* This is valid provided that $f(t)$ is continuous, except possibly for a finite number of finite discontinuities, for $t > 0$, and is of exponential order.

Now, assuming that the limit of $f(t)/t$ exists as $t \to 0^+$, and that $f(t)$ is piecewise continuous and of exponential order as before, we may let c become infinite; then

$$\int_p^\infty g(p) \, dp = \int_0^\infty e^{-pt} \frac{f(t)}{t} \, dt = L \left\{ \frac{f(t)}{t} \right\}. \tag{19}$$

This result gives, for instance, from (7) with $a = 1$,

$$L \left\{ \frac{\sin t}{t} \right\} = \int_p^\infty \frac{dp}{p^2 + 1} = [\arctan p]_p^\infty$$

$$= \frac{\pi}{2} - \arctan p = \operatorname{arccot} p.$$

Since, by (10), division of a transform by p corresponds to integration of a function from 0 to t, we get

$$L \left\{ \int_0^t \frac{\sin t}{t} \, dt \right\} = L\{\operatorname{Si}(t)\} = \frac{\operatorname{arccot} p}{p}. \tag{20}$$

The integral function denoted by $\operatorname{Si}(t)$ is called the *sine-integral* function. It arises in various physical applications, and its values are given in certain tables, including those of Jahnke-Emde.

115. Applications. To illustrate the manner in which the Laplace transform may be used in solving linear ordinary differential equations with constant coefficients, we consider Problem 18 following Art. 27. The planar motion involved there is given by the system of equations

$$D^2 x = 2y, \qquad D^2 y = -2x, \tag{1}$$

where $D = d/dt$ and t is time, accompanied by the initial conditions

$$x = -1, \qquad y = 0, \qquad Dx = 0, \qquad Dy = 0, \tag{2}$$

for $t = 0$. Elimination of y from equations (1) gives

$$D^4 x = 2D^2 y = -4x,$$

or

$$D^4 x + 4x = 0. \tag{3}$$

Corresponding to $t = 0$, we also get, from (1) and (2),

$$x = -1, \qquad Dx = 0, \qquad D^2 x = 2y = 0, \qquad D^3 x = 2Dy = 0. \tag{4}$$

The problem is thus reduced to that of finding the solution of the fourth order equation (3) which satisfies the initial conditions (4). Once that solution $x = f(t)$ has been determined, the first of equations (1) yields $y = \frac{1}{2} D^2 x = \frac{1}{2} f''(t)$.

Now, by relation (11) of Art. 114, together with conditions (4), the Laplace transform of D^4x is

$$L\{D^4x\} = p^4 L\{x\} - p^3,$$

and consequently

$$L\{D^4x + 4x\} = p^4 L\{x\} - p^3 + 4L\{x\} = 0,$$

$$L\{x\} = \frac{p^3}{p^4 + 4}.$$

Resolving this rational algebraic function of the parameter p into partial fractions, we find

$$\frac{p^3}{p^4 + 4} = \frac{1}{2}\left(\frac{p - 1}{p^2 - 2p + 2} + \frac{p + 1}{p^2 + 2p + 2}\right),$$

so that

$$L\{x\} = \frac{1}{2}\left[\frac{p - 1}{(p - 1)^2 + 1} + \frac{p + 1}{(p + 1)^2 + 1}\right].$$

Formula (15) of Art. 114 thus yields immediately

$$x = \tfrac{1}{2}(e^t \cos t + e^{-t} \cos t) = \cos t \cosh t, \tag{5}$$

whence we get

$$y = \tfrac{1}{2}D^2 x = -\sin t \sinh t. \tag{6}$$

These relations, (5) and (6), are the desired equations of the path of the particle.

Using formula (16), it is also sometimes possible to solve a linear ordinary differential equation, whose coefficients are non-constant polynomials in the independent variable. As an example, consider Bessel's equation of order zero (cf. equations (9) and (11), Art. 107),

$$ty'' + y' + ty = 0, \tag{7}$$

accompanied by the initial conditions

$$y = 1, \qquad y' = 0, \tag{8}$$

for $t = 0$. By (16) and (11), Art. 114, we have

$$L\{ty''\} = -\frac{d}{dp}[p^2 g(p) - p] = -p^2 g'(p) - 2pg(p) + 1,$$

where $g(p)$ denotes the transform of $y = f(t)$.   Likewise,

$$L\{y'\} = pg(p) - 1,$$

and

$$L\{ty\} = -\frac{d}{dp} g(p) = -g'(p).$$

Hence the transformed equation, corresponding to (7) and (8), is

$$-p^2 g' - 2pg + 1 + pg - 1 - g' = 0,$$

or

$$(p^2 + 1) \frac{dg}{dp} + pg = 0.$$

Separating the variables and integrating, we find

$$\frac{dg}{g} + \frac{p \, dp}{p^2 + 1} = 0,$$

$$\ln g + \tfrac{1}{2} \ln (p^2 + 1) = \ln c,$$

say, where c is a constant.   Consequently our Laplace transform is of the form

$$g(p) = \frac{c}{\sqrt{p^2 + 1}}. \tag{9}$$

Now, by the binomial series, for $p > 1$ (Peirce, 750),

$$g(p) = \frac{c}{p}\left(1 + \frac{1}{p^2}\right)^{-\frac{1}{2}} = \frac{c}{p}\left(1 - \frac{1}{2p^2} + \frac{1 \cdot 3}{2 \cdot 4 p^4} - \cdots\right)$$

$$= c \sum_{n=0}^{\infty} \frac{(-1)^n (2n)!}{2^{2n}(n!)^2 p^{2n+1}}.$$

Applying formula (3), Art. 114, to this transform series, we get

$$y = f(t) = c \sum_{n=0}^{\infty} \frac{(-1)^n t^{2n}}{2^{2n}(n!)^2}.$$

Both of the initial conditions (8) are satisfied by taking $c = 1$, and the summation is readily identified as the series for the Bessel function $J_0(t)$.   Relation (9) thus yields a new transform formula,

$$L\{J_0(t)\} = \frac{1}{\sqrt{p^2 + 1}}. \tag{10}$$

Another application of the Laplace transformation is to the evaluation of certain integrals. Consider, for example, the function

$$f(t) = \int_0^\infty \frac{\sin^2 tx}{x^2} \, dx. \tag{11}$$

For convenience, we replace $\sin^2 tx$ by its equivalent, $\frac{1}{2}(1 - \cos 2tx)$. Then, assuming it to be permissible to interchange the process of transforming (11) as a function of t and that of integration with respect to x, we get (from (3) and (7), Art. 114)

$$L\{f(t)\} = \frac{1}{2} \int_0^\infty \left[\frac{1}{px^2} - \frac{p}{x^2(p^2 + 4x^2)} \right] dx$$

$$= \int_0^\infty \frac{2 \, dx}{p(p^2 + 4x^2)} = \left[\frac{1}{p^2} \arctan \frac{2x}{p} \right]_0^\infty = \frac{\pi}{2p^2}.$$

Therefore, from (3), Art. 114,

$$f(t) = \int_0^\infty \frac{\sin^2 tx}{x^2} \, dx = \frac{\pi t}{2}. \tag{12}$$

When $t = 1$, (12) yields Peirce's formula 486. Incidentally, it may be remarked that the substitution $y = tx$ in (11) gives

$$f(t) = t \int_0^\infty \frac{\sin^2 y}{y^2} \, dy,$$

so that $f(t)$ is indeed of the form kt, where k is a constant; the Laplace transformation thus serves to evaluate k (that is, Peirce's integral 486) as $\pi/2$.

As a final application, one which serves to illustrate the use of Laplace transforms in solving partial differential equations, we reconsider the resonant forced vibrations of the string of Art. 92. We wish now to find an analytic solution of the equation

$$\frac{\partial^2 y}{\partial t^2} = a^2 \frac{\partial^2 y}{\partial x^2}, \tag{13}$$

satisfying the boundary and initial conditions

$$y(x, 0) = 0, \qquad \frac{\partial y}{\partial t}\bigg]_{t=0} = 0, \qquad y(L, t) = 0,$$

$$y(0, t) = A \sin (a\pi t/L). \tag{14}$$

Let $G(x, p)$ denote the Laplace transform of $y(x, t)$ with regard to the variable t:

$$L\{y(x, t)\} = G(x, p) = \int_0^\infty e^{-pt} y(x, t)\, dt.$$

Then we have, from the first two of conditions (14) and relation (11) of Art. 114,

$$L\left\{\frac{\partial^2 y}{\partial t^2}\right\} = p^2 L\{y(x, t)\} = p^2 G(x, p).$$

Moreover, assuming that the processes of integration with respect to t and of differentiation with respect to x are interchangeable in order,

$$L\left\{\frac{\partial^2 y}{\partial x^2}\right\} = \int_0^\infty e^{-pt} \frac{\partial^2 y}{\partial x^2}\, dt$$
$$= \frac{\partial^2}{\partial x^2}\left[\int_0^\infty e^{-pt} y(x, t)\, dt\right] = \frac{\partial^2 G}{\partial x^2}.$$

Accordingly, (13) is transformed into

$$p^2 G = a^2 \frac{\partial^2 G}{\partial x^2}.$$

Since the parameter p is independent of x, this transformed equation is, in effect, a linear ordinary differential equation with constant coefficients, and therefore (Art. 10)

$$G(x, p) = e^{xp/a} K_1(p) + e^{-xp/a} K_2(p), \tag{15}$$

where K_1 and K_2 may be functions of p (cf. the transmission line problem of Art. 113).

The transforms of the last two of conditions (14) are

$$G(L, p) = 0, \qquad G(0, p) = \frac{A(a\pi/L)}{p^2 + (a^2\pi^2/L^2)}. \tag{16}$$

Therefore, from (15),

$$e^{Lp/a} K_1 + e^{-Lp/a} K_2 = 0, \qquad K_1 + K_2 = G(0, p).$$

Solving this pair of linear algebraic equations in K_1 and K_2, we easily find

$$K_1(p) = \frac{G(0, p)}{1 - e^{-2Lp/a}} = (1 + e^{-2Lp/a} + e^{-4Lp/a} + \cdots)G(0, p),$$

$$K_2(p) = -\frac{e^{-2Lp/a} G(0, p)}{1 - e^{-2Lp/a}} = -(e^{-2Lp/a} + e^{-4Lp/a} + \cdots)G(0, p).$$

Inserting these expressions in (15), we get

$$G(x, p) = [e^{-xp/a} + e^{-(2L+x)p/a} + e^{-(4L+x)p/a} + \cdots]G(0, p)$$
$$- [e^{-(2L-x)p/a} + e^{-(4L-x)p/a} + \cdots]G(0, p). \quad (17)$$

We have now to determine the effect of multiplying a transform by an exponential function e^{-cp}, where c is a positive constant. For any function $f(t)$ possessing a tra sform $g(p)$, we have, by definition,

$$g(p) = \int_0^\infty e^{-pt}f(t)\, dt.$$

Hence

$$e^{-cp}g(p) = \int_0^\infty e^{-p(t+c)}f(t)\, dt.$$

Letting $s = t + c$, we then get

$$e^{-cp}g(p) = \int_c^\infty e^{-ps}f(s - c)\, ds$$
$$= \int_0^c 0 \cdot ds + \int_c^\infty e^{-ps}f(s - c)\, ds.$$

We define a new function $f_c(s)$, as follows:

$$f_c(s) = 0, \qquad 0 < s < c; \quad (18)$$
$$f_c(s) = f(s - c), \qquad s > c;$$

then

$$e^{-cp}g(p) = \int_0^\infty e^{-ps}f_c(s)\, ds. \quad (19)$$

Consequently, if $g(p)$ is the Laplace transform of $f(t)$, $e^{-cp}g(p)$ is the transform of $f_c(t)$, where $f_c(s)$ is given by (18). The function $f_c(t)$ may be called a *translation function*, for its graph is that of $f(t)$ translated a distance c to the right, augmented by the segment of the t-axis between 0 and c.

Applying these findings to relation (17), and remembering that $G(x, p)$ and $G(0, p)$ denote the transforms of the required functions $y(x, t)$ and $y(0, t) = f(t) = A \sin (a\pi t/L)$, respectively, we obtain

$$y(x, t) = f_{x/a}\left(t - \frac{x}{a}\right) + f_{(2L+x)/a}\left(t - \frac{2L + x}{a}\right)$$
$$+ f_{(4L+x)/a}\left(t - \frac{4L + x}{a}\right) + \cdots - f_{(2L-x)/a}\left(t - \frac{2L - x}{a}\right)$$
$$- f_{(4L-x)/a}\left(t - \frac{4L - x}{a}\right) - \cdots. \quad (20)$$

All the translation functions appearing here obey the defining conditions (18). If we introduce the symbolism sint θ to denote the *translation-sine function*, which is such that sint $\theta = 0$ when $\theta < 0$, and sint $\theta = \sin \theta$ for $\theta \geqq 0$, we may then write

$$y(x, t) = A \left[\text{sint} \frac{\pi(at - x)}{L} + \text{sint} \frac{\pi(at - x - 2L)}{L} \right.$$

$$+ \text{sint} \frac{\pi(at - x - 4L)}{L} + \cdots - \text{sint} \frac{\pi(at + x - 2L)}{L}$$

$$\left. - \text{sint} \frac{\pi(at + x - 4L)}{L} - \cdots \right]. \quad (21)$$

This is the desired analytic expression for $y(x, t)$. For every pair of values of x and t, equation (21) will contain a finite number of non-zero terms; when $at - x < 2(n - 1)L$, the nth and following terms in the first (positively signed) set will vanish, and when $at + x < 2mL$, the mth and following terms in the second (negatively signed) set will vanish, since only those terms involving positive angles can contribute to the value of $y(x, t)$. For example, at the end of the first cycle of oscillation of the left-hand end of the string, the displacement of the midpoint of the string is

$$y\left(\frac{L}{2}, \frac{2L}{a}\right) = A\left(\sin\frac{3\pi}{2} - \sin\frac{\pi}{2}\right) = -2A;$$

after two periods,

$$y\left(\frac{L}{2}, \frac{4L}{a}\right) = A\left(\sin\frac{7\pi}{2} + \sin\frac{3\pi}{2} - \sin\frac{5\pi}{2} - \sin\frac{\pi}{2}\right) = -4A;$$

and so on.

PROBLEMS

Determine the Laplace transforms of each of the functions in Problems 1–6.

1. $at - \sin at$.   **2.** $\sin at - at \cos at$.

3. $\sin at + at \cos at$.   **4.** $\sin at \sinh at$.

5. $(t - a)^n \qquad (t > a)$.   **6.** $t^2 \sin at$.

7. If $g(p)$ is the Laplace transform of $f(t)$, show that $ag(ap - b)$ is the transform of $e^{bt/a}f(t/a)$.

8. If $f(t)$ is a periodic function, with period T, so that $f(t + T) \equiv f(t)$, show that the Laplace transform of $f(t)$ is given by

$$\sum_{n=0}^{\infty} e^{-nTp} \int_0^T e^{-ps}f(s) \, ds = \frac{\int_0^T e^{-ps}f(s) \, ds}{1 - e^{-Tp}}.$$

9. Using the result of Problem 8, show that

$$L\{|\sin at|\} = \frac{a \coth (\pi p/2a)}{p^2 + a^2}.$$

10. Show that

$$L\{tJ_1(t)\} = \frac{1}{(p^2 + 1)^{3/2}},$$

where $J_1(t)$ is the Bessel function of first order, (a) directly from the series expansion of $J_1(t)$ and relation (3), Art. 114; (b) using the fact that $J_1(t) = -J_0'(t)$, together with relations (11) and (16), Art. 114.

11. Show that $f(p)/F(p)$, where $F(p) = (p - a_1)(p - a_2)\cdots(p - a_n)$, a's all different constants, and where $f(p)$ is a polynomial of degree less than n, is the Laplace transform of the function

$$\sum_{k=1}^{n} \frac{f(a_k)e^{a_k t}}{F'(a_k)}.$$

This is the analog of Heaviside's expansion theorem (equation (7), Art. 108).

12. Show that the Laplace transform of the *cosine-integral function*, defined as

$$\text{Ci}\ (t) = -\int_t^\infty \frac{\cos x}{x}\, dx,$$

is $-[\ln (p^2 + 1)]/2p$. *Hint:* Let $x = ty$, and transform $\cos yt$.

13. The *exponential-integral function* is defined as

$$\text{Ei}\ (t) = \int_{-\infty}^t \frac{e^x}{x}\, dx.$$

Show that the Laplace transform of $\text{Ei}(-t)$ is $-[\ln (p + 1)]/p$.

Using the Laplace transformation, find the solution of each of the linear differential equations in Problems 14–19, subject to the given initial conditions.

14. $y'' - 3y' + 2y = 0$; $t = 0$, $y = 0$, $y' = 1$.
15. $y''' + 2y'' - y' - 2y = 0$; $t = 0$, $y = 1$, $y' = 2$, $y'' = -2$.
16. $y'' + 2y' + 2y = 0$; $t = 0$, $y = 0$, $y' = 1$.
17. $y^{\text{iv}} - y = 0$; $t = 0$, $y = 2$, $y' = 2$, $y'' = 0$, $y''' = 0$.
18. $ty'' - y' + ty = 0$; $t = 0$, $y = 0$, $y' = 0$.
19. $ty'' + (1 - 2n)y' + ty = 0$; $t = 0$, $y = 0$, $y' = 0$ $(n > 1)$.

Evaluate each of the integrals in Problems 20–22. (Cf. Peirce's formulas 484, 490, 491.)

20. $\int_0^\infty \frac{\sin tx}{x}\, dx$ $(t > 0)$.

21. $\int_0^\infty \frac{\cos tx}{1 + x^2}\, dx$ $(t > 0)$.

22. $\int_0^\infty \frac{\sin tx}{\sqrt{x}}\, dx$ $(t > 0)$.

23. In the vibrating string problem of Art. 115, show that, theoretically, $y(L/2, 2nL/a) = -2nA$ for every positive integer n.

24. Using relation (21), Art. 115, verify the computations tabulated in Art. 92.

Units and Dimensional Analysis

In this book, as in others dealing with physical problems, a variety of physical quantities and units are employed. Often one physical quantity may be expressed in terms of other quantities regarded as more fundamental, so that functional dependencies arise. New entities are sometimes defined by such relationships.

For example, in the centimeter-gram-second (c.g.s.) system, the dyne is defined as that unit of force which, acting on a mass of 1 gram, produces an acceleration of 1 cm./sec.^{2} Similarly, in the foot-pound-second (f.p.s.) system, the poundal is defined as that unit of force which, acting on a mass of 1 lb., produces an acceleration of 1 ft./sec.^{2} In both systems, acceleration is further expressible in terms of the more basic concepts of length and time.

When changing from one system of units to another, it is necessary to use suitable conversion factors. In mechanics and heat, relations between c.g.s. and f.p.s. units are needed. For convenient reference, the principal mechanical and thermal units employed in this book, and the corresponding conversion factors, are listed here:

QUANTITY	C.G.S. UNITS	F.P.S. UNITS	CONVERSION FACTORS
Mass	gram	pound	1 lb. = 453.6 gm.
Length	centimeter	foot	1 ft. = 30.48 cm.
Force	dyne	poundal	1 pdl. = 13,826 dynes
Energy, work	erg	foot-pound	1 ft-lb. = 1.356 × 10^7 ergs
Power	watt	horsepower	1 hp. = 745.7 watts
			1 watt = 10^7 ergs/sec.
Quantity of heat	calorie	B.t.u.	1 B.t.u. = 252 cal.

In electricity and magnetism, relations among electromagnetic units (e.m.u. ab units), electrostatic units (e.s.u., stat units), and the practical units (such as volt and ampere) are required:

QUANTITY	CONVERSION FACTORS
Potential difference	1 statvolt = 2.998 × 10^{10} abvolts = 299.8 volts
Current	1 abamp. = 2.998 × 10^{10} statamp. = 10 amp.
Electric charge	1 abcoul. = 2.998 × 10^{10} statcoul. = 10 coulombs
Resistance	1 statohm = 8.988 × 10^{20} abohms = 8.988 × 10^{11} ohms
Inductance	1 stathenry = 8.988 × 10^{20} abhenries = 8.988 × 10^{11} henries
Capacitance	1 abfarad = 8.988 × 10^{20} statfarads = 10^9 farads

The fact that various physical quantities are expressible in terms of certain fundamental quantities gives rise to the concept of dimensionality. In mechanics, the fundamental quantities are commonly taken as mass (M), length (L), and time (T). We give here the dimensions of some of the mechanical and geometric quantities that are frequently used.

Quantity	Dimension
Acceleration	LT^{-2}
Angular acceleration	T^{-2}
Angular momentum	ML^2T^{-1}
Angular velocity	T^{-1}
Area	L^2
Curvature	L^{-1}
Density	ML^{-3}
Energy (work)	ML^2T^{-2}
Force	MLT^{-2}
Frequency	T^{-1}
Moment (torque)	ML^2T^{-2}
Moment of inertia	ML^2 or L^4
Momentum	MLT^{-1}
Power	ML^2T^{-3}
Velocity	LT^{-1}
Volume	L^3

Sometimes force (F), instead of mass (M), is regarded as the third basic quantity in mechanics, with length (L) and time (T) retained as the other two. Then mass is a derived quantity whose dimension is $FL^{-1}T^2$, power has the dimension FLT^{-1}, and so on. We shall not discuss this system of dimensions further, since only the M-L-T system is used throughout this book.

In heat and thermodynamics, it is usual to augment the three mechanical units (M, L, T) by temperature (θ). For convenience, thermal units are sometimes employed; then quantity of heat (H) is also taken as a fundamental quantity. However, if we regard heat as a form of energy, so that it has the mechanical dimension ML^2T^{-2}, it suffices to express thermal quantities in terms of M, L, T, and θ.

Quantity	Thermal Units	Mechanical Units
Entropy, gas constant	$H\theta^{-1}$	$ML^2T^{-2}\theta^{-1}$
Quantity of heat	H	ML^2T^{-2}
Specific heat (per unit mass)	$HM^{-1}\theta^{-1}$	$L^2T^{-2}\theta^{-1}$
Temperature gradient	$L^{-1}\theta$	$L^{-1}\theta$
Thermal conductivity	$HL^{-1}T^{-1}\theta^{-1}$	$MLT^{-3}\theta^{-1}$

The dimensions of electrical and magnetic quantities may be expressed in terms of M, L, T and Q, where Q represents electric charge or quantity of electricity.

APPENDIX 525

Quantity	Dimension
Capacitance	$M^{-1}L^{-2}T^2Q^2$
Conductance	$M^{-1}L^{-2}TQ^2$
Current	$T^{-1}Q$
Electric field intensity	$MLT^{-2}Q^{-1}$
Inductance	ML^2Q^{-2}
Magnetic field intensity	$L^{-1}T^{-1}Q$
Potential difference	$ML^2T^{-2}Q^{-1}$
Resistance	$ML^2T^{-1}Q^{-2}$

The concept of dimensionality has one application in checking the "balance" of a differential or functional equation or in determining the dimension of a quantity appearing in such an equation. Thus, in the differential equation of a damped mechanical vibration,

$$\frac{m}{g}\frac{d^2x}{dt^2} = -k^2x - K\frac{dx}{dt},$$

each term has the dimension of mass M. Hence, since x has the dimension L and dx/dt has the dimension LT^{-1}, we see that k^2 and K have the dimensions ML^{-1} and $ML^{-1}T$, respectively.

The methods of dimensional analysis also enable us to predict the form of a functional relation in many instances. As an elementary mechanical illustration, consider the simple pendulum. The period of oscillation t may conceivably depend upon the length a of the pendulum, its mass m, its amplitude of swing α, and the acceleration of gravity g:

$$t = f_1(a, m, \alpha, g).$$

Now the dimensions of these five quantities are as follows:

Quantity:	t	a	m	α	g
Dimension:	T	L	M	0	LT^{-2}

(The angle α is a pure number, the ratio of two lengths, and therefore has no dimension.) Since M appears only in the mass itself, we see immediately that a change in the unit of mass cannot be compensated by any corresponding change in the units of the other quantities, whence it appears that t is independent of m. The functional relation will then be of the form

$$t = f_2(a, \alpha, g).$$

We may note next that L appears only in a and g, and to the same power in each. Hence we conclude that a and g can be present only in the ratio a/g, so that

$$t = f_3(a/g, \alpha).$$

But the dimension of a/g is T^2, whereas we need T as the dimension of t. Therefore we have

$$t = f_4(\alpha)\sqrt{\frac{a}{g}}.$$

The form of $f_4(\alpha)$, being dimensionless, cannot be determined by dimensional analysis; we have found, however (Chapter III), that α is involved in an elliptic integral, and our discussion then led to just the last form of functional relation determined above.

We consider now a more systematic method of determining the form of a functional relation, taking as an example a problem in the kinetic theory of gases. Suppose that we wish to find the pressure p exerted by a perfect gas. Conceivably p will depend upon the mass m of the gas atom, the density ρ of the gas, the temperature θ, and the gas constant K which expresses the average kinetic energy of an atom as a function of temperature. We have then the following quantities:

Quantity:	$p.$	m	ρ	θ	K
Dimension:	$ML^{-1}T^{-2}$	M	ML^{-3}	θ	$ML^2T^{-2}\theta^{-1}$

Assume that the pressure p is expressible as a product of powers of the other four quantities,* so that we have

$$p = km^x\rho^y\theta^zK^w,$$

where k is a dimensionless constant and x, y, z, w are exponents to be determined. Using the dimensions of our five quantities, we then get the identity

$$ML^{-1}T^{-2} \equiv M^x(ML^{-3})^y\theta^z(ML^2T^{-2}\theta^{-1})^w$$

$$\equiv M^{x+y+w}L^{-3y+2w}T^{-2w}\theta^{z-w}.$$

We therefore have the system of equations

$$x + y + w = 1, \qquad -3y + 2w = -1,$$

$$-2w = -2, \qquad z - w = 0,$$

from which we easily find $x = -1$, $y = 1$, $z = 1$, $w = 1$. Hence the desired relation is

$$p = k\frac{\rho\theta K}{m}.$$

As a final example, consider the problem of finding the energy W stored in a condenser of capacitance C, holding a charge q, the potential difference between the plates being V. We then have:

Quantity:	W	C	q	V
Dimension:	ML^2T^{-2}	$M^{-1}L^{-2}T^2Q^2$	Q	$ML^2T^{-2}Q^{-1}$

Assuming a relation of the form

$$W = kC^xq^yV^z,$$

---

* The validity of this assumption may be established on other grounds; see P. W. Bridgman, "Dimensional Analysis," Chap. II.

where k is again a dimensionless constant, we get

$$ML^2T^{-2} \equiv (M^{-1}L^{-2}T^2Q^2)^x Q^y (ML^2T^{-2}Q^{-1})^z$$
$$\equiv M^{-x+z}L^{-2x+2z}T^{2x-2z}Q^{2x+y-z},$$

which yields the equations

$$-x + z = 1, \qquad -2x + 2z = 2, \qquad 2x - 2z = -2, \qquad 2x + y - z = 0.$$

We see immediately that the first three of these equations are equivalent, so that we have only two independent equations in three unknowns. This would seem to indicate that the energy W can be expressed in terms of two of the three quantities C, q, and V. In fact, if we set $x = 0$, we find $y = 1$ and $z = 1$, whence

$$W = kqV;$$

setting $y = 0$, there is found $x = 1$ and $z = 2$, and consequently

$$W = kCV^2;$$

if $z = 0$, $x = -1$ and $y = 2$, so that

$$W = k\frac{q^2}{C}.$$

All these relations are correct, for the quantities C, q, and V are functionally related: $q = $ (const.)CV, as may easily be checked dimensionally.

We have considered here only a few systems of dimensions and the elements of the subject of dimensional analysis. More extensive treatments will be found in Section 3 of the "Handbook of Engineering Fundamentals," edited by O. W. Eshbach, and in Bridgman's "Dimensional Analysis."

ANSWERS TO PROBLEMS

Arts. 1–3. Page 9

1. $(x^4 + c)y^4 + 1 = 0.$
3. $y^2 + \cos 2x = c.$
5. $1/(2 - y) = \sqrt{1 + x} + c.$
7. $y = \tan(\sin x + c).$
9. $xy = x^2 + c.$
11. $y = x^2 y^2 + c.$
13. $y = \frac{1}{2}x(\ln x + c).$
15. $y - xy^2 = cx.$
17. $\ln[(x + y)/(x - y)] = 3x^2 + c.$
19. $x \sin y = y + c.$
21. $y(2xy + c) + x = 0.$
23. $y^2 - xe^{-y} = c.$

2. $e^{3y} = x^3 + c.$
4. $\sin y = c \sin x.$
6. $\ln y = \frac{1}{2}\ln^2 x + c.$
8. $(4 + y^2)(1 - x^2) = c.$
10. $4xy = x^2 + y^2 + c.$
12. $2y^3 - x = cy.$
14. $(x^2 - y^2)^2 = 4x + c.$
16. $y = x \tan(c - x).$
18. $y - x\sqrt{y} = cx.$
20. $2y = x(x^2 + y^2 + c).$
22. $x^2 y = y^3 + c.$
24. $y \cos x = x^2 + c$

Arts. 4–5. Pages 15–16

1. $y^3 = x^3(c - \ln x).$
3. $\cos(y/x) = cx.$
5. $y(\csc x + \cot x) = x + c.$
7. $y = x^2(\ln x + c).$
9. $y = \cos x + cx.$
11. $2\sqrt{x/y} = \ln y + c.$
13. $y = x \sin(c - \ln x).$
15. $x = y + 1 + ce^y.$
17. $\cot(y/x) = c - \ln x.$
19. $y + \sqrt{x^2 + y^2} = cx^2.$
21. $x^2 y = y^3 + c.$
23. $x = y \ln cy.$

2. $y = (4x + c)e^{2x}.$
4. $y = c/\sqrt{x} - 3/x.$
6. $4x^2 + y^2 = cx^3.$
8. $x^2 y = x^4 + c.$
10. $y = x \ln(\ln x + c).$
12. $x^2 y = 2\ln^2 x + c.$
14. $y = x + c \sin x.$
16. $(x - e^y)(y - 1) = c.$
18. $\ln^2(y/x) = 2\ln x + c.$
20. $2x + y = c(x - y)^4.$
22. $y \cos x = x^2 + c.$

24. (a) $2x + y - 5 = c(x - y - 1)^4$; (b) $5\ln(4x + 8y - 7) = 4x - 8y + c.$
25. $3x^2 + x^3 y = cy.$

Art. 6. Pages 18–19

1. $y = 2\sin x - x \cos x - 2x^4 + c_1 x + c_2.$
2. $y = c_2 e^{c_1 x}.$
3. $y = \ln x + c_1/x + c_2.$
4. $y = \ln \cos(x + c_1) + c_2.$
5. $(x - c_1)^2 + (y - c_2)^2 = 4.$
6. $y = x \ln^2 x + c_1 x \ln x + c_2 x - 3\ln x + c_3.$
7. $y = -\frac{1}{2}\ln(c_1 - x^2) + c_2.$
8. $y + c_1 \ln(y - c_1) = 2x + c_2.$
9. $y^3 = c_1 x + c_2.$
10. $c_1 y + \cos(x + c_2) = 1.$

11. $y = c_1 \sin kx + c_2 \cos kx$.   **12.** $\ln (1 + c_1 y) = c_1 x + c_2$.

13. $\ln (c_1 y - 1) + c_1 y = c_1{}^2 x + c_2$.

14. $y = \frac{1}{2}x^2 - c_1 \ln [(c_1 + x^2)/(c_1 - x^2)] + c_2$.

15. $y = c_1 \sec (2x + c_2)$.   **16.** $c_1(y - x) + 2 \tan^{-1} c_1 x = c_2$.

17. $y = -\frac{1}{2} \ln (x^2 + c_1) + c_2$.   **18.** $y = x^2 + 2c_1 x + 2c_1{}^2 \ln (x - c_1) + c_2$.

19. $(x - c_2)^2 + y^2 = c_1$.   **20.** $\ln \tan (c_1 y + c_2) \pm x = c_3$.

Art. 7. Pages 32–38

1. $3xy^2 + x^3 = c'$.   **2.** $x = \frac{1}{2}y + \frac{5}{4} - \frac{7}{4}e^{2y-2}$.

3. $y^4 = c'(2x^2 - y^2)$.   **4.** $\frac{1}{2} \ln (x^2 + y^2) \pm \arctan (y/x) = c'$.

6. 2.88 ft./sec., 1.05 ft.   **7.** 105 ft./sec.

8. 2.42 ft./sec.   **9.** 6.68 ft.

10. $L = v_1^2 /(2v_1 - v_2)$.

11. (a) $v = L(1 - e^{-gt/L})$ ft./sec.; (b) 0.301.

12. 2.15 sec.   **13.** 0.0748 sec.

14. 0.295 sec.   **15.** 6.49 sec.

20. 1.12 sec.   **22.** 4.71 sec.

23. 34.5 min.   **24.** (a) 1000 dynes; (b) 0.214 sec.

25. 27.5 min.   **26.** (a) 36.7 lb.; (b) 0.980 lb./gal.

27. (a) 61.3 min.; (b) 141 lb.   **28.** 118 lb.

29. 4.75 lb./gal.   **30.** 38.6 gal.

31. 150 lb.   **32.** 10.9 lb.

33. 18.3 min.   **34.** (a) 1.29×10^7 cal./hr.; (b) 63.4°.

35. 1.60 cm.   **36.** 28.3°.

37. 67,000 cal./hr.; 55,000 cal./hr.   **39.** 2 min. 28 sec.

40. (a) 0.475 amp.; (b) 0.299 amp.   **41.** 8 volts.

42. 149 volts.   **43.** (a) 43.0 volts; (b) 0.120, 2.18 sec.

44. $I = E(e^{-at} - e^{-Rt/L})/(R - aL)$ amp.; $t = L \ln (R/aL)/(R - aL)$ sec.

45. (a) 3.68 amp.; (b) 3.64 amp.   **46.** -0.0135 amp.; 0.000068 coul.

47. 95.8%.   **48.** (a) 1.55; (b) 1.60.

49. (a) 11.3 min.; (b) 13.5 min.   **50.** 25:1.

51. 29.3%.   **52.** (b) 8.00 lb./in.²

53. 17.8 mi.   **54.** 64.9 lb./ft.³

55. Max. defl. $= qL^4/384EI$ ft.   **56.** $(qL + 2P)L^3/384EI$ ft.

57. $EIy = Px(3L^2 - x^2)/6 + qx(4L^3 - x^3)/24$.

58. $0.422L$ ft.   **59.** Above.

60. $EIy = 10x^3 - 5x^4/6 - 640x/3$; 3.37 ft.

61. $EIy = 1920 - 640x/3 - 5(12 - x)^4/6$.

62. 1 ft.   **63.** $76P/3EI$ ft.

64. 20 lb.   **65.** $\frac{7}{5}$.

66. $\frac{3}{20}$.   **67.** $2wkL^5/5Eh^3$ ft.

69. (a) $6EILy = P(L - c)x(x^2 - 2cL + c^2)$; $6EILy = Pc(L - x)(c^2 - 2Lx + x^2)$;
(b) $(Pc/3EIL)[(L^2 - c^2)/3]^{3/2}$.

Arts. 8–9. Pages 46–47

1. $3x(\cos x + \sin x) - 3 \cos x - 4 \sin x - 15$.

2. $2 \sec^2 x \tan x + 2 \sec^2 x - 3 \tan x + 2(3x^2 + 2x - 2)/x^3$.

3. $2 \ln 2x + (x^3 - 5x^2 + 2x - 18)/x^4$. **4.** $4e^{-x}(\cos x - \sin x) + 8e^{2x}$.

5. $\ln \cos x - 24 \tan^4 x - 31 \tan^2 x - 2 \tan x - 7$.

6. 0. **7.** $6 + 18x + 6x^2$.

8. $-7 \cos x - 3 \sin x$. **9.** $12x + 12x^2 + 4x^3$.

10. 0. **11.** $e^x(\cos x - 4 \sin x)$.

12. 0. **13.** $-10xe^{-2x}$.

14. 0. **15.** 0.

16. $-4e^{3x} \cos 2x$. **17.** 0.

18. 0. **19.** $(a + \ln a)^r a^x$.

Art. 10. Pages 53–54

1. $y = c_1 e^{-2x} + c_2 e^{-3x}$. **2.** $y = c_1 e^{3x} + c_2 e^{-x/2}$.

3. $y = c_1 + c_2 e^x + c_3 e^{3x}$. **4.** $y = c_1 e^x + c_2 e^{-x} + c_3 e^{3x}$.

5. $y = (c_1 + c_2 x)e^{x/3}$. **6.** $y = c_1 + (c_2 + c_3 x)e^{x/2}$.

7. $y = (c_1 + c_2 x + c_3 x^2)e^{2x}$. **8.** $y = c_1 + c_2 x + (c_3 + c_4 x)e^x$.

9. $y = c_1 + c_2 \sin 3x + c_3 \cos 3x$. **10.** $y = e^{2x}(c_1 \sin x + c_2 \cos x)$.

11. $y = c_1 e^x + e^{-2x}(c_2 \sin 3x + c_3 \cos 3x)$.

12. $y = c_1 + (c_2 + c_3 x) \sin 2x + (c_4 + c_5 x) \cos 2x$.

13. $y = c_1 + c_2 x + c_3 e^{\sqrt{2}x} + c_4 e^{-\sqrt{2}x}$.

14. $y = c_1 e^{-2x} + e^x(c_2 \sin \sqrt{3}\, x + c_3 \cos \sqrt{3}\, x)$.

15. $y = c_1 + c_2 x + c_3 x^2 + c_4 e^{2x}$. **16.** $y = c_1 + c_2 x + c_3 \sin 2x + c_4 \cos 2x$.

17. $y = c_1 e^{3x} + c_2 e^{-3x} + c_3 \sin 3x + c_4 \cos 3x$.

18. $y = c_1 + c_2 x + c_3 x^2 + c_4 \sin 3x + c_5 \cos 3x$.

19. $y = c_1 + c_2 x + (c_3 + c_4 x)e^{\sqrt{2}x} + (c_5 + c_6 x)e^{-\sqrt{2}x}$.

20. $y = e^x(c_1 \sin x + c_2 \cos x) + e^{-x}(c_3 \sin x + c_4 \cos x)$.

Art. 11. Pages 67–68

1. $y = c_1 e^{2x} + c_2 e^{-2x} + e^x - x$. **2.** $y = c_1 e^{2x} + c_2 e^{3x} + 2x^2 - xe^{2x}$.

3. $y = c_1 + c_2 x + c_3 e^{-x} + x^3 - 2xe^{-x}$.

4. $y = c_1 \sin x + c_2 \cos x + x \sin x + \cos 2x$.

5. $y = e^{-x}(c_1 \sin 2x + c_2 \cos 2x + \sin x) - 2$.

6. $y = c_1 e^{2x} + c_2 e^{-2x} + c_3 \sin x + c_4 \cos x + \sin 2x + 2xe^{-2x}$.

7. $y = c_1 + c_2 x + (c_3 + c_4 x)e^x + 3x^2 e^x - x^2$.

8. $y = c_1 + c_2 \sin 2x + c_3 \cos 2x + 2x^3 - x \sin 2x$.

9. $y = c_1 e^{2x} + c_2 e^{-x/2} + x^3 e^{2x} - xe^{2x} + 6e^x$.

10. $y = c_1 e^{-x} + c_2 e^{-3x} + x \sin x - xe^{-x}$.

11. $y = c_1 + c_2 x + c_3 \sin x + c_4 \cos x + 3x^3 - 2x \cos x$.

12. $y = e^{2x}(c_1 \sin x + c_2 \cos x + x \sin x) - 1$.

13. $y = e^{4x}(2/x^2 + c_1 x + c_2)$. **14.** $y = (c_1 + c_2 x - \ln \cos x)e^{2x}$.

15. $y = c_1 \sin 3x + c_2 \cos 3x + 2 - 3x \sin 3x - \cos 3x \ln \cos 3x$.

16. $y = c_1 \sin x + c_2 \cos x + 8 \sin x \ln (\csc x + \cot x) + 3x$.

17. $y = e^{-x}[c_1 \sin 2x + c_2 \cos 2x - \cos 2x \ln (\sec 2x + \tan 2x)] + \frac{5}{8}e^x$.

18. $y = c_1 + c_2 \sin x + c_3 \cos x - \ln (\sec x + \tan x) - \sin x \ln \cos x + x \cos x$.

19. $y = c_1 + c_2 e^x + c_3 e^{-x} + 4 \ln (e^x + 1) - 4x - 2 + 2e^x \ln (e^x + 1) - 2xe^x + 2e^{-x} \ln (e^x + 1)$.

20. $y = e^x[c_1 + c_2 \sin x + c_3 \cos x - \ln (\csc x + \cot x) - x \sin x - \cos x \ln \sin x]$.

Arts. 12–13. Page 73

1. $y = c_1 x + c_2/x^2 - 2 + \frac{1}{4}x^2$.   **2.** $y = c_1/\sqrt{x} + c_2 x^2 - x - x^2 \ln x$.

3. $y = (c_1 + c_2 \ln x)x + 3x \ln^2 x + 2x^2$.

4. $y = [c_1 \sin (2 \ln x) + c_2 \cos (2 \ln x)]/x + 2 - 1/x$.

5. $y = c_1 x^2 + [c_2 \sin (\sqrt{3} \ln x) + c_3 \cos (\sqrt{3} \ln x)]/x - x + \frac{1}{2}$.

6. $y = (c_1 + c_2 \ln x)x + c_3/x + x^2 \ln x - \frac{7}{3}x^2 - 2x \ln^2 x$.

7. $y = (c_1 + c_2 \ln x + c_3 \ln^2 x + \frac{1}{5} \ln^5 x)x^2$.

8. $y = c_1(2x - 1) + c_2(2x - 1)^2 - (2x - 1) \ln (2x - 1) + \frac{1}{2}$.

9. $y = 2,\ z = \frac{1}{2}e^{2x} - 4x + c_1$.

10. $y = 2x^2 - 3c_1 e^x + 3x + c_2,\ z = c_1 e^x - 1$.

11. $y = 2e^x \sin x,\ z = \frac{1}{2}e^x(\cos x - 5 \sin x)$.

12. $y = (c_1 + c_2 x)e^{-x} + c_3 e^{2x} - \frac{1}{4}e^x,\ z = -2(c_1 + c_2 x + c_2)e^{-x} + c_3 e^{2x} - \frac{1}{2}e^x$.

13. $y = (c_1 + c_2 x)e^x + (c_3 - x)e^{-x},\ z = -c_2 e^x + (2x - 3 - 2c_3)e^{-x} + 1$.

14. $y = x^2 + c_1,\ z = -3x,\ w = 6$.

15. $y = c_1 e^x + c_2 e^{-x/2} \sin (\frac{1}{2}\sqrt{3}x + \alpha),\ z = c_1 e^x + c_2 e^{-x/2} \sin (\frac{1}{2}\sqrt{3}\,x + \alpha + \frac{2}{3}\pi),$
$w = c_1 e^x + c_2 e^{-x/2} \sin (\frac{1}{2}\sqrt{3}\,x + \alpha + \frac{4}{3}\pi)$.

16. $y = c_1 x^{22} + c_2/x^2 - 1,\ z = -\frac{5}{2}c_1 x^{22} + \frac{7}{2}c_2/x^2 + 5$.

17. $y = c_1 x + c_2/x^2 + 2,\ z = \frac{3}{5}c_2/x^2 + 4x - 1$.

18. $y = c_1 x + c_2/x^4 + \frac{2}{5}x \ln x,\ z = \frac{3}{2}c_1 x - c_2/x^4 + \frac{3}{5}x \ln x + \frac{1}{5}x$.

19. $y = c_1 x + c_2/x^2 - \frac{4}{3}x \ln x,\ z = -2c_1 x + 4c_2/x^2 + \frac{8}{3}x \ln x + \frac{8}{3}x + 5$.

20. $y = c_1 x^2 + c_2 x^{\frac{3}{5}} + \cos \ln x - \sin \ln x,\ z = c_1 x^2 + \frac{22}{15}c_2 x^{\frac{3}{5}} + 2 \cos \ln x + \sin \ln x$.

Art. 14. Pages 86–93

1. $\sqrt{2}$ ft.; $2\pi/3$ sec.

2. $2\pi\sqrt{L/g}$ sec.; $\theta = \alpha \cos (t\sqrt{g/L})$ rad.

3. $2\sqrt{g/L} \sin (\alpha/2)$ rad./sec.   **4.** 11.3 ft./sec.

5. 2.01 ft./sec.   **6.** 0.561 sec.; $x = 0.244 \cos 11.2t$ ft.

7. 66.5 lb.   **8.** (a) 42.2 min.; (b) 14.1 min.

9. $x = \frac{1}{4}e^{-2\sqrt{g}\,t}(\sqrt{2} \sin \sqrt{2g}\,t + \cos \sqrt{2g}\,t)$ ft.

10. 3.98 lb./ft.   **11.** $a = 0.0351,\ b = 5.03$.

12. 1.81, 14.5 lb.   **13.** 0.198 sec.

14. 0.00294.   **15.** $(D^2 + 9.37D + 39.5)x = 0$.

16. -9.82 ft./sec.^{2} **17.** (a) -9.16 ft./sec.; (b) -8 ft./sec.

18. Yes: $K = 29.8$ lb. sec./ft.   **19.** 49.1′.

20. 80.4%.   **21.** 1.28 ft.

22. (a) $x = \frac{3}{2}e^{-2t} - e^{-3t}$ ft.; (b) 0.437 ft.

23. (a) 0.549 sec.; (b) 2.16 ft.   **24.** 3 sec.; -0.893 ft.

25. (a) $(Ce^{-at} \sin \omega t)/(b^2 - a^2 - \omega^2)$; (b) $-(Cte^{-at} \cos \omega t)/2\omega$.

26. (a) -1.93 ft.; (b) -3.14 ft.   **27.** -0.364 ft.

28. 0.462 ft. above.   **29.** $\frac{1}{4}$ lb.

30. (a) 0.952 ft.; (b) 1.025 ft.

31. (a) $4\sqrt{g}$ lb. sec./ft.; (b) $x = (\frac{1}{2} + \sqrt{g}\,t)e^{-2\sqrt{g}\,t} - \frac{1}{2} \cos 2\sqrt{g}\,t$ ft.

32. 0.705 ft./sec.   **33.** 0.875 ft.

36. (a) 0.0000460 coul., 0.0841 amp.; (b) 0.00000783 coul., 0.0225 amp.;
(c) 0.0000151 coul., 0.0421 amp.

37. 0.0168 amp.

38. $I_c = -0.0410$, $I_P = 0.0701$ amp.

39. 0.691.

40. 0.00972 amp.

41. $Q = E_0[(R\omega_1 \cos \omega_1 t + (\omega X + aR) \sin \omega_1 t)e^{-at} - X\omega_1 \sin \omega t - R\omega_1 \cos \omega t]/$
$\omega\omega_1 Z^2$ coul.; $\omega = \sqrt{4LC - 2R^2C^2}/2LC$ rad./sec. for resonance.

42. $Q = E_0[(R + (\omega X + aR)t)e^{-at} - X \sin \omega t - R \cos \omega t]/\omega Z^2$ coul.

43. $Q = E_0[(\omega X + aR + \omega_2 R)e^{-(a-\omega_2)t}/2\omega_2 - (\omega X + aR - \omega_2 R)e^{-(a+\omega_2)t}/2\omega_2 -$
$X \sin \omega t - R \cos \omega t]/\omega Z^2$ coul.

44. (b) $I_1 = 1.67$ amp., $I_2 = 0.505$ amp.

45. L_1 must be decreased by $1/C\omega^2$ henries.

46. $\Delta I_{1P} = E_0\omega C_1(1 - L_2 C_2 \omega^2) \cos \omega t$, $\Delta I_{2P} = E_0 M C_1 C_2 \omega^3 \cos \omega t$;
$\Delta = (L_1 L_2 - M^2)C_1 C_2 \omega^4 - (L_1 C_1 + L_2 C_2)\omega^2 + 1$.

47. 38.5 lb.

48. 9.05 ft.

49. $(v_0^2 \sin^2 \alpha)/2g$ ft.; $(v_0^2 \sin 2\alpha)/g$ ft.

50. $x = wv_0(1 - e^{-Kgt/w})(\cos \alpha)/Kg$, $y = -wt/K +$
$w(Kv_0 \sin \alpha + w)(1 - e^{-Kgt/w})/K^2g$;
$(wv_0 \sin \alpha)/Kg - (w^2/K^2g) \ln [(Kv_0 \sin \alpha + w)/w]$ ft.

51. $x = \frac{3}{8}[\sqrt{2} + (2 - \sqrt{2}) \cos 5\sqrt{2g} t]$ ft.

54. $x = \frac{1}{2}x_0(e^{\omega t} + e^{-\omega t}) + (v_0/2\omega - g/4\omega^2)(e^{\omega t} - e^{-\omega t}) + (g/2\omega^2) \sin \omega t$; S.H.M.
for $x_0 = 0$, $v_0 = g/2\omega$.

55. (a) $u = k/h^2 + (1/r_0 - k/h^2) \cos \theta$; (b) $u = (e^{\sqrt{k-h^2}\theta/h} + e^{-\sqrt{k-h^2}\theta/h})/2r_0$
$(k > h^2)$; $u = 1/r_0$ $(k = h^2)$; $u = (1/r_0) \cos (\sqrt{h^2 - k} \,\theta/h)$ $(k < h^2)$.

56. (b) $u \ln (r_1/r_2) = u_1 \ln (r/r_2) + u_2 \ln (r_1/r)$; (c) 94.6°.

57. (b) $u = (r_2 u_2 - r_1 u_1)/(r_2 - r_1) + r_1 r_2(u_1 - u_2)/(r_2 - r_1)r$; (c) 94.3°.

58. 1.40, 1.07.

59. $\Delta x_{1P} = [(k_1 + k_2)g^2 - w_2\omega^2 g]A \sin \omega t$, $\Delta x_{2P} = k_1 g^2 A \sin \omega t$; $\Delta = w_1 w_2 \omega^4 -$
$(k_1 w_1 + k_2 w_1 + k_1 w_2)g\omega^2 + k_1 k_2 g^2$; two values.

60. 0.910 ft.

61. (b) (i) $x = 2 \cos 2t$, $y = -2 \sin 2t$; (ii) $x = \sin 8t$, $y = \cos 8t$.

63. (b) 0.365 in.

Arts. 15–17. Pages 99–100

2. 0; 1; 0; 0; 0; 0; 1; ln 2.

4. $1/\sqrt{x^2 + 1}$; $\pm 1/\sqrt{x^2 - 1}$; $1/(1 - x^2)$; $\pm 1/x\sqrt{1 - x^2}$; $\pm 1/x\sqrt{x^2 + 1}$,
$x \lessgtr 0$; $1/(1 - x^2)$.

7. 0.498.

8. (1, 1.22), (−1, −1.45).

9. 1.

Arts. 18–22. Pages 106–107

1. (a) 24.5 ft./sec.; (b) 14.0 ft.; (c) 4.63 ft.; (d) 6.91 sec.

2. 2.73 sec.

3. 53.7 ft./sec.; 1.80 sec.

4. 4.69 sec.; 138 ft./sec.

5. 7.99 ft./sec.; 6.61 ft.

6. 0.645 ft.

8. 6.52 ft./sec.

9. 0.185 sec.

10. 0.0834 ft.; 2.01 ft./sec.

11. 3.31 ft.; 1.06 ft./sec.

12. (b) 0.843.

13. (a) 13.2 in., 21.2 in.; (b) 6.65 in., 13.8 in.

14. $\frac{1}{2}a\sqrt{3}$.

15. 0.95 in.

16. 0.71 in.

17. $wEI(1 + \theta^2/2 - \text{sech } \theta - \theta \tanh \theta)/P^2 + QL(\theta - \tanh \theta)/P\theta$, $\theta = L\sqrt{P/EI}$.

Arts. 23–27.   Pages 122–124

1. (a) 11.8 ft.; (b) 37.6 ft.; (c) 25.3 lb., 40.3 lb.

2. 18.8 ft.

3. 85.5 ft.

6. (a) 0.293 cm.; (b) 0.143 cm.

8. ($\pm 0.552L$, $0.464y_0$).

9. (a) 389 rad./sec., 882 rad./ sec.; (b) $0.707y_0$, $0.544y_0$.

10. (a) 101 volts, 0.00151 amp.; (b) 151 volts, 0.101 amp.

11. 0.577 amp.

12. (a) 649 volts, 0.586 amp.; (b) 88 mi.; (c) 566 mi.

13. 161×10^{-6} cm.^{3}/sec.

14. -5.82 ft./sec.; 1.38 ft. from O.

15. 1.14 sec.$^{-1}$

17. $x = 2(\cosh t + \cos t)$, $y = 2(\cosh t - \cos t)$; (4.17, 2.01).

18. (a) $x = -\cos t \cosh t$, $y = \sin t \sinh t$; (b) (3.83, 3.70).

19. (a) $y = y_0[\cos \alpha x \cosh \alpha x + (\sin \alpha L \cos \alpha L + \sinh \alpha L \cosh \alpha L)(\sin \alpha x \cosh \alpha x - \cos \alpha x \sinh \alpha x)/(\cos^2 \alpha L + \cosh^2 \alpha L) + (\cos^2 \alpha L - \cosh^2 \alpha L)(\sin \alpha x \sinh \alpha x)/(\cos^2 \alpha L + \cosh^2 \alpha L)]$, $\alpha^4 = k/4EI$, $P = 8EI\alpha^3 y_0(\sin \alpha L \cos \alpha L + \sinh \alpha L \cosh \alpha L)/(\cos^2 \alpha L + \cosh^2 \alpha L)$;
(b) $k = 8.80$ lb./in.^{2}, $y_L = 0.434$ in.

Arts. 28–30.   Pages 135–138

1. $\pi/2$, no max.; 1, $\pi/2$.

3. $[F(k, \phi) - E(k, \phi)]/k^2$; $(K - E)/k^2$.

4. 1.02.

7. 2.62.

8. 0.623.

9. 0.398.

12. (a) 1.41; (b) 1.19.

13. 1.004.

14. (a) 3.82; (b) (2.68, 0.442), (3.60, -0.442).

15. 0.553.

16. 1.58 sec.; 4.54% decrease.

17. 0.134 sec.

18. (a) 93°; (b) 0.168 sec.

19. 0.462 sec.

20. 1.12.

21. 1.08 ft.

22. $2\sqrt{2}\, F[\frac{1}{2}\sqrt{2}$, $\sin^{-1}(\sqrt{2} \sin c)]$; 5.24.

23. 3.10.

24. (b) 0.462 sec.

25. 0.329 sec.

26. (a) 5.24; (b) 0.584.

27. (a) $2E(\sqrt{n^2 - 1}/n)$; (b) 9.69, 6.68.

28. (a) $2.935a^2$; (b) $0.413a^2$.

Arts. 31–35.   Pages 154–155

1. 49° 27'; 36°.

2. (a) 0.31 cm.; (b) 0.40 cm.; (c) 0.30 cm.

3. (a) 130° 42'; (b) $0.392L$ in.

4. $0.258L$ in.

5. (a) 0.48 lb.; (b) 3.9 in.

6. 1.6 lb.

7. (a) 4.35 in.; (b) 2.40 in.; (c) 2.01 in.; (d) 1.18 in.

8. 3.91 in.

9. 0.164 lb., 7.63 in.

10. (a) 1.01 ft., 0.75 ft.; (b) 264 pdl., 4.69 ft.

11. 0.764.

12. 0.810.

13. 4.02.

14. 0.985.

15. 0.74 sec.

Arts. 36–40.   Pages 178–179

1. (a) $x - x^3/2! + \cdots + (-1)^{n-1}x^{2n-1}/(2n-2)! + \cdots,\ |x| < \infty$;
(b) $x^2 - x^6/3! + \cdots + (-1)^{n-1}x^{4n-2}/(2n-1)! + \cdots,\ |x| < \infty$; (c) $1 + x$
$-\cdots + (\sqrt{2})^n \cos(n\pi/4)x^n/n! + \cdots,\ |x| < \infty$; (d) $1 + x + x^2/2 + x^3/3$
$+ 5x^4/24 + \cdots,\ |x| < \infty$; (e) $x + x^3/3 + \cdots + x^{2n-1}/(2n-1) + \cdots$,
$|x| < 1$; (f) $1 + x^2/2 + x^3/2 + x^4/3 + \cdots,\ |x| < \infty$.

2. (a) 0.7468; (b) 0.6205; (c) $x - x^2/2^2 + x^3/3^2 - x^4/4^2 + \cdots$; (d) 0.2838;
(e) 0.3103; (f) 0.2126.

3. (a) $y + y^3/6 + 3y^5/40 + \cdots$; (b) $y + y^2/4 + y^3/72 + y^4/576 + \cdots$.

4. 0.659. **5.** (1.45, 0.339).

6. 1.06. **7.** 2.78.

8. 0.241. **9.** 0.105 ft./sec.

10. 0.216. **11.** 1.468.

12. 0.5417. **13.** 0.503 sec.

14. 7.62×10^{-15} erg/cm.^{3} deg.^{4} **16.** (a) 2.17 in., 12.6 in.; (b) 0.990 in.

17. (b) 3.75.

Arts. 41–42.   Pages 185–187

1. $y_4 = 1 + x + x^2 + x^3/3 + x^4/12 + x^5/120;\ y = 2e^x - 1 - x$.

2. 1.78. **3.** 8.76 ft./sec.

4. 12.4 lb. **7.** $y = c_1 \cosh \sqrt{x} + c_2 \sinh \sqrt{x}$.

8. $y = c_1(1 + x) + c_2\sqrt{x}$. **9.** $y = c_1/(1 - x) + c_2/x$.

10. $y = c_1 e^x + c_2 \sqrt{x}$. **12.** 1.53 sec.

13. 1.97 sec. **14.** (a) 0.311 in.; (b) 0.290 in.

Arts. 43–45.   Page 196

1. $\dfrac{\pi}{4} - \dfrac{2}{\pi}\left(\cos x + \dfrac{1}{3^2}\cos 3x + \dfrac{1}{5^2}\cos 5x + \cdots\right) + \sin x - \tfrac{1}{2}\sin 2x + \tfrac{1}{3}\sin 3x$
$-\cdots$.

2. $-\pi^2 - 8\left(\cos x + \dfrac{1}{3^2}\cos 3x + \dfrac{1}{5^2}\cos 5x + \cdots\right) + \dfrac{2}{\pi}\left[\left(\dfrac{3\pi^2}{1} - \dfrac{4}{1^3}\right)\sin x +\right.$
$\left. \dfrac{\pi^2}{2}\sin 2x + \left(\dfrac{3\pi^2}{3} - \dfrac{4}{3^3}\right)\sin 3x + \dfrac{\pi^2}{4}\sin 4x + \cdots\right]$.

3. $\dfrac{\sinh \pi}{\pi}\left[1 + 2\sum_{n=1}^{\infty}\dfrac{(-1)^n}{n^2+1}(\cos nx - n \sin nx)\right]$.

4. $-1 + \pi \sin x - \tfrac{1}{2}\cos x + 2\sum_{n=2}^{\infty}\dfrac{\cos nx}{n^2-1}$.

5. $\dfrac{2\sqrt{2}}{\pi}\left[1 - 2\sum_{n=1}^{\infty}\dfrac{\cos nx}{4n^2-1}\right]$. **6.** $\dfrac{\sin a\pi}{a\pi}\left[1 + 2a^2\sum_{n=1}^{\infty}\dfrac{(-1)^n \cos nx}{a^2-n^2}\right]$.

7. $\dfrac{2}{\pi}\left[1 - 2\sum_{n=1}^{\infty}\dfrac{\cos 2nx}{4n^2-1}\right]$. **8.** $\dfrac{1}{\pi} + \tfrac{1}{2}\sin x - \dfrac{2}{\pi}\sum_{n=1}^{\infty}\dfrac{\cos 2nx}{4n^2-1}$.

9. $\dfrac{\pi^2}{3} + 4\sum_{n=1}^{\infty}\dfrac{(-1)^n}{n^2}\cos nx$. **10.** $2\sum_{n=2}^{\infty}\dfrac{(-1)^n}{n^2+1}$.

Arts. 46–48. Page 204

1. $\dfrac{2}{\pi}\left[\left(\dfrac{\pi^2}{1}-\dfrac{4}{1^3}\right)\sin x-\dfrac{\pi^2}{2}\sin 2x+\left(\dfrac{\pi^2}{3}-\dfrac{4}{3^3}\right)\sin 3x-\dfrac{\pi^2}{4}\sin 4x+\cdots\right];$

$\dfrac{\pi^2}{3}-4\left(\cos x-\dfrac{1}{2^2}\cos 2x+\dfrac{1}{3^2}\cos 3x-\dfrac{1}{4^2}\cos 4x+\cdots\right).$

2. $\dfrac{2}{\pi}\displaystyle\sum_{n=1}^{\infty}\dfrac{n[1-(-1)^n e^\pi]}{n^2+1}\sin nx;\ \dfrac{e^\pi-1}{\pi}-\dfrac{2}{\pi}\sum_{n=1}^{\infty}\dfrac{1-(-1)^n e^\pi}{n^2+1}\cos nx.$

3. $\dfrac{4}{\pi}\displaystyle\sum_{n=1}^{\infty}\dfrac{(-1)^{n+1}}{(2n-1)^2}\sin(2n-1)x;\ \dfrac{\pi}{4}-\dfrac{2}{\pi}\sum_{n=1}^{\infty}\dfrac{\cos 2(2n-1)x}{(2n-1)^2}.$

4. $\left(\dfrac{4}{\pi}+\dfrac{8}{\pi^2}\right)\sin\dfrac{\pi x}{2}-\dfrac{2}{\pi}\sin\dfrac{2\pi x}{2}+\left(\dfrac{4}{3\pi}+\dfrac{8}{3^2\pi^2}\right)\sin\dfrac{3\pi x}{2}-\dfrac{2}{2\pi}\sin\dfrac{4\pi x}{2}+\cdots.$

5. $-\dfrac{2}{\pi}\displaystyle\sum_{n=1}^{\infty}\dfrac{\sin 2n\pi x}{n};\ -\dfrac{8}{\pi^2}\sum_{n=1}^{\infty}\dfrac{\cos(2n-1)\pi x}{(2n-1)^2}.$

6. $1+(2\pi\sin 1)\displaystyle\sum_{n=1}^{\infty}\dfrac{(-1)^{n+1}n\sin n\pi x}{n^2\pi^2-1};\ \csc 1=2\pi\sqrt{2}\sum_{n=1}^{\infty}\dfrac{(-1)^{n+1}n\sin(n\pi^2/4)}{n^2\pi^2-1}.$

7. $\dfrac{3}{2}-\dfrac{4}{\pi^2}\displaystyle\sum_{n=1}^{\infty}\dfrac{1}{(2n-1)^2}\cos\dfrac{(2n-1)\pi x}{2}-\dfrac{2}{\pi}\sum_{n=1}^{\infty}\dfrac{1}{n}\sin\dfrac{n\pi x}{2}.$

8. $\dfrac{8}{\pi^2}\displaystyle\sum_{n=1}^{\infty}\dfrac{\cos\frac12(2n-1)\pi x}{(2n-1)^2}.$

9. $-\dfrac{32}{\pi^3}\left(\sin\dfrac{\pi x}{2}+\dfrac{\pi^2}{8}\sin\dfrac{2\pi x}{2}+\dfrac{1}{3^3}\sin\dfrac{3\pi x}{2}+\dfrac{\pi^2}{16}\sin\dfrac{4\pi x}{2}+\cdots\right);$

$\pi^2=32\left(1-\dfrac{1}{3^3}+\dfrac{1}{5^3}-\dfrac{1}{7^3}+\cdots\right).$

10. $-\dfrac{2}{3}-\dfrac{16}{\pi^2}\displaystyle\sum_{n=1}^{\infty}\dfrac{(-1)^{n+1}\cos(n\pi x/2)}{n^2}.$

11. $-\dfrac{64}{\pi^3}\displaystyle\sum_{n=1}^{\infty}\dfrac{\sin\frac12(2n-1)\pi x}{(2n-1)^3}.$ **12.** $-\dfrac{4}{3}+\dfrac{8}{\pi^2}\displaystyle\sum_{n=1}^{\infty}\dfrac{\cos n\pi x}{n^2}.$

13. $\dfrac{2}{\pi^3}\left[\left(\dfrac{\pi^2}{1}-\dfrac{4}{1^3}\right)\sin \pi x+\dfrac{\pi^2}{2}\sin 2\pi x+\left(\dfrac{\pi^2}{3}-\dfrac{4}{3^3}\right)\sin 3\pi x+\dfrac{\pi^2}{4}\sin 4\pi x-\cdots\right].$

14. $\dfrac{1}{3}+\dfrac{4}{\pi^2}\displaystyle\sum_{n=1}^{\infty}\dfrac{\cos n\pi x}{n^2};\ \pi^2=6\left(1+\dfrac{1}{2^2}+\dfrac{1}{3^2}+\cdots\right).$

Arts. 49–51. Page 213

5. $1.30+0.92\cos x-0.42\cos 2x+0.18\cos 3x+1.10\sin x-0.68\sin 2x-$
$0.21\sin 3x.$

Art. 52. Page 217

3. $\dfrac{2\sqrt{2}\,L^4w}{\pi^5 EI}\left(1+\dfrac{1}{3^5}-\dfrac{1}{5^5}-\dfrac{1}{7^5}+\cdots\right).$

4. 1.02 in. **5.** 0.279 in., 0.283 in., 0.280 in.; 4.5 ft.

Arts. 53–56.   Pages 224–227

2. (a) 0.893; (b) 0.451; (c) 1.31; (d) 0.222.

4. 2.85.

5. 5.24.

6. 3.01.

7. 0.431.

8. 3.50.

9. 8.13.

10. (a) $2\Gamma(1 + 1/2n)\Gamma(1/2m)/m\Gamma(1 + 1/2m + 1/2n)$; (b) 1.18.

11. 0.275.

13. $\sqrt{\pi}\,\Gamma(1/n)/n\Gamma(\frac{1}{2} + 1/n)$; 1.31.

14. $\sqrt{\pi}\,a^{\frac{1}{2}n+1}\Gamma(1/n)/2n\Gamma(\frac{3}{2} + 1/n)$; 78.5.

16. 6.01; (2.89, 1.13).

17. 0.356; 0.340.

18. 0.421.

23. 4.38.

24. 1.05.

25. 0.607.

26. 2.22 sec.; 1.69 sec.

27. 37.9 min.

28. 0.327 sec.

29. 0.457 sec.

30. 5.43 sec.

31. (a) 0.736 sec.; (b) 0.126 sec.

32. $\sqrt{\pi/(2n-2)}\,\Gamma[(n+1)/(2n-2)]/\Gamma[n/(n-1)]$; 1.11 sec.

33. $\sqrt{\pi/(2n+2)}\,\Gamma[1/(n+1)]/\Gamma[(n+3)/(2n+2)]$; 1.57 sec.

34. $\Gamma(a)\Gamma(b)\Gamma(c)/\Gamma(a+b+c+1)$.

35. $\frac{1}{6}$; $(\frac{1}{4}, \frac{1}{4}, \frac{1}{4})$; $\frac{1}{30}$.

Arts. 57–64.   Pages 245–247

1. 0.2239; 0.4401; 0.9903.

6. 0.3367.

10. $\sqrt{2/\pi x}[(3 - x^2)\sin x - 3x\cos x]/x^2$; 0.1374.

14. $c_1 = \sqrt{2/\pi}$, $c_2 = 0$.

15. 0.390.

16. 0.545.

20. $x^3\,d^4y/dx^4 + 2x^2\,d^3y/dx^3 - x\,d^2y/dx^2 + dy/dx + x^3y = 0$.

26. 0.36 in.; 1° 28′.

27. 1.86.

Art. 65.   Pages 256–257

5. $x^5 = \frac{8}{63}P_5(x) + \frac{4}{9}P_3(x) + \frac{3}{7}P_1(x)$.

Arts. 66–67.   Pages 266–268

1. 0.693.

2. 1.64.

3. 0.785.

4. 0.458.

5. −0.218.

8. 0.216.

10. (b) $A = \int_1^2 (\sin y\,dy)/y^2$.

11. 0.690.

12. $\mu = 1/h\sqrt{2}$.

14. $\frac{1}{4}$.

16. 2.83.

17. (a) $\sqrt{2}$; (b) 0.208 sec.

Arts. 68–70.   Pages 279–280

1. $y = \dfrac{y_0}{4}\left(3\sin\dfrac{\pi x}{L}\cos\dfrac{a\pi t}{L} - \sin\dfrac{3\pi x}{L}\cos\dfrac{3a\pi t}{L}\right)$.

2. (a) $\dfrac{v_0 L}{12a\pi}\left(9\sin\dfrac{\pi x}{L}\sin\dfrac{a\pi t}{L} - \sin\dfrac{3\pi x}{L}\sin\dfrac{3a\pi t}{L}\right)$; (b) 0.081 in.

3. (a) $\dfrac{24L^3}{\pi^4 a} \displaystyle\sum_{n=1}^{\infty} \dfrac{1}{(2n-1)^4} \sin \dfrac{(2n-1)\pi x}{L} \sin \dfrac{(2n-1)a\pi t}{L}$; (b) 0.314 in

4. $\dfrac{3L^3}{25\pi^3} \displaystyle\sum_{n=1}^{\infty} \dfrac{(-1)^{n+1}}{n^3} \sin \dfrac{n\pi x}{L} \cos \dfrac{na\pi t}{L}$. **5.** 0.235 in.

6. $\dfrac{18m}{a\pi^3} \displaystyle\sum_{n=1}^{\infty} \dfrac{1}{n^3} \left(\sin \dfrac{n\pi}{3} + \sin \dfrac{2n\pi}{3} \right) \sin \dfrac{n\pi x}{3} \cos \dfrac{na\pi t}{3}$.

10. $\dfrac{8SL}{\pi^2 E} \displaystyle\sum_{n=1}^{\infty} \dfrac{(-1)^n}{(2n-1)^2} \sin \dfrac{(2n-1)\pi x}{2L} \cos \dfrac{(2n-1)a\pi t}{2L}$.

12. $-\dfrac{16gL^2}{a^2\pi^3} \displaystyle\sum_{n=1}^{\infty} \dfrac{1}{(2n-1)^3} \sin \dfrac{(2n-1)\pi x}{2L} \cos \dfrac{(2n-1)a\pi t}{2L}$.

Art. 71.   Pages 284–286

1. (a) $\dfrac{200}{\pi} \displaystyle\sum_{n=1}^{\infty} \dfrac{(-1)^{n+1}}{n} \sin \dfrac{n\pi x}{L} \cdot e^{-n^2\pi^2\alpha^2 t/L^2}$; (b) 4.76°.

2. (a) $x + \dfrac{80}{\pi} \displaystyle\sum_{n=1}^{\infty} \dfrac{(-1)^{n+1}}{n} \sin \dfrac{n\pi x}{40} \cdot e^{-n^2\pi^2\alpha^2 t/1600}$; (b) 12.7°.

3. (a) $50 + \dfrac{100x}{L} - \dfrac{200}{\pi} \displaystyle\sum_{n=1}^{\infty} \dfrac{1}{2n-1} \sin \dfrac{(2n-1)\pi x}{L} \cdot e^{-(2n-1)^2\pi^2\alpha^2 t/L^2}$; (b) 65.7°.

4. (a) $25 + \dfrac{50x}{L} - \dfrac{50}{\pi} \displaystyle\sum_{n=1}^{\infty} \dfrac{1}{n} \sin \dfrac{2n\pi x}{L} \cdot e^{-4n^2\pi^2\alpha^2 t/L^2}$; (b) 28.9°.

5. $\dfrac{8000}{\pi^5} \displaystyle\sum_{n=1}^{\infty} \dfrac{12 - (2n-1)^2\pi^2}{(2n-1)^5} \sin \dfrac{(2n-1)\pi x}{10} \cdot e^{-(2n-1)^2\pi^2\alpha^2 t/100}$.

6. 7.52°. **7.** 32.3°.

8. 88.7°. **9.** 7.73 min.

10. $Ax + \dfrac{8AL}{\pi^2} \displaystyle\sum_{n=1}^{\infty} \dfrac{(-1)^n}{(2n-1)^2} \sin \dfrac{(2n-1)\pi x}{2L} \cdot e^{-(2n-1)^2\pi^2\alpha^2 t/4L^2}$.

15. $2\pi\alpha^2 u_0 e^{-Bt} \displaystyle\sum_{n=1}^{\infty} \dfrac{(-1)^n n}{BL^2 + n^2\pi^2\alpha^2} \sin \dfrac{n\pi x}{L} \cdot e^{-n^2\pi^2\alpha^2 t/L^2}$.

18. $\dfrac{8ca^2}{\pi^3 r} \displaystyle\sum_{n=1}^{\infty} \dfrac{1}{(2n-1)^3} \sin \dfrac{(2n-1)\pi r}{a} \cdot e^{-(2n-1)^2\pi^2\alpha^2 t/a^2}$.

19. $A + \dfrac{2aA}{\pi r} \displaystyle\sum_{n=1}^{\infty} \dfrac{(-1)^n}{n} \sin \dfrac{n\pi r}{a} \cdot e^{-n^2\pi^2\alpha^2 t/a^2}$.

Art. 72.   Pages 292–293

1. $0.278u_0$.

2. $\dfrac{200}{\pi} \displaystyle\sum_{n=1}^{\infty} \dfrac{(-1)^{n+1}}{(2n-1)^2} \left(\dfrac{r}{10} \right)^{2n-1} \sin (2n-1)\theta$.

3. 31.5°. **4.** $100 \sin (\pi x/8) \cdot e^{-\pi y/8}$.

5. (a) $\dfrac{40}{\pi} \displaystyle\sum_{n=1}^{\infty} \dfrac{1}{2n-1} \sin \dfrac{(2n-1)\pi x}{10} \cdot e^{-(2n-1)\pi y/10}$; (b) 8.1 cm., 2.8 cm.

7. $\dfrac{512}{\pi^3} \displaystyle\sum_{n=1}^{\infty} \dfrac{1}{(2n-1)^3} \sin \dfrac{(2n-1)\pi x}{8} \cdot e^{-(2n-1)\pi y/8}$.

8. $\dfrac{12000}{\pi^3} \displaystyle\sum_{n=1}^{\infty} \dfrac{(-1)^{n+1}}{n^3} \sin \dfrac{n\pi x}{10} \cdot e^{-n\pi y/10}$.

9. $\dfrac{800}{\pi^2} \displaystyle\sum_{n=1}^{\infty} \dfrac{(-1)^{n+1}}{(2n-1)^2} \sin \dfrac{(2n-1)\pi x}{10} \cdot e^{-(2n-1)\pi y/10}$.

10. $25.0°$, $6.79°$.

11. $\dfrac{4a}{\pi^2} \displaystyle\sum_{n=1}^{\infty} \dfrac{(-1)^{n+1}}{(2n-1)^2 \sinh (2n-1)\pi} \sin \dfrac{(2n-1)\pi x}{a} \sinh \dfrac{(2n-1)\pi y}{a}$.

12. $\dfrac{3200}{\pi^3} \displaystyle\sum_{n=1}^{\infty} \dfrac{1}{(2n-1)^3 \sinh \frac{1}{2}(2n-1)\pi} \sin \dfrac{(2n-1)\pi x}{20} \sinh \dfrac{(2n-1)\pi y}{20}$.

13. $\dfrac{400}{\pi^3} \displaystyle\sum_{n=1}^{\infty} \dfrac{(-1)^{n+1}(2n-1)\pi - 2}{(2n-1)^3 \sinh (4n-2)\pi} \sinh \dfrac{(2n-1)\pi x}{10} \sin \dfrac{(2n-1)\pi y}{10}$.

Arts. 73–74.   Pages 304–305

3. $p = p_0 - 9\rho(x^2 + y^2)^2/2g$.   **4.** $p = p_0 - \rho/2g(x^2 + y^2)$.

5. $1200 - 1.2x - \dfrac{2200}{\pi} \displaystyle\sum_{n=1}^{\infty} \dfrac{(-1)^n}{n} \sin \dfrac{n\pi x}{1000} \cdot \epsilon^{-n^2\pi^2 t/10^6 rC}$.

6. $\dfrac{1.2}{r} + \dfrac{2.2}{r} \displaystyle\sum_{n=1}^{\infty} (-1)^n \cos \dfrac{n\pi x}{1000} \cdot \epsilon^{-n^2\pi^2 t/10^6 rC}$.

7. 0.007 amp., 0.144 amp.   **8.** 5.3%, 61.7%, 87.1%.

9. $2.72 \displaystyle\sum_{n=1}^{\infty} \dfrac{1 - \epsilon^{-1} \cos n\pi}{1 + n^2\pi^2} \cos \dfrac{n\pi x}{100} \cdot \epsilon^{-100t}(\cos 100n\pi t - n\pi \sin 100n\pi t) +$
$0.859\epsilon^{-100t}$.

Arts. 75–76.   Pages 320–321

1. (a) -4.9, -14, 27 lines/cm.^{2}; (b) 8.1 watts.
4. 0.125, 0.095, 0.075, 0.061 lb./ft.^{3} **5.** 0.159, 0.144, 0.133, 0.125 lb./ft.^{3}

Art. 77.   Page 324

5. $8a^2h \displaystyle\sum_{n=1}^{\infty} \dfrac{J_0(\alpha_n r/a)}{\alpha_n^3 J_1(\alpha_n)} \cos \dfrac{c\alpha_n t}{a}$.

Art. 78.   Pages 328–329

1. $50[1 + (r/a) \cos \theta]$.

2. $u_0 \left[\dfrac{1}{2} + \dfrac{3}{4} \left(\dfrac{r}{a}\right) \cos \theta - \dfrac{7}{32} \left(\dfrac{r}{a}\right)^3 (5 \cos^3 \theta - 3 \cos \theta) + \right.$
$\left. \dfrac{11}{256} \left(\dfrac{r}{a}\right)^5 (63 \cos^5 \theta - 70 \cos^3 \theta + 15 \cos \theta) + \cdots \right]$.

3. $\frac{200}{3}[1 - (r/a)^2 P_2(\cos \theta)]$.

5. $u_0 \left[\dfrac{3}{2}\left(\dfrac{r}{a}\right) P_1(\cos\theta) - \dfrac{7}{8}\left(\dfrac{r}{a}\right)^3 P_3(\cos\theta) + \dfrac{11}{16}\left(\dfrac{r}{a}\right)^5 P_5(\cos\theta) - \cdots \right].$

6. $u_0 \left[1 - r^2 P_2(\cos\theta) + \dfrac{r^4}{2!} P_4(\cos\theta) - \dfrac{r^6}{3!} P_6(\cos\theta) + \cdots \right].$

8. $\frac{1}{5}u_0[3xe^{-2kt} + (5x^3 - 3x)e^{-12kt}].$

Arts. 83–86. Pages 369–371

7. $\displaystyle\iiint_V \left[u\left(\dfrac{\partial^2 w}{\partial x^2} + \dfrac{\partial^2 w}{\partial y^2} + \dfrac{\partial^2 w}{\partial z^2}\right) + \dfrac{\partial u}{\partial x}\dfrac{\partial w}{\partial x} + \dfrac{\partial u}{\partial y}\dfrac{\partial w}{\partial y} + \dfrac{\partial u}{\partial z}\dfrac{\partial w}{\partial z} \right] dV =$

$\displaystyle\iint_S u\left(\dfrac{\partial w}{\partial x}\cos\alpha + \dfrac{\partial w}{\partial y}\cos\beta + \dfrac{\partial w}{\partial z}\cos\gamma \right) dS;$

$\displaystyle\iiint_V \left[u\left(\dfrac{\partial^2 w}{\partial x^2} + \dfrac{\partial^2 w}{\partial y^2} + \dfrac{\partial^2 w}{\partial z^2}\right) - w\left(\dfrac{\partial^2 u}{\partial x^2} + \dfrac{\partial^2 u}{\partial y^2} + \dfrac{\partial^2 u}{\partial z^2}\right) \right] dV =$

$\displaystyle\iint_S \left[\left(u\dfrac{\partial w}{\partial x} - w\dfrac{\partial u}{\partial x} \right)\cos\alpha + \left(u\dfrac{\partial w}{\partial y} - w\dfrac{\partial u}{\partial y} \right)\cos\beta + \right.$

$\left. \left(u\dfrac{\partial w}{\partial z} - w\dfrac{\partial u}{\partial z} \right)\cos\gamma \right] dS.$

8. $\rho\dfrac{\partial^2 \mathbf{v}}{\partial t^2} = (a+b)\nabla u + b\nabla^2\mathbf{v}.$

Arts. 87–89. Pages 386–387

2. Points where $y = \sigma$.

5. 57.

7. 32.18, 0.04.

4. (a) 0.021; (b) 0.942.

6. 1.743, 0.005.

8. 2.1 in., 39.8 in.

9. (a) 83.288, 0.021; (b) 0.014; (c) 3, 4; (d) 0.774.

10. $97°\,36'\,39.45''$; $2.05''$, $1.38''$.

Art. 90. Pages 391–394

1. 24.4 mm.^{3}

2. $p = 2.28 + 0.1879w$ lb.; 30 lb.; -0.01, 0.32.

3. $y = 54.9 + 0.500x$ gr.; -0.7, 4.83.

4. $y = 0.0476 + 0.00407P$ in.

5. $R = 6.7 + 0.0092V^2$ lb./ton.

6. $b/a = 1.063 - 0.0505r$.

7. $M = 0.3793 + 0.675r$; 0.0006.

8. $Q = 101 - 51e^{-t/50}$ lb.

10. 24.7 ft.

11. $x = -1.172$, $y = 1.039$.

12. 1.960 ohms.

13. $x = 7.1$, $y = 3.9$, $z = 2.3$ gr.

14. $e = (3.15t + 0.0035t^2) \times 10^{-6}$ volt.

15. $21°\,13'\,28.36''$.

Arts. 91–92. Pages 402–403

6. 0.7652.

8. $-6.00A$.

7. 6.06 sec.

12. $53.7°$, $47.1°$, $42.0°$, $37.8°$, $34.1°$.

Arts. 93–96. Pages 418–419

6. (b) $(4n+1)\pi/2 + i\cosh^{-1}2$, n an integer or zero.

8. (b) $\sinh^{-1}2 + 2n\pi i$, $-\sinh^{-1}2 + (2n+1)\pi i$, n an integer or zero.

9. (b) $\sinh^{-1}1 + (4n+1)\pi i/2$, $-\sinh^{-1}1 + (4n+3)\pi i/2$, n an integer or zero.

Arts. 97–101. Pages 436–437

5. (b) $(D^2 + R_1^2 - R_2^2 - R^2)/2D$, $(D^2 - R_1^2 + R_2^2 - R^2)/2D$, R^2/D;
$R^4 = D^4 + R_1^4 + R_2^4 - 2(D^2 R_1^2 + D^2 R_2^2 + R_1^2 R_2^2)$.

7. $V = c(u^3 - 3uv^2)$, $S = c(3u^2v - v^3)$.

8. $V = c(u^4 - 6u^2v^2 + v^4)$, $S = c(4u^3v - 4uv^3)$.

10. $u = c(V^2 - S^2)$, $v = 2cVS$. Streamlines and equipotentials are confocal parabolas; focus at O, u-axis as common axis.

Arts. 102–105. Pages 459–460

5. $\frac{2}{9}$, $(-1 \pm \sqrt{3}\, i)/9$.

Arts. 106–107. Pages 468–469

1. $y = 3t^2$.

2. $y = e^{3t}$.

3. $y = 2e^t - 3e^{-t} - t$.

4. $y = (3e^{3t} + 29e^{-t})/4$.

5. $y = t^2 + e^t - e^{-2t}$.

Art. 108. Pages 475–476

1. $y = 2 + \sin t - \cos t$.

2. $y = 3 \sin t - (1 + t) \cos t$.

3. $y = 2 - e^t + 3e^{-t} + e^{2t}$.

4. $y = 1 + 2t - \sin t + 2 \cos t$.

5. $y = e^t + \sin t + \cos t - 1$.

Arts. 109–111. Pages 491–492

1. (a) $I_1 = \frac{5}{3}(4 - 3e^{-t} - e^{-3t})$, $I_2 = \frac{5}{3}(2 - 3e^{-t} + e^{-3t})$; (b) $I_1 = \frac{1}{20}(8 \sin t - 6 \cos t + 5e^{-t} + e^{-3t})$, $I_2 = \frac{1}{20}(2 \sin t - 4 \cos t + 5e^{-t} - e^{-3t})$.

2. (a) $i_1 = \frac{10}{3}(3 - e^{-t/2} - 2e^{-2t})$, $i_2 = \frac{10}{3}(e^{-t/2} - e^{-2t})$, $i_3 = \frac{10}{3}(3 - 2e^{-t/2} - e^{-2t})$; (b) $i_1 = \frac{1}{51}(18 \cos 2t + 21 \sin 2t - e^{-t/2} - 17e^{-2t})$, $i_2 = \frac{1}{102}(15 \cos 2t + 9 \sin 2t + 2e^{-t/2} - 17e^{-2t})$, $i_3 = \frac{1}{102}(21 \cos 2t + 33 \sin 2t - 4e^{-t/2} - 17e^{-2t})$.

3. (a) $I_1 = \frac{1}{15}(1 - 6e^{-100t} + 8e^{-150t})$, $I_2 = \frac{1}{15}(1 - 3e^{-100t} + 2e^{-150t})$; (b) $I_2 = 0.0060 \sin 120\pi t - 0.0081 \cos 120\pi t - 0.0210e^{-100t} + 0.0291e^{-150t}$.

4. (a) $A_{11} = \frac{1}{36}(27 - 4e^{-t} - 5e^{-10t})$, $A_{12} = \frac{1}{36}(9 - 4e^{-t} - 5e^{-10t})$, $A_{13} = \frac{1}{9}(e^{-t} - e^{-10t})$; (b) $I_3 = \frac{1}{585}(99 \cos 5t + 27 \sin 5t + 5e^{-t} - 104e^{-10t})$.

5. 0.153, 0.051, 0.102, 0.024, 0.078 amp.

Arts. 112–113. Pages 509–510

7. 99.7°.

8. 0.100, 0.0791, 0.0645, 0.0466 amp.

Arts. 114–115. Pages 521–522

1. $a^3/p^2(p^2 + a^2)$.

2. $2a^3/(p^2 + a^2)^2$.

3. $2ap^2/(p^2 + a^2)^2$.

4. $2a^2p/(p^4 + 4a^4)$.

5. $e^{-ap}\Gamma(n + 1)/p^{n+1}$.

6. $2a(3p^2 - a^2)/(p^2 + a^2)^3$.

14. $y = e^{2t} - e^t$.

15. $y = e^t + e^{-t} - e^{-2t}$.

16. $y = e^{-t} \sin t$.

17. $y = e^t + \cos t + \sin t$.

18. $y = ct J_1(t)$.

19. $y = ct^n J_n(t)$.

20. $\pi/2$.

21. $\pi e^{-t}/2$.

22. $\sqrt{\pi/2t}$.

Index

INDEX

547

Reversion of series, 166
Riemann, *see* Cauchy
Riemann-Weber, 269
R.m.s. value, 205
Robinson, *see* Whittaker
Rodrigues's formula, 251
Rope wound on drum, 33
Rorty, 372
Rotating shaft, 113
Rotation, of a fluid, 296
Rothe, Ollendorf, and Pohlhausen, 423
Rümelin, 121

Saturation current, 120
Savart, *see* Biot
Scalar, 330
Scalar field, 347
Scalar product, 333
Scarborough, 394
Schiele's pivot, 103
Schwarz-Christoffel transformation, 419 ff., 454
Series, addition of, 161
  alternating, 159
  combination of, 205
  comparison test for, 158
  convergence of, 157
    absolute, 158
    uniform, 167
  differentiation of, 164, 171
  division of, 162
  Fourier, 188 ff.
    half-range, 198, 202
  identical, 165
  infinite, 156 ff., 448
  integration of, 164, 170
  Laurent's, 451
  Maclaurin's, 159
  multiplication of, 161
  of Bessel functions, 236
  of Legendre polynomials, 254
  power, 159 ff.
  ratio test for, 158
  region of convergence of, 157
  reversion of, 166
  sum of, 157
  Taylor's, 159, 449
  trigonometric, 188 ff.
Shaft, rotating, 113
Shear, 29

Shearer, *see* Carse
Shifting formula, 498
Shots fired at target, 373
Simple beam, 29, 214
Simple harmonic motion, 75
  amplitude of, 75
  frequency of, 75
  period of, 75
Simultaneous differential equations, 2, 70
Sine-integral function, 515
Singular points, 451
  essential, 451
  isolated, 451
Smail, 159, 167
Solenoid, eddy currents inside, 305
Solution of differential equation, 2
  general, 2
  particular, 2
Soucek, Howe, and Mavis, 174
Specific heat, 281
Sphere, heat flow in, 286
Spring constant, 79
Standard deviation, 379
  of the mean, 385
Stat units, 523
Statistical probability, 373
Steady state, 24, 117, 282, 289
Stefan-Boltzmann law, 179
Stokes's theorem, 357
Stream function, 420
Streamlines, 297, 492
String, vibrating, 273, 398, 503, 518
Sum, of series, 157
Superposition, principle of, 482
Surface tension, 111, 140
Suspended cable, 107
Sutro weir, 174
Swinging cord, 145
Systems of units, 21, 523

Target, shots fired at, 373
Taylor's operator, 499
Taylor's series, 159, 449
Taylor's theorem, 449
Telegraph equations, 302
Telephone equations, 301
Temperature gradient, 24
Tension, surface, 111, 140
Test, comparison, 158